Middle School 2-2
2학기 전과정

중간 + 기말
적중100 plus

영어 기출문제집

영어 중 2

비상 | 김진완

▶ **교과서 확인학습**　교과서 학습목표 달성 및 구문에 대한 완벽 이해
▶ **실력평가 대비서**　수시 또는 단원평가 대비 다양한 형태의 문제풀이
▶ **서술형평가 대비**　점증하는 주관식 또는 서술형 평가에 대비한 사전 연습
▶ **창의사고력 문제**　스토리텔링 능력 제고를 위한 사고력 향상 문제풀이
▶ **교과서 파헤치기**　교과서 지문에 대한 완벽 이해와 습득을 위한 무한 반복

Best Collection

2학기 전과정

적중 100 plus

영어 기출문제집

중2

비상 | 김진완

Best Collection

구성과 특징

교과서의 주요 학습 내용을 중심으로 학습 영역별 특성에 맞춰 단계별로 다양한 학습 기회를 제공하여
단원별 학습능력 평가는 물론 중간 및 기말고사 시험 등에 완벽하게 대비할 수 있도록 내용을 구성

Words & Expressions

Step1   Key Words 단원별 핵심 단어 설명 및 풀이
         Key Expression 단원별 핵심 숙어 및 관용어 설명
         Word Power 반대 또는 비슷한 뜻 단어 배우기
         English Dictionary 영어로 배우는 영어 단어

Step2   실력평가 단원별 수시평가 대비 주관식, 객관식 문제풀이

Step3   서술형 대비 학업성취도 및 수행능력평가 대비 서술형 문제풀이

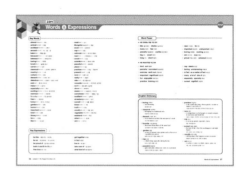

Conversation

Step1   핵심 의사소통 소통에 필요한 주요 표현 방법 요약
         핵심 Check 기본적인 표현 방법 및 활용능력 확인

Step2   대화문 익히기 교과서 대화문 심층 분석 및 확인

Step3   교과서 확인학습 빈칸 채우기를 통한 문장 완성 능력 확인

Step4   기본평가 시험대비 기초 학습 능력 평가

Step5   실력평가 단원별 수시평가 대비 주관식, 객관식 문제풀이

Step6   서술형 대비 학업성취도 및 수행능력평가 대비 서술형 문제풀이

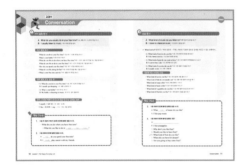

Grammar

Step1   주요 문법 단원별 주요 문법 사항과 예문을 알기 쉽게 설명
         핵심 Check 기본 문법사항에 대한 이해 여부 확인

Step2   기본평가 시험대비 기초 학습 능력 평가

Step3   실력평가 단원별 수시평가 대비 주관식, 객관식 문제풀이

Step4   서술형 대비 학업성취도 및 수행능력평가 대비 서술형 문제풀이

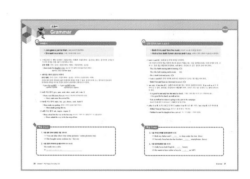

Reading

Step1   구문 분석 단원별로 제시된 문장에 대한 구문별 분석과 내용 설명
         확인문제 문장에 대한 기본적인 이해와 인지능력 확인

Step2   확인학습A 빈칸 채우기를 통한 문장 완성 능력 확인

Step3   확인학습B 제시된 우리말을 영어로 완성하여 작문 능력 키우기

Step4   실력평가 단원별 수시평가 대비 주관식, 객관식 문제풀이

Step5   서술형 대비 학업성취도 및 수행능력평가 대비 서술형 문제풀이
         교과서 구석구석 교과서에 나오는 기타 문장까지 완벽 학습

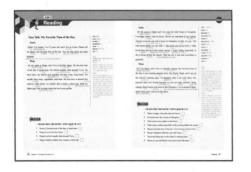

Composition

|영역별 핵심문제|

단어 및 어휘, 대화문, 문법, 독해 등 각 영역별 기출문제의 출제 유형을 분석하여 실전에 대비하고 연습할 수 있도록 문제를 배열

|단원별 예상문제|

기출문제를 분석한 후 새로운 시험 출제 경향을 더하여 새롭게 출제될 수 있는 문제를 포함하여 시험에 완벽하게 대비할 수 있도록 준비

|서술형 실전 및 창의사고력 문제|

학교 시험에서 점차 늘어나는 서술형 시험에 집중 대비하고 고득점을 취득하는데 만전을 기하기 위한 학습 코너

|단원별 모의고사|

영역별, 단계별 학습을 모두 마친 후 실전 연습을 위한 모의고사

교과서 파헤치기

- **단어Test1~3** 영어 단어 우리말 쓰기, 우리말을 영어 단어로 쓰기, 영영풀이에 해당하는 단어와 우리말 쓰기
- **대화문Test1~2** 대화문 빈칸 완성 및 전체 대화문 쓰기
- **본문Test1~5** 빈칸 완성, 우리말 쓰기, 문장 배열연습, 영어 작문하기 복습 등 단계별 반복 학습을 통해 교과서 지문에 대한 완벽한 습득
- **구석구석지문Test1~2** 지문 빈칸 완성 및 전문 영어로 쓰기

Explore Your Feelings!

🎤 의사소통 기능

- 좋지 않은 감정을 느끼게 된 원인 묻기

  A: You look down today. What's the matter?

  B: I got a haircut but it's too short.

- 고민을 해결할 방법 제안하기

  A: I've gained weight lately.

  B: I think you should exercise regularly.

🎤 언어 형식

- 현재완료

  They **have been** best friends since childhood.

- 목적격 관계대명사

  I'm sure there is a reason **that** we don't know about.

Words & Expressions

Key Words

- **advice**[ədváis] 몡 조언
- **advise**[ədváiz] 동 조언하다, 충고하다
- **alone**[əlóun] 분 홀로, 혼자
- **avoid**[əvɔ́id] 동 피하다
- **bar**[bɑːr] 몡 (특정 음식이나 음료를 파는) 전문점
- **contact**[kántækt] 몡 접촉, 닿음
- **difficult**[dífikʌlt] 혱 어려운
- **elementary**[èləméntəri] 혱 초보의, 초급의
- **explain**[ikspéin] 동 설명하다
- **fear**[fiər] 몡 두려움, 공포
- **fight**[fait] 동 싸우다
- **forgive**[fərgív] 동 용서하다
- **haircut**[hɛ́ərkʌt] 몡 이발, 머리 깎기
- **hate**[heit] 동 싫어하다
- **hurt**[həːrt] 동 다치게 하다, 아프게 하다
- **limit**[límit] 몡 한계, 제한
- **line**[lain] 몡 (연극, 영화의) 대사
- **matter**[mǽtər] 몡 문제
- **mean**[miːn] 동 의도하다, 작정하다

- **messy**[mési] 혱 어질러진, 더러운
- **mirror**[mírər] 몡 거울
- **pack**[pæk] 동 싸다, 꾸리다
- **reason**[ríːzn] 몡 이유, 까닭
- **repeat**[ripíːt] 동 반복하다
- **share**[ʃɛər] 동 공유하다, 나누다
- **since**[sins] 전 ~부터, ~ 이후
- **snack**[snæk] 몡 간식
- **solve**[sɑlv] 동 풀다, 해결하다
- **stand**[stænd] 동 참다, 견디다
- **stuff**[stʌf] 몡 물건
- **suggestion**[səgdʒéstʃən] 몡 제안
- **toothache**[túːθeik] 몡 치통
- **upset**[ʌ́pset] 혱 속상한, 마음이 상한
- **wise**[waiz] 혱 현명한
- **worry**[wə́ːri] 동 걱정하다 몡 걱정
- **yell**[jel] 동 소리치다, 소리 지르다
- **yet**[jet] 분 아직

Key Expressions

- **face a problem** 문제에 직면하다
- **focus on** ~에 집중하다
- **gain weight** 체중이 늘다
- **in the end** 결국, 마침내
- **let it go** 그쯤 해 두다, 내버려 두다
- **lunch break** 점심시간
- **make a mistake** 실수하다
- **on purpose** 고의로, 일부러

- **point out** 지적하다
- **put ~ down** ~을 깎아내리다
- **set an alarm** 자명종을 맞추다
- **shut down** (기계가) 멈추다, 정지하다
- **stay up late** 늦게까지 자지 않고 있다
- **up and down** 좋다가 나쁘다가 하는
- **wake up** 잠에서 깨다
- **work out** 해결하다

Word Power

※ 서로 반대되는 뜻을 가진 어휘

- ☐ **easy** 쉬운 ↔ **difficult** 어려운
- ☐ **hate** 싫어하다 ↔ **like** 좋아하다
- ☐ **wise** 현명한 ↔ **stupid** 어리석은
- ☐ **upset** 속상한, 마음이 상한 ↔ **relieved** 안도하는
- ☐ **messy** 어질러진, 더러운 ↔ **clean** 깔끔한
- ☐ **avoid** 피하다 ↔ **face** 맞서다

- ☐ **pack** 싸다, 꾸리다 ↔ **unpack** (꾸러미, 짐을) 풀다
- ☐ **alone** 혼자 ↔ **together** 함께
- ☐ **limited** 한정된 ↔ **limitless** 무한의, 무제한의
- ☐ **on purpose** 고의로 ↔ **by accident** 우연히
- ☐ **elementary** 초급의, 초보의 ↔ **advanced** 상급의, 고등의
- ☐ **gain weight** 체중이 늘다 ↔ **lose weight** 체중이 줄다

English Dictionary

- ☐ **advice** 조언
  → an opinion or a suggestion about what somebody should do in a particular situation
  누군가가 특정한 상황에서 해야 하는 것에 대한 의견 또는 제안

- ☐ **avoid** 피하다
  → to keep away from somebody/something; to try not to do something
  누군가 또는 무언가로부터 멀리하다; 무언가를 하지 않으려고 하다

- ☐ **contact** 접촉
  → the state of touching something
  무언가를 만지는 상태

- ☐ **elementary** 초급의
  → in or connected with the first stages of a course of study
  학업 과정에서 첫 번째 단계에 관련된

- ☐ **forgive** 용서하다
  → to stop feeling angry with somebody who has done something to harm, annoy or upset you
  당신에게 해롭게 하거나 화나게 하거나 또는 불안하게 하는 무언가를 한 사람에게 화내는 감정을 그만두다

- ☐ **hate** 싫어하다
  → to dislike something very much
  무언가를 매우 싫어하다

- ☐ **hurt** 다치게 하다
  → to cause physical pain to somebody/yourself; to injure somebody/yourself
  누군가 또는 당신 자신에게 신체적 고통을 야기하다; 누군가 또는 당신 자신을 부상을 입히다

- ☐ **line** 대사
  → the words spoken by an actor in a play or film/movie
  연극 또는 영화에서 배우에 의해 이야기되는 말

- ☐ **messy** 어질러진, 더러운
  → dirty and/or untidy
  더러운, 그리고[또는] 정돈되지 않은

- ☐ **repeat** 반복하다
  → to say or write something again or more than once
  무언가를 다시 또는 한번 이상 말하거나 쓰다

- ☐ **share** 공유하다
  → to have or use something at the same time as somebody else
  다른 누군가와 동시에 무언가를 갖거나 사용하다

- ☐ **suggestion** 제안
  → an idea or a plan that you mention for somebody else to think about
  다른 누군가가 그것에 관해 생각하도록 당신이 언급한 의견 또는 계획

- ☐ **toothache** 치통
  → a pain in one of your teeth
  치아의 아픔

- ☐ **yell** 소리 지르다
  → to shout loudly, for example because you are angry, excited, frightened or in pain
  예를 들어 당신이 화가 나거나, 흥분하거나, 깜짝 놀라거나 고통을 당하고 있기 때문에 크게 소리 지르다

서답형

01 다음 짝지어진 단어의 관계가 같도록 빈칸에 알맞은 말을 쓰시오.

> easy : difficult = like : h_____

중요

02 다음 중 밑줄 친 부분의 뜻풀이가 바르지 <u>않은</u> 것은?

① I didn't want to go there <u>alone</u>. 혼자, 홀로
② The sport is dangerous because there is a lot of body <u>contact</u>. 접촉
③ You can overcome your <u>fear</u> of water. 두려움
④ Susan will <u>forgive</u> the rude boy. 용서하다
⑤ I can't memorize my <u>lines</u> at all. 선

서답형

03 다음 우리말에 맞게 빈칸에 알맞은 말을 쓰시오.

(1) 밤에 혼자 다니지 마세요.
  ➡ Don't walk round _____ at night.
(2) 내가 무대에 섰을 때, 나는 대사를 잊어버렸다.
  ➡ When I was on the stage, I forgot my _____.
(3) 여기 제한 속도는 60km/h이다.
  ➡ The speed _____ is 60km/h here.
(4) 저는 여섯 살 때 이후부터 여기에 살고 있습니다.
  ➡ I've lived here _____ I was six years old.

04 다음 영영풀이가 가리키는 것을 고르시오.

> an opinion or a suggestion about what somebody should do in a particular situation

① matter   ② fear
③ mirror   ④ stuff
⑤ advice

서답형

05 다음 우리말에 맞게 주어진 단어를 사용하여 영작하시오.

(1) 나는 추위를 별로 잘 참지 못한다. (very, stand)
  ➡ _____
(2) 그들은 그 문제에 대해 이야기했다. (matter)
  ➡ _____
(3) 제게 조언 좀 주세요. (some, please)
  ➡ _____
(4) 그녀가 내게 먼저 물어보지 않고 내 물건을 사용해서 나는 화가 났다. (stuff, upset)
  ➡ _____
  _____

중요

06 다음 주어진 문장의 밑줄 친 stand와 같은 의미로 쓰인 것은?

> I can't <u>stand</u> his arrogant attitude.

① You don't have to <u>stand</u>. Just sit down.
② Let's <u>stand</u> up and talk about it now.
③ The old buildings <u>stand</u> in front of the library.
④ Can you <u>stand</u> the pain?
⑤ Tall trees <u>stand</u> on the riverside.

01 다음 빈칸에 들어갈 말을 〈보기〉에서 찾아 쓰시오.

> a pain in one of your teeth

➡ _____

02 다음 우리말에 맞게 빈칸에 알맞은 말을 쓰시오.

(1) 우리의 점심시간은 12시부터 1시까지이다.
  ➡ Our _____ is from twelve to one.
(2) 나는 너의 조언을 받아들여 집에 일찍 들어갔다.
  ➡ I took your _____ and went home early.
(3) 난 그녀의 마음을 아프게 하고 싶지 않다.
  ➡ I don't want to _____ her feelings.

03 다음 문장의 빈칸에 들어갈 말을 〈보기〉에서 골라 쓰시오.

> ┤ 보기 ├
>
> gain weight / in the end / focus on / on purpose

(1) He broke his glasses _____.
(2) You can _____ because of lack of sleep.
(3) We should _____ the changes in the global market.
(4) _____, I accepted his suggestion.

04 다음 우리말을 주어진 단어를 이용하여 영작하시오.

(1) 그는 때때로 사람들을 깎아내린다. (puts)
  ➡ _____
(2) 그녀는 항상 내 실수들을 지적한다. (points)
  ➡ _____
(3) 잠자리에 들기 전에 자명종을 맞춰라. (set)
  ➡ _____

05 다음 우리말과 일치하도록 주어진 어구를 배열하여 완성하시오.

(1) 내 보고서의 몇몇 실수들을 지적해 주어 고마워요.
  (you / mistakes / my / in / report / out / pointing / thank / for / some)
  ➡ _____
(2) 여기 여러분의 대본이 있으니 대사를 연습하세요.
  (your / practice / so / your / here / scripts / are / lines)
  ➡ _____
(3) 내가 전화한 이유는 토요일 계획에 대해 묻기 위해서였다.
  (for / the reason / to / the plans / ask / called / I / Saturday / was / about)
  ➡ _____
  _____
(4) 화재의 위험을 피하기 위해 조치를 취하는 것은 중요하다.
  (avoid / is / to / it / important / to / take / the risk / fire / measures / of)
  ➡ _____
  _____

1 좋지 않은 감정을 느끼게 된 원인 묻기

A You look down today. What's the matter? (너 오늘 침울해 보여. 무슨 일 있어?)

B I got a haircut but it's too short. (머리를 잘랐는데 너무 짧아.)

■ "What's the matter?"는 상대방의 기분이 언짢아 보일 때 무슨 일이 있는지 혹은 좋지 않은 기분의 원인을 묻고자 할 때 사용된다. 예를 들어, 상대방의 기분이 안 좋아 보일 때 "What's the matter? You look upset."과 같이 말한다.

좋지 않은 감정을 느끼게 된 원인 묻기

- What's wrong? (무슨 일이에요?)
- Is something the matter? (무슨 문제가 있나요?)
- Is there something wrong? (무슨 일이에요?)
- Why do you look so sad[mad]? (왜 그렇게 슬퍼[화나] 보이니?)
- What's the problem with you? (무슨 일이야?)

핵심 Check

1. 다음 우리말과 일치하도록 빈칸에 알맞은 말을 쓰시오.

(1) **A:** You look so _____. _____? (매우 초조해 보여. 무슨 일이야?)

　　B: I dropped my mom's new glasses and broke them. (내가 엄마의 새 안경을 떨어뜨렸는데 그게 깨졌어.)

(2) **A:** _____? (왜 그렇게 슬퍼 보이니?)

　　B: I didn't pass the test. I don't know what to do. (시험을 통과하지 못했어. 나는 무엇을 해야 할지 모르겠어.)

(3) **A:** You don't look good today. Is there something _____? (너 오늘 좋아 보이지 않아. 무슨 일이야?)

　　B: I can't sleep well at night. _____? (밤에 잠을 잘 잘 수 없어. 내가 무엇을 해야 할까?)

② 고민을 해결할 방법 제안하기

A I've gained weight lately. (나는 최근에 체중이 늘었어.)

B I think you should exercise regularly. (내 생각에 네가 규칙적으로 운동을 해야 할 것 같아.)

■ "I think you should ~."는 뭔가 고민하고 있거나 어려움을 겪고 있는 사람에게 그 문제에 대한 해결책을 제안할 때 사용된다. 예를 들어, 친구와 말다툼을 한 후 고민하고 있는 친구에게 문제를 해결할 방안을 제시하고 싶다면 "I think you should talk to your friend first."와 같이 말할 수 있다.

고민을 해결할 방법 제안하기

• Why don't you talk to your father first? (먼저 아빠와 이야기해 보는 게 어때?)

• How about playing a video game? (비디오 게임을 하는 것이 어때?)

• If I were you, I'd go to bed first and think about it later. (내가 너라면 나는 먼저 잠자리에 들고 나중에 생각할래.)

• What about setting an alarm before you go to bed? (잠자리에 들기 전에 알람을 맞추는 게 어때?)

• I recommend writing a letter to your friend. (나는 네 친구에게 편지 쓰는 걸 추천해.)

• I advise you to meet her personally. (나는 네가 개인적으로 그녀를 만나보는 것을 권해.)

핵심 Check

2. 다음 우리말과 일치하도록 빈칸에 알맞은 말을 쓰시오.

(1) **A:** My face turns red when I'm in front of many people. (저는 많은 사람들 앞에 서면 얼굴이 빨개져요.)

   B: _____ take a deep breath first. (내 생각에 네가 먼저 깊게 숨을 쉬어야 할 것 같아.)

(2) **A:** I'm really bad at making eye contact. (저는 정말로 눈을 마주치는 것을 잘 못해요.)

   B: I _____ you to practice looking into your own eyes in the mirror. (나는 네가 거울에서 네 눈을 보는 것을 연습하길 충고해.)

(3) **A:** I want a better style. (나는 더 나은 스타일을 원해요.)

   B: _____ look for magazines with fashion tips? (패션 정보가 있는 잡지를 찾아보는 게 어때?)

Listen & Talk 1-B

Jane: You look tired. ❶What's the matter?

Mike: I didn't have breakfast this morning. I'm so hungry.

Jane: Oh, ❷that's too bad. We still have two more hours ❸until lunch break.

Mike: Our school should have a snack bar. Then, we could have a quick breakfast or snacks.

Jane: I think so, too. How can we ❹make that suggestion?

Mike: We can post it on the suggestion board.

Jane: 너 피곤해 보인다. 무슨 일 있어?

Mike: 오늘 아침에 밥을 못 먹었어. 너무 배가 고파.

Jane: 오, 안됐다. 점심시간까지 아직 두 시간도 더 남았는데.

Mike: 우리 학교도 매점이 있어야 돼. 그러면 간단히 아침이나 간식을 먹을 수 있잖아.

Jane: 내 생각도 그래. 어떻게 하면 우리가 그 제안을 할 수 있을까?

Mike: 우리는 이걸 제안 게시판에 올릴 수 있어.

❶ 상대방의 기분이 언짢아 보일 때 무슨 일이 있는지 혹은 좋지 않은 기분의 원인을 묻고자 한다. What's the problem with you? 등으로 바꾸어 쓸 수 있다.

❷ 유감을 나타내는 표현으로 I'm sorry to hear that. 등으로 바꾸어 쓸 수 있다.

❸ until: ~까지, ~이 되기까지

❹ make a suggestion: 제안을 하다

Check(√) True or False

(1) There isn't a snack bar in Jane's school.   T ☐ F ☐

(2) Mike is going to have lunch with Jane soon.   T ☐ F ☐

Communication

Solomon: Hello, you're ❶on the air.

Amy: Hi, Solomon. I'm Amy.

Solomon: Hi, Amy. What's the matter?

Amy: I ❷hate sharing my room with my little sister. She uses my ❸stuff without asking me first. What should I do?

Solomon: Hmm.... I think you should tell her your feelings. And you should also make some rules with your sister.

Amy: Oh, I'll try ❹that. Thanks for the advice.

Solomon: 안녕하세요. (방송에) 연결되었습니다.

Amy: 안녕하세요, Solomon. 전 Amy라고 해요.

Solomon: 안녕하세요, Amy. 무슨 일 있어요?

Amy: 전 여동생이랑 제 방을 같이 쓰는 게 싫어요. 그 애는 제게 먼저 물어보지도 않고 제 물건을 쓰거든요. 제가 어떻게 해야 할까요?

Solomon: 흠.... 제 생각엔 당신의 기분을 여동생에게 말해야 할 것 같아요. 그리고 여동생과 몇 가지 규칙을 만들어 봐요.

Amy: 오, 그렇게 할게요. 조언 감사해요.

❶ on the air: 방송 중에

❷ hate은 to부정사와 동명사 모두를 목적어로 취할 수 있다.

❸ stuff: 물건

❹ that은 Solomon의 조언으로 제시된 여동생에게 기분을 이야기하는 것과 여동생과 몇 가지 규칙을 만들어 보는 것을 가리킨다.

Check(√) True or False

(3) Amy is upset because of her little sister.   T ☐ F ☐

(4) Solomon thinks that Amy should share her stuff with her little sister.   T ☐ F ☐

Listen & Talk 1-A-1

M: You don't look so happy today. What's the matter?

W: I wore my sister's favorite T-shirt. But I got grape juice on ❶it.

M: Oh, no. Did you tell your sister?

W: No, ❷not yet. I don't know ❸what to do.

❶ it은 her sister's favorite T-shirt를 가리킨다.
❷ not yet: 아직 (~ 않다)
❸ what to do = what I should do

Listen & Talk 1-A-2

Sora: David, you look ❶down today. What's the matter?

David: I got a haircut but it's too short. I look ❷funny.

Sora: ❸Take off your hat and let me see. (pause) Oh, it looks fine.

David: Really? I guess ❹I'm just not used to it yet.

❶ down: 우울한(= depressed, gloomy)
❷ funny: 우스꽝스러운, 우스운, cf. fun: 즐거운, 재미있는
❸ take off: ~을 벗다
❹ be used to ~: ~에 익숙하다

Listen & Talk 2 A-1

Sujin: I don't know how to do better in math. Can you give me some ❶advice?

Jake: How do you study for tests?

Sujin: I just solve a lot of problems.

Jake: Well, don't solve everything. I think you should ❷focus on the ❸ones you got wrong.

❶ advice: 조언, cf. advise: 조언하다
❷ focus on: ~에 집중하다
❸ ones는 problems를 가리킨다.

Listen & Talk 2 A-2

Emily: I was late for class again. I just can't ❶wake up in the morning.

Tom: Do you ❷set an alarm?

Emily: Yeah, but I ❸turn ❹it off and go back to sleep.

Tom: I think you should put ❹it far from your bed. That way, you'll have to ❺get out of bed.

❶ wake up: 잠에서 깨다
❷ set an alarm: 자명종을 맞추다
❸ turn off: ~을 끄다 (↔ turn on: ~을 켜다)
❹ it은 alarm을 가리킨다.
❺ get out of ~: ~에서 나오다

Listen & Talk 2 B

Eric: Ms. Morris, I just can't ❶stop playing computer games. What should I do?

Ms. Morris: Well, ❷why don't you use a special program? When you set a time limit, the computer ❸shuts down at that time.

Eric: Oh, that's a good idea.

Ms. Morris: And I think you should move the computer out of your room and into the living room.

Eric: I think I should. Thank you for the advice, Ms. Morris.

❶ stop+동명사: ~하던 것을 멈추다, cf. stop+to부정사: ~하기 위해 멈추다
❷ why don't you ~?: ~하는 게 어때?
❸ shut down: (기계가) 멈추다, 정지하다

다음 우리말과 일치하도록 빈칸에 알맞은 말을 쓰시오.

Listen & Talk 1-A-1

M: You _____ _____ so happy today. What's the _____?

W: I _____ my sister's favorite T-shirt. But I _____ grape juice on it.

M: Oh, no. Did you tell your sister?

W: No, not yet. I don't know _____ _____ _____.

Listen & Talk 1-A-2

Sora: David, you _____ _____ today. _____ _____ _____?

David: I got a _____ but it's too short. I look _____.

Sora: _____ _____ your hat and let me see. (*pause*) Oh, it looks fine.

David: Really? I guess I'm just not _____ _____ it yet.

Listen & Talk 1-B

Jane: You look _____. What's the matter?

Mike: _____ _____ _____ _____ _____ _____ _____ _____. I'm so hungry.

Jane: Oh, that's _____ _____. We still have two more hours until _____ _____.

Mike: Our school should have a _____ _____. Then, we could have a quick breakfast or snacks.

Jane: I think so, too. How can we _____ that _____?

Mike: We can _____ it on the suggestion board.

Listen & Talk 2 A-1

Sujin: I don't know _____ _____ _____ better in math. Can you give me some _____?

Jake: How do you study for tests?

Sujin: I just _____ a lot of problems.

Jake: Well, don't _____ everything. I think you should _____ _____ the _____ you _____ wrong.

해석

M: 너 오늘은 별로 행복해 보이지가 않네. 무슨 일 있어?

W: 언니가 가장 좋아하는 티셔츠를 입었어. 그런데 거기에 포도 주스를 쏟았지 뭐야.

M: 오, 저런. 너희 언니에게 말했어?

W: 아니, 아직. 내가 뭘 해야 할지 모르겠어.

Sora: David, 너 오늘 침울해 보여. 무슨 일 있어?

David: 머리를 잘랐는데 너무 짧아. 우스꽝스럽게 보여.

Sora: 모자를 벗으면 내가 한 번 볼게. 오, 괜찮아 보이는데.

David: 정말? 난 아직 익숙해지지 않은 것 같아.

Jane: 너 피곤해 보인다. 무슨 일 있어?

Mike: 오늘 아침에 밥을 못 먹었어. 너무 배가 고파.

Jane: 오, 안됐다. 점심시간까지 아직 두 시간도 더 남았는데.

Mike: 우리 학교도 매점이 있어야 돼. 그러면 간단히 아침이나 간식을 먹을 수 있잖아.

Jane: 내 생각도 그래. 어떻게 하면 우리가 그 제안을 할 수 있을까?

Mike: 우리는 이걸 제안 게시판에 올릴 수 있어.

Sujin: 수학을 더 잘하는 방법을 모르겠어. 나에게 조언을 좀 해 줄래?

Jake: 시험을 목표로 어떻게 공부해?

Sujin: 난 그냥 많은 문제를 풀어 봐.

Jake: 글쎄, 전부 풀지 마. 내 생각엔 네가 틀린 문제들에 집중해야 할 것 같아.

Listen & Talk 2 A-2

Emily: I was _____ _____ class again. I just can't _____ _____ in the morning.

Tom: Do you _____ _____ _____?

Emily: Yeah, but I _____ _____ _____ and go back to sleep.

Tom: I think you should put it _____ _____ your bed. _____ _____, you'll have to get out of bed.

해석

Emily: 나 또 수업에 늦었어. 난 정말 아침에 못 일어나겠어.
Tom: 자명종은 맞춰 두는 거야?
Emily: 응, 그렇지만 자명종을 끄고 다시 잠들게 돼.
Tom: 내 생각엔 자명종을 침대에서 멀리 떨어진 곳에 두어야 할 것 같아. 그러면 침대에서 일어날 수밖에 없을 거야.

Listen & Talk 2 B

Eric: Ms. Morris, I just can't _____ _____ _____ _____. _____ _____ _____ _____?

Ms. Morris: Well, why don't you use a special program? When you _____ a time _____, the computer _____ _____ at that time.

Eric: Oh, that's a good idea.

Ms. Morris: And _____ _____ _____ _____ move the computer _____ _____ your room and _____ the living room.

Eric: I think I should. Thank you for the _____, Ms. Morris.

Eric: Morris 선생님, 저 컴퓨터 게임하는 것을 멈출 수가 없어요. 제가 어떻게 해야 할까요?
Mr. Morris: 음, 특별한 프로그램을 써 보는 게 어떨까? 네가 시간 제한을 정해 두면 컴퓨터가 그 시간에 맞춰 종료돼.
Eric: 오, 좋은 생각이네요.
Mr. Morris: 그리고 내 생각엔 컴퓨터를 네 방에서 거실로 옮겨 두어야 할 것 같아.
Eric: 제 생각에도 그래야 할 것 같아요. Morris 선생님, 조언해 주셔서 감사합니다.

Communication

Solomon: Hello, you're _____ _____ _____.

Amy: Hi, Solomon. I'm Amy.

Solomon: Hi, Amy. What's the _____?

Amy: I hate _____ my room _____ my little sister. She uses my _____ without asking me first. What should I do?

Solomon: Hmm.... I think you should tell her your _____. And you should also _____ _____ _____ with your sister.

Amy: Oh, _____ _____ _____. Thanks for the advice.

Solomon: 안녕하세요. (방송에) 연결되었습니다.
Amy: 안녕하세요, Solomon. 전 Amy라고 해요.
Solomon: 안녕하세요, Amy. 무슨 일 있어요?
Amy: 전 여동생이랑 제 방을 같이 쓰는 게 싫어요. 그 애는 제게 먼저 물어보지도 않고 제 물건을 쓰거든요. 제가 어떻게 해야 할까요?
Solomon: 흠.... 제 생각엔 당신의 기분을 여동생에게 말해야 할 것 같아요. 그리고 여동생과 몇 가지 규칙을 만들어 봐요.
Amy: 오, 그렇게 할게요. 조언 감사해요.

Conversation 시험대비 기본평가

01 다음 대화가 자연스럽게 이어지도록 순서대로 배열하시오.

> (A) Do you set an alarm?
> (B) I think you should put it far from your bed. That way, you'll have to get out of bed.
> (C) Yeah, but I turn it off and go back to sleep.
> (D) I was late for class again. I just can't wake up in the morning.

➡ _____

[02~04] 다음 대화를 읽고 물음에 답하시오.

Jane: You look tired. What's the matter?
Mike: (A) I didn't have breakfast this morning. I'm so hungry.
Jane: (B) Oh, that's too bad. We still have two more hours until lunch break.
Mike: (C) Then, we could have a quick breakfast or snacks.
Jane: (D) ⓐI think so, too. How can we make that suggestion?
Mike: (E) We can post it on the suggestion board.

02 위 대화의 (A)~(E) 중 주어진 문장이 들어가기에 적절한 곳은?

> Our school should have a snack bar.

① (A) ② (B) ③ (C) ④ (D) ⑤ (E)

03 위 대화의 밑줄 친 ⓐ와 바꾸어 쓸 수 있는 것을 모두 고르시오.

① I'm against it. ② I'm with you in what you say.
③ That's not right. ④ I agree with you.
⑤ This won't work.

04 위 대화의 내용과 일치하지 않는 것은?
① Mike는 아침을 먹지 않아 피곤해 보인다.
② Jane과 Mike는 곧 점심을 먹을 예정이다.
③ 학교에 매점이 없다.
④ Mike는 매점이 있다면 간단히 아침이나 간식을 먹을 수 있을 것이라고 생각한다.
⑤ Jane과 Mike는 제안 게시판에 매점 설치 제안을 할 수 있다.

[01~03] 다음 대화를 읽고 물음에 답하시오.

> Tom: You don't look so happy today. (A) <u>What's the matter?</u>
> Sue: I wore my sister's favorite T-shirt. But I got grape juice on it.
> Tom: Oh, no. Did you tell your sister?
> Sue: No, not yet. I don't know what to do.

01 위 대화의 밑줄 친 (A)와 바꾸어 쓰기에 <u>어색한</u> 것은?

① What's the problem with you?
② What's wrong?
③ Is there something wrong?
④ Is something the matter?
⑤ What do you do?

02 위 대화에서 Sue의 심정으로 적절한 것은?

① worried　　② joyful　　③ lonely
④ happy　　⑤ pleased

03 위 대화의 내용과 일치하도록 빈칸을 완성하시오.

> Sue looked so worried because she got grape juice on ＿＿＿＿＿＿＿＿＿＿＿.

[04~06] 다음 대화를 읽고 물음에 답하시오.

> Jane: You look tired. What's the matter?
> Mike: I didn't have breakfast this morning. I'm so hungry.
> Jane: Oh, (A)<u>that's too bad.</u> We still have two more hours until lunch break.
> Mike: Our school should have a snack bar. Then, we could have a quick breakfast or snacks.
> Jane: I think so, too. How can we make that suggestion?
> Mike: We can post it on the suggestion board.

04 위 대화에서 주어진 영영풀이가 나타내는 말을 찾아 쓰시오. 〔서답형〕

> an idea or a plan that you mention for somebody else to think about

➡ ＿＿＿＿＿＿＿＿＿＿＿＿＿

05 How can Jane and Mike make the suggestion? 〔서답형〕

➡ ＿＿＿＿＿＿＿＿＿＿＿＿＿＿

06 위 대화의 밑줄 친 (A)와 바꾸어 쓸 수 있는 것을 <u>모두</u> 고르시오.

① I'm sorry to hear that.
② but I'm afraid I can't.
③ what a pity!
④ no problem.
⑤ don't mention it.

07 다음 대화가 자연스럽게 이어지도록 순서대로 배열하시오. 〔서답형〕

> (A) Take off your hat and let me see. (*pause*) Oh, it looks fine.
> (B) I got a haircut but it's too short. I look funny.
> (C) You look down today. What's the matter?
> (D) Really? I guess I'm just not used to it yet.

➡ ＿＿＿＿＿＿＿＿＿＿＿＿＿

[08~09] 다음 대화를 읽고 물음에 답하시오.

Sujin: I don't know how to do better in math. (a)Can you give me some advice?

Jake: How do you study for tests?

Sujin: I just solve a lot of problems.

Jake: Well, don't solve everything. (A)_____
_____

서답형

08 위 대화의 빈칸 (A)에 들어갈 말을 보기에 주어진 단어를 모두 배열하여 완성하시오.

┌─ 보기 ─┐
you / should / ones / you / got / the / wrong / think / focus / I / on

➡ _____

09 위 대화의 밑줄 친 (a)와 바꾸어 쓸 수 없는 것은?

① What should I do?

② Would you give me some tips?

③ Would you advise me?

④ Will you give me a hint as to what I should do?

⑤ What can I do for you?

[10~12] 다음 대화를 읽고 물음에 답하시오.

Eric: Ms. Morris, I just can't stop ⓐto play computer games. What should I do?

Ms. Morris: Well, (A)why don't you use a special program?(how) When you set a time ⓑlimit, the computer ⓒ shuts down at that time.

Eric: Oh, that's a good idea.

Ms. Morris: And I think you should move the computer ⓓout of your room and ⓔinto the living room.

Eric: I think I should. I'll try that. Thank you for the advice, Ms. Morris.

서답형

10 위 대화의 밑줄 친 ⓐ~ⓔ 중 대화의 흐름상 어색한 것을 찾아 바르게 고치시오.

➡ _____

서답형

11 위 대화의 밑줄 친 (A)와 의미가 같도록 주어진 단어를 사용하여 다시 쓰시오.

➡ _____

12 위 대화의 내용과 일치하지 않는 것은?

① Eric은 컴퓨터 게임을 멈추지 못해 고민이다.

② Ms. Morris는 Eric에게 특별한 프로그램을 사용해 볼 것을 추천한다.

③ 특별한 프로그램은 시간을 정해 두면 컴퓨터가 그 시간에 맞춰 종료된다.

④ Ms. Morris는 Eric이 컴퓨터를 거실에서 그의 방으로 옮길 것을 조언한다.

⑤ Eric은 Ms. Morris의 조언을 실행해 볼 것이다.

[13~14] 다음 대화를 읽고 물음에 답하시오.

Emily: I was late for class again. I just can't wake up in the morning.

Tom: Do you set an alarm?

Emily: Yeah, but I turn it off and go back to sleep.

Tom: I think you should put it far from your bed. That way, you'll have to get out of bed.

서답형

13 Why was Emily late for class?

➡ _____

서답형

14 Why does Tom advise Emily to put an alarm far from the bed?

➡ _____

[01~03] 다음 대화를 읽고 물음에 답하시오.

Solomon: Hello, (A)you're on the air.
Amy: Hi, Solomon. I'm Amy.
Solomon: Hi, Amy. What's the matter?
Amy: I hate sharing my room with my little sister. She uses my stuff without asking me first. What should I do?
Solomon: Hmm.... I think you should tell her your feelings. And you should also make some rules with your sister.
Amy: Oh, I'll try that. Thanks for the advice.

01 위 대화의 밑줄 친 (A)의 의미를 우리말로 쓰시오.

➡ _____

02 Why doesn't Amy like sharing her room with her little sister?

➡ _____

_____

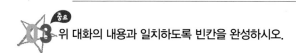 위 대화의 내용과 일치하도록 빈칸을 완성하시오.

Amy: I'm so upset with my sister who uses my stuff without asking me first. I hate sharing my room with her.
Solomon: If I were you, I'd _____

_____ .

[04~05] 다음 대화를 읽고 물음에 답하시오.

Sujin: I don't know how to do better in math. Can you give me some advice?
Jake: How do you study for tests?
Sujin: I just solve a lot of problems.
Jake: Well, don't solve everything. I think you should focus on the ones you got wrong.

04 What's the matter with Sujin?

➡ _____

05 What is Jake's advice to do better in math?

➡ _____

06 다음 대화를 읽고 대화의 내용과 일치하도록 다음 표를 완성하시오.

Eric: Ms. Morris, I just can't stop playing computer games. What should I do?
Ms. Morris: Well, why don't you use a special program? When you set a time limit, the computer shuts down at that time.
Eric: Oh, that's a good idea.
Ms. Morris: And I think you should move the computer out of your room and into the living room.
Eric: I think I should. Thank you for the advice, Ms. Morris.

⬇

Student Name	Eric
Date	August 24th
Problem	(A) _____ .
Advice	(1) Use a special program to (B) _____ . (2) Move the computer from (C) _____ to (D) _____ .

Grammar

① 현재완료

> • I **have read** 500 books since I was six. 여섯 살 이후로 나는 책을 500권 읽었다.
> • My father **has never** been to a grocery store. 나의 아버지는 식료품점에 가 본 적이 없다.

■ 현재완료는 과거의 사건이 현재까지 영향을 미칠 때 사용한다. 'have[has]+p.p.'의 형태로, 부정형은 'have[has] not+p.p.'이며, 의문형은 'Have[Has]+주어+p.p. ~?'로 나타낸다.

  • The man **has worked** for the company since 2010. 그 남자는 2010년 이래로 그 회사를 위해 일해 왔다.

  • **Have** you ever **been** to China? 너는 중국에 가 본 적 있니?

■ 현재완료는 '완료, 경험, 계속, 결과'의 네 가지 용법으로 쓰인다. 완료 용법은 'just, already, yet'과 같은 부사와 주로 함께 쓰이며, 경험은 'ever, never, once, before' 등과 같은 부사와 함께 쓰인다. 'How long ~?'으로 묻는 질문이나 'for+기간', 'since+특정 시점'은 현재완료의 계속 용법에 속한다. 결과 용법은 특별한 부사와 어울리지 않고 과거에 발생한 사건으로 인하여 현재까지 영향을 미치고 있는 상태를 나타낼 때 결과 용법으로 본다.

  • The boy **has drunk** the milk already. 그 소년은 벌써 우유를 마셨다. 〈완료〉

  • David **has played** ping-pong for an hour. David는 한 시간 동안 탁구를 쳤다. 〈계속〉

  • We **have seen** the program several times. 우리는 그 프로그램을 몇 번 본 적이 있다. 〈경험〉

  • The girls **have gone** to Busan. 그 소녀들은 부산에 가고 없다. 〈결과〉

*have[has] been to와 have[has] gone to의 사용에 유의하자. '~에 가 본 적이 있다'는 경험은 have[has] been to로 표현하고, '~에 가고 없다'는 결과는 have[has] gone to로 표현한다.

■ 현재완료는 과거의 일이 현재까지 영향을 미칠 때 쓰는 시제이므로 과거를 나타내는 어구인 yesterday, last year, ~ ago 등과 함께 쓸 수 없다.

  • Jane has met Tom yesterday. (X)

  • Jane met Tom yesterday.　　(O)

핵심 Check

1. 다음 우리말과 일치하도록 빈칸에 알맞은 말을 쓰시오.

  (1) Jason은 세 시간 동안 공부하고 있다.

  ➡ Jason _____ _____ for three hours.

  (2) 그 비행기는 막 도착했다.

  ➡ The plane _____ just _____.

  (3) 나는 어제 이후로 아무것도 하지 않았다.

  ➡ I _____ _____ nothing since yesterday.

② 목적격 관계대명사

> • There is a man **whom** my sister likes. 내 여동생이 좋아하는 남자가 있어.
>
> • The flowers **which** you take care of are beautiful. 네가 돌보는 꽃들은 아름다워.

■ 관계대명사는 두 개의 문장을 하나로 이어주는 접속사 역할을 하면서 동시에 (대)명사 역할을 한다. 전치사의 목적어 혹은 동사의 목적어였던 (대)명사를 목적격 관계대명사로 만들어 문장을 하나로 이어준다.

- This is the book **that** Ms. Han recommended. 〈동사의 목적어〉
  이것이 한 선생님이 추천하신 책이다.

- He is the only friend **that** I can rely on. 〈전치사의 목적어〉
  그는 내가 의지할 수 있는 유일한 친구이다.

■ 목적격 관계대명사 who(m), which는 that으로 대체할 수 있으며, 생략 가능하다. 관계대명사가 전치사의 목적어로 사용된 경우 전치사는 동사 뒤에 그대로 두거나, 전치사를 관계대명사 앞으로 보낼 수 있다. 단, 전치사를 관계대명사 앞으로 보낸 경우 관계대명사 that을 쓸 수 없고 관계대명사를 생략할 수 없음에 유의한다.

- Do you know the woman (**who/whom/that**) Maria is talking to? 너는 Maria가 대화하고 있는 여자를 아니?

- The bag (**which/that**) he brought the other day smells bad. 그가 지난번에 가져온 가방에서 나쁜 냄새가 난다.

- I have the wallet (**which/that**) Tom was looking **for**. Tom이 찾던 지갑을 내가 가지고 있어.
  = I have the wallet **for which** Tom was looking.

- The subject (**which/that**) I am interested **in** is English. 내가 흥미를 느끼는 과목은 영어이다.
  = The subject **in which** I am interested is English.

핵심 Check

2. 다음 우리말과 일치하도록 빈칸에 알맞은 말을 쓰시오.

(1) 네가 만든 그 샌드위치는 맛있어 보인다.

➡ The sandwich _____ _____ _____ looks delicious.

(2) 이것은 그가 나에게 사 준 목걸이야.

➡ This is the necklace _____ _____ _____ for me.

(3) Helen이 함께 온 저 남자를 아니?

➡ Do you know the man _____ _____ _____ _____?

01 다음 문장에서 어법상 <u>어색한</u> 부분을 바르게 고쳐 쓰시오.

(1) When have you left the place?

_____ ➡ _____

(2) Mr. Pang who the children love teach how to swim to them.

_____ ➡ _____

(3) I did this work for a long time until now. So I know about the work well.

_____ ➡ _____

(4) The knife whom you used is very sharp.

_____ ➡ _____

02 적절한 관계사를 이용하여 다음 두 문장을 하나의 문장으로 쓰시오.

star in: ~에서 주연을 맡다

(1) Have you found the pen? You lost it.

➡ _____

(2) Did she take the class? James taught the class.

➡ _____

(3) I want to meet the boy. You speak highly of him.

➡ _____

(4) Molly likes the movie. Tom Cruise starred in the movie.

➡ _____

03 주어진 어구를 바르게 배열하여 다음 우리말을 영어로 쓰시오. 필요하다면 단어를 추가하거나 변형하시오.

(1) 나는 아직 점심을 다 먹지 않았다. (yet / finished / lunch / I / my / haven't)

➡ _____

(2) 그녀는 그 교회에 두 번 가봤어. (two / she / times / been / has / the church)

➡ _____

(3) 나는 내가 가지고 있던 모든 돈을 그녀에게 주었다. (that / I / I / had / all the money / her / gave)

➡ _____

(4) 우리가 제출한 보고서는 어디에 있나요? (in / where / hand / is / which / we / the report)

➡ _____

01 다음 중 빈칸에 들어갈 말로 가장 적절한 것은?

> A: Have you seen her lately?
> B: _____

① Yes, I do.　　② No, I don't.
③ Yes, I saw.　　④ Yes, I have.
⑤ No, I have.

02 다음 우리말을 영어로 바르게 옮긴 것은?

> 너는 Jamie가 쓴 책을 읽고 싶니?

① Have you wanted to read the book which Jamie has written?
② Do you want to the book that Jamie was writing?
③ Did you wrote the book that Jamie read?
④ Did you read the book that Jamie wrote?
⑤ Do you want to read the book which Jamie wrote?

03 다음 중 빈칸에 들어갈 말로 가장 적절한 것은?

> Tyler has studied Economy _____.

① last year　　② the other day
③ since yesterday　　④ last week
⑤ a year ago

서답형
04 다음 두 문장을 한 문장으로 쓸 때 빈칸을 완성하시오.

> • I like the dress.
> • You want to buy the dress.

➡ I _____.

05 다음 우리말을 영어로 바르게 옮기지 <u>않은</u> 것은?

① 네가 악수한 그 소년은 누구니?
→ Who is the boy that you shook hands with?
② 나는 그녀를 한 번 만난 적 있어.
→ I have met her once.
③ 그는 그녀를 3년 동안 알아왔습니다.
→ He has known her for three years.
④ 그들은 네가 만든 기계를 좋아해.
→ They like the machine that you made.
⑤ 너는 서울에 가 본 적이 있니?
→ Have you ever gone to Seoul?

06 다음 중 어법상 바르지 <u>않은</u> 것은?

① Katherine likes the music which her friends don't like.
② Kelly has met Julian a few minutes ago.
③ Can you tell me the story that Tom told you?
④ Have you eaten the food before?
⑤ Did you buy the pants that you wanted to buy?

07 다음 중 빈칸에 들어갈 말로 가장 적절한 것은?

> Jina has paid the bill _____ five years.

① since　　② already　　③ for
④ just　　⑤ almost

서답형

08 다음 우리말을 영어로 쓸 때 빈칸에 알맞은 말을 세 단어로 쓰시오.

> 그들은 네가 파티에 초대한 사람들이니?
> ➡ Are they the people _____ to the party?

중요

09 다음 빈칸에 들어갈 말이 바르게 짝지어진 것은?

> • _____ you ever met a famous person like Justin Bieber?
> • Brad _____ to Italy. He is enjoying his vacation.

① Have – was   ② Have – has gone
③ Did – have been   ④ Did – went
⑤ Did – want to go

10 다음 두 문장을 하나의 문장으로 바르게 표현한 것은?

> They began to talk about the subject two hours ago. They still talk about it.

① They talked about the subject two hours ago.
② They talked about the subject until now.
③ They have talked about the subject since two hours.
④ They have talked about the subject for two hours.
⑤ They have just talked about the subject.

서답형

11 다음 두 문장을 하나의 문장으로 쓰시오.

> • Tell me about the people.
> • You met them in the hospital.

➡ _____

_____

12 다음 중 현재완료의 용법이 <u>다른</u> 하나는?

① They have just finished their work.
② He has already signed up for the class.
③ Jena has seen the menu for 20 minutes.
④ Melissa has not passed the test yet.
⑤ Brad has checked the schedule already.

중요

13 다음 중 밑줄 친 부분을 생략할 수 <u>없는</u> 것은?

① The boys <u>that</u> you are looking at are my children.
② The cat <u>that</u> is resting on the chair looks so cute.
③ My car was made in the company <u>that</u> Paul works for.
④ The candy <u>that</u> the girl is eating was made by me.
⑤ The cup <u>that</u> Amelia likes to use is on the shelf.

14 다음 빈칸에 가장 적절한 말을 고르시오.

> Look at the man and the dog _____ are walking together.

① which   ② who   ③ what
④ that   ⑤ whom

서답형

15 주어진 어구를 바르게 배열하여 다음 우리말을 영어로 쓰시오.

> 네가 나에게 보낸 그 편지는 아직 도착하지 않았어.
> (yet / the letter / has / that / not / to me / arrived / sent / you)

➡ _____

16 (A)~(C)에서 어법상 옳은 것끼리 바르게 짝지어진 것은?

> • Ted has used the computer (A)[for / since] he was a high school student.
> • What (B)[did you do / have you done] last weekend?
> • Clara (C)[has painted / painted] the wall twice until now.

① for – did you do – has painted
② for – did you do – painted
③ for – have you done – has painted
④ since – did you do – has painted
⑤ since – have you done – painted

17 다음 중 밑줄 친 부분의 쓰임이 다른 하나는?

① Do you know the girl that is making something with clay?
② The fact that is well known to us is that she is a great cook.
③ I don't know about the party that was planned by Jane.
④ The man likes to see the movie that was filmed at Sydney.
⑤ I don't care about the information that Sarah told us.

18 다음 중 빈칸에 들어갈 말이 바르게 짝지어진 것은?

> The company considers publishing a book _____ David _____ three years ago.

① who – has written
② whose – wrote
③ which – wrote
④ that – has wrote
⑤ that – is writing

19 다음 주어진 단어를 활용하여 우리말을 영어로 쓰시오.

> 전에 인도에 가 본 적이 있나요? (ever)

➡ _____

20 다음 중 어법상 바르지 <u>않은</u> 것은?

① Maria has learned math for three years.
② Can you give me back the pen that you borrowed from me?
③ Mina has had lunch a few minutes ago.
④ I have made my own jacket once.
⑤ The plants that you have just watered look beautiful.

21 다음 두 문장을 하나의 문장으로 쓰시오.

> I lost my cap. And I still don't have it.

➡ _____

22 다음 두 문장을 하나의 문장으로 쓰시오.

> • The I-pad was my birthday present.
> • I got it from my father.

➡ _____
_____

23 주어진 단어를 바르게 배열하여 문장을 완성하시오.

> The toys (with / that / play / the children) look dirty.

➡ _____

01 주어진 단어를 이용하여 다음 두 문장을 하나의 문장으로 표현하시오.

> It was sunny yesterday. It is still sunny today. (since)

➡ _____

02 다음 우리말에 맞도록 빈칸에 알맞은 말을 써서 문장을 완성하시오.

> 네가 마시고 있는 그 차 어때?
> ➡ How do you like the tea _____
> _____ _____ _____ ?

03 주어진 단어를 어법에 맞게 빈칸에 각각 쓰시오.

> ago   for   since

> • Julia has known Karl _____ 2015.
> • We have discussed the problem _____ a couple of hours.
> • Tom and Jane got married sixteen years _____.
> • We have known each other _____ we were young.

04 주어진 어구를 바르게 배열하여 다음 우리말을 영어로 쓰시오.

> 사람들이 찾던 그 실종 소년이 어젯밤 집으로 왔습니다.
> (were / the missing boy / whom / looking / people / for / last night / home / came)

➡ _____

_____

05 다음 대화의 빈칸에 알맞은 말을 쓰시오.

> A: How long _____ _____ _____ in this house?
> B: We moved into this house two years _____. So we _____ _____ in this house _____ two years.

06 자연스러운 문장이 되도록 관계대명사를 이용하여 하나의 문장으로 연결하시오. that은 사용하지 마시오.

> • What is the name of the man?
> • This is the car.
> • Where is the red sweater?

> • My friend hopes to buy it someday.
> • I put it in my drawer.
> • You want to meet him.

➡ (1) _____

_____

(2) _____

_____

(3) _____

_____

07 다음 우리말을 영어로 쓰시오.

> A: 너는 전에 코끼리를 본 적이 있니?
> B: 아니, 본 적 없어.

➡ _____

➡ _____

08 다음 문장에서 어법상 <u>틀린</u> 것을 고쳐 문장을 다시 쓰시오.

(1) Have you thrown a party for her yesterday?

➡ _____

(2) I have gone to Boston many times.

➡ _____

(3) The sandwich who he made for us is very delicious.

➡ _____

_____

09 다음 상황을 읽고 한 문장으로 표현하시오.

Yesterday Kevin lost his umbrella. So he doesn't have it now.

➡ _____

10 적절한 관계사를 이용하여 다음 두 문장을 한 문장으로 쓸 때 빈칸을 완성하시오.

(1) There isn't much information. You can get it.

➡ There _____.

(2) I gave Tim the pants. He always liked them.

➡ I _____.

(3) Is he the man? You respect him very much.

➡ Is _____?

11 다음 우리말을 8 단어로 이루어진 영어 문장으로 쓰시오.

이것은 우리 아빠가 만드신 책상이야.

➡ _____

12 다음 문장에서 생략 가능한 것을 생략하여 문장을 다시 쓰시오.

(1) The tennis game that he played yesterday was great.

➡ _____

(2) Do you know the boy who is talking with your sister?

➡ _____

(3) The subject which Jane is interested in is history and Korean.

➡ _____

13 다음 빈칸에 알맞은 말을 4 단어로 쓰시오.

그녀는 좋아하지 않는 음식에는 손도 대지 않는다.

➡ She never touches the food _____

_____.

14 다음 상황을 읽고 빈칸에 알맞은 말을 쓰시오.

I lost my shoes last week. I still don't have them. In other words, I _____ _____ my shoes.

15 우리말에 맞게 빈칸에 알맞은 말을 세 단어로 쓰시오.

네가 참석한 파티에 얼마나 많은 사람들이 있었니?

= How many people were there at the party _____ _____ _____?

Reading

Voices in Our Mind

Bella is 15 years old this year and these days her feelings are going up

and down. Today, she looks down. Let's listen to Bella's feelings and

find out why.

Day 1

Anger: What a day! I can't believe Jenny yelled at Bella after the

school play.

Sadness: Well, that's because Bella forgot her lines on stage.

Anger: Jenny pointed out the mistake that Bella made. How could she

do that in front of everyone?

Joy: But I'm sure Jenny did not mean to hurt Bella. They have been

best friends since elementary school. Remember?

Anger: That's what I'm saying. A true friend would never put Bella

down like that.

Fear: I'm worried that they are not going to be friends anymore.

Joy: Come on, Fear. Don't go too far. We'll see.

up and down: 좋다가 나쁘다가 하는
yell: 소리치다, 소리 지르다
line: (연극, 영화의) 대사
point out: 지적하다
make a mistake: 실수하다
in front of: ~ 앞에서
mean: 의도하다, 작정하다
hurt: 다치게 하다, 아프게 하다
since: ~부터, ~ 이후
put ~ down: ~을 깎아내리다

확인문제

● 다음 문장이 본문의 내용과 일치하면 T, 일치하지 않으면 F를 쓰시오.

1 Bella's feelings are going up and down lately. ☐

2 Jenny yelled at Bella during the school play. ☐

3 Bella couldn't remember her lines on stage. ☐

4 Bella shouted at Jenny in front of others. ☐

5 Bella has known Jenny since elementary school. ☐

28 Lesson 5. Explore Your Feelings!

Day 2

Anger: I can't forgive Jenny. She didn't say a word to Bella.

Fear: Jenny didn't even look at her. Jenny has never been this cold
　　　　　　　　　 심지어　　　　　　　　　과거부터 여태껏 이렇게 차가웠던 적이 없었다는 의미의 현재완료 – '경험'
　　before.

Sadness: Bella ate alone during lunch today. Poor Bella!
　　　　　　　　　　　　　　　　　　　　　　　　　　　　가엾은

Joy: Jenny is Bella's best friend. I'm sure there is a reason that we
　　　　　　　　　　　　　　　　　　　　　　　　　　　　　　　목적격 관계대명사(which 대체 가능)
　　don't know about.

Anger: I can't stand this any longer. Bella should just go and tell her
　　　　 not ~ any longer: 더 이상 ~ 않다(= no longer)
　　about her feelings.

Fear: I don't want Bella to be hurt again. She should let it go.
　　　　 want+목적어+to부정사: 목적어가 V하는 것을 원하다　　　　　　그쯤 해 두다, 내버려 두다
Joy: They are good friends. They will work it out.
　　　　　　　　　　　　　　　　　　└ 해결하다 ┘

Day 3

Joy: Whew! I'm so happy that they are talking again.
　　　 I'm so happy that ~: ~하니 참 기쁘다
Anger: Yeah, Bella went to Jenny and talked to her first.

Joy: Jenny didn't avoid Bella on purpose.
　　　　　　　　　　　　　　　　 고의로

Sadness: Yeah, Jenny didn't know a way to say sorry.
　　　　　　　　　　　　　　　　 형용사로 쓰인 to부정사로 a way 수식
Fear: I hope Bella doesn't have any more problems like this.
　　　 hope (that): 명사절을 이끄는 접속사 that 생략　　　　　　전치사: ~와 비슷한
Joy: Me, too. But problems are part of growing up. Just like this
　　　 나도 그래.　　　　　　　　　　　동명사: 전치사 of의 목적어　　이번과 꼭 마찬가지로
　　time, Bella will face the problems, solve them, and become wiser
　　in the end.

확인문제

- 다음 문장이 본문의 내용과 일치하면 T, 일치하지 <u>않으면</u> F를 쓰시오.

1　Jenny said nothing to Bella on the second day. ☐

2　Jenny was cold towards Bella several times. ☐

3　Anger wants Bella to go to Jenny to talk about her feelings. ☐

4　Fear thinks Bella needs to be hurt. ☐

5　Bella and Jenny finally made up. ☐

6　Fear wants Bella not to have any more problems. ☐

---

forgive: 용서하다
alone: 홀로, 혼자
reason: 이유, 까닭
stand: 참다, 견디다
let it go: 그쯤 해 두다, 내버려 두다
work out: 해결하다
avoid: 피하다
on purpose: 고의로, 일부러
grow up: 성장하다
face a problem: 문제에 직면하다
in the end: 결국, 마침내

● 우리말을 참고하여 빈칸에 알맞은 말을 쓰시오.

1 Bella is 15 _____ _____ this year and _____ _____ _____ her feelings are _____ _____ _____ _____.

2 Today, she _____ _____.

3 Let's listen to Bella's _____ and _____ _____ _____.

Day 1

4 Anger: _____ _____ _____! I can't believe Jenny _____ _____ Bella _____ the school play.

5 Sadness: Well, that's _____ Bella _____ her _____ on stage.

6 Anger: Jenny pointed out the mistake _____ _____ _____.

7 How _____ she do that _____ _____ _____ everyone?

8 Joy: But I'm sure Jenny _____ _____ _____ _____ _____ Bella.

9 They _____ _____ best friends _____ elementary school. Remember?

10 Anger: That's _____ I'm _____.

11 A true friend _____ _____ _____ Bella down like that.

12 Fear: I'm worried _____ they are _____ _____ _____ _____ _____ anymore.

13 Joy: Come on, Fear. Don't go _____ _____. We'll _____.

Day 2

14 Anger: I can't _____ Jenny. She didn't _____ _____ _____ to Bella.

15 Fear: Jenny didn't _____ _____ _____ her

1 Bella는 올해 15세이고 요즘 그 애의 기분은 좋다가 안 좋다가 한다.

2 오늘 그 애는 우울해 보인다.

3 Bella의 감정에 귀 기울여 보고 그 이유를 알아보자.

Day 1

4 Anger: 정말 끔찍한 하루야! 학교 연극이 끝난 후 Jenny가 Bella에게 소리를 지르다니 믿을 수가 없어.

5 Sadness: 글쎄, 그건 Bella가 무대에서 그녀의 대사를 잊어버렸기 때문이잖아.

6 Anger: Jenny는 Bella가 저지른 실수를 지적했잖아.

7 어떻게 모든 사람 앞에서 그렇게 할 수가 있니?

8 Joy: 하지만 난 Jenny가 Bella에게 상처를 주려고 했던 건 아니었다고 확신해.

9 그들은 초등학교 때부터 가장 친한 친구였잖아. 기억하지?

10 Anger: 내 말이 바로 그거야.

11 진정한 친구라면 절대로 그런 식으로 Bella를 깎아내리지 않을 거야.

12 Fear: 나는 그들이 더 이상 친구로 지내지 않을까봐 걱정돼.

13 Joy: 자, Fear. 너무 극단적으로 생각하지 마. 곧 알게 되겠지.

Day 2

14 Anger: 난 Jenny를 용서할 수 없어. 그 애는 Bella에게 한마디도 말을 안 했어.

15 Fear: Jenny는 심지어 Bella를 쳐다 보지도 않았어.

16 Jenny _____ _____ _____ this cold before.

17 Sadness: Bella _____ _____ _____ lunch today. Poor Bella!

18 Joy: Jenny is Bella's _____ _____ .

19 I'm sure there is a reason _____ _____ _____ _____ _____ .

20 Anger: I can't _____ this _____ _____ .

21 Bella should just _____ and _____ her _____ her feelings.

22 Fear: I don't want Bella _____ _____ _____ again.

23 She should _____ _____ _____ .

24 Joy: They are good friends. They will _____ _____ .

Day 3

25 Joy: Whew! I'm so happy _____ they _____ _____ again.

26 Anger: Yeah, Bella went to Jenny and _____ _____ _____ first.

27 Joy: Jenny didn't _____ Bella _____ _____ .

28 Sadness: Yeah, Jenny didn't know _____ _____ _____ sorry.

29 Fear: I hope Bella doesn't have _____ _____ _____ like this.

30 Joy: Me, too. But problems are _____ _____ _____ .

31 _____ _____ this time, Bella will _____ the problems, _____ _____ , and become _____ in the end.

16 Jenny가 전에 이렇게 차가웠던 적이 없었어.

17 Sadness: Bella는 오늘 점심시간에 혼자 밥을 먹었잖아. 가엾은 Bella!

18 Joy: Jenny는 Bella의 가장 친한 친구야.

19 나는 우리가 모르는 어떤 이유가 있다고 확신해.

20 Anger: 나는 더 이상 이 상황을 못 참아.

21 Bella는 일단 가서 Jenny에게 자신의 감정을 말해야 해.

22 Fear: 나는 Bella가 또다시 상처받는 걸 원하지 않아.

23 그 애는 그냥 내버려 두어야 해.

24 Joy: 그 애들은 좋은 친구야. 그 애들이 잘 해낼 거야.

Day 3

25 Joy: 휴! 나는 그 애들이 다시 이야기하게 되어 무척 기뻐.

26 Anger: 그래, Bella가 Jenny에게 가서 그 애에게 먼저 말을 걸었지.

27 Joy: Jenny는 일부러 Bella를 피한 게 아니었어.

28 Sadness: 맞아, Jenny는 사과하는 방법을 몰랐던 거야.

29 Fear: 나는 Bella에게 이번과 같은 문제가 더 이상 없기를 바라.

30 Joy: 나도 그래. 하지만 문제들은 성장의 일부야.

31 이번과 꼭 마찬가지로 Bella는 문제들에 직면하게 될 거고, 그것들을 해결할 거고, 그리고 결국 더 현명해질 거야.

● 우리말을 참고하여 본문을 영작하시오.

1 Bella는 올해 15세이고 요즘 그 애의 기분은 좋다가 안 좋다가 한다.

➡ _____

2 오늘 그 애는 우울해 보인다.

➡ _____

3 Bella의 감정에 귀 기울여 보고 그 이유를 알아보자.

➡ _____

Day 1

4 Anger: 정말 끔찍한 하루야! 학교 연극이 끝난 후 Jenny가 Bella에게 소리를 지르다니 믿을 수가 없어.

➡ _____

5 Sadness: 글쎄, 그건 Bella가 무대에서 그녀의 대사를 잊어버렸기 때문이잖아.

➡ _____

6 Anger: Jenny는 Bella가 저지른 실수를 지적했잖아.

➡ _____

7 어떻게 모든 사람 앞에서 그렇게 할 수가 있니?

➡ _____

8 Joy: 하지만 난 Jenny가 Bella에게 상처를 주려고 했던 건 아니었다고 확신해.

➡ _____

9 그들은 초등학교 때부터 가장 친한 친구였잖아. 기억하지?

➡ _____

10 Anger: 내 말이 바로 그거야.

➡ _____

11 진정한 친구라면 절대로 그런 식으로 Bella를 깎아내리지 않을 거야.

➡ _____

12 Fear: 나는 그들이 더 이상 친구로 지내지 않을까봐 걱정돼.

➡ _____

13 Joy: 자, Fear. 너무 극단적으로 생각하지 마. 곧 알게 되겠지.

➡ _____

Day 2

14 Anger: 난 Jenny를 용서할 수 없어. 그 애는 Bella에게 한마디도 말을 안 했어.

➡ _____

15 Fear: Jenny는 심지어 Bella를 쳐다보지도 않았어.

➡ _____

16 Jenny가 전에 이렇게 차가웠던 적이 없었어.
➡ _____

17 Sadness: Bella는 오늘 점심시간에 혼자 밥을 먹었잖아. 가엾은 Bella!
➡ _____

18 Joy: Jenny는 Bella의 가장 친한 친구야.
➡ _____

19 나는 우리가 모르는 어떤 이유가 있다고 확신해.
➡ _____

20 Anger: 나는 더 이상 이 상황을 못 참아.
➡ _____

21 Bella는 일단 가서 Jenny에게 자신의 감정을 말해야 해.
➡ _____

22 Fear: 나는 Bella가 또다시 상처받는 걸 원하지 않아.
➡ _____

23 그 애는 그냥 내버려 두어야 해.
➡ _____

24 Joy: 그 애들은 좋은 친구야. 그 애들이 잘 해낼 거야.
➡ _____

Day 3

25 Joy: 휴! 나는 그 애들이 다시 이야기하게 되어 무척 기뻐.
➡ _____

26 Anger: 그래, Bella가 Jenny에게 가서 그 애에게 먼저 말을 걸었지.
➡ _____

27 Joy: Jenny는 일부러 Bella를 피한 게 아니었어.
➡ _____

28 Sadness: 맞아, Jenny는 사과하는 방법을 몰랐던 거야.
➡ _____

29 Fear: 나는 Bella에게 이번과 같은 문제가 더 이상 없기를 바라.
➡ _____

30 Joy: 나도 그래. 하지만 문제들은 성장의 일부야.
➡ _____

31 이번과 꼭 마찬가지로 Bella는 문제들에 직면하게 될 거고, 그것들을 해결할 거고, 그리고 결국 더 현명해질 거야.
➡ _____

[01~06] 다음 글을 읽고 물음에 답하시오.

Bella is 15 years old this year and these days her feelings are going up and down. Today, she looks (A)_____. Let's listen to Bella's feelings and find out why.

Day 1

Anger: What a day! I can't believe Jenny yelled at Bella after the school play.

Sadness: Well, that's because Bella forgot her lines on stage.

Anger: Jenny pointed out the mistake (B)_____ Bella made. How could she do (C)that in front of everyone?

Joy: But I'm sure Jenny did not mean to hurt Bella. They have been best friends (D)_____ elementary school. Remember?

Anger: That's what I'm saying. A true friend would never put Bella down like that.

Fear: I'm worried that they are not going to be friends anymore.

Joy: Come on, Fear. Don't go too far. We'll see.

01 빈칸 (A)에 알맞은 말을 위 글에서 찾아 쓰시오.

➡ _____

02 다음 중 빈칸 (B)에 들어갈 말로 적절한 것을 <u>모두</u> 고르시오.

① which ② that ③ who
④ what ⑤ whose

03 밑줄 친 (C)가 의미하는 것을 우리말로 쓰시오.

➡ _____

04 다음 중 빈칸 (D)에 들어갈 말과 <u>다른</u> 말이 들어가는 것은?

① We have known you _____ you were a baby.
② I have studied English _____ 2010.
③ You have sung the same song _____ an hour.
④ They have played the computer game _____ 5 o'clock.
⑤ He has exercised regularly _____ he was in college.

05 다음 중 위 글을 읽고 답할 수 <u>없는</u> 것은?

① How old is Bella?
② How are Bella's feelings these days?
③ What did Jenny do to Bella today?
④ Why did Bella forget her lines on stage?
⑤ What is Joy sure about?

06 다음 질문의 답을 위 글에서 찾아 쓰시오.

> **Q:** Why did Jenny yell at Bella after the school play?

➡ _____

[07~10] 다음 글을 읽고 물음에 답하시오.

Anger: I can't forgive Jenny. She didn't say a word to Bella.

Fear: Jenny didn't even look at ⓐher. (A) <u>Jenny has never been this cold before.</u>

Sadness: Bella ate alone during lunch today. Poor Bella!

Joy: Jenny is ⓑher best friend. I'm sure there is a reason that we don't know about.

Anger: I can't stand this any longer. Bella should just go and tell ⓒ<u>her</u> about ⓓ <u>her</u> feelings.

Fear: I don't want ⓔ<u>her</u> to be hurt again. She should let it go.

Joy: They are good friends. They will work it out.

07 다음 중 밑줄 친 (A)에서 쓰인 현재완료와 그 쓰임이 같은 것은?

① We <u>have</u> just <u>left</u> the restaurant.
② How long <u>have</u> you <u>been</u> here?
③ Helen <u>has</u> never <u>met</u> the mailman.
④ I <u>have lost</u> it, so I don't know where it is.
⑤ <u>Has</u> he <u>finished</u> his project yet?

08 밑줄 친 ⓐ~ⓔ에서 지칭하는 바가 <u>다른</u> 하나는?

① ⓐ   ② ⓑ   ③ ⓒ   ④ ⓓ   ⑤ ⓔ

09 다음 중 위 글의 내용과 일치하지 <u>않는</u> 것은?

① Jenny said nothing to Bella.
② Jenny didn't look at Bella even once.
③ Anger doesn't want to bear the situation.
④ Fear thinks Bella should let Jenny go.
⑤ Joy is hopeful about Jenny and Bella.

서답형
10 다음과 같이 풀이되는 말을 위 글에서 찾아 쓰시오.

to stop being angry with someone and stop blaming

➡ _____

[11~14] 다음 글을 읽고 물음에 답하시오.

Joy: Whew! I'm so happy that they are talking again.

Anger: Yeah, Bella went to Jenny and talked to her first.

Joy: Jenny didn't avoid Bella (A)____ purpose.

Sadness: Yeah, Jenny didn't know a way to say sorry.

Fear: I hope Bella doesn't have any more problems like this.

Joy: Me, too. But problems are (B)성장의 일부. Just like this time, Bella will face the problems, solve them, and become wiser (C)<u>in the end</u>.

11 다음 중 빈칸 (A)에 들어갈 말과 같은 말이 들어가는 것은?

① She is not satisfied _____ the result.
② Don't give _____. You can do it.
③ She will take part _____ the race.
④ He came up _____ a great idea.
⑤ I'm cold. Can you turn _____ the heater?

서답형
12 밑줄 친 우리말 (B)를 영어로 쓰시오. (4단어)

➡ _____

13 다음 중 밑줄 친 (C)를 대신할 수 있는 것은?

① at last   ② suddenly
③ fortunately ④ lastly
⑤ lately

서답형
14 Write the reason why Joy is so happy. Fill in the blank with six words.

➡ Joy is happy because _____
_____

[15~19] 다음 글을 읽고 물음에 답하시오.

Bella is 15 years old this year and these days her feelings are going up and down. Today, she looks down. Let's (A)[listen / listen to] Bella's feelings and find out why.

Day 1

Anger: What a day! I can't believe Jenny yelled at Bella after the school play.

Sadness: Well, (B)[that's because / that's why] Bella forgot her @lines on stage.

Anger: Jenny pointed out the mistake that Bella made. How could she do that in front of everyone?

Joy: But I'm sure Jenny did not mean to hurt Bella. They (C)[were / have been] best friends since elementary school. Remember?

Anger: That's what I'm saying. A true friend would never put Bella down like that.

Fear: I'm worried that they are not going to be friends anymore.

Joy: Come on, Fear. Don't go too far. We'll see.

15 (A)~(C)에서 어법상 옳은 것끼리 바르게 짝지은 것은?

① listen – that's because - were
② listen – that's why – were
③ listen – that's because – have been
④ listen to – that's because – have been
⑤ listen to – that's why – have been

16 According to the passage, how does Bella feel these days?

➡ _____

17 What is Fear worried about? Answer in English with a full sentence.

➡ _____

_____

18 다음 중 밑줄 친 @를 풀이한 말로 가장 적절한 것은?

① a long thin mark which is drawn on a surface
② a line of written words, for example in a play or film
③ a long thin mark that appears on someone's skin as they grow older
④ the edge, outline, or shape of something
⑤ a row of people or things next to each other or behind each other

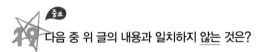

19 다음 중 위 글의 내용과 일치하지 않는 것은?

① Bella feels depressed today.
② Jenny shouted at Bella.
③ Joy is sure that Jenny intended to hurt Bella.
④ Jenny pointed out Bella's mistake in front of everyone.
⑤ Bella made a mistake on stage.

[20~23] 다음 글을 읽고 물음에 답하시오.

Anger: I can't forgive Jenny. She didn't say a word to Bella.

Fear: Jenny didn't even look at her. Jenny has never been this cold before.

Sadness: Bella ate alone during lunch today. Poor Bella!

Joy: Jenny is Bella's best friend. I'm sure there is a reason (A)that we don't know about.

Anger: I can't stand this any longer. Bella should just go and tell her about her feelings.

Fear: I don't want Bella to be hurt again. She should let it go.

Joy: They are good friends. They will work it out.

20 다음 중 밑줄 친 (A)와 쓰임이 다른 하나는?

① The cheese that you ate is not mine.

② People that participate in the game look happy.

③ The car that he wants to sell is a little old.

④ I will pay you back the money that you lent to me.

⑤ The news that he won first prize is true.

서답형

21 글의 내용에 맞게 빈칸에 알맞은 말을 쓰시오.

Sadness feels sorry for Bella because
_____.

서답형

22 What does Anger want Bella to do about her problem? Answer in English with a full sentence.

➡ _____

_____

23 다음 중 글의 내용과 일치하는 것은?

① Fear doesn't want to bear the situation.

② Fear is afraid that Bella will be hurt again.

③ Joy thinks Bella has to find another good friend.

④ Anger is upset by the fact that Bella ate alone.

⑤ Sadness wants Bella to tell her feelings.

[24~27] 다음 글을 읽고 물음에 답하시오.

Day 3

Joy: Whew! I'm so ⓐhappy that they are talking again.

Anger: Yeah, Bella went to Jenny and talked to her first.

Joy: Jenny didn't ⓑavoid Bella on purpose.

Sadness: Yeah, Jenny didn't know a way to say ⓒsorry.

Fear: I hope Bella doesn't have any more problems like (A)this.

Joy: Me, too. But problems are part of growing up. Just like this time, Bella will ⓓavoid the problems, ⓔsolve them, and become wiser in the end.

24 밑줄 친 ⓐ~ⓔ 중 글의 흐름상 어색한 것은?

① ⓐ   ② ⓑ   ③ ⓒ   ④ ⓓ   ⑤ ⓔ

중요

25 밑줄 친 (A)가 의미하는 것으로 가장 적절한 것은?

① Bella가 Jenny에게 화를 낸 것

② Jenny와 Bella가 서로 이야기하지 않는 것

③ Jenny가 Bella에게 사과하지 않은 것

④ Bella가 Jenny에게 먼저 다가간 것

⑤ Bella가 Jenny를 일부러 피한 것

서답형

26 글의 내용에 맞게 다음 빈칸에 알맞은 말을 쓰시오.

According to Joy, Bella will become
_____ by solving problems with Jenny.

서답형

27 다음은 Jenny에게 Bella가 한 말이다. 빈칸에 알맞은 말을 쓰시오.

We _____ _____ _____ to each other for two days. Now I want to solve the problem between us.

[01~05] 다음 글을 읽고, 물음에 답하시오.

Bella is 15 years old this year and these days her feelings are going up and down. Today, she looks down. Let's listen to Bella's feelings and find out (A)why.

Day 1

Anger: What a day! I can't believe Jenny yelled at Bella after the school play.

Sadness: Well, that's because Bella forgot her lines on stage.

Anger: (B)Jenny pointed out the mistake that Bella made. How could she do that in front of everyone?

Joy: But I'm sure Jenny did not mean to hurt Bella. (C)They became best friends in elementary school. They are still best friends. Remember?

Anger: That's what I'm saying. A true friend would never put Bella down like that.

Fear: I'm worried that they are not going to be friends anymore.

Joy: Come on, Fear. Don't go too far. We'll see.

01 밑줄 친 (A)가 의미하는 것을 완전한 문장으로 쓰시오.

➡ _____

02 밑줄 친 (B)를 두 문장으로 나누어 쓰시오.

➡ _____

➡ _____

03 밑줄 친 문장 (C)를 하나의 문장으로 쓰시오.

➡ _____

04 What mistake did Bella make? Answer in English with a full sentence.

➡ _____

05 다음 물음에 완전한 문장의 영어로 답하시오.

Q: What did Jenny do to Bella after the school play?

➡ _____

[06~08] 다음 글을 읽고 물음에 답하시오.

Day 2

Anger: I can't forgive Jenny. She didn't say a word to Bella.

Fear: Jenny didn't even look at her. Jenny has never been this cold before.

Sadness: Bella ate alone during lunch today. Poor Bella!

Joy: Jenny is Bella's best friend. I'm sure there is a reason that we don't know about.

Anger: I can't stand this any longer. Bella should just go and tell her about her feelings.

Fear: I don't want Bella to be hurt again. She should let it go.

Joy: They are good friends. They will work it out.

06 What did Jenny do to Bella on the second day? Answer in English with a full sentence.

➡ _____

➡ _____

위 글의 표현을 이용하여 다음 우리말을 영어로 쓰시오.

> 나는 전에 나의 가장 친한 친구를 용서해 본 적이 있다.

➡ _____

08 다음 물음에 'It's because'를 사용하여 답하시오.

> Q: Why does Sadness say "Poor Bella"?

➡ _____

[09~11] 다음 글을 읽고 물음에 답하시오.

Day 3
Joy: Whew! I'm so happy that they are talking again.
Anger: Yeah, Bella went to Jenny and talked to her first.
Joy: Jenny didn't avoid Bella on purpose.
Sadness: Yeah, Jenny didn't know a way to say sorry.
Fear: I hope Bella doesn't have any more problems like this.
Joy: Me, too. But problems are part of growing up. Just like this time, Bella will face the problems, solve them, and become wiser in the end.

09 다음 질문에 대한 답을 위 글의 내용에 맞게 완성하시오.

> Q: How did Bella make up with Jenny?
> A: _____,
>   so they cleared up the misunderstanding.

10 다음 빈칸에 알맞은 말을 쓰시오.

> According to Joy, the problems _____ _____ _____ help us to become wiser.

 Fill in the blank with the reason why Jenny avoided Bella.

> Jenny avoided Belly because _____
> _____.

[12~15] 다음 글을 읽고 물음에 답하시오.

Dear Worry Doll,
 (A)_____ I'm worried about my terrible math grades. I (B)(have) this problem since last year. I want to do better in math. But when I try to study math, I just can't focus on it. (C)무엇을 해야 할지 모르겠어. I have not had a good night's sleep because of (D)this worry. Can you take my worries away?

12 다음 두 문장을 하나의 문장으로 바꿔 빈칸 (A)에 쓰시오.

> • I want to tell you a problem.
> • I have a problem.

➡ _____

13 (B)에 주어진 동사를 어법에 맞게 고쳐 쓰시오.

➡ _____

14 to부정사를 이용하여 밑줄 친 우리말 (C)를 영어로 쓰시오.

➡ _____

15 밑줄 친 (D)가 의미하는 것을 위 글에서 찾아 쓰시오.

➡ _____

Wrap up 1

Mr. Jones: Daisy, you're late again.

Daisy: I'm really sorry, Mr. Jones. I stayed up late again last night.

Mr. Jones: Well, I think you should try to go to bed earlier.

try to+동사원형: ~하려고 노력하다. cf. try ~ing: (시험 삼아) ~해 보다

You should also pack your bag the night before, so you can save time in

시간을 절약하다

the morning.

Daisy: Okay, Mr. Jones. I'll try your advice.

구문해설 • stay up late: 늦게까지 자지 않고 깨어 있다 • pack: (짐을) 싸다 • advice: 조언

Read & Think

Bella: Jenny, I was upset when you pointed out my mistake in front of others.

때를 나타내는 부사절 접속사   other people

But I'm sure you didn't mean to hurt my feelings.

Jenny: I'm so sorry, Bella. Thanks for coming up to me first.

전치사의 목적어(동명사)

구문해설 • upset: 화난 • point out: 지적하다 • mistake: 실수 • in front of: ~ 앞에서

• others: 다른 사람들 • mean to V: V을 의도하다

Think and Write

Dear Worry Doll,

I want to tell you a problem that I have. I'm worried about my terrible math

목적격 관계대명사

grades. I have had this problem since last year. I want to do better in math.

현재완료(계속)   since+특정 시점   to부정사를 목적어로 취하는 동사

But when I try to study math, I just can't focus on it. I don't know what to do.

무엇을 해야 할지(= what I should do)

I have not had a good night's sleep because of this worry. Can you take my

현재완료 부정문

worries away?

구문해설 • terrible: 끔찍한, 형편없는 • grade: 성적. 점수 • better: 더 나은 • because of: ~ 때문에

• take A away: A를 없애 주다

해석

Mr. Jones: Daisy, 너 또 지각이구나.

Daisy: Jones 선생님, 정말 죄송해요. 어젯밤에 또 늦게까지 자지 않고 깨어 있었어요.

Mr. Jones: 음, 내 생각엔 넌 더 일찍 잠자리에 들려고 노력해야 할 것 같구나. 또 전날 밤에 가방을 싸 둔다면 아침에 시간을 절약할 수 있어.

Daisy: 알겠어요, Jones 선생님. 조언해 주신 것을 해 볼게요.

Bella: Jenny야, 네가 다른 사람들 앞에서 내 잘못을 지적했을 때 화가 났었어. 그렇지만 난 네가 내게 상처를 주려고 일부러 그런 게 아니라고 믿어.

Jenny: Bella야, 미안해. 먼저 내게 와 줘서 고마워.

걱정 인형에게.

나는 너에게 내가 가진 문제를 말하고 싶어. 나는 나의 끔찍한 수학 성적이 걱정 돼. 나는 작년부터 이 문제를 가지고 있어. 나는 수학을 더 잘하고 싶어. 하지만 내가 수학을 공부하려고 하면, 나는 그것에 집중할 수 없어. 무엇을 해야 할지 모르겠어. 이 걱정 때문에 밤에 잠도 잘 못 자. 내 걱정을 없애 줄 수 있겠니?

영역별 핵심문제

01 다음 영영풀이가 가리키는 것을 고르시오.

> to stop feeling angry with somebody who has done something to harm, annoy or upset you

① give
② forgive
③ receive
④ fight
⑤ share

02 다음 중 밑줄 친 부분의 뜻풀이가 바르지 <u>않은</u> 것은?

① A bear can <u>grow up</u> to two meters in height. 성장하다
② I usually <u>gain weight</u> in winter. 체중이 늘다
③ They won the Olympic medal <u>in the end</u>. 결국
④ John pushed me hard <u>on purpose</u>. 실수로
⑤ I'll <u>let it go</u> this time. 내버려두다

03 다음 우리말을 주어진 단어를 이용하여 영작하시오.

(1) 너는 가까이에 있는 문제에 집중해야 한다. (hand, problem, on)

　➡ _____

(2) 우리는 또 다시 문제에 직면할 수 있다. (face)

　➡ _____

(3) 아이들이 요즘은 아주 빠르게 성장한다. (so, these, up, fast)

　➡ _____

04 다음 짝지어진 단어의 관계가 같도록 빈칸에 알맞은 말을 쓰시오.

> wise : stupid = advanced : _____

05 다음 주어진 문장의 밑줄 친 lines와 같은 의미로 쓰인 것은?

> It is difficult for me to memorize the <u>lines</u> perfectly.

① The red <u>lines</u> refer to the main roads on the map.
② I was embarrassed when I forgot my <u>lines</u>.
③ I'm not good at drawing <u>lines</u> without a ruler.
④ I think the cable <u>lines</u> seem to be damaged.
⑤ I found out just dots and <u>lines</u> on this picture.

06 다음 문장에 공통으로 들어갈 말을 고르시오.

> • I'm sorry, but I didn't _____ it.
> • I hate the man who is _____ about money.
> • Are there any _____s of contacting Mike?

① stand
② mean
③ check
④ fight
⑤ point

Conversation

[07~08] 다음 대화를 읽고 물음에 답하시오.

> Emily: I was (A)[late / lately] for class again. I just can't wake up in the morning.
>
> Tom: Do you set an alarm?
>
> Emily: Yeah, but I turn it (B)[on / off] and go back to sleep.
>
> Tom: I think you should put it (C)[close to / far from] your bed. That way, you'll have to get out of bed.

07 위 대화의 빈칸 (A)~(C)에 알맞은 말로 짝지어진 것은?

	(A)	(B)	(C)
①	late	on	close to
②	late	off	far from
③	late	off	close to
④	lately	off	far from
⑤	lately	on	close to

08 위 대화의 내용과 일치하지 <u>않는</u> 것은?

① Emily는 전에도 수업에 늦은 적이 있다.
② Emily는 아침에 일어나는 데 어려움을 겪고 있다.
③ Emily는 자명종을 잘못 맞추어 놓는다.
④ Emily는 자명종을 끄고 다시 잠든다.
⑤ Tom은 Emily에게 자명종을 침대에서 멀리 둘 것을 조언한다.

09 다음 대화의 내용과 일치하도록 Amy의 일기를 완성하시오.

> Solomon: Hello, you're on the air.
>
> Amy: Hi, Solomon. I'm Amy.
>
> Solomon: Hi, Amy. What's the matter?
>
> Amy: I hate sharing my room with my little sister. She uses my stuff without asking me first. What should I do?
>
> Solomon: Hmm.... I think you should tell her your feelings. And you should also make some rules with your sister.
>
> Amy: Oh, I'll try that. Thanks for the advice.

> Mon, 26th Aug, 2019
>
> I was upset again because my little sister used my stuff without asking me first. I didn't want to (A)_____ anymore. To solve this problem, I called Solomon and asked him to give me his (B)_____. He advised me to (C)_____ _____.
> It was a great advice for me and I decided to try that.

10 다음 대화가 자연스럽게 이어지도록 순서대로 배열하시오.

> (A) No, not yet. I don't know what to do.
> (B) Oh, no. Did you tell your sister?
> (C) You don't look so happy today. What's the matter?
> (D) I wore my sister's favorite T-shirt. But I got grape juice on it.

➡ _____

[11~12] 다음 대화를 읽고 물음에 답하시오.

> Eric: (A) Ms. Morris, I just can't stop playing computer games. What should I do?
>
> Ms. Morris: (B) When you set a time limit, the computer shuts down at that time.
>
> Eric: (C) Oh, that's a good idea.
>
> Ms. Morris: (D) And I think you should move the computer out of your room and into the living room.
>
> Eric: (E) I think I should. Thank you for the advice, Ms. Morris.

11 위 대화의 (A)~(E) 중 주어진 문장이 들어가기에 적절한 곳은?

> Well, why don't you use a special program?

① (A)　② (B)　③ (C)　④ (D)　⑤ (E)

12 위 대화를 읽고 대답할 수 <u>없는</u> 것은?

① What's the matter with Eric?
② Why can't Eric stop playing computer games?
③ Why does Ms. Morris recommend using a special program?
④ Where will Eric move his computer?
⑤ Where does Eric use his computer?

[13~14] 다음 대화를 읽고 물음에 답하시오.

> Sora: David, you look down today. What's the matter?
> David: I got a haircut but it's too short. I look funny.
> Sora: Take off your hat and let me see. (*pause*) Oh, it looks fine.
> David: Really? I guess I'm just not used to it yet.

13 Why did David feel down?

➡ _____

14 What did Sora think about David's haircut?

➡ _____

Grammar

15 다음 중 that이 들어가기에 가장 적절한 곳은?

> The watch (①) you are looking for (②) is (③) on the table (④) in your room (⑤).

①　　②　　③　　④　　⑤

16 다음 우리말을 영어로 바르게 옮기지 <u>않은</u> 것은?

> 그들은 김 선생님이 영어를 가르친 학생들이다.

① They are the students who Mr. Kim taught English.
② They are the students to whom Mr. Kim taught English.
③ They are the students Mr. Kim taught English.
④ They are the students whom Mr. Kim taught English.
⑤ They are the students who taught Mr. Kim English.

17 다음 빈칸에 들어갈 말로 적절한 것을 <u>모두</u> 고르시오.

> The suitcase _____ she brought into this room is similar to mine.

① who　　② which　　③ that
④ whose　　⑤ whom

18 괄호 안의 단어를 바르게 배열하여 문장을 완성하시오.

> The person (about / I / most / whom / care) is not her but you.

➡ _____

19 다음 문장을 읽고 알 수 있는 것을 <u>모두</u> 고르시오.

> Jason has just come back home from his journey.

① Jason has gone on his journey.

② Jason went on a journey.

③ Jason wants to go on his journey.

④ Jason has not arrived at his home yet.

⑤ Jason is at his home now.

20 다음 중 서로 의미가 같지 <u>않은</u> 것은?

① I didn't see her. I still don't know where she is.

→ I have not seen her lately.

② Paul is the man. I work with him.

→ Paul is the man I work with.

③ I lost my umbrella. But I have it now.

→ I have lost my umbrella.

④ The coffee is too hot. June is drinking it.

→ The coffee which June is drinking is too hot.

⑤ Where is the jacket? You have had it since 2010.

→ Where is the jacket you have had since 2010?

21 다음 중 주어진 문장의 현재완료와 쓰임이 같은 것은?

> Mike <u>has visited</u> this place many times.

① Yumi <u>has</u> just <u>read</u> the book.

② He <u>has written</u> many books since 1990.

③ They <u>have watched</u> the movie for an hour.

④ Tom <u>has cleaned</u> his room already.

⑤ We <u>have been</u> to Washington.

22 다음 대화의 빈칸에 알맞은 말을 네 단어로 쓰시오.

> A: Where is Sally?
>
> B: Oh, _____ her home.
>
> A: Do you mean she is not here now?
>
> A: Yes.

23 다음 중 어법상 바르지 <u>않은</u> 것은?

① The bread Susan is baking smells good.

② They have noticed it more than twice until now.

③ How long have you waited for her yesterday?

④ Where are all the guests whom you invited?

⑤ Can you tell me the secret which Katherine told you?

24 다음 두 문장을 하나의 문장으로 쓰시오.

> • I will read the book.
> • I borrowed it from the library.

➡ _____

Reading

[25~28] 다음 글을 읽고 물음에 답하시오.

Bella is 15 years old this year and these days her feelings are going up and down. Today, she looks down. Let's listen to Bella's feelings and find out why.

Day 1

Anger: What a day! I can't believe Jenny yelled at Bella after the school play.

Sadness: Well, that's because Bella forgot her lines on stage.

Anger: Jenny pointed out the mistake (A)that Bella made. How could she do that in front of everyone?

Joy: But I'm sure Jenny did not mean to hurt Bella. They have been best friends since elementary school. Remember?

Anger: That's what I'm saying. A true friend would never put Bella down like that.

Fear: I'm worried that they are not going to be friends anymore.

Joy: Come on, Fear. (B)Don't go too far. We'll see.

25 다음 중 밑줄 친 (A)와 쓰임이 같은 것은?

① Do you think that he is honest?
② Jimmy believes that she stole the bag.
③ This is the man that I admire very much.
④ The fact that she is older than me doesn't matter.
⑤ How do you know that he came back?

26 다음 중 밑줄 친 (B)의 의미로 가장 적절한 것은?

① Don't go farther than I expected.
② Don't think that you can go as far as you want.
③ Bella should run away as far as possible.
④ Don't think that they are not going to be friends anymore.
⑤ Try to be nice to the friends in need.

27 According to the conversation, what did Bella forget on stage? Answer in English with a full sentence.

➡ _____

28 다음 중 위 글을 읽고 답할 수 <u>없는</u> 것은?

① How does Bella look today?
② Who yelled at Bella today?
③ Who pointed out Bella's mistake?
④ Who is Bella's best friend?
⑤ What is the name of the school play?

[29~31] 다음 글을 읽고 물음에 답하시오.

Joy: Whew! I'm so happy that they are talking again.

Anger: Yeah, Bella went to Jenny and talked to her first.

Joy: Jenny didn't avoid Bella (A)on purpose.

Sadness: Yeah, Jenny didn't know a way to say sorry.

Fear: I hope Bella doesn't have any more problems like this.

Joy: Me, too. But problems are part of growing up. Just like this time, Bella will face the problems, solve them, and become wiser in the end.

29 다음 중 밑줄 친 (A)를 대신하여 쓸 수 있는 것은?

① all of sudden   ② by accident
③ intentionally   ④ by mistake
⑤ immediately

30 주어진 어구를 바르게 배열하여 Bella와 Jenny가 처해 있던 문제의 결과를 쓰시오.

Bella and Jenny / each other / with / up / finally / made

➡ _____

31 위 글의 내용과 일치하지 <u>않는</u> 것은?

① Joy feels happy because Bella is talking with Jenny again.
② It was Bella that went to Jenny and talked to her first.
③ Jenny didn't know how to say sorry.
④ Bella doesn't want to face problems like this.
⑤ Problems are part of growth.

[01~02] 다음 대화를 읽고 물음에 답하시오.

> Sujin: I don't know how to do better in math.
>   (A)_____
> Jake: How do you study for tests?
> Sujin: I just solve a lot of problems.
> Jake: Well, don't solve everything. (B)I think you should focus on the ones you got wrong.

출제율 90%

01 위 대화의 빈칸 (A)에 들어가기에 어색한 것은?

① What should I do to improve my math?
② Would you give me some tips for me?
③ Could you tell me what to do?
④ How can I help you?
⑤ Can you give me some advice?

출제율 95%

02 위 대화의 밑줄 친 (B)와 바꾸어 쓰기가 어색한 것은?

① Why don't you focus on the ones you got wrong?
② How about focusing on the ones you got wrong?
③ You had better focus on the ones you got wrong.
④ You need to focus on the ones you got wrong.
⑤ You don't have to focus on the ones you got wrong.

[03~05] 다음 대화를 읽고 물음에 답하시오.

> Jane: You look tired. What's the matter?
> Mike: I didn't have breakfast this morning. I'm so hungry.
> Jane: Oh, that's too bad. We still have two more hours until lunch break.
> Mike: Our school should have a snack bar. Then, we could have a quick breakfast or snacks.

> Jane: I think so, too. How can we make that suggestion?
> Mike: We can post it on the suggestion board.

출제율 90%

03 Why doesn't Mike look good?

➡ _____

출제율 85%

04 How long should Jane and Mike wait for lunch break?

➡ _____

출제율 90%

05 What can Jane and Mike do if there is a snack bar in school?

➡ _____

[06~07] 다음 대화를 읽고 물음에 답하시오.

> Solomon: Hello, you're on the air.
> Amy: Hi, Solomon. I'm Amy.
> Solomon: Hi, Amy. What's the matter?
> Amy: I hate sharing my room with my little sister. She uses my stuff without asking me first. What should I do?
> Solomon: Hmm.... _____ And you should also make some rules with your sister.
> Amy: Oh, I'll try that. Thanks for the advice.

출제율 95%

06 위 대화의 빈칸에 들어갈 말을 주어진 단어를 배열하여 완성하시오.

┌─ 보기 ┐
feelings / you / tell / your / her / I / think / should
└──────┘

➡ _____

07 위 대화를 읽고 알 수 <u>없는</u> 것은?

① Why did Amy call Solomon?

② What's wrong with Amy?

③ Why didn't Amy like sharing her room with her little sister?

④ What is Solomon's advice?

⑤ How will Amy make up with her little sister?

[08~09] 다음 대화를 읽고 물음에 답하시오.

Julia: Kevin, you look so nervous. What's the matter?

Kevin: I dropped my mom's new glasses and broke them.

Julia: (A)_____ So, your mom also knows about it?

Kevin: Not yet. I can't tell her about it. What should I do?

Julia: Just tell her first before she finds out about it.

08 위 대화에서 나타난 Kevin의 심경으로 적절한 것은?

① relieved　　　② lonely

③ worried　　　④ surprised

⑤ angry

09 위 대화의 빈칸 (A)에 들어갈 말로 적절한 것을 <u>모두</u> 고르시오.

① I'm very disappointed.

② I'm sorry to hear that.

③ I can't stand it.

④ Oh, that's terrible.

⑤ What a relief!

---

10 다음 대화가 자연스럽게 이어지도록 순서대로 배열하시오.

(A) Okay, Mr. Jones. I'll try your advice.

(B) Daisy, you're late again.

(C) Well, I think you should try to go to bed earlier. You should also pack your bag the night before, so you can save time in the morning.

(D) I'm really sorry, Mr. Jones. I stayed up late again last night.

➡ _____

---

11 다음 중 주어진 문장에 쓰인 현재완료와 쓰임이 <u>다른</u> 것은?

They <u>have</u> not <u>passed</u> the test yet.

① There <u>has</u> just <u>been</u> a car accident.

② Nick <u>has</u> already <u>heard</u> about the news.

③ Karl <u>has</u> just <u>parked</u> his car in the parking lot.

④ Lora <u>has traveled</u> alone many times.

⑤ We <u>have</u> not <u>decided</u> what to do yet.

12 〈보기〉와 같이 하나의 문장을 둘로 나누어 쓰시오.

┤ 보기 ├

Who is the woman whom your sister wants to talk to?

➡ Who is the woman? Your sister wants to talk to her.

(1) Where is the man who you cheered for?

➡ _____

(2) The car that Tony Stark drives in the movie is very expensive.

➡ _____

13 다음 빈칸에 공통으로 들어갈 말로 가장 적절한 것은?

> - This is the key _____ Christine gave to me.
> - I know the boy _____ you met at a dance party.

① who　　② which　　③ whom
④ whose　　⑤ that

14 다음 중 어법상 바르지 않은 것은?

① The train has left already.
② That is the famous building which Antonio Gaudi built.
③ Do you know about the book that Joe is reading it?
④ When did you get the phone call?
⑤ I have not had dinner with her for a month.

15 다음 밑줄 친 부분 중 생략할 수 없는 것은?

① Everything that he told you is true.
② It is not easy to find the money that someone stole from you.
③ Where is the milk that Mom put in the refrigerator?
④ The information that you found is very valuable to us.
⑤ She wants me to buy a jacket that has many pockets.

16 다음 두 문장을 여섯 단어로 이루어진 하나의 문장으로 표현하시오.

> I lost my cell phone. I still can't find it until now.

➡ _____

17 주어진 문장과 같은 의미가 되도록 빈칸에 알맞은 말을 쓰시오.

> We began to see this movie two hours ago. And we still see it.
> = We _____ _____ this movie _____ two hours.

[18~21] 다음 글을 읽고, 물음에 답하시오.

> Day 2
> Anger: I can't forgive Jenny. She didn't say a word to Bella.
> Fear: Jenny didn't even look (A)[at / after] her. Jenny has never been this cold before.
> Sadness: Bella ate alone (B)[while / during] lunch today. Poor Bella!
> Joy: Jenny is Bella's best friend. @I'm sure there is a reason that we don't know about.
> Anger: I can't stand this any longer. Bella should just go and tell her about her feelings.
> Fear: I don't want Bella to be hurt again. She should let it go.
> Joy: They are good friends. They will (C)[work it out / work out it].

18 (A)~(C)에서 어법상 옳은 것끼리 바르게 짝지은 것은?

① at – while – work it out
② at – during – work out it
③ at – during – work it out
④ after – during – work out it
⑤ after – while – work it out

19 밑줄 친 문장 @를 두 문장으로 나누어 쓰시오.

➡ _____

➡ _____

출제율 95%

20 다음 중 위 글의 내용과 일치하지 <u>않는</u> 것은?

① Jenny said nothing to Bella on the second day.

② Jenny has not been this cold to Bella before.

③ Bella didn't have lunch today.

④ Anger wants Bella to tell her feelings to Jenny.

⑤ Joy thinks Bella and Jenny are good friends.

출제율 90%

21 위 글의 내용에 맞게 다음 물음에 완전한 문장의 영어로 답하시오.

> **Q:** What does Fear want for Bella?

➡ _____

[22~24] 다음 글을 읽고 물음에 답하시오.

Day 3

Joy: Whew! I'm so happy that they are talking again.

Anger: Yeah, Bella went to Jenny and talked to her first.

Joy: Jenny didn't avoid Bella on purpose.

Sadness: Yeah, Jenny didn't know a way (A)<u>to say</u> sorry.

Fear: I hope Bella doesn't have any more problems like this.

Joy: Me, too. But problems are part of growing up. Just like this time, Bella will face the problems, solve them, and become wiser in the end.

출제율 100%

22 다음 중 밑줄 친 (A)와 쓰임이 같은 것은?

① Tom went to the office <u>to get</u> the job.

② I want you <u>to make</u> up your mind.

③ David decided <u>to finish</u> the project.

④ I am so happy <u>to see</u> you again.

⑤ I have something <u>to talk</u> to you.

출제율 95%

23 What does Fear hope? Answer in English with a full sentence.

➡ _____

_____

출제율 90%

24 다음 중 위 글의 내용과 일치하지 <u>않는</u> 것은?

> ①Thanks to Bella's effort, Bella and Jenny were back to being friends. ② Bella told Jenny about her feelings first. ③Owing to Bella's courage, she found out that Jenny avoided her on purpose. ④She just didn't know a good way to say sorry. ⑤Bella will become wiser by solving problems like this.

①　　②　　③　　④　　⑤

[25~26] 다음 글을 읽고 물음에 답하시오.

Dear Worry Doll,

I want to tell you a problem (A)_____ I have. I'm worried about my terrible math grades. (B)_____ I want to do better in math. But when I try to study math, I just can't focus on it. I don't know what to do. I have not had a good night's sleep because of this worry. Can you take my worries away?

출제율 90%

25 다음 중 빈칸 (A)에 들어갈 말로 적절한 것을 <u>모두</u> 고르시오.

① that　　② what　　③ who

④ which　　⑤ whom

출제율 90%

26 다음 두 문장을 하나의 문장으로 바꿔 빈칸 (B)에 쓰시오.

> I had this problem last year. I still have it.

➡ _____

[01~03] 다음 대화를 읽고 물음에 답하시오.

Eric: Ms. Morris, I just can't stop playing computer games. (A)제가 어떻게 해야 할까요?(should)

Ms. Morris: Well, why don't you use a special program? When you set a time limit, the computer shuts down at that time.

Eric: Oh, that's a good idea.

Ms. Morris: And I think you should move the computer out of your room and into the living room.

Eric: I thinks I should. Thank you for the advice, Ms. Morris.

01 위 대화의 밑줄 친 (A)의 우리말을 주어진 단어를 사용하여 영작하시오.

➡ _____

02 What happens if Eric sets a time limit using the special program?

➡ _____

03 Where does Ms. Morris advise Eric to move the computer?

➡ _____

_____

04 다음 우리말을 영어로 각각 쓰시오.

(1) 너는 부산에 가 본 적이 있니?
(2) 그녀는 부산에 가고 없습니다.

➡ (1) _____
(2) _____

05 자연스러운 문장이 되도록 관계대명사를 이용하여 하나의 문장으로 바꿔 쓰시오.

- The box is not that heavy.
- The restaurant is crowded with people.
- The children are very noisy.

- Paul runs it.
- She is lifting it.
- I take care of them.

➡ _____

➡ _____

➡ _____

06 알맞은 질문으로 대화를 완성하시오.

A: _____

B: We have known each other for 10 years.

➡ _____

07 주어진 어구를 바르게 배열하여 다음 우리말을 영어로 쓰시오.

Tom이 바라보고 있는 그 소녀는 Danny의 친구이다.
(Danny's friend / is / is / looking / whom / the girl / at / Tom)

➡ _____

다음 우리말에 맞도록 빈칸에 알맞은 말을 네 단어로 쓰시오.

> Jimmy가 쓰고 있는 헬멧은 나의 것과 비슷해.
> = The helmet _____
>   is similar to mine.

09 다음 대화의 빈칸에 알맞은 말을 쓰시오.

> A: How long _____ your brother
>   _____ golf?
> B: He learned golf _____ he was seven
>   years old. So he _____ _____
>   golf _____ five years.

[10~14] 다음 글을 읽고 물음에 답하시오.

> Bella is 15 years old this year and these days her feelings are going up and down. Today, she looks down. Let's listen to Bella's feelings and find out why.
> Day 1
> Anger: What a day! I can't believe Jenny yelled at Bella after the school play.
> Sadness: Well, (A)that's because Bella forgot her lines on stage.
> Anger: Jenny pointed out the mistake that Bella made. How could she do that in front of everyone?
> Joy: But I'm sure Jenny did not mean to hurt Bella. They have been best friends since elementary school. Remember?
> Anger: That's what I'm saying. (B)_____
>   _____
> Fear: I'm worried that they are not going to be friends anymore.
> Joy: Come on, Fear. Don't go too far. We'll see.

10 밑줄 친 (A)가 의미하는 것을 위 글에서 찾아 쓰시오.

➡ _____

11 주어진 어구를 바르게 배열하여 빈칸 (B)에 들어갈 말을 쓰시오.

> (that / would / down / Bella / like / never / put / a true friend)

➡ _____

12 주어진 어구를 바르게 배열하여 다음 대화를 완성하시오.

> A: Bella, why are you so upset?
> B: I am upset because _____
>   _____.
>   And she even shouted loudly.
>   (everyone / Jenny / my mistake / out / in / of / front / pointed)

★13 위 글을 읽고 사건의 순서를 바르게 나열하시오.

> ⓐ Jenny yelled at Bella.
> ⓑ Bella was sad because of it.
> ⓒ Bella forgot her lines during the play.

➡ _____

14 다음 우리말에 맞게 빈칸에 알맞은 말을 7 단어로 쓰시오.

> 초등학교 때부터 알아온 Jenny는 나의 가장 친한 친구이다.
> ➡ Jenny _____
>   is my best friend.

01 다음 대화의 내용과 일치하도록 Mike의 일기를 완성하시오.

> Jane: You look tired. What's the matter?
>
> Mike: I didn't have breakfast this morning. I'm so hungry.
>
> Jane: Oh, that's too bad. We still have two more hours until lunch break.
>
> Mike: Our school should have a snack bar. Then, we could have a quick breakfast or snacks.
>
> Jane: I think so, too. How can we make that suggestion?
>
> Mike: We can post it on the suggestion board.

Mon, Sep 23rd, Sunny

I got up late and almost missed the bus. Fortunately, I wasn't late for school. But I felt so tired and hungry because (A)_____ in the morning. Even worse, I had to wait for (B)_____ for lunch break. I thought (C)_____ for hungry students. When I talked about it with Jane, she agreed with my idea. I made a plan to post my idea on (D)_____ soon.

02 주어진 어구와 현재완료 시제를 이용하여 자신과 친구에 관한 여러 가지 이야기를 써 보시오.

> argue with a friend   visit one's house   have a snow fight
>
> know him or her since   be to a concert before

(1) _____

(2) _____

(3) _____

(4) _____

(5) _____

03 다음 Ryan의 글을 읽고 주어진 어휘를 이용하여 빈칸을 채우시오.

> Hi. I'm Ryan. My family moved to New York in 2008 and we still live in New York. I took trip to Spain in 2011 and 2012 with my family. And Cooper, our dog, became a member of our family in 2013. He likes to play with a ball. Also, I became friends with John in 2016. He is my best friend.

(1) Ryan _____ for more than ten years. (live)

(2) Ryan _____ twice. (be)

(3) Ryan _____ 2013. (raise)

(4) Ryan _____ 2016. (know each other)

단원별 모의고사

01 다음 우리말에 맞게 빈칸에 알맞은 말을 쓰시오.

(1) 저는 제안을 하고 싶습니다.
➡ I'd like to make a _____.

(2) 결코 같은 실수를 반복하지 마라.
➡ Never _____ the same mistake.

(3) 약속을 지키지 못한 걸 용서해 주세요.
➡ Please _____ me for breaking my promise.

02 다음 문장에 공통으로 들어갈 말을 고르시오. (대·소문자 무시)

- I've been busy _____ I came here.
- _____ I'm driving my car, I'll drop by your office.
- _____ when are you a member of the dance club?

① for   ② at
③ because   ④ from
⑤ since

03 다음 문장의 빈칸에 들어갈 말을 〈보기〉에서 골라 쓰시오.

┌─ 보기 ─┐
up and down / work out / stay up late / wake up
└────────┘

(1) Did you _____ last night?
(2) Life goes _____.
(3) I _____ early in the morning.
(4) We can _____ any problem.

04 다음 문장의 빈칸에 들어갈 말을 〈보기〉에서 골라 쓰시오.

┌─ 보기 ─┐
pack / explain / fight / worry / yell
└────────┘

(1) I'll _____ the details of this product.
(2) You should not _____ or run in the museum.
(3) You don't have to _____ about this matter. Everything will be fine.
(4) I have to _____ for my business trip.
(5) My brother and I used to _____ like cat and dog.

[05~06] 다음 대화를 읽고 물음에 답하시오.

Sora: David, you look ⓐdown today. What's the matter?

David: I got a haircut but it's too short. I look funny.

Sora: Take off your hat and let me see. (*pause*) Oh, it looks fine.

David: Really? I guess I'm just not used to it yet.

05 위 대화의 밑줄 친 ⓐdown과 같은 의미로 쓰인 것은?

① Don't look down on me.
② When I feel down, I usually listen to music.
③ You don't need to write it down.
④ I jumped down off the second floor.
⑤ Would you turn the music down?

06 위 대화의 내용과 일치하는 것은?

① Sora needed a haircut.
② The boy really likes his haircut.
③ Sora takes off her hat to show her haircut to David.
④ David doesn't feel good because of his new hairstyle.
⑤ Sora used to have a short haircut.

[07~08] 다음 대화를 읽고 물음에 답하시오.

Solomon: Hello, you're on the air.
Amy: (A) Hi, Solomon. I'm Amy.
Solomon: (B) Hi, Amy. What's the matter?
Amy: (C) She uses my stuff without asking me first. What should I do?
Solomon: (D) Hmm.... I think you should tell her your feelings. And you should also make some rules with your sister.
Amy: (E) Oh, I'll try that. Thanks for the advice.

07 위 대화의 (A)~(E) 중 주어진 문장이 들어가기에 적절한 곳은?

I hate sharing my room with my little sister.

① (A) ② (B) ③ (C) ④ (D) ⑤ (E)

08 위 대화의 내용과 일치하지 <u>않는</u> 것은?

① Amy is talking to Solomon face to face.
② Amy has difficulty sharing her room with her little sister.
③ Amy's sister used Amy's stuff without asking her first.
④ Solomon advises Amy to tell her feelings to her sister.
⑤ Solomon recommends making some rules with her sister to Amy.

09 다음 대화의 내용과 일치하도록 다음 표의 빈칸을 완성하시오.

Jane: You look tired. What's the matter?
Mike: I didn't have breakfast this morning. I'm so hungry.
Jane: Oh, that's too bad. We still have two more hours until lunch break.
Mike: Our school should have a snack bar. Then, we could have a quick breakfast or snacks.
Jane: I think so, too. How can we make that suggestion?
Mike: We can post it on the suggestion board.

⬇

Let's Make a Better School	
Title	Many students are hungry!
Name	Mike, Jane
Suggestion	Some students don't have (A)_____, so they get (B)_____ in the morning. We should (C)_____.

[10~11] 다음 대화를 읽고 물음에 답하시오.

Mr. Jones: Daisy, you're late again.
Daisy: I'm really sorry, Mr. Jones. I stayed up late again last night.
Mr. Jones: Well, I think you should try to go to bed earlier. You should also pack your bag the night before, so you can save time in the morning.
Daisy: Okay, Mr. Jones. I'll try your advice.

10 Why is Daisy late again?

➡ _____

11 According to Mr. Jones, what should Daisy do to save time in the morning?

➡ _____

12 다음 주어진 우리말과 일치하도록 주어진 단어를 모두 배열하여 영작하시오.

(1) 나는 더 이상 그와 일하는 것을 견딜 수 없다.
(stand / him / more / working / any / I / with / can't)

➡ _____

(2) Minho는 영어로 된 대사를 외워야 한다.
(English / lines / memorize / Minho / his / to / in / has)

➡ _____

(3) 나는 그가 내 실수들을 지적했을 때 당황스러웠다.
(mistakes / he / pointed / I / my / was / when / embarrassed / out)

➡ _____

13 다음 빈칸에 알맞은 말이 바르게 짝지어진 것은?

- I have known Chris _____ I was in college.
- They have made the video _____ about three hours.

① for – for
② since – already
③ since – for
④ already – for
⑤ just – since

14 다음 우리말을 영어로 바르게 옮기지 <u>않은</u> 것은?

① 네가 어제 입은 외투는 멋져 보였어.
→ The jacket you wore yesterday looked fancy.
② 이곳에 얼마나 오랫동안 있었던 거야?
→ How long have you been here?
③ 네가 찾던 책이 여기에 있어.
→ The book you were looking for is here.
④ Tina는 그녀의 고향으로 가고 없습니다.
→ Tina has gone to her hometown.
⑤ 나는 네가 말하고 있는 사람을 알지 못해.
→ I don't know the person whom you are talking.

15 다음 중 어법상 바르지 <u>않은</u> 것은?

① There are some rules you have to keep.
② The apple juice which you drank this morning was made by my mom.
③ Ann has never worn the scarf.
④ I ate nothing since yesterday.
⑤ The music that I often listen to is very sad.

16 주어진 어구를 바르게 배열하여 다음 우리말을 영어로 쓰시오.

네가 나에게 사 주었던 그 케이크를 나는 방금 먹었어.
(me / I / for / have / bought / you / just / that / eaten / the cake)

➡ _____

17 주어진 단어를 이용하여 다음 문장을 하나의 문장으로 표현하시오.

I lost my gold necklace. I can't find it. (yet)

➡ _____

[18~20] 다음 글을 읽고 물음에 답하시오.

Bella is 15 years old this year and these days her feelings are going up and down. Today, she looks down. Let's listen to Bella's feelings and find out why.

Day 1

Anger: What a day! I can't believe Jenny yelled at Bella after the school play.

Sadness: Well, that's because Bella forgot her lines on stage.

Anger: Jenny pointed out the mistake that Bella made. How could she do that in front of everyone?

Joy: But I'm sure Jenny did not mean to hurt Bella. They have been best friends since elementary school. Remember?

Anger: That's what I'm saying. A true friend would never put Bella down like that.

Fear: I'm worried that they are not going to be friends anymore.

Joy: Come on, Fear. Don't go too far. We'll see.

18 다음은 Bella의 일기이다. 위 글의 내용과 일치하지 <u>않는</u> 것은?

①I was upset today. ②It was because of Jenny. ③She pointed out the mistake I made during the school play. ④And she even yelled at me during the play. ⑤ There were other people around us. I was so embarrassed.

①   ②   ③   ④   ⑤

19 위 글의 내용에 맞게 대화의 빈칸에 알맞은 말을 쓰시오.

A: Bella, did Jenny point out your mistake in a quiet place?
B: _____, _____. _____
_____.

20 다음 중 위 글의 내용과 일치하지 <u>않는</u> 것은?

① Bella forgot her lines on stage.
② It was Jenny that pointed out the mistake Bella made.
③ Joy believes that Jenny didn't intend to hurt Bella.
④ Jenny looks gloomy because of Bella.
⑤ Anger thinks Jenny is not Bella's true friend.

[21~23] 다음 글을 읽고 물음에 답하시오.

Day 2

Anger: I can't forgive Jenny. She didn't say a word to Bella.

Fear: Jenny didn't even look at her. Jenny has never been this cold before.

Sadness: Bella ate alone during lunch today. Poor Bella!

Joy: Jenny is Bella's best friend. I'm sure there is a reason that we don't know about.

Anger: I can't (A)_____ this any longer. Bella should just go and tell her about her feelings.

Fear: I don't want Bella to be hurt again. She should let it go.

Joy: They are good friends. They will work it out.

21 주어진 영영풀이를 참고하여 빈칸 (A)에 철자 s로 시작하는 단어를 쓰시오.

to be able to accept or deal well with a difficult situation

➡ _____

22 다음 중 둘째 날 일어난 일과 관련이 <u>없는</u> 것은?

① Jenny didn't say a word to Bella.
② Bella was cold toward Jenny.
③ Bella talked to Jenny first.
④ Bella ate lunch alone.
⑤ Jenny didn't look at Bella at all.

23 위 글의 내용에 맞게 다음 물음에 대한 답을 완성하시오.

Q: Why does Joy think Bella and Jenny will work it out?
A: Joy thinks that way because _____
_____.

Lesson 6

Doors to the Wild

 의사소통 기능

- 궁금한 일 표현하기

  A: This flower is bigger than a person.

  B: Yeah. **I'm curious about** the flower.

- 비교해 표현하기

  A: We got a new puppy yesterday.

  B: Oh, he's so small!

  A: Yeah. He's **as small as** my hand.

 언어 형식

- 가주어(it) ~ 진주어(to부정사)

  It is dangerous **to stay** alone in such a wild area.

- 원급 비교

  Stella's eyes were **as bright as** stars.

Words & Expressions

Key Words

- **adventurous** [ædvéntʃərəs] 형 모험심이 강한
- **allow** [əláu] 동 허락하다
- **appear** [əpíər] 동 나타나다
- **approach** [əpróutʃ] 동 다가가다, 다가오다
- **attack** [ətǽk] 동 공격하다
- **attract** [ətrǽkt] 동 끌다, ~을 끌어당기다
- **bat** [bæt] 명 박쥐
- **blind** [blaind] 형 눈 먼, 맹인인
- **careless** [kɛ́ərlis] 형 부주의한
- **curious** [kjúəriəs] 형 궁금한, 호기심이 많은
- **dangerous** [déindʒərəs] 형 위험한
- **dead** [ded] 형 죽은
- **dolphin** [dɑ́lfin] 명 돌고래
- **feed** [fi:d] 동 밥[우유]을 먹이다, 먹이를 주다
- **female** [fí:meil] 형 암컷의
- **friendship** [fréndʃip] 명 우정
- **giant** [dʒáiənt] 형 거대한
- **ginger** [dʒíndʒər] 명 생강
- **hole** [houl] 명 구멍
- **huge** [hju:dʒ] 형 거대한
- **humorous** [hjú:mərəs] 형 재미있는, 유머러스한
- **insect** [ínsekt] 명 곤충, 벌레
- **language** [lǽŋgwidʒ] 명 언어
- **lifeless** [láiflis] 형 죽은, 생명이 없는
- **probably** [prɑ́bəbli] 부 아마
- **pumpkin** [pʌ́mpkin] 명 호박
- **rescue** [réskju:] 명 구조
- **restless** [réstlis] 형 가만히 못 있는
- **seem** [si:m] 동 ~처럼 보이다
- **sense** [sens] 명 감각
- **sheet** [ʃi:t] 명 (종이) 한 장
- **shelter** [ʃéltər] 명 보호소
- **snake** [sneik] 명 뱀
- **strength** [streŋkθ] 명 힘
- **tail** [teil] 명 꼬리
- **thick** [θik] 형 두꺼운
- **throughout** [θru:áut] 전 ~ 동안, ~ 내내
- **tongue** [tʌŋ] 명 혀
- **trunk** [trʌŋk] 명 (코끼리의) 코
- **unbelievably** [ʌnbəlívəbli] 부 믿을 수 없을 정도로
- **whale** [hweil] 명 고래
- **wild** [waild] 형 야생의 명 야생

Key Expressions

- **be born** 태어나다
- **become part of** ~의 일원이 되다
- **care for** ~을 돌보다
- **give a presentation** 발표하다
- **keep one's eyes on** ~에서 눈을 떼지 않다
- **millions of** 수백만의
- **next to** ~ 옆에
- **take a picture of** ~의 사진을 찍다
- **tell the difference** 차이를 구별하다
- **thanks to** ~ 덕분에

Word Power

※ 서로 반대되는 뜻을 가진 어휘

- ☐ **careful** 주의 깊은 ↔ **careless** 부주의한
- ☐ **allow** 허락하다 ↔ **prohibit** 금지하다
- ☐ **safe** 안전한 ↔ **dangerous** 위험한
- ☐ **giant** 거대한 ↔ **tiny** 작은
- ☐ **male** 수컷의 ↔ **female** 암컷의
- ☐ **humorous** 재미있는 ↔ **boring** 지루한

- ☐ **tail** 꼬리 ↔ **head** 머리
- ☐ **thick** 두꺼운 ↔ **thin** 얇은
- ☐ **appear** 나타나다 ↔ **disappear** 사라지다
- ☐ **attack** 공격하다 ↔ **defend** 방어하다
- ☐ **alive** 살아 있는 ↔ **dead** 죽은
- ☐ **believable** 믿을 수 있는 ↔ **unbelievable** 믿을 수 없는

English Dictionary

- ☐ **allow** 허락하다
  - → to let somebody/something do something; to let something happen or be done
  - 누군가나 무언가가 어떤 것을 하게 하다; 무언가가 일어나게 하거나 이루어지게 하다

- ☐ **approach** 다가가다
  - → to come near to somebody/something in distance or time
  - 거리상 또는 시간상으로 누군가나 무언가에 가까이 오다

- ☐ **blind** 눈 먼, 맹인인
  - → not able to see
  - 볼 수 없는

- ☐ **careless** 부주의한
  - → not giving enough attention and thought to what you are doing, so that you make mistakes
  - 당신이 하고 있는 것에 충분한 주의나 생각을 기울이지 않아서 당신이 실수하도록 하는

- ☐ **curious** 호기심이 많은
  - → having a strong desire to know about something
  - 무언가에 대해 알고 싶은 강한 욕구를 가진

- ☐ **dead** 죽은
  - → no longer alive
  - 더 이상 살아 있지 않은

- ☐ **feed** 먹이를 주다
  - → to give food to a person or an animal
  - 사람이나 동물에게 먹을 것을 주다

- ☐ **friendship** 우정

  - → the feeling or relationship that friends have; the state of being friends
  - 친구들이 갖고 있는 감정 또는 관계; 친구인 상태

- ☐ **insect** 곤충
  - → any small creature with six legs and a body divided into three parts
  - 6개의 다리와 3부분으로 나누어지는 몸을 가진 작은 생명체

- ☐ **rescue** 구조하다
  - → to save somebody/something from a dangerous or harmful situation
  - 누군가나 무언가를 위험하거나 해로운 상황으로부터 구하다

- ☐ **shelter** 보호소
  - → a structure built to give protection, especially from the weather or from attack
  - 특히 날씨나 공격으로부터 보호하기 위해 지어진 구조물

- ☐ **tail** 꼬리
  - → the part that sticks out and can be moved at the back of the body of a bird, an animal or a fish
  - 새, 동물, 또는 물고기의 몸통의 뒷부분에서 튀어나와 움직여질 수 있는 부분

- ☐ **tongue** 혀
  - → the soft part in the mouth that moves around, used for tasting, swallowing, speaking, etc.
  - 입안에서 이리저리 움직이는, 맛을 보거나 삼키거나 말을 하는 데 사용되는 부드러운 부분

- ☐ **trunk** (코끼리의) 코
  - → the long nose of an elephant
  - 코끼리의 긴 코

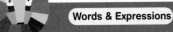

서답형
01 다음 짝지어진 단어의 관계가 같도록 빈칸에 알맞은 말을 쓰시오.

> giant : tiny = thick : _____

02 다음 영영풀이가 가리키는 것을 고르시오.

> not able to see

① deaf   ② blind
③ disabled   ④ dead
⑤ blank

중요
03 다음 중 밑줄 친 부분의 뜻풀이가 바르지 <u>않은</u> 것은?

① Bears look cute, but they are very <u>dangerous</u>. 위험한
② All the trees were either <u>lifeless</u> or leafless. 생명이 없는
③ I worked <u>throughout</u> the night. ~ 동안
④ Many monkeys <u>appear</u> at your Town Center. 사라지다
⑤ <u>Unbelievably</u>, owls can rotate their heads 270 degrees! 믿을 수 없게도

서답형
04 다음 우리말에 맞게 빈칸에 알맞은 말을 쓰시오.

(1) 코끼리는 음식을 집기 위해 코를 이용한다.
　➡ The elephant uses its _____ to pick up food.
(2) 고래는 등으로 물을 내뿜고 있다.
　➡ The _____ is spouting water from its back.
(3) 암컷 사자들이 대부분의 사냥을 한다.
　➡ _____ lions do most of the hunting.

서답형
05 다음 우리말을 주어진 단어를 이용하여 영작하시오.

(1) 코끼리는 좀처럼 사람들을 공격하지 않는다. (rarely, humans)
　➡ _____
(2) 구조팀이 정시에 도착했다. (on)
　➡ _____
(3) 이 반지들은 우리의 우정을 상징한다. (symbolize)
　➡ _____

06 다음 주어진 문장의 밑줄 친 bat과 같은 의미로 쓰인 것은?

> <u>Bats</u> can fly well in the dark.

① He suddenly struck the man with a baseball <u>bat</u>.
② This <u>bat</u> is made of wood.
③ Do you know how to swing the <u>bat</u>?
④ The sounds made by <u>bats</u> are bounced back to them.
⑤ My father bought me a <u>bat</u> instead of a glove.

중요
07 다음 문장에 공통으로 들어갈 말을 고르시오.

> • I love your _____ of humor.
> • I met the chef suffering from losing his _____ of smell.
> • If you _____ danger, you must start to run.

① sense   ② touch
③ feel   ④ idea
⑤ approach

01 다음 짝지어진 단어의 관계가 같도록 빈칸에 알맞은 말을 쓰시오.

> safe : dangerous = careful : _____

02 다음 영영풀이가 가리키는 것을 고르시오.

> to give food to a person or an animal

① feed ② fit ③ seed
④ eat ⑤ dine

03 다음 우리말에 맞게 빈칸에 알맞은 말을 쓰시오. (한 칸에 한 단어씩 쓸 것.)

(1) 나는 이번 주말에 고양이들을 돌볼 것이다.
➡ I'll _____ _____ cats this weekend.

(2) Sue는 Mike에게서 눈을 떼지 못했다.
➡ Sue kept _____ _____ on Mike.

(3) 나는 우리 가족의 사진을 찍고 싶다.
➡ I want to _____ _____ _____
of my family.

04 다음 문장의 빈칸에 들어갈 말을 〈보기〉에서 골라 쓰시오.

> ┤ 보기 ├
> probably / seem / feed / female / allow

(1) You _____ to be in a good mood.
(2) We should _____ kids to have thinking time.
(3) _____ gorillas are half the size of the males.
(4) Don't _____ bread to the ducks.
(5) You have _____ heard of Vincent van Gogh.

05 다음 우리말에 맞게 주어진 단어를 사용하여 영작하시오.

(1) 부주의한 운전자는 불이 빨간색으로 바뀐 것을 보지 못했다. (light)
➡ _____

(2) 아이들은 그들 주위에 있는 모든 것에 호기심이 있다. (around)
➡ _____

(3) 우리 부모님은 내가 컴퓨터 게임하는 것을 허락하지 않을 것이다. (won't)
➡ _____

06 다음 주어진 우리말과 일치하도록 주어진 단어를 모두 배열하여 영작하시오.

(1) 나는 지난 주말에 지역 동물 보호소를 방문했다.
(last / a / visited / I / animal / weekend / shelter / local)
➡ _____

(2) 그는 그때 가만히 있지 않았다.
(that / he / restless / time / at / was)
➡ _____

(3) 우리는 더 모험심을 갖고 강해질 필요가 있다.
(need / more / we / be / to / and / stronger / adventurous)
➡ _____

Conversation

① 궁금한 일 표현하기

> **A** This flower is bigger than a person. 이 꽃은 사람보다 더 크다.
> **B** Yeah. I'm curious about the flower. 응. 나는 이 꽃이 궁금해.

- "I'm curious about ~."은 놀랍거나 특별한 것에 대하여 호기심이 있다는 것을 표현할 때 사용된다. 예를 들어, 어떤 음식이 맛있어서 그 요리법이 궁금할 경우 "I'm curious about the recipe."와 같이 말한다.

궁금한 일 표현하기

- I wonder what this dish is made of. 나는 이 요리가 무엇으로 만들어졌는지 궁금해.
- I'm interested to know about the amazing dog that can speak English.
  나는 영어를 말할 수 있는 이 놀라운 개에 대해 알고 싶어.
- Can someone tell me about the dog that saved a girl from a fire?
  누가 나에게 화재로부터 한 소녀를 구한 개에 대해 이야기해 줄 수 있니?

핵심 Check

1. 다음 주어진 우리말과 일치하도록 빈칸을 완성하시오.

   (1) **A**: Look at this. This bird laughs like a person. (이것 좀 봐. 이 새는 사람처럼 웃어.)

   B: Oh, I'm _____ _____ the bird. (오, 나는 이 새가 궁금해.)

   C: Me, too. _____ _____ more about it. (나도 그래. 이것에 대해 더 읽어 보자.)

   (2) **A**: This horse guided the _____. (이 말이 맹인들을 안내했어.)

   B: Oh, I _____ how he could do it. (오, 나는 어떻게 그가 이것을 했는지 궁금해.)

   C: So do I. Let's listen to the story more. (나도 그래. 이야기를 더 들어보자.)

   (3) **A**: Bees _____ with each other by dancing. (벌들은 춤을 추며 서로 의사소통을 해.)

   B: Really? How do they do it? _____ _____ _____ _____.
   (정말? 그들은 그것을 어떻게 해? 나는 그 방법이 궁금해.)

   C: Me, too. Let's watch this video and _____ _____.
   (나도 그래. 이 비디오를 보고 알아보자.)

2 비교해 표현하기

A We got a new puppy yesterday. 우리 어제 새 강아지를 데려왔어.

B Oh, he's so small! 오. 그는 정말 작다!

A Yeah. He's as small as my hand. 응. 그는 내 손만큼 작아.

■ "as ~ as"는 사람이나 사물들의 유사한 특징을 비교할 때 사용된다. 예를 들어, 친구의 동생을 만났을 때 동생의 키가 친구와 거의 비슷하다면 "Your brother is as tall as you."와 같이 말할 수 있다.

비교해 표현하기

- Your shoes and mine are the same. 네 신발과 내 것이 같구나.
- Our math teacher and PE teacher are alike. 우리 수학 선생님과 체육 선생님은 비슷하다.
- Mammoths are similar to elephants. 매머드들은 코끼리들과 비슷하다.

핵심 Check

2. 다음 주어진 우리말과 일치하도록 빈칸을 완성하시오.

(1) **A:** Let's play a guessing game. It's a fruit. (수수께끼 하자. 이것은 과일이야.)

   B: How _____ is it? (얼마나 커?)

   C: It's _____ _____ _____ a basketball. (농구공만큼 커.)

(2) **A:** What _____ is it? (무슨 색이야?)

   B: It's _____ _____ _____ _____ _____. (장미꽃만큼 붉은색이야.)

   C: I think it's a strawberry. (딸기라고 생각해.)

(3) **A:** The ants can smell things _____ _____ _____ _____. Aren't they surprising? (개미들은 개만큼 냄새를 잘 맡을 수 있어요. 놀랍지 않나요?)

   B: Yes. I want _____ _____ _____ _____ _____.
   (네. 나는 그들에 대해 더 알고 싶어요.)

Listen & Talk 1-B

Clare: Do you think we can be friends with lions, Todd?

Todd: No, Clare. I don't think so.

Clare: Well, I watched a video clip about ❶friendship between two men and a lion.

Todd: Really? ❷I'm curious about the story. Can you tell me more?

Clare: The two men raised a baby lion and sent ❸her back into the wild. When the men and the lion met a year later, ❸she remembered them.

Todd: Wow, that's so ❹touching.

Clare: 우리가 사자와 친구가 될 수 있을 거라고 생각해, Todd?

Todd: 아니, Clare. 난 그렇게 생각하지 않아.

Clare: 음, 나 두 남자와 사자 사이의 우정에 대한 동영상을 봤어.

Todd: 정말? 그 이야기가 궁금해. 더 얘기해 줄 수 있어?

Clare: 두 남자가 아기 사자를 길러서 야생으로 돌려보냈대. 일 년 후에 그 남자들과 사자가 만났을 때, 그 사자는 그들을 기억했다는 거야.

Todd: 와, 정말 감동적이구나.

❶ friendship: 우정
❷ 궁금한 것을 나타내는 표현으로 "I'd be interested to know about the story." 또는 "I want to know about the story."로 바꾸어 표현할 수 있다.
❸ her와 she는 a baby lion을 가리킨다.
❹ touching: 감동적인 (= moving)

Check(√) True or False

(1) A baby lion was raised by the two men before going back to the wild.　　T ☐ F ☐

(2) Clare was moved by a video clip about friendship between two men and a lion.　　T ☐ F ☐

Communication

Emily: Hello, Dr. Watson. Can you tell us about your study?

Dr. Watson: I study animals ❶that lived millions of years ago.

Emily: Oh, I'm curious about those animals. Were there any interesting ❷ones?

Dr. Watson: Yes, there were many. This is the giant kangaroo. ❸It lived in Australia. ❸It was ❹as heavy as three men and ❸it couldn't jump well.

Emily: That's amazing!

Emily: 안녕하세요, Watson 박사님. 박사님의 연구에 대해 이야기해 주시겠어요?

Dr. Watson: 전 수백만 년 전에 살았던 동물들을 연구합니다.

Emily: 오, 전 그 동물들이 궁금해요. 흥미로운 동물들이 있었나요?

Dr. Watson: 네, 많이 있었죠. 이 동물은 '자이언트 캥거루'입니다. 호주에서 살았어요. 사람 세 명만큼 무거웠고, 잘 뛰지 못했어요.

Emily: 그거 정말 놀랍군요!

❶ that은 주격 관계대명사로 which로 바꾸어 쓸 수 있다.
❷ ones는 animals를 가리킨다.
❸ It은 모두 'the giant kangaroo'를 가리킨다.
❹ 'as+원급+as' 구문으로 '~만큼 …한'을 의미한다.

Check(√) True or False

(3) Emily wanted to know about the animals that lived millions of years ago.　　T ☐ F ☐

(4) The giant kangaroo was much heavier than three men.　　T ☐ F ☐

Listen & Talk 1 A-1

Ryan: Judy, did you choose a topic for your science project?

Judy: Not yet. ❶How about you, Ryan?

Ryan: I'm curious about weather change. So I'm thinking about doing the project on ❷that.

Judy: ❷That's an interesting topic!

❶ '너는 어때?'를 의미하며 'What about you?'로 바꾸어 쓸 수 있다.
❷ that은 weather change를 가리킨다.

Listen & Talk 1 A-2

Jane: ❶Look at this picture of a huge flower.

Tom: Wow, ❷it is bigger than a person.

Jane: Yeah. I'm really curious about this flower. It also says here that the flower smells very bad, but ❸insects love the smell.

Tom: Hmm, I wonder why.

❶ look at: ~을 보다
❷ it은 a huge flower를 가리킨다.
❸ insect: 곤충, 벌레

Listen & Talk 2 A-1

Dylan: Look at this picture, Mina. We got a new puppy yesterday. He's only two weeks old.

Mina: Oh, Dylan, ❶he's so small!

Dylan: Yeah. He's as small as my hand now, but he'll get ❷much bigger in ❸a few months.

Mina: Wow, puppies grow very quickly.

❶ he는 a new puppy를 가리킨다.
❷ much는 비교급을 강조하는 표현으로 even, a lot, still, far 등으로 바꾸어 쓸 수 있다.
❸ a few+셀 수 있는 명사: 조금의, few+셀 수 있는 명사: 거의 없는

Listen & Talk 2 A-2

Kelly: George, ❶that red house over there is my grandparents' house.

George: Wow, the tree by the house is really big.

Kelly: ❷Actually, that tree is as old as me, thirteen years old.

George: How do you know ❸that, Kelly?

Kelly: My grandfather ❹planted the tree in 2004 when I ❺was born.

❶ that은 지시형용사로 '저, 그'를 뜻한다.
❷ actually: 실제로
❸ that은 'That tree is as old as Kelly, thirteen years old.'를 나타낸다.
❹ plant: 심다
❺ be born: 태어나다

Listen & Talk 2 B-2

Toby: Hi, I'm Toby. I'm going to ❶give a presentation about the blue whale. ❷It's ❸the biggest sea animal in the world. How big is ❷it? Well, ❷it's about 30m long. That means ❷it's longer than a basketball court. Another interesting thing is that its ❹tongue is as heavy as an elephant! Surprising, isn't it?

❶ give a presentation: 발표하다
❷ it은 모두 the blue whale을 가리킨다.
❸ the biggest는 '가장 큰'을 의미하며 최상급을 나타낸다.
❹ tongue: 혀

● 다음 우리말과 일치하도록 빈칸에 알맞은 말을 쓰시오.

Listen & Talk 1 A-1

Ryan: Judy, did you choose a _____ for your science project?

Judy: Not yet. How about you, Ryan?

Ryan: _____ _____ _____ _____ _____. So I'm thinking about _____ the project on that.

Judy: That's an interesting topic!

해석

Ryan: Judy, 너 과학 과제로 할 주제 골랐어?
Judy: 아직. 너는 어때, Ryan?
Ryan: 나는 날씨 변화가 궁금하거든. 그래서 난 그것에 관한 과제를 하려고 생각 중이야.
Judy: 주제가 흥미로운걸!

Listen & Talk 1 A-2

Jane: Look at this picture of a _____ flower.

Tom: Wow, it is _____ than a person.

Jane: Yeah. I'm really _____ _____ this flower. It also _____ here that the flower smells very bad, but _____ love the smell.

Tom: Hmm, I wonder _____.

Jane: 이 커다란 꽃 사진을 봐.
Tom: 와, 사람보다 더 크네.
Jane: 그래. 나는 이 꽃이 정말 궁금해. 또 여기에 나와 있는데 그 꽃은 냄새가 매우 고약하지만 벌레들은 그 냄새를 좋아한대.
Tom: 흠, 이유가 궁금하다.

Listen & Talk 1 B

Clare: Do you think we can _____ _____ with lions, Todd?

Todd: No, Clare. I don't _____ _____.

Clare: Well, I watched a video clip about _____ between two men and a lion.

Todd: Really? I'm _____ _____ the story. Can you tell me more?

Clare: The two men _____ a baby lion and sent her _____ into the _____. When the men and the lion met _____ _____ _____, she remembered them.

Todd: Wow, that's so _____.

Clare: 우리가 사자와 친구가 될 수 있을 거라고 생각해, Todd?
Todd: 아니, Clare. 난 그렇게 생각하지 않아.
Clare: 음, 나 두 남자와 사자 사이의 우정에 대한 동영상을 봤어.
Todd: 정말? 그 이야기가 궁금해. 더 얘기해 줄 수 있어?
Clare: 두 남자가 아기 사자를 길러서 야생으로 돌려보냈대. 일 년 후에 그 남자들과 사자가 만났을 때, 그 사자는 그들을 기억했다는 거야.
Todd: 와, 정말 감동적이구나.

Listen & Talk 2 A-1

Dylan: Look at this picture, Mina. We got a new _____ yesterday. He's only two weeks old.

Mina: Oh, Dylan, he's _____ _____!

Dylan: Yeah. He's _____ _____ _____ _____ my hand now, but he'll get _____ _____ in a few months.

Mina: Wow, puppies _____ very quickly.

Dylan: 이 사진 좀 봐, 미나야. 우리 어제 새 강아지를 데리고 왔어. 그 강아지는 2주밖에 안됐어.
Mina: 오, Dylan, 걔 너무 조그맣다!
Dylan: 맞아. 그 애는 지금 내 손만큼 작지만, 몇 달 뒤에는 훨씬 더 커질 거야.
Mina: 와, 강아지들은 정말 빨리 크네.

Listen & Talk 2 A-2

Kelly: George, that red house _____ _____ is my grandparents' house.

George: Wow, the tree by the house is _____ _____.

Kelly: Actually, that tree is _____ _____ _____ _____, thirteen years old.

George: How do you know that, Kelly?

Kelly: My grandfather _____ the tree in 2004 when I _____ _____.

Kelly: George, 저기에 있는 빨간 집이 우리 할아버지와 할머니 댁이야.
George: 와, 집 옆에 있는 나무가 굉장히 크네.
Kelly: 사실, 저 나무의 나이는 나랑 같아서 수령이 13년 되었어.
George: 그걸 어떻게 알아, Kelly?
Kelly: 할아버지께서 내가 태어난 해인 2004년에 그 나무를 심으셨거든.

Listen & Talk 2 B

Toby: Hi, I'm Toby. I'm going to _____ _____ _____ about the blue whale. It's _____ _____ sea animal in the world. How big is it? Well, it's about 30m long. That means it's _____ _____ a basketball court. Another interesting thing is that its tongue is _____ _____ _____ an elephant! Surprising, _____ _____?

Toby: 안녕하세요, 저는 Toby입니다. 저는 흰긴수염고래에 대해서 발표를 하려고 해요 그 고래는 세상에서 가장 큰 바다 동물이에요. 얼마나 크냐고요? 음, 길이가 30미터 정도 돼요. 그 말은 그 고래가 농구 경기장보다 길다는 뜻이에요. 또 다른 흥미로운 점은 그 고래의 혀가 코끼리만큼 무겁다는 거예요! 놀랍죠, 그렇지 않나요?

Communication

Emily: Hello, Dr. Watson. Can you tell us about your study?

Dr. Watson: I study animals that lived _____ _____ years ago.

Emily: Oh, I'm _____ about those animals. Were there _____ interesting ones?

Dr. Watson: Yes, there were _____. This is the giant kangaroo. It lived in Australia. It was _____ _____ _____ three men and it couldn't jump well.

Emily: That's _____!

Emily: 안녕하세요, Watson 박사님. 박사님의 연구에 대해 이야기해 주시겠어요?
Dr Watson: 전 수백만 년 전에 살았던 동물들을 연구합니다.
Emily: 오, 전 그 동물들이 궁금해요. 흥미로운 동물들이 있었나요?
Dr Watson: 네, 많이 있었죠. 이 동물은 '자이언트 캥거루'입니다. 호주에서 살았어요. 사람 세 명만큼 무거웠고, 잘 뛰지 못했어요.
Emily: 그거 정말 놀랍군요!

[01~02] 다음 대화를 읽고 물음에 답하시오.

Ryan: Judy, did you choose a topic for your science project?

Judy: Not yet. How about you, Ryan?

Ryan: I'm curious about weather change. So I'm thinking about doing the project on (a)that.

Judy: ＿＿＿＿＿＿＿ (A) ＿＿＿＿＿＿＿

01 위 대화의 빈칸 (A)에 들어갈 말로 나머지와 의도가 다른 것은?

① Sounds like an interesting topic!

② How interesting the topic is!

③ What an interesting topic!

④ I think it should be an interesting topic.

⑤ That's an interesting topic!

02 위 대화의 밑줄 친 (a)가 가리키는 말을 찾아 쓰시오.

➡ ＿＿＿＿＿＿＿＿＿＿＿＿＿

[03~04] 다음 글을 읽고 물음에 답하시오.

Toby: Hi, I'm Toby. I'm going to give a presentation about the blue whale. It's the ＿＿(A)＿＿ (big) sea animal in the world. How big is it? Well, it's about 30m long. That means it's ＿＿(B)＿＿ (long) than a basketball court. Another interesting thing is that its tongue is as heavy as an elephant! Surprising, isn't it?

03 위 글의 빈칸 (A)와 (B)에 주어진 단어를 알맞은 형태로 쓰시오.

(A) ＿＿＿＿＿＿＿＿＿　(B) ＿＿＿＿＿＿＿＿＿

04 위 글의 내용과 일치하지 않는 것은?

① Toby explains the blue whale.

② There is nothing bigger than the blue whale in the sea.

③ The blue whale is 30m long.

④ The basketball court is longer than the blue whale.

⑤ The blue whale's tongue is as heavy as an elephant.

[01~02] 다음 대화를 읽고 물음에 답하시오.

Ryan: Judy, did you choose a topic for your science project?

Judy: Not yet. How about you, Ryan?

Ryan: (A)나는 날씨 변화가 궁금하거든. So I'm thinking about doing the project on that.

Judy: That's an interesting topic!

서답형

01 위 대화의 밑줄 친 (A)의 우리말을 주어진 단어를 모두 배열하여 영작하시오.

┌─ 보기 ├─

curious / weather / about / I'm / change

➡ _____

02 위 대화의 내용과 일치하지 <u>않는</u> 것은?

① Judy hasn't decided her topic for the science project.

② Ryan is thinking about weather change for the science project.

③ Ryan is interested in weather change.

④ Judy thinks that the weather change is an interesting topic.

⑤ Judy is interested in weather change.

03 다음 글의 내용과 일치하도록 표의 빈칸을 완성하시오.

Toby: Hi, I'm Toby. I'm going to give a presentation about the blue whale. It's the biggest sea animal in the world. How big is it? Well, it's about 30m long. That means it's longer than a basketball court. Another interesting thing is that its tongue is as heavy as an elephant! Surprising, isn't it?

↓

How big is the blue whale?	
Size	It's the (1)_____ sea animal in the world.
Length	It's (2)_____ long. It's longer than (3)_____ _____.
Interesting point	(4)_____ _____

[04~05] 다음 대화를 읽고 물음에 답하시오.

Jane: Look at this picture of a huge flower.

Tom: Wow, it is bigger than a person.

Jane: Yeah. I'm really curious about this flower. It also says here that the flower smells very bad, but __(A)__s love the smell.

Tom: Hmm, I wonder why.

서답형

04 위 대화의 빈칸 (A)에 다음 주어진 영영풀이가 나타내는 말을 <u>쓰시오</u>.

any small creature with six legs and a body divided into three part

➡ _____

중요

05 위 대화를 읽고 대답할 수 <u>없는</u> 것은?

① What are Jane and Tom looking at?

② What does Jane want to know about?

③ What is bigger than a person in the picture?

④ Why do insects like the smell of the huge flower?

⑤ How does the huge flower smell?

[06~07] 다음 대화를 읽고 물음에 답하시오.

> Dylan: Look at this picture, Mina. We got a new puppy yesterday. He's only two weeks old.
>
> Mina: Oh, Dylan, he's so small!
>
> Dylan: Yeah. He's as (A)[small / smaller] as my hand now, but he'll get (B)[many / much] bigger in a few months.
>
> Mina: Wow, puppies grow very (C)[quick / quickly].

06 위 대화의 괄호 (A)~(C)에 알맞은 말로 바르게 짝지어진 것은?

① small – many – quick
② small – much – quickly
③ smaller – much – quick
④ smaller – much – quickly
⑤ smaller – many – quick

07 위 대화의 내용과 일치하지 <u>않는</u> 것은?

① Dylan은 어제 새 강아지를 얻었다.
② Dylan은 새 강아지를 직접 Mina에게 보여주고 있다.
③ 강아지는 2주 밖에 안됐다.
④ 강아지는 Dylan의 손만큼 작다.
⑤ 강아지는 정말 빨리 큰다.

[08~09] 다음 대화를 읽고 물음에 답하시오.

> Clare: Do you think we can be friends with lions, Todd?
>
> Todd: No, Clare. I don't think so.
>
> Clare: Well, I watched a video clip about friendship between two men (A)[and / or] a lion.

> Todd: Really? I'm curious about the story. Can you tell me more?
>
> Clare: The two men raised a baby lion and (B) [sending / sent] her back into the wild. When the men and the lion met a year later, she remembered them.
>
> Todd: Wow, ⓐ<u>that</u>'s so (C)[touched / touching].

08 위 대화의 괄호 (A)~(C)에 알맞은 말로 바르게 짝지어진 것은?

① and – sending – touched
② and – sent – touching
③ and – sent – touched
④ or – sent – touching
⑤ or – sending – touched

09 위 대화의 밑줄 친 ⓐ가 가리키는 것을 우리말로 쓰시오.

➡ _____

10 다음 대화의 내용과 일치하지 <u>않는</u> 것은?

> Kelly: George, that red house over there is my grandparents' house.
>
> George: Wow, the tree by the house is really big.
>
> Kelly: Actually, that tree is as old as me, thirteen years old.
>
> George: How do you know <u>that</u>, Kelly?
>
> Kelly: My grandfather planted the tree in 2004 when I was born.

① The house of Kelly's grandparents is red.
② There is a tree by the red house.
③ The tree is thirteen years old.
④ Kelly's grandfather planted the tree when Kelly was born.
⑤ The tree is as old as Kelly's grandparents.

[01~03] 다음 글을 읽고 물음에 답하시오.

> **Toby:** Hi, I'm Toby. I'm going to give a presentation about the blue whale. It's the biggest sea animal in the world. How big is it? Well, it's about 30m long. That means it's longer than a basketball court. Another interesting thing is that its tongue is as heavy as an elephant! Surprising, isn't it?

01 How long is the blue whale?

➡ _____

02 Which is longer, a blue whale or a basketball court?

➡ _____

03 중요 What is the blue whale's tongue as heavy as?

➡ _____

04 다음 대화의 내용과 일치하도록 빈칸을 완성하시오.

> **Jane:** Look at this picture of a huge flower.
> **Tom:** Wow, it is bigger than a person.
> **Jane:** Yeah. I'm really curious about this flower. It also says here that the flower smells very bad, but insects love the smell.
> **Tom:** Hmm, I wonder why.

⬇

> Jane found out a flower which is (A)_____ than a person in the (B)_____. Interestingly, the flower smells very bad but (C)_____ are fond of its smell. Tom was curious about why (D)_____ _____ _____ _____ .

[05~06] 다음 대화를 읽고 물음에 답하시오.

> **Clare:** Do you think we can be friends with lions, Todd?
> **Todd:** No, Clare. I don't think so.
> **Clare:** Well, I watched a video clip about friendship between two men and a lion.
> **Todd:** Really? I'm curious about the story. Can you tell me more?
> **Clare:** The two men raised a baby lion and sent her back into the wild. When the men and the lion met a year later, she remembered them.
> **Todd:** Wow, that's so touching.

05 중요 What was the video clip Clare watched about?

➡ _____

_____

06 What did the lion remember?

➡ _____

07 고난이도 다음 대화가 자연스럽게 이어지도록 순서대로 배열하시오.

> (A) I'm curious about weather change. So I'm thinking about doing the project on that.
> (B) Not yet. How about you, Ryan?
> (C) That's an interesting topic!
> (D) Judy, did you choose a topic for your science project?

➡ _____

Grammar

① 가주어 It

> • **It** is good **to read** many books. 많은 책을 읽는 것은 좋다.
> • **It** was hard **to stop** the machine. 그 기계를 멈추는 것은 어려웠다.

■ to부정사구가 문장의 주어로 쓰여 주어가 길어진 경우, 주어부를 문장의 맨 뒤로 보내고 이 자리에 It을 쓰는 것이 가주어 It이다.

- **To exercise** early in the morning is helpful.
  = It is helpful **to exercise** early in the morning. 아침 일찍 운동하는 것은 도움이 된다.

■ 가주어 It은 따로 해석하지 않으며 to부정사구를 주어로 해석해야 한다. to부정사구의 부정은 'not+to V'로 나타낸다.

- **It** is wrong **to lie** to your friend. 친구에게 거짓말하는 것은 나쁘다.
- **It** was hard **to remember** all the appointments. 모든 약속을 기억하는 것은 어려웠다.
- **It** is useful **to know** how to use the copy machine. 복사기를 사용하는 방법을 아는 것은 유용하다.
- **It** is necessary **not to skip** meals. 식사를 거르지 않는 것이 필요하다.

■ to부정사구가 주어인 경우 가주어 It을 사용하여 문장을 만드는 것과 마찬가지로, that절이 주어인 경우에도 가주어 It을 사용할 수 있다.

- **That** he should miss his family is natural.
  = **It** is natural **that** he should miss his family. 그가 그의 가족을 그리워하는 것은 당연하다.

핵심 Check

1. 다음 우리말과 일치하도록 빈칸에 알맞은 말을 쓰시오.

(1) 운동을 규칙적으로 하는 것은 중요하다.
➡ _____ is important _____ _____ regularly.

(2) 놀이공원에 가는 것은 즐겁다.
➡ _____ is amusing _____ _____ to the amusement park.

(3) 걷는 동안 휴대 전화기를 사용하지 않는 것이 중요하다.
➡ _____ is important _____ _____ _____ your phone while walking.

② 원급 비교

> • Sally is **as** smart **as** Minju. Sally는 민주만큼 똑똑하다.
> • They were **as** hungry **as** Tom. 그들은 Tom만큼 배가 고팠다.

■ 'as ~ as' 원급 비교는 두 개의 대상을 비교할 때 정도가 같을 경우 사용할 수 있는 표현이다. 'as+형용사/부사의 원급+as'로 '~만큼 …한[하게]'라고 해석한다. 앞에 쓰인 as는 '그러한, 똑같은 정도로'라는 의미의 부사이며, 뒤에 쓰이고 있는 as는 '~와 같이'라는 의미로 접속사이다.

- Julia came **as** late **as** you. Julia는 너만큼 늦게 왔어.
- Robert is **as** tall **as** Chuck. Robert는 Chuck만큼 키가 크다.

■ 원급 비교의 부정인 'not as[so]+원급+as ~'는 '~만큼 …하지 않은[않게]'라는 의미로, 비교하는 두 대상의 정도가 같지 않을 경우 쓸 수 있다.

- Your pie was **not as** delicious **as** his pie. 너의 파이는 그의 파이만큼 맛있지 않았어.
- She doesn't talk **as** loudly **as** Jason. 그녀는 Jason만큼 크게 말하지 않는다.

■ 동등 비교를 이용하여 비교의 배수 표현이 가능하다. '배수사(twice, three times)+as+형용사/부사+as'의 형태이며 '~의 몇 배만큼 …한'이라는 의미로 쓰인다.

- This balloon is **twice as** big **as** that balloon. 이 풍선은 저 풍선보다 두 배만큼 크다.
- This mountain is **three times as** high **as** Namsan. 이 산은 남산보다 세 배 높다.

■ 원급을 이용한 관용 표현을 알아두자. 'as+원급+as possible'은 '가능한 한 ~한[하게]'라고 해석되고 이는 'as+원급+as+주어+can[could]'와 같다.

- Call me **as** often **as possible**. 가능한 한 자주 전화하렴.

핵심 Check

2. 다음 우리말과 일치하도록 빈칸에 알맞은 말을 쓰시오.

(1) 그들은 우리만큼 가난하지 않아.
➡ They are ＿＿ ＿＿ ＿＿ ＿＿ we are.

(2) 그 치마는 이 바지보다 두 배 비싸.
➡ The skirt is ＿＿ ＿＿ ＿＿ ＿＿ these pants.

(3) 그녀는 나만큼 춤을 잘 춘다.
➡ She dances ＿＿ ＿＿ ＿＿ I.

01 다음 문장에서 어법상 어색한 부분을 바르게 고치시오.

(1) It is important to being fair and truthful.

_____ ➡ _____

(2) He is as simply as a child.

_____ ➡ _____

(3) It is essential drive carefully.

_____ ➡ _____

(4) It is three time as expensive as the watch.

_____ ➡ _____

02 다음 우리말에 맞게 빈칸에 알맞은 말을 쓰시오.

(1) 소풍을 가는 것은 친구들과 노는 것만큼 재미있다.

➡ Going on a picnic is _____ _____ _____ playing with friends.

(2) 그 강은 나일강만큼 길지 않다.

➡ The river is _____ _____ _____ _____ the Nile.

(3) 이 바지는 너의 바지보다 두 배 더 따뜻하다.

➡ These pants are _____ _____ _____ yours.

(4) 사탕은 아이스크림만큼 달콤하다.

➡ Candies are _____ _____ _____ ice cream.

03 주어진 단어를 바르게 배열하여 다음 우리말을 영어로 쓰시오. 필요하다면 단어를 추가하시오.

(1) 어려움에 처한 사람들을 돕는 것은 중요합니다.

(in need / it / people / help / important / is)

➡ _____

(2) 서로를 돕는 것은 이득이 된다. (help / it / each / beneficial / is / other)

➡ _____

(3) 그는 너만큼 어리석지 않아.

(are / is / you / foolish / as / he / as / not)

➡ _____

(4) 그 영화는 'Amazing Amy'만큼 지루하지 않다.

(Amazing Amy / is / boring / the movie / as / as / not)

➡ _____

01 다음 중 빈칸에 들어갈 말로 알맞지 <u>않은</u> 것은?

> Kathy is as _____ as Polly.

① lovely   ② friendly
③ lonely   ④ diligent
⑤ kindly

02 다음 중 밑줄 친 부분의 쓰임이 <u>다른</u> 하나는?

① <u>It</u> is my favorite hobby to play the violin.
② <u>It</u> was lucky to meet you there.
③ <u>It</u> is under the sofa in the living room.
④ <u>It</u> is hard to play tennis every day.
⑤ <u>It</u> is fun to play computer games.

03 다음 우리말을 영어로 바르게 옮긴 것은?

> 그는 가능한 한 빨리 달렸다.

① He ran as fastly as he could.
② He runs as fastly as he can.
③ He runs as fast as he can.
④ He ran as fast as he can.
⑤ He ran as fast as he could.

서답형
04 주어진 단어를 바르게 배열하여 다음 우리말을 영어로 쓰시오. 필요하다면 단어를 추가하시오.

> 한 시간에 그 퍼즐을 푸는 것은 어렵다.
> (difficult / an hour / in / it / the puzzle / is / solve)

➡ _____

05 다음 중 빈칸에 알맞은 것을 바르게 묶은 것은?

> • It is fun _____ a foreign language.
> • Eating well is _____ sleeping well.

① learn – as important
② learning – as importantly as
③ as learning – as importance
④ to learn – as important as
⑤ to learn – important

06 to부정사를 이용하여 다음 우리말을 영어로 쓸 때, 다섯 번째로 오는 단어는?

> 자전거를 타는 것은 좋은 운동이다.

① good   ② exercise   ③ to
④ ride   ⑤ a

07 다음 중 어법상 <u>틀린</u> 문장은?

① It is my dream to travel around the world.
② Sophia is not as clever as you are.
③ Sunsets are as beautiful as sunrises.
④ It is easy to make them believe it.
⑤ The water in this cup is not as clearer as the water in that cup.

서답형
08 주어진 단어를 활용하여 다음 우리말을 영어로 쓰시오.

> 밤늦게 밖에 혼자 나가는 것은 위험하다.
> (it / outside / late at night)

➡ _____

09 다음 중 표에 관한 내용으로 바르지 <u>않은</u> 것은?

	Age	Height	Weight
Jason	15	170cm	70kg
Mike	14	170cm	64kg
Paul	15	165cm	64kg

① Jason is as old as Paul.

② Mike is not as heavy as Jason.

③ Paul is not as tall as Mike.

④ Jason is as heavy as Paul.

⑤ Mike is as tall as Jason.

10 다음 빈칸에 들어갈 말로 가장 적절한 것은?

It is a pity _____ Helen broke her arm.

① to   ② so   ③ what

④ that   ⑤ which

11 다음 중 우리말 전환이 바르지 <u>않은</u> 것은?

① 네 시계는 내 시계만큼 정확해.

　→ Your watch is as accurate as mine.

② 축구를 보는 것은 재미있어.

　→ It is fun to watch football.

③ John이 나에게 거짓말을 한 것은 사실이야.

　→ It is true John to lie to me.

④ 그는 그녀보다 두 배 많은 물을 가지고 있다.

　→ He has two times as much water as she has.

⑤ 그녀의 머리카락은 나만큼 길지 않다.

　→ Her hair is not as long as mine.

서답형

12 주어진 단어를 활용하여 다음 두 문장을 하나의 문장으로 표현하시오.

• Alex gets up at 6 a.m.
• I get up at 6 a.m., too.

➡ _____ (carly)

13 다음 중 어법상 바르지 <u>않은</u> 것은?

①It is ②impolite ③to not pay attention ④to ⑤what others are saying.

①   ②   ③   ④   ⑤

14 다음 중 빈칸에 들어갈 말로 가장 적절한 것은?

Zach is more nervous than Clara.
= Clara _____ Zach.

① is as nervous as

② is more nervous than

③ is much more nervous

④ is not as nervous as

⑤ is as nervously as

15 다음 중 밑줄 친 부분의 쓰임이 <u>다른</u> 하나는?

① They wanted to see me <u>to ask</u> some questions.

② It is your duty to wash the car every day <u>to keep</u> it clean.

③ Jack went to Paris <u>to study</u> fashion.

④ Polly cooked food for us <u>to make</u> us happy.

⑤ It is necessary <u>to attend</u> the meeting.

16 다음 중 빈칸에 들어갈 말이 바르게 짝지어진 것은?

• It is true _____ Kelvin bought a new car.
• You watch TV too much. I don't watch _____ you.

① to – much TV

② that – as many TV as

③ to – TV as much as

④ that – TV as much as

⑤ to – as many TV as

17 다음 우리말을 영어로 바르게 옮긴 것을 고르시오.

> 안전수칙을 따르는 것은 중요합니다.

① It is important to obey rules.
② It is important obey safety rules.
③ It is important to obeying safety rules.
④ It is important to obey safety rules.
⑤ It is important obeyed safety rules.

18 원급 비교를 이용하여 다음 대화의 빈칸에 알맞은 말을 쓰시오.

> A: How tall are you?
> B: I'm 165cm tall.
> A: Oh, then you _____
> my brother. He is 170cm tall.

19 다음 중 서로 의미가 통하지 <u>않는</u> 것은?

① It is not easy to learn French.
= To learn French is not easy.
② Riding a bike is really exciting.
= It is really exciting to ride a bike.
③ Your watch is more expensive than mine.
= My watch is as expensive as yours.
④ It is my job to protect you.
= Protecting you is my job.
⑤ I think sun flowers are not as pretty as roses.
= I think roses are prettier than sun flowers.

서답형

20 주어진 단어를 활용하여 다음 우리말을 영어로 쓰시오.
(8 words)

> 네가 그녀를 걱정하는 것은 당연해.
> (it / natural / worry about)

➡ _____

21 다음 문장과 같은 의미의 문장으로 가장 적절한 것은?

> Kelly works harder than Julia.

① Julia works as hard as Kelly.
② Julia works harder than Kelly.
③ Julia doesn't work hard.
④ Julia doesn't work as hard as Kelly.
⑤ Julia doesn't want to work hard.

22 다음 중 어법상 바르지 <u>않은</u> 문장의 개수는?

> ⓐ It is lucky to seeing the man make a speech.
> ⓑ Jim sings as good as Miranda.
> ⓒ Brad makes pies as often as you do.
> ⓓ It is a pity that she made a mistake.
> ⓔ It is difficult find her right suit.

① 1개   ② 2개   ③ 3개   ④ 4개   ⑤ 5개

23 다음 두 문장을 하나의 문장으로 바르게 표현한 것은?

> • David has ten friends.
> • Gloria has five friends.

① David has as many friends as Gloria.
② Gloria has as many friends as David.
③ David hasn't as many friends as Gloria.
④ Gloria hasn't as many friends as David.
⑤ Gloria has more friends than David has.

서답형

24 주어진 단어를 활용하여 다음 우리말을 영어로 쓰시오.

> 이 물을 마시는 것은 안전합니다. (it)

➡ _____

Grammar **77**

01 원급 비교를 이용하여 다음 두 문장을 하나의 문장으로 표현할 때 빈칸에 알맞은 말을 쓰시오.

> Jinsu has three balloons. I have six balloons.
> ➡ I _____ .

02 주어진 단어를 활용하여 다음 우리말을 영어로 쓰시오.

> 이 산의 꼭대기까지 걷는 것이 가능하다.
> (it / the top of this mountain)
>
> ➡ _____

03 원급 비교를 이용하여 다음 주어진 문장과 같은 의미가 되도록 빈칸을 완성하시오.

> You have more money than me.
> = I don't have _____ you.

04 다음 문장과 같은 의미의 문장을 완성하시오.

> To wear a helmet is safe.
> = It _____ .

05 다음 빈칸에 알맞은 말을 다섯 단어로 쓰시오.

> Mr. Jackson is 90 years old. Mrs. Jackson is 91 years old. So, Mr. Jackson _____ Mrs. Jackson.

06 다음은 Peter의 자기소개 중 일부이다. 주어진 단어를 활용하여 영어로 쓰시오.

> 안경 없이 무언가를 보는 것은 힘듭니다. 나는 안경이 없으면 박쥐만큼 앞이 보이지 않아요.
> (it / hard / something / without / blind)
>
> ➡ _____
>
> _____

07 다음 문장과 같은 의미의 문장을 각각 쓰시오.

(1) That we try to save energy is important.
   ➡ _____
(2) To get there in time is impossible.
   ➡ _____
(3) To hear her singing was difficult.
   ➡ _____
(4) To want to be rich without working hard is foolish.
   ➡ _____
   _____
(5) To play with matches is unsafe.
   ➡ _____

08 다음 글의 빈칸에 알맞은 말을 쓰시오.

> This box weighs 10 grams. A feather weighs 10 grams. So this box _____ a feather. Anyone can move it

09 주어진 단어를 어법과 내용에 맞게 빈칸에 쓰시오.

이름	Mike	John	Betty
키	168cm	180cm	168cm
몸무게	75kg	75kg	50kg
신발사이즈	280mm	270mm	270mm

(1) Mike _____ John. (tall)

(2) John's shoes _____ Mike's. (big)

(3) Betty's shoes _____ John's. (big)

(4) John _____ Mike. (heavy)

(5) Mike _____ Betty. (tall)

(6) Betty _____ Mike and John. (heavy)

10 주어진 단어를 바르게 배열하여 다음 우리말을 영어로 쓰시오. 필요하다면 단어를 추가하시오.

> 지구에 사는 동물을 보호할 필요가 있다.
> (it / the animals / is / protect / necessary / on Earth)

➡ _____

11 다음 대화의 빈칸에 알맞은 말을 세 단어로 쓰시오.

> A: What did you have for lunch?
> B: I ate pizza. It was _____ ice, so I had to heat it.

12 다음 빈칸에 알맞은 말을 다섯 단어로 쓰시오.

> A: Was it _____ ?
> B: Yes, it was. Answering his questions was not difficult.

13 다음 주어진 어구를 이용하여 빈칸을 알맞게 채우시오.

> enter a cage   feed animals
> take a zoo tour   take pets to the zoo

(1) 동물들에게 먹이를 주는 것은 잘못된 것이다.
➡ It is _____.

(2) 동물원 관람을 하는 것은 흥미진진하다.
➡ It is _____.

(3) 우리에 들어가는 것은 위험하다.
➡ It is _____.

(4) 애완동물을 동물원에 데려가는 것은 안전하지 않다.
➡ It is _____.

14 대화의 빈칸에 알맞은 말을 쓰시오.

> A: My rope is one meter long.
> B: Oh, then your rope _____ _____ _____ _____ my rope. My rope is 50cm long. But Suji's rope is the same as mine. Her rope _____ _____ _____ _____ _____ .

15 주어진 단어를 활용하여 다음 대화를 우리말에 맞게 완성하시오

> A: _____
> 연을 날리는 것은 재미있니?(fun)
> B: Yes, it is. Flying a kite _____.
> 응, 그래. 연을 날리는 것은 컴퓨터 게임을 하는 것만큼 재미있어. (fun)

A: _____

B: _____

The Footprints of a Baby Elephant

Date/Time: July 8th / 2:35 p.m.

Notes: Today was my first day in Africa. I took lots of pictures of
넓은 범위 앞에서 쓰이는 전치사 　　　　= many

elephants. This morning, I found an elephant group by a small water
　　　　　　　　　　　　　　　　　　～ 옆에

hole. I saw a baby elephant drinking water beside her mother. Her eyes
지각동사+목적어+Ving

were as bright as stars. I gave her a name, Stella. Around noon, I saw
as+원급+as: ～만큼 …한

a group of lions approaching Stella. The elephants stood around Stella
지각동사+목적어+Ving

and made a thick wall. Thanks to them, Stella was safe.
　　　　　　　　　Thanks to+ 명사: ～ 덕분에

Date/Time: July 12th / 7:20 p.m.

Notes: Around sunset, I heard a strange sound. I followed the sound

and found Stella crying next to her mom. She was lying dead and
find+목적어+Ving: 목적어의 상태를 설명하기 위하여 현재분사를 사용　　　　　　자동사 lie의 주격보어

Stella was alone. It is dangerous to stay alone in such a wild area.
　　　　　　　　　가주어 It　　　　　진주어 to V

What's more, it was going to be dark soon. Elephants can't see well at
비인칭 주어(날짜, 날씨, 거리, 명암 등을 나타낼 때)　　　코끼리가 밤에 잘 볼 수 없는 것은 일반적인 사실이므로 현재시제로 씀

night. So Stella could easily be attacked. I called the elephant shelter
　　　　　　　　　　　조동사가 있는 수동태

and asked for help. I decided to stay by her until the rescue team came.
　　　　　　　　　to부정사를 목적어로 취하는 동사　　　시간 부사절 접속사(～할 때까지)

take a picture of ～의 사진을 찍다

hole 구덩이

bright 밝은

approach 다가가다

thick 두꺼운

sunset 해질녘

strange 이상한

follow ～을 따라가다

dead 죽은

dangerous 위험한

wild area 야생 지역

what's more 더욱이

attack ～을 공격하다

shelter 보호소

rescue 구조

확인문제

● 다음 문장이 본문의 내용과 일치하면 T, 일치하지 <u>않으면</u> F를 쓰시오.

1   The writer gave a name, Stella, to a baby elephant. ☐

2   The writer saw many elephants drink water by the river. ☐

3   The baby elephant was protected by other elephants. ☐

4   Stella's mom was found dead in the morning. ☐

Date/Time: July 12th / 10:40 p.m.

Notes: The night was dark and quiet. I kept my eyes on Stella with
_{수단을 나타내는 전치사}
my night camera. Stella was still next to her mom. She was touching
_{~ 옆에(= beside. by)}   _{과거진행형}
her mom's lifeless body with her nose. It was sad to see Stella staying
_{~으로}   _{가주어 It}   _{진주어 to V}
close to her mom. I hope Stella stays safe throughout the night.
_{= I hope (that) 명사절 접속사 생략}

Date/Time: July 13th / 6:00 a.m.

Notes: A new elephant group appeared and Stella approached them.
_{타동사 (approach to x)}
At first, I thought that they would not let Stella in their group. But I
_{명사절 접속사}   _{~을 들여놓다}
was wrong. An elephant, probably the oldest female allowed Stella to
_{the+최상급: 가장 ~한}   _{allow+목적어+to V: 목적어가 V하도록 허락하다}
become part of the group. The other elephants also seemed to welcome
_{나머지 모든}   _{~인 것처럼 보였다}
Stella. Unbelievably, one of the female elephants fed Stella. She cared
_{feed-fed-fed}
for Stella as warmly as Stella's mom did. This was such an amazing
_{as+원급+as: ~만큼 …한}   _{어순: such+a(n)+형용사+명사}
moment!

keep one's eyes on ~에서 눈을 떼지 않다

still 여전히

lifeless 죽은. 생명이 없는

throughout ~ 동안, ~ 내내

appear 나타나다

probably 아마도

become part of ~의 일원이 되다

welcome 환영하다. 반기다

unbelievably 믿을 수 없을 정도로

feed 밥[우유]을 먹이다. 먹이를 주다

확인문제

• 다음 문장이 본문의 내용과 일치하면 T, 일치하지 않으면 F를 쓰시오.

1   It was dark and noisy on the night of July 12. ☐

2   The writer kept watching Stella with his glasses. ☐

3   Stella stayed close to her mother on the night of July 12. ☐

4   A new elephant group approached Stella first. ☐

5   One of the female elephants let Stella in their group. ☐

6   Stella was fed by a female elephant. ☐

7   Some elephants didn't like Stella. ☐

● 우리말을 참고하여 빈칸에 알맞은 말을 쓰시오.

Date/Time: July 8th / 2:35 p.m.

1 Notes: Today _____ _____ _____ day _____ Africa.

2 I _____ lots of _____ _____ elephants.

3 This morning, I _____ an elephant group _____ a small water hole.

4 I _____ a baby elephant _____ water _____ her mother.

5 Her eyes _____ as _____ as stars.

6 I _____ _____ a name, Stella.

7 Around noon, I _____ a group of lions _____ Stella.

8 The elephants _____ _____ Stella and made _____ _____ wall.

9 Thanks to _____, Stella was _____.

Date/Time: July 12th / 7:20 p.m.

10 Notes: _____ sunset, I _____ a strange sound.

11 I _____ the sound and _____ Stella _____ next to her mom.

12 She was _____ _____ and Stella was _____.

13 _____ is dangerous _____ _____ alone _____ such a wild area.

14 _____ _____, _____ was going to be dark soon.

15 Elephants can't _____ _____ at night.

날짜/시간: 7월 8일, 오후 2시 35분

1 기록: 오늘은 내가 아프리카에 온 첫날이었다.

2 나는 코끼리 사진을 많이 찍었다.

3 오늘 아침에 나는 작은 물웅덩이 옆에 있는 한 코끼리 무리를 발견했다.

4 나는 아기 코끼리 한 마리가 엄마 옆에서 물을 마시고 있는 것을 보았다.

5 그 코끼리의 눈이 별처럼 밝았다.

6 나는 그 코끼리에게 Stella란 이름을 붙여 주었다.

7 정오 즈음에 나는 사자 한 무리가 Stella에게 다가가는 것을 보았다.

8 코끼리들은 Stella 주위에 둘러서서 두꺼운 벽을 만들었다.

9 그 코끼리들 덕분에 Stella는 안전했다.

날짜/시간: 7월 12일, 오후 7시 20분

10 기록: 해질녘에 나는 이상한 소리를 들었다.

11 나는 그 소리를 따라갔고 Stella가 자신의 엄마 옆에서 울고 있는 것을 발견했다.

12 엄마는 죽어서 누워 있었고, Stella는 혼자였다.

13 이러한 야생 지역에서 혼자 있는 것은 위험하다.

14 더욱이 곧 어두워질 것이었다.

15 코끼리들은 밤에 잘 볼 수 없다.

16 So Stella could _____ _____ _____ .

17 I called _____ _____ _____ and _____ _____ help.

18 I decided _____ _____ by her _____ the rescue team came.

Date/Time: July 12th / 10:40 p.m.

19 Notes: The night _____ _____ and _____ .

20 I _____ my eyes _____ Stella with my night camera.

21 Stella was _____ _____ _____ her mom.

22 She _____ _____ her mom's lifeless body _____ her nose.

23 _____ was sad _____ _____ Stella _____ close to her mom.

24 I hope Stella _____ _____ throughout the night.

Date/Time: July 13th / 6:00 a.m.

25 Notes: A new elephant group _____ and Stella _____ them.

26 At first, I thought _____ they would not _____ Stella _____ their group.

27 But I was _____ .

28 An elephant, probably _____ _____ _____ allowed Stella _____ _____ part of the group.

29 _____ _____ _____ also seemed to welcome Stella.

30 Unbelievably, one of the female _____ _____ Stella.

31 She cared for Stella _____ _____ _____ Stella's mom _____ .

32 This was _____ _____ _____ moment!

16 그래서 Stella는 쉽게 공격을 받을 수 있었다.

17 나는 코끼리 보호소에 전화를 해서 도움을 요청했다.

18 나는 구조대가 올 때까지 Stella 곁에 머물기로 결정했다.

날짜/시간: 7월 12일, 오후 10시 40분

19 기록: 밤은 어둡고 조용했다.

20 나는 야간용 카메라를 이용해서 Stella를 계속 지켜보았다.

21 Stella는 여전히 엄마 곁에 있었다.

22 Stella는 코로 엄마의 죽은 몸을 어루만지고 있었다.

23 Stella가 엄마 가까이에 머물고 있는 것을 보는 것은 슬픈 일이었다.

24 나는 Stella가 밤새도록 안전하게 있기를 바란다.

날짜/시간: 7월 13일, 오전 6시

25 기록: 새로운 코끼리 무리가 나타났고, Stella는 그 무리에 다가갔다.

26 처음에 나는 그 코끼리들이 Stella를 자신의 무리로 받아들이지 않을 것이라고 생각했다.

27 그러나 내 생각이 틀렸다.

28 아마도 가장 나이가 많은 암컷인 듯한 코끼리 한 마리가 Stella가 그 무리의 일원이 되도록 허락했다.

29 다른 코끼리들도 Stella를 반기는 것처럼 보였다.

30 믿을 수 없게도, 암컷 코끼리 중의 한 마리가 Stella에게 젖을 먹였다.

31 그 코끼리는 Stella의 엄마만큼 따뜻하게 Stella를 보살폈다.

32 이것은 너무나 놀라운 순간이었다.

● 우리말을 참고하여 본문을 영작하시오.

날짜/시간: 7월 8일, 오후 2시 35분

1 기록: 오늘은 내가 아프리카에 온 첫날이었다.

➡ _____

2 나는 코끼리 사진을 많이 찍었다.

➡ _____

3 오늘 아침에 나는 작은 물웅덩이 옆에 있는 한 코끼리 무리를 발견했다.

➡ _____

4 나는 아기 코끼리 한 마리가 엄마 옆에서 물을 마시고 있는 것을 보았다.

➡ _____

5 그 코끼리의 눈이 별처럼 밝았다.

➡ _____

6 나는 그 코끼리에게 Stella란 이름을 붙여 주었다.

➡ _____

7 정오 즈음에 나는 사자 한 무리가 Stella에게 다가가는 것을 보았다.

➡ _____

8 코끼리들은 Stella 주위에 둘러서서 두꺼운 벽을 만들었다.

➡ _____

9 그 코끼리들 덕분에 Stella는 안전했다.

➡ _____

날짜/시간: 7월 12일, 오후 7시 20분

10 기록: 해질녘에 나는 이상한 소리를 들었다.

➡ _____

11 나는 그 소리를 따라갔고 Stella가 자신의 엄마 옆에서 울고 있는 것을 발견했다.

➡ _____

12 엄마는 죽어서 누워 있었고, Stella는 혼자였다.

➡ _____

13 이러한 야생 지역에서 혼자 있는 것은 위험하다.

➡ _____

14 더욱이 곧 어두워질 것이었다.

➡ _____

15 코끼리들은 밤에 잘 볼 수 없다.

➡ _____

16 그래서 Stella는 쉽게 공격을 받을 수 있었다.
➡ _____

17 나는 코끼리 보호소에 전화를 해서 도움을 요청했다.
➡ _____

18 나는 구조대가 올 때까지 Stella 곁에 머물기로 결정했다.
➡ _____

날짜/시간: 7월 12일, 오후 10시 40분
19 기록: 밤은 어둡고 조용했다.
➡ _____

20 나는 야간용 카메라를 이용해서 Stella를 계속 지켜보았다.
➡ _____

21 Stella는 여전히 엄마 곁에 있었다.
➡ _____

22 Stella는 코로 엄마의 죽은 몸을 어루만지고 있었다.
➡ _____

23 Stella가 엄마 가까이에 머물고 있는 것을 보는 것은 슬픈 일이었다.
➡ _____

24 나는 Stella가 밤새도록 안전하게 있기를 바란다.
➡ _____

날짜/시간: 7월 13일, 오전 6시
25 기록: 새로운 코끼리 무리가 나타났고, Stella는 그 무리에 다가갔다.
➡ _____

26 처음에 나는 그 코끼리들이 Stella를 자신의 무리로 받아들이지 않을 것이라고 생각했다.
➡ _____

27 그러나 내 생각이 틀렸다.
➡ _____

28 아마도 가장 나이가 많은 암컷인 듯한 코끼리 한 마리가 Stella가 그 무리의 일원이 되도록 허락했다.
➡ _____

29 다른 코끼리들도 Stella를 반기는 것처럼 보였다.
➡ _____

30 믿을 수 없게도, 암컷 코끼리 중의 한 마리가 Stella에게 젖을 먹였다.
➡ _____

31 그 코끼리는 Stella의 엄마만큼 따뜻하게 Stella를 보살폈다.
➡ _____

32 이것은 너무나 놀라운 순간이었다.
➡ _____

[01~03] 다음 글을 읽고 물음에 답하시오.

Date/Time: July 8th / 2:35 p.m.
Notes: Today was my first day in Africa. I took lots of pictures of elephants. This morning, I found an elephant group by a small water hole. I saw a baby elephant drinking water beside her mother. Her eyes were as bright as stars. I gave her a name, Stella. Around noon, I saw a group of lions approaching Stella. The elephants stood around Stella and made a thick wall. Thanks to them, Stella was safe.

중요

01 다음 중 위 글에서 찾아볼 수 없는 것은?

① a person who is taking picture of elephants
② an elephant group near a small water hole
③ a group of lions approaching a baby elephant
④ elephants protecting a baby elephant
⑤ a small elephant sucking its mother's milk

02 다음 중 위 글을 읽고 답할 수 있는 것은?

① How did the writer get to Africa?
② When did the writer take notes?
③ What is the writer's name?
④ How many elephants did the writer see?
⑤ How many lions were there?

서답형

03 What did the writer find on the morning of July 8?

➡ _____

_____

[04~07] 다음 글을 읽고 물음에 답하시오.

Date/Time: July 12th / 7:20 p.m.
Notes: Around sunset, I heard a strange sound. I followed the sound and found Stella crying next to her mom. She was lying dead and Stella was alone. It is dangerous ___(A)___ alone in such a wild area. ___(B)___, it was going to be dark soon. Elephants can't see well at night. So Stella could easily be attacked. I called the elephant shelter and asked for help. I decided to stay by her until the rescue team came.

서답형

04 빈칸 (A)에 들어갈 알맞은 말을 위 글에서 찾아 어법에 맞게 쓰시오.

➡ _____

05 다음 중 빈칸 (B)에 들어갈 말로 적절하지 않은 것은?

① What's more   ② Furthermore
③ However   ④ In addition
⑤ Besides

중요

06 다음 중 위 글의 내용과 일치하지 않는 것은?

① The writer heard a strange sound around sunset.
② The writer found Stella crying on July 12.
③ Stella was left alone in a wild area.
④ Luckily, Stella can see well at night.
⑤ The writer called the elephant shelter to ask for help.

서답형

07 다음과 같이 풀이되는 말을 위 글에서 찾아 쓰시오.

> a building designed to give protection from bad weather, danger, or attack

➡ _____

[08~10] 다음 글을 읽고 물음에 답하시오.

> Date/Time: July 12th / 10:40 p.m.
> Notes: The night was dark and quiet. I kept my eyes ____(A)____ Stella with my night camera. Stella was still next to her mom. She was touching her mom's lifeless body with her nose. It was sad to see Stella stay close to her mom. I hope Stella stays safe throughout the night.

08 다음 중 빈칸 (A)에 들어갈 말과 같은 말이 들어가는 것은?

① Did you turn _____ all the lights when you went out of the room?
② I am really looking forward _____ visiting the place.
③ Jason was full _____ justice and courage.
④ Put _____ your mask, or you will catch a cold.
⑤ She needs to pick _____ her sister at the airport.

서답형

09 위 글의 내용과 일치하도록 빈칸에 알맞은 말을 쓰시오.

> A: What made you sad?
> B: _____ _____ _____ _____
> _____ _____ _____ made me really sad.

중요

10 다음 중 위 글의 내용과 일치하는 것은?

① The writer wasn't interested in Stella at all.
② Stella left her mother as soon as possible.
③ The writer took care of Stella.
④ Stella's mom was dead.
⑤ Stella spent the night in a shelter.

[11~13] 다음 글을 읽고 물음에 답하시오.

> Date/Time: July 13th / 6:00 a.m.
> Notes: A new elephant group appeared and Stella approached them.
> (A) Unbelievably, one of the female elephants fed Stella. She cared for Stella as warmly as Stella's mom did.
> (B) An elephant, probably the oldest female allowed Stella to become part of the group.
> (C) At first, I thought that they would not let Stella in their group. But I was wrong.
> (D) The other elephants also seemed to welcome Stella.
> This was _____ⓐ_____!

서답형

11 자연스러운 글이 되도록 (A)~(D)를 바르게 나열하시오.

➡ _____

12 다음 중 빈칸 ⓐ에 들어갈 말로 가장 적절한 것은?

① amazing such a moment
② such amazing a moment
③ such an amazing moment
④ an amazing such moment
⑤ a moment such amazing

13 Which one is TRUE about the passage?

① The new elephant group didn't accept Stella.

② Stella moved near to the new elephant group.

③ All the elephants didn't like Stella except one elephant.

④ Stella didn't want to be part of the group.

⑤ The writer's guess about the elephants was right.

[14~17] 다음 글을 읽고 물음에 답하시오.

Date/Time: July 8th / 2:35 p.m.
Notes: Today was my first day in Africa. I took ____(A)____ pictures of elephants. This morning, I found an elephant group by a small water hole. ① I saw a baby elephant drinking water beside her mother. ② Her eyes were as bright as stars. ③ I gave her a name, Stella. ④ Around noon, I saw a group of lions approaching Stella. ⑤ Thanks to them, Stella was safe.

14 다음 중 빈칸 (A)에 들어갈 말로 적절하지 <u>않은</u> 것은?

① a number of   ② a lot of

③ lots of   ④ many

⑤ much

15 위 글의 ①~⑤ 중 주어진 문장이 들어가기에 가장 적절한 곳은?

The elephants stood around Stella and made a thick wall.

①   ②   ③   ④   ⑤

서답형

16 다음 물음에 완전한 문장의 영어로 답하시오.

Q: Where did the writer write this diary?

➡ _____

17 다음 중 위 글의 내용과 일치하지 <u>않는</u> 것은?

① The writer found an elephant group beside a small water hole.

② The writer took many pictures of elephants.

③ The writer decided to call the mother elephant Stella.

④ A group of lions approached Stella.

⑤ The writer found a group of lions around noon.

[18~21] 다음 글을 읽고 물음에 답하시오.

Date/Time: July 12th / 7:20 p.m.
Notes: Around sunset, I heard a strange sound. I followed the sound and found Stella crying next to her mom. She was lying dead and Stella was alone. (A)To stay alone in such a wild area was dangerous. What's more, (B)it was going to be dark soon. Elephants can't see well at night. So Stella could easily be attacked. I called the elephant shelter and asked for help. I decided to stay by her until the rescue team came.

서답형

18 위 글의 밑줄 친 (A)와 같은 의미의 문장을 완성하시오.

It _____.

19 다음 중 밑줄 친 (B)와 쓰임이 <u>다른</u> 것은?

① It was Saturday afternoon.

② It is cloudy and windy.

③ It is ten miles to Boston.

④ It is dark outside.

⑤ It is difficult to solve the problem.

20 According to the passage, why could Stella be attacked easily at night? Use the phrase 'it's because.'

➡ _____

21 다음 중 위 글을 읽고 답할 수 있는 것은?

① What can elephants do well?

② What was Stella doing in the morning?

③ Whom did the writer call?

④ When did the rescue team come?

⑤ What did the writer see around noon?

[22~23] 다음 글을 읽고 물음에 답하시오.

Date: June 15th, 2019
Write about what you saw:
Today, I saw a plant. It is called a pitcher plant. It is bright green and red. It looks like a pitcher. As for its size, it is about 15cm long. It is as long as my hand. (A)벌레잡이 식물이 곤충을 먹는 것을 보는 것은 흥미로워.

22 Which is NOT true about the passage?

① The writer wrote about a pitcher plant.

② A pitcher plant is bright green and red.

③ The writer's hand is about 15cm long.

④ A pitcher plant is two times as long as the writer's hand.

⑤ A pitcher plant eats insects.

23 주어진 단어를 활용하여 밑줄 친 우리말 (A)를 영어로 쓰시오.

(it / interesting)

➡ _____

[24~26] 다음 글을 읽고 물음에 답하시오.

Date/Time: July 12th / 10:40 p.m.
Notes: The night was dark and quiet. I ①kept my eyes on Stella with my night camera. Stella was still next to her mom. She was touching her mom's lifeless body with her nose. ②It was sad to see Stella ③staying close to her mom. I hope Stella stays ④safely throughout the night.
Date/Time: July 13th / 6:00 a.m.
Notes: A new elephant group ⑤appeared and Stella approached them. At first, I thought that they would not let Stella in their group. But I was wrong. An elephant, probably the oldest female allowed Stella to become part of the group. The other elephants also seemed to welcome Stella. Unbelievably, one of the female elephants fed Stella. She cared for Stella as ___(A)___ as Stella's mom did. This was such an amazing moment!

24 빈칸 (A)에 warm의 알맞은 어형을 쓰시오.

➡ _____

25 ①~⑤ 중 어법상 바르지 않은 것은?

①   ②   ③   ④   ⑤

26 다음 중 위 글의 내용을 잘못 이해한 사람은?

① Jason: I'm so sorry that Stella's mom was dead.

② Claire: It was so lucky that Stella spent the night safely.

③ Jim: Unlike the writer, I thought the new elephant group would not accept Stella.

④ Brad: The female elephant which fed Stella is so generous.

⑤ David: I am happy to see Stella become part of the new group.

[01~04] 다음 글을 읽고 물음에 답하시오.

Date/Time: July 8th / 2:35 p.m.
Notes: Today was my first day in Africa. I took lots of pictures of elephants. This morning, I found an elephant group by a small water hole. I saw a baby elephant drinking water beside her mother. _____(A)_____
I gave her a name, Stella. Around noon, I saw a group of lions approaching Stella. The elephants stood around Stella and made a thick wall. Thanks to them, Stella was safe.

01 원급 비교를 이용하여 다음 두 문장을 하나의 문장으로 만들어 빈칸 (A)를 채우시오.

> Her eyes were bright. They were bright like stars.

➡ _____

02 According to the passage, how did the elephant group protect Stella from the lions?

➡ _____

03 다음 대화의 빈칸을 알맞게 채우시오.

> A: When did the writer _____ _____
> _____ _____ _____?
> B: It was around noon.

04 다음은 글쓴이가 아프리카에서 돌아와서 한 말이다. 위 글의 표현을 활용하여 영어로 쓰시오. 주어진 단어를 활용하시오.

> 사자 한 무리가 Stella에게 다가가는 것을 보는 것은 무서웠어. (it / scare)

➡ _____
_____

[05~08] 다음 글을 읽고 물음에 답하시오.

Date/Time: July 12th / 7:20 p.m.
Notes: Around sunset, I heard a strange sound. I followed the sound and found Stella crying next to her mom. She was lying dead and Stella was alone. It is dangerous to stay alone in such a wild area. What's more, it was going to be dark soon. Elephants can't see well at night. So Stella could easily be attacked. I called the elephant shelter and asked for help. _____(A)_____ until the rescue team came.

05 주어진 단어를 바르게 배열하여 빈칸 (A)에 들어갈 말을 완성하시오.

> (by / stay / I / to / her / decided)

➡ _____

06 According to the passage, what did the writer find when he followed the strange sound? Answer in English with a full sentence.

➡ _____

07 Write the reason why the writer called the elephant shelter and asked for help. Answer in Korean.

➡ _____
_____

08 원급 비교와 주어진 단어를 활용하여 다음 우리말을 8 단어로 이루어진 한 문장의 영어로 쓰시오.

> 나는 밤에 코끼리만큼 잘 볼 수 없다. (blind)

➡ _____

[09~14] 다음 글을 읽고 물음에 답하시오.

Date/Time: July 12th / 10:40 p.m.

Notes: The night was dark and quiet. I kept my eyes on Stella with my night camera. Stella was still next to her mom. She was touching her mom's lifeless body with her nose. ⓐ<u>To see Stella staying close to her mom was sad.</u> I hope Stella stays safe throughout the night.

Date/Time: July 13th / 6:00 a.m.

Notes: A new elephant group appeared and Stella approached them. At first, I thought that ⓑ<u>they</u> would not let Stella in their group. But I was wrong. An elephant, probably the oldest female allowed Stella to become part of the group. The other elephants also seemed to welcome Stella. Unbelievably, one of the female elephants fed Stella. _____ (A) _____.

This was such an amazing moment!

09 원급 비교를 이용하여 주어진 문장과 같은 의미의 문장을 빈칸 (A)에 쓰시오.

> She cared for Stella warmly like her mother did.

➡ _____

10 밑줄 친 문장 ⓐ와 같은 의미의 문장을 완성하시오.

> It _____ .

11 밑줄 친 ⓑ가 가리키는 것을 위 글에서 찾아 쓰시오.

➡ _____

12 According to the passage, what was Stella doing next to her mother during the night? Answer in English with a full sentence.

➡ _____

_____

13 다음 물음에 완전한 문장의 영어로 답하시오.

> Q: What appeared in front of Stella?

➡ _____

14 When Stella approached a new elephant group, what did the writer think at first? Answer in English.

➡ _____

_____

[15~16] 다음 글을 읽고 물음에 답하시오.

Plant Diary

Date: June 15th, 2019

Write about what you saw:

Today, I saw a plant. It is called a pitcher plant. It is bright green and red. It looks like a pitcher. As for its size, it is about 15cm long. It is as long as my hand. It is interesting that the plant attracts insects and eats them.

15 According to the passage, how long is the writer's hand? Answer in English with a full sentence.

➡ _____

16 According to the passage, what does the plant look like?

➡ _____

해석

Read and Think

Some lions tried to attack Stella. The elephant group made a thick wall to
　　　　　　 ~하려고 애썼다
protect her.
to부정사의 부사적 용법 – 목적 (~하기 위해서)
Stella was crying next to her dead mother. I watched her all night.
　　　　　　　　　　　　　　　　　　　　　　　　　 밤새도록
The oldest female elephant of a new group allowed Stella to become part of
　　　　　　　　　　　　　　　　　　 allow+목적어+to부정사: 목적어가 V하도록 허락했다
them.

사자 몇 마리가 Stella를 공격하려고 했다. 코끼리 무리는 Stella를 보호하기 위해 두꺼운 벽을 만들었다. Stella는 그녀의 죽은 엄마 옆에서 울고 있었다 나는 밤새도록 그녀를 지켜보았다. 새로운 무리의 가장 나이 많은 암컷 코끼리는 Stella를 그들의 일원이 되도록 허락했다.

구문해설　• attack: 공격하다　• thick: 두꺼운　• protect: 보호하다　• dead: 죽은
　　　　 • allow: ~을 허락하다

Think & Write C

Plant Diary

Date: June 15th, 2019

Write about what you saw:

Today, I saw a plant. It is called a pitcher plant. It is bright green and red. It
　　　　　　　　　　　 ~라고 불린다
looks like a pitcher. As for its size, it is about 15cm long. It is as long as my
look like+명사: ~처럼 보이다　　　　　　　　 인칭대명사
hand. It is interesting that the plant attracts insects and eats them.
　　　　　 가주어　　　　　 진주어

식물 일기
날짜: 6월 15일, 2019년
네가 본 것을 써 봐.
오늘, 나는 식물 하나를 봤다. 그것은 벌레잡이 식물이라고 불린다. 그것은 밝은 녹색에 붉은색이다. 그것은 항아리처럼 생겼다. 크기에 대해 말하자면, 그것은 대략 15cm이다. 그것은 내 손만큼 길다. 그 식물이 벌레를 끌어들이고 그것들을 먹는 것은 흥미롭다.

구문해설　• look like: ~처럼 보이다　• pitcher: 항아리　• as for: ~에 대해서 말하자면
　　　　 • about: 대략　• interesting: 흥미로운　• attract: 끌어들이다

Wrap Up 1

Minho: Look! Isn't that a sea horse?
　　　　　　　　 부정의문문
Sue: Actually, no. It's a sea dragon.
　　　　 actual+-ly
Minho: Oh, really? I'm curious about the difference between them.
　　　　　　　　　　　 ~을 궁금해 하다　　　　　　 = a sea horse and a sea dragon
Sue: Look at the tail carefully. A sea dragon has a straight one, and but a sea
　　　　　　　　　　　　　　　　　　　　　　　　　　 = tail
horse does not.
뒤에 have a straight tail이 생략되어 있음.
Minho: Oh, I can tell the difference now!
　　　　　　　　 = 차이를 구별하다

Minho: 봐! 저거 해마 아니야?
Sue: 사실은 아니야. 그건 해룡이야.
Minho: 아, 정말? 난 그 둘의 차이점이 궁금해.
Sue: 꼬리를 주의해서 봐. 해룡은 꼬리가 곧지만, 해마는 그렇지 않아.
Minho: 오, 나 이제 차이를 구별할 수 있겠다!

구문해설　• sea horse: 해마　• sea dragon: 해룡　• tail: 꼬리　• straight: 곧은

01 다음 영영풀이가 가리키는 것을 고르시오.

> the soft part in the mouth that moves around, used for tasting, swallowing, speaking, etc.

① tongue   ② knee   ③ lap
④ tooth   ⑤ lip

02 다음 중 밑줄 친 부분의 뜻풀이가 바르지 <u>않은</u> 것은?

① He dug a <u>hole</u> in the garden. 구멍
② Jane is using a ladder to <u>approach</u> the sign. 다가가다
③ The <u>thick</u> mud walls block the sunlight. 얇은
④ Tom got a dog from an animal <u>shelter</u>. 보호소
⑤ Wild animals usually avoid human sounds. 야생의

03 다음 우리말에 맞게 빈칸에 알맞은 말을 쓰시오.

(1) 동물 구조 팀이 강에서 캥거루를 구조했다.
  ➡ An animal _____ team saved a kangaroo from the river.
(2) 긴 꼬리가 치타가 균형을 잡을 수 있도록 도와준다.
  ➡ A long _____ helps the cheetah to keep its balance.
(3) 그녀는 온 힘을 다해 그 밧줄을 당겼다.
  ➡ She pulled on the rope with all her _____.

04 다음 주어진 문장의 밑줄 친 approach와 같은 의미로 쓰인 것은?

> Nobody could <u>approach</u> the President.

① She took the wrong <u>approach</u> to the problem.
② Don't wait for kids to come, <u>approach</u> them first.
③ What is the best <u>approach</u> to the learning of English?
④ His <u>approach</u> was not effective to solve this problem.
⑤ I think the best <u>approach</u> is the conversation.

05 다음 우리말과 일치하도록 주어진 어구를 모두 배열하여 영작하시오.

(1) 작은 소년 옆에 있는 소녀를 아니?
(the little / the / next / girl / to / you / know / do / boy)
  ➡ _____
(2) 전 세계 수백만의 사람들이 인터넷을 사용한다.
(use / people / the Internet / the world / millions / around / of)
  ➡ _____
_____
(3) 그녀는 그녀의 딸 사진을 찍는 것을 아주 좋아한다.
(her / she / daughter / take / of / to / a / picture / loves)
  ➡ _____

06 다음 문장에 들어갈 말을 〈보기〉에서 찾아 순서대로 쓰시오.

> ┌── 보기 ──┐
> receive / give / keep / tell /
> appear / attract

- I was asked to (A)_____ a presentation in English class.
- It is hard for me to (B)_____ the difference between two dogs.
- During the game, I had to (C)_____ my eyes on the ball.

Conversation

[07~08] 다음 대화를 읽고 물음에 답하시오.

Jane: ⓐLook at this picture of a huge flower.

Tom: Wow, it is ⓑmore big than a person.

Jane: Yeah. I'm really ⓒcurious about this flower. It also says here that the flower ⓓsmells very bad, but insects love the smell.

Tom: Hmm, I wonder ⓔwhy.

07 위 대화의 ⓐ~ⓔ 중 어법상 어색한 것을 찾아 바르게 고치시오.

➡ _____

08 위 대화의 내용과 일치하지 <u>않는</u> 것은?

① Jane and Tom are looking at the huge flower in the garden.

② The huge flower is bigger than a person.

③ Jane wants to know the huge flower more.

④ The huge flower smells very bad.

⑤ The insects love the smell of the huge flower.

09 다음 주어진 문장 뒤에 대화가 자연스럽게 이어지도록 순서대로 배열하시오.

> Do you think we can be friends with lions?

(A) Wow, that's so touching.

(B) No, I don't think so.

(C) Really? I'm curious about the story. Can you tell me more?

(D) Well, I watched a video clip about friendship between two men and a lion.

(E) The two men raised a baby lion and sent her back into the wild. When the men and the lion met a year later, she remembered them.

➡ _____

10 다음 대화를 읽고 Dr. Watson이 소개한 자이언트 캥거루의 특징을 우리말로 간략하게 서술하시오.

Emily: Hello, Dr. Watson. Can you tell us about your study?

Dr. Watson: I study animals that lived millions of years ago.

Emily: Oh, I'm curious about those animals. Were there any interesting ones?

Dr. Watson: Yes, there were many. This is the giant kangaroo. It lived in Australia. It was as heavy as three men and it couldn't jump well.

Emily: That's amazing!

➡ _____
_____

[11~13] 다음 대화를 읽고 물음에 답하시오.

Dylan: Look at this picture, Mina. We got a new puppy yesterday. He's only two weeks old.

Mina: Oh, Dylan, he's so small!

Dylan: Yeah. ⓐ그는 지금 내 손만큼 작다(as, small), but he'll get (A) bigger in a few months.

Mina: Wow, puppies grow very quickly.

11 위 대화의 빈칸 (A)에 들어갈 말로 어색한 것은?

① much　　② very　　③ a lot
④ far　　⑤ even

12 위 대화의 밑줄 친 ⓐ의 우리말을 주어진 단어를 사용하여 영어로 쓰시오.

➡ _____

13 위 대화를 읽고 대답할 수 없는 것은?

① What did Dylan get yesterday?
② How old is the new puppy?
③ How small is the new puppy now?
④ What is Dylan showing to Mina?
⑤ What should Dylan do to take care of the puppy?

Grammar

14 다음 중 빈칸에 들어갈 말로 가장 적절한 것은?

It is wrong _____ bad things about friends.

① say　　　　　② to say
③ to saying　　④ that
⑤ to

15 다음 중 어법상 바르지 않은 것은?

A: Was ①it fun ②to watching a baseball game?
B: Yes, it ③was. I like ④watching a baseball game ⑤a lot.

①　　②　　③　　④　　⑤

16 다음 중 문장의 전환이 바르지 않은 것은?

① To take a trip to another country is fun.
　= It is fun to take a trip to another country.
② Washing all the dishes is difficult.
　= It is difficult to wash all the dishes.
③ It is good to help people in the poor countries.
　= To help people in the poor countries are good.
④ James is not as thin as Paul.
　= Paul is thinner than James.
⑤ The man is heavier than the woman.
　= The woman is not as heavy as the man.

17 주어진 단어를 활용하여 다음 우리말을 일곱 단어로 이루어진 한 문장의 영어로 쓰시오.

물 없이 사는 것은 불가능하다.
(impossible / live)

➡ _____

18 다음은 남자와 여자 30명씩을 대상으로 선호하는 과일을 물은 설문조사 결과이다. 표를 제대로 분석하지 못한 사람은?

	Apple	Grape	Orange
men	8	14	8
women	8	7	15

① 민수: Men like apples as much as women.
② 은서: Women don't like oranges as much as men.
③ 혜진: Men like grapes two times as much as women.
④ 현우: Men like apples as much as oranges.
⑤ 청아: Men don't like oranges as much as women.

19 주어진 단어를 활용하여 다음 우리말을 7단어로 이루어진 한 문장의 영어로 쓰시오.

> 그녀가 노래 부르는 것을 듣는 것은 어려웠다.
> (difficult / hear / it)

➡ _____

20 다음 중 밑줄 친 부분의 쓰임이 다른 하나는?

① It is my duty to clean my room every day.
② It is interesting that you think her beautiful.
③ It is fun to see them playing together.
④ It was boring to hear him talk.
⑤ It was found on the table.

21 다음 문장을 하나의 문장으로 바르게 표현한 것은?

> James's dog is three years old. My dog is three years old, too.

① James's dog is older than my dog.
② James's dog is not as old as my dog.
③ James's dog is two times as old as my dog.
④ James's dog is as old as my dog.
⑤ My dog is not as old as James's dog.

22 다음 중 빈칸에 들어갈 말로 적절한 것을 고르시오.

> It was exciting _____ a soccer game at the stadium.

① to watching   ② watches
③ watch   ④ watched
⑤ to watch

[23~26] 다음 글을 읽고 물음에 답하시오.

> Date/Time: July 8th / 2:35 p.m.
> Notes: Today was my first day in Africa. I took lots of pictures of elephants. This morning, I found an elephant group by a small water hole. I saw a baby elephant (A)[drinking / to drink] water beside her mother. Her eyes were as (B)[bright / brightly] as stars. I gave her a name, Stella. Around noon, I saw a group of lions approaching Stella. The elephants stood around Stella and made a thick wall. Thanks to (C)[it / them], Stella was safe.

23 (A)~(C)에서 어법상 옳은 것끼리 바르게 짝지은 것은?

① drinking – bright – it
② drinking – brightly – it
③ drinking – bright – them
④ to drink – bright – them
⑤ to drink – brightly – it

24 What name did the writer give to the baby elephant? Answer in English with a full sentence.

➡ _____

25 다음 중 위 글을 읽고 답할 수 없는 것은?

① What did the writer see on his first day in Africa?
② What did the writer find this morning?
③ Where was the group of elephants on the morning of July 8?
④ What was the baby elephant doing beside her mother?
⑤ How many lions were approaching Stella?

26 위 글의 내용에 맞게 빈칸에 알맞은 말을 쓰시오.

> A: Why did the elephants make a thick wall around the baby elephant?
> B: It's because they wanted _____ _____ _____ _____ _____ from _____.

27 다음 주어진 문장이 들어가기에 가장 적절한 곳은?

> But I was wrong.

①   ②   ③   ④   ⑤

28 (A)~(C)에서 어법상 옳은 것끼리 바르게 짝지은 것은?

① beside – approached – was
② besides – approached to – was
③ beside – approached – did
④ besides – approached to – did
⑤ beside – approached to – did

[27~30] 다음 글을 읽고 물음에 답하시오.

Date/Time: July 12th / 10:40 p.m.
Notes: The night was dark and quiet. I kept my eyes on Stella with my night camera. Stella was still (A)[beside / besides] her mom. She was touching her mom's lifeless body with her nose. It was sad to see Stella staying close to her mom. I hope Stella stays safe throughout the night.
Date/Time: July 13th / 6:00 a.m.
Notes: A new elephant group appeared and Stella (B)[approached / approached to] them. ① At first, I thought that they would not let Stella in their group. ② An elephant, probably the oldest female allowed Stella to become part of the group. ③ The other elephants also seemed to welcome Stella. ④ Unbelievably, one of the female elephants fed Stella. ⑤ She cared for Stella as warmly as Stella's mom (C)[was / did]. This was such an amazing moment!

29 위 글의 내용에 맞게 빈칸에 알맞은 말을 쓰시오.

> A: It was really surprising that _____ _____ _____ _____ _____ _____ _____.
> B: She is really generous. Although Stella was not her baby, she took care of her like Stella's mom.

30 다음 중 위 글의 내용과 일치하지 <u>않는</u> 것은?

① It was dark and quiet on the night of July 12.
② The writer had a night camera.
③ The writer hoped Stella would stay safe.
④ Stella stayed by her mom without touching her.
⑤ The writer didn't expect that the new elephant group would let Stella in their group.

출제율 95%

01 다음 문장의 빈칸에 들어갈 말을 〈보기〉에서 골라 쓰시오.

┌─ 보기 ─┐
careless / humorous / sheet / blind / wild
└─────┘

(1) We laughed at the comedian's _____ stories.

(2) I'm sorry to hurt your feelings by my _____ words.

(3) It's dangerous to stay alone in a _____ area.

(4) I'm as _____ as a bat without my glasses.

(5) We should prepare a _____ to draw the picture.

출제율 90%

02 다음 우리말을 주어진 단어를 이용하여 영작하시오.

(1) 야생 동물은 위험할 수 있다. (be)

➡ _____

(2) 우리는 유머 감각을 가질 필요가 있다. (need)

➡ _____

(3) 동물원에서 동물들에게 먹이를 주지 마라. (don't, feed)

➡ _____

[03~04] 다음 대화를 읽고 물음에 답하시오.

Minho: Look! Isn't that a sea horse?
Sue: Actually, no. It's a sea dragon.
Minho: Oh, really? I'm curious about the difference between them.
Sue: Look at the tail carefully. A sea dragon has a straight one, but a sea horse does not.
Minho: Oh, I can (A)tell the difference now!

출제율 85%

03 위 대화의 밑줄 친 (A)tell과 같은 의미로 쓰인 것은?

① Would you tell me the truth?
② Why don't you tell everyone your story?
③ I can't tell you from your twin sister.
④ Don't tell me what to do.
⑤ Many doctors tell us that we should not eat too much.

출제율 95%

04 해마와 해룡을 어떻게 구분할 수 있는지 우리말로 설명하시오.

➡ _____

[05~06] 다음 대화를 읽고 물음에 답하시오.

Emily: (A) Hello, Dr. Watson. Can you tell us about your study?
Dr. Watson: (B) I study animals that lived millions of years ago.
Emily: (C) Were there any interesting ones?
Dr. Watson: (D) Yes, there were many. This is the giant kangaroo. It lived in Australia. It was as heavy as three men and it couldn't jump well.
Emily: (E) That's amazing!

출제율 100%

05 위 대화의 (A)~(E) 중 주어진 문장이 들어가기에 가장 적절한 곳은?

Oh, I'm curious about those animals.

① (A) ② (B) ③ (C) ④ (D) ⑤ (E)

06 위 대화의 내용과 일치하지 <u>않는</u> 것은?

① Dr. Watson studies animals which lived millions of years ago.

② Emily wants to know what Dr. Watson studies.

③ The giant kangaroo lived in Australia.

④ The giant kangaroo was not able to jump well.

⑤ The giant kangaroo was heavier than three men.

[07~08] 다음 대화를 읽고 물음에 답하시오.

Kelly: George, (A)[which / that] red house over there is my grandparents' house.

George: Wow, the tree by the house is really big.

Kelly: Actually, that tree is (B)[so / as] old as me, thirteen years old.

George: How do you know that, Kelly?

Kelly: My grandfather (C)[plant / planted] the tree in 2004 when I was born.

07 위 대화의 괄호 (A)~(C)에 알맞은 말을 바르게 쓰시오.

(A) _____ (B) _____ (C) _____

08 위 대화를 읽고 대답할 수 <u>없는</u> 것은?

① What color is the house of Kelly's grandparents?

② What is there by the house of Kelly's grandparents?

③ How old is the tree that Kelly's grandfather planted?

④ When was Kelly born?

⑤ What tree did Kelly's grandfather plant in 2004?

[09~10] 다음 대화를 읽고 물음에 답하시오.

Ryan: Judy, did you choose a topic for your science project?

Judy: Not yet. How about you, Ryan?

Ryan: I'm curious about weather change. So I'm thinking about doing the project on that.

Judy: That's an interesting topic!

09 What are Judy and Ryan talking about?

➡ _____

10 What is Ryan wondering about?

➡ _____

11 다음 중 주어진 문장의 밑줄 친 부분과 그 쓰임이 같은 것은?

> <u>It</u> is necessary to say no sometimes.

① <u>It</u> is a long and thin object.

② <u>It</u> is dark and humid.

③ <u>It</u> was interesting to talk with him.

④ <u>It</u> was my parents' wedding anniversary.

⑤ <u>It</u> made me angry and upset.

12 다음 중 어법상 바르지 <u>않은</u> 것은?

① It is dangerous to talk with a stranger.

② Jane earns two times as much money as Tom.

③ That is fun to get along with friends.

④ This pen is as cheap as the pencil.

⑤ It is necessary to start at once.

13 주어진 단어를 활용하여 다음 우리말을 영어로 쓰시오.

> 밤에 그 사물을 보는 것은 가능했다.
> (it / the object)

➡ _____

14 다음 문장과 같은 의미의 문장은?

> Jill knows more people than me.

① I know more people than Jill.
② Jill doesn't know as many people as I do.
③ I don't know as many people as Jill does.
④ Jill knows as many people as I do.
⑤ Jill knows twice as many people as I do.

15 다음 중 어법상 바르지 <u>않은</u> 것은?

> ①It was impossible ②understand him ③because he spoke ④too fast. He spoke ⑤as fast as a train.

①   ②   ③   ④   ⑤

16 주어진 단어를 바르게 배열하여 다음 우리말을 영어로 쓰시오. 필요하면 단어를 추가하시오.

> 이 방은 저 방보다 대략 두 배 더 크다.
> (that one / this room / about / large / as / is / two times)

➡ _____

17 주어진 단어를 활용하여 다음 우리말을 영어로 쓰시오.

> 물고기가 물속에서 수영하는 것을 보는 것은 아주 멋졌다.
> (it / wonderful / fish)

➡ _____

[18~23] 다음 글을 읽고 물음에 답하시오.

> Date/Time: July 12th / 7:20 p.m.
> Notes: Around sunset, I heard a (A)[joyful / strange] sound. I followed the sound and found Stella crying next to her mom. She was lying dead and Stella was alone. ⓐ이러한 야생 지역에서 혼자 있는 것은 위험하다. What's more, it was going to be (B)[dark / bright] soon. Elephants can't see well at night. So Stella could easily be attacked. I called the elephant shelter and asked for help. I decided to stay by her until the rescue team came.
> Date/Time: July 12th / 10:40 p.m.
> Notes: The night was dark and quiet. I kept my eyes on Stella with my night camera. Stella was still next to her mom. She was touching her mom's (C)[lively / lifeless] body with her nose. (D)It was sad to see Stella staying close to her mom. I hope Stella stays safe throughout the night.

18 주어진 단어를 활용하여 밑줄 친 우리말 ⓐ를 영어로 쓰시오.

> (it / stay / such)

➡ _____

19 (A)~(C)에서 글의 흐름상 자연스러운 것끼리 바르게 짝지은 것은?
출제율 100%

① joyful – dark – lively
② joyful – bright – lifeless
③ joyful – dark – lifeless
④ strange – dark – lifeless
⑤ strange – bright – lively

20 다음 중 밑줄 친 (D)와 쓰임이 다른 것은?
출제율 90%

① It was my fault to give her the message.
② It is his job to make us delicious food.
③ It is used to make cheese and yogurt.
④ It is amazing to see them talking with delight.
⑤ It is interesting that you gave her your diary.

21 Which is NOT true about the passage?
출제율 95%

① The writer heard Stella crying in the evening.
② Stella was crying beside her mother.
③ It was the elephant shelter that the writer called.
④ Stella was touching her dead mom with her nose.
⑤ Stella left her mom as soon as it was getting dark.

22 다음 중 위 글을 읽고 찾아볼 수 없는 것을 모두 고르시오.
출제율 95%

① a baby elephant crying beside her dead mother
② some elephants protecting Stella at night
③ the writer staying near Stella to watch her
④ the rescue team approaching Stella
⑤ the writer calling the elephant shelter

23 다음 물음에 완전한 문장의 영어로 답하시오.
출제율 90%

Q: What did the writer hear around sunset?

➡ _____

[24~25] 다음 글을 읽고 물음에 답하시오.

Plant Diary
Date: June 15th, 2019
Write about what you saw:
Today, I saw a plant. It is called a pitcher plant. It is bright green and red. It looks like a pitcher. As for its size, it is about 15cm long. It is as long as my hand. (A)그 식물이 곤충을 끌어들이고 그것들을 먹는 것은 흥미롭다.

24 주어진 단어를 활용하여 밑줄 친 우리말 (A)를 영어로 쓰시오.
출제율 95%

(it / that / insects)

➡ _____
_____

25 다음 중 위 글을 읽고 답할 수 없는 것은?
출제율 100%

① What did the writer see today?
② What is the plant called?
③ What does the plant look like?
④ How does the plant attract insects?
⑤ How long is the writer's hand?

[01~03] 다음 대화를 읽고 물음에 답하시오.

> **Kelly:** George, that red house over there is my grandparents' house.
>
> **George:** Wow, the tree by the house is really big.
>
> **Kelly:** Actually, that tree is as ⓐolder as me, thirteen years old.
>
> **George:** How do you know that, Kelly?
>
> **Kelly:** My grandfather planted the tree in 2004 when I ⓑborn.

01 위 대화의 밑줄 친 ⓐ와 ⓑ를 어법상 바르게 고쳐 쓰시오.

ⓐ _____ ⓑ _____

02 How old is the tree by the red house?

➡ _____

03 What did Kelly's grandfather do when Kelly was born?

➡ _____

04 주어진 단어를 바르게 배열하여 다음 우리말을 영어로 쓰시오. 필요하면 단어를 추가하시오.

> 학급 친구들에게 친절하게 대하는 것은 중요하다.
> (be / is / it / your / kind / important / classmates / to)

➡ _____

05 괄호 안의 단어를 활용하여 다음 두 문장을 하나의 문장으로 쓰시오.

> • A yellow pencil is only one dollar.
> • A green pencil is only one dollar, too.
> (cheap)

➡ _____

06 다음 대화의 빈칸에 알맞은 말을 다섯 단어로 쓰시오.

> **A:** Is it _____?
> **B:** Sure. Living without electricity is not that easy, but possible.

➡ _____

07 다음 대화를 읽고 주어진 단어를 활용하여 문장을 완성하시오.

> **A:** When do you usually go to bed, Brian?
> **B:** I go to bed at 9 p.m. How about you, June?
> **A:** Oh, I go to bed at 9 p.m., too.

➡ Brian _____ June. (early)

08 다음 대화의 빈칸에 알맞은 말을 쓰시오.

> **A:** Did you play soccer better than them?
> **B:** No. I didn't play soccer _____ _____ _____ them. They were very good players.

09 다음 대화를 읽고 빈칸에 알맞은 말을 쓰시오.

> A: I think Helen is sick.
> B: Why do you say so?
> A: Her face looks like a sheet. It is too white.

➡ Helen's face is _____ a sheet.

[10~12] 다음 글을 읽고 물음에 답하시오.

> Date/Time: July 8th / 2:35 p.m.
> Notes: Today was my first day in Africa. I took ①lots of pictures of elephants. This morning, I found an elephant group by a small water hole. I saw a baby elephant ②drinking water beside her mother. Her eyes were as bright as stars. I gave her a name, Stella. Around noon, I saw a group of lions ③approaching Stella. The elephants stood around Stella and made ④a thick wall. Thanks to them, Stella was ⑤in danger.

10 위 글의 표현을 활용하여 다음 우리말을 영어로 쓰시오.

> 나의 눈은 그녀의 눈만큼 밝지 않아.

➡ _____

11 What approached Stella? Answer in English with a full sentence.

➡ _____

12 ①~⑤ 중 글의 흐름상 어색한 것을 바르게 고쳐 쓰시오.

➡ _____

[13~15] 다음 글을 읽고 물음에 답하시오.

> Date/Time: July 13th / 6:00 a.m.
> Notes: A new elephant group appeared and Stella approached them. At first, I thought that they would not let Stella in their group. But I was wrong. An elephant, probably the oldest female allowed Stella to become part of the group. The other elephants also seemed to welcome Stella. Unbelievably, one of the female elephants fed Stella. (A)그녀는 Stella의 엄마만큼 따뜻하게 Stella를 보살폈다. This was such an amazing moment!

13 주어진 단어를 활용하여 밑줄 친 우리말 (A)를 영어로 쓰시오.

> (care / as / as / Stella's mom / do)

➡ _____
_____

14 위 글의 내용과 일치하도록 빈칸에 알맞은 말을 쓰시오.

> Q: What did the oldest elephant do for Stella?
> A: She let _____ _____ _____
> _____ _____ .

15 다음은 아프리카에서 돌아온 글쓴이의 말이다. 글의 내용에 맞게 빈칸에 알맞은 말을 쓰시오.

> When I saw Stella approaching a new elephant group, I thought it was impossible that they _____ _____ _____ _____ their group. But it didn't go as I thought. I was really relieved.

01 다음 대화의 내용과 일치하도록 Mina의 일기를 완성하시오.

> Clare: Do you think we can be friends with lions, Todd?
> Todd: No, Clare. I don't think so.
> Clare: Well, I watched a video clip about friendship between two men and a lion.
> Todd: Really? I'm curious about the story. Can you tell me more?
> Clare: The two men raised a baby lion and sent her back into the wild. When the men and the lion met a year later, she remembered them.
> Todd: Wow, that's so touching.

> Mon, Oct 7th, 2019
> I was so touched by the story Clare told me today. I didn't think that we could be friends with (A)_____. Then, Clare introduced the video clip about (B)_____ between two men and a lion. When I heard that the baby lion remembered the two men who (C)_____, I felt so moved.

02 주어진 어구와 가주어 it을 이용하여 여러 가지 문장을 쓰시오.

> to see elephants protect a baby elephant
> to read that the female elephant took care of Stella
> to see the new elephants accept Stella as a group member

(1) _____
(2) _____
(3) _____

03 다음 식물에 관하여 읽고 식물 관찰 일지를 완성하시오.

> Name: Moss Ball   Color: dark green
> Size: about 4cm   An interesting fact: It floats up when it gets enough sunlight.

> Plant Diary
> Today, I saw a plant. It is called _____. It is _____. It looks _____ a small ball. As for its size, it is _____. It is _____ a ping-pong ball. It is interesting that _____.

단원별 모의고사

01 다음 대화가 자연스럽게 이어지도록 순서대로 배열하시오.

> (A) Oh, Dylan, he's so small!
> (B) Wow, puppies grow very quickly.
> (C) Yeah. He's as small as my hand now, but he'll get much bigger in a few months.
> (D) Look at this picture, Mina. We got a new puppy yesterday. He's only two weeks old.

➡ _____

[02~04] 다음 대화를 읽고 물음에 답하시오.

> **Emily:** Hello, Dr. Watson. Can you tell us about your study?
> **Dr. Watson:** I study animals that lived millions of years ago.
> **Emily:** Oh, I'm curious about those animals. Were there any interesting ones?
> **Dr. Watson:** Yes, there were many. This is the giant kangaroo. It lived in Australia. It was as heavy as three men and it couldn't jump well.
> **Emily:** That's amazing!

02 What does Dr. Watson study?

➡ _____

_____

03 Where did the giant kangaroo live?

➡ _____

04 How heavy was the giant kangaroo?

➡ _____

[05~06] 다음 대화를 읽고 물음에 답하시오.

> **Clare:** Do you think we can be friends with lions, Todd?
> **Todd:** (A) No, Clare. I don't think so.
> **Clare:** (B) Well, I watched a video clip about friendship between two men and a lion.
> **Todd:** (C) Can you tell me more?
> **Clare:** (D) The two men raised a baby lion and sent her back into the wild. When the men and the lion met a year later, she remembered them.
> **Todd:** (E) Wow, that's so touching.

05 위 대화의 (A)~(E) 중 주어진 문장이 들어가기에 적절한 곳은?

> Really? I'm curious about the story.

① (A) ② (B) ③ (C) ④ (D) ⑤ (E)

06 위 대화의 내용과 일치하는 것은?

① Todd thought that people can be friends with lions.
② Clare watched the video clip about friendship of two men.
③ The two men brought up a baby lion in the wild.
④ When the two men met the lion a year later, they were afraid of her.
⑤ Todd is touched by the story about friendship between two men and a lion.

[07~08] 다음 대화를 읽고 물음에 답하시오.

> **Jane:** Look at this picture of a huge flower.
> **Tom:** Wow, it is bigger than a person.
> **Jane:** Yeah. I'm really curious about this flower. It also says here that the flower smells very bad, but insects love the smell.
> **Tom:** Hmm, I wonder why.

07 What is Jane curious about?

➡ _____

08 How does the huge flower smell?

➡ _____

09 다음 문장의 빈칸에 들어갈 말을 〈보기〉에서 골라 쓰시오.

┤ 보기 ├

become part of / give a presentation /
thanks to / next to / tell the difference

(1) Can you _____ between the twin?

(2) I want to _____ the dancing club.

(3) Who will _____ first?

(4) The tree _____ the red house is planted by my father.

(5) _____ your help, I could finish my work early.

[10~11] 다음 대화를 읽고 물음에 답하시오.

Kelly: George, that red house over there is my grandparents' house.

George: Wow, the tree by the house is really big.

Kelly: Actually, _____(A)_____, thirteen years old.

George: How do you know that, Kelly?

Kelly: My grandfather planted the tree in 2004 when I was born.

10 위 대화의 빈칸 (A)에 들어갈 말을 〈보기〉에 주어진 단어를 모두 배열하여 영작하시오.

┤ 보기 ├

as / me / is / as / that / tree / old

➡ _____

11 What are Kelly and George talking about?

① the house of Kelly's grandparents
② the tree by the red house
③ the color of the big house
④ how big the tree by the red house is
⑤ how old Kelly's grandparents are

12 다음 대화가 자연스럽게 이어지도록 순서대로 배열하시오.

(A) That's amazing!

(B) I study animals that lived millions of years ago.

(C) Hello, Dr. Watson. Can you tell us about your study?

(D) Oh, I'm curious about those animals. Were there any interesting ones?

(E) Yes, there were many. This is the giant kangaroo. It lived in Australia. It was as heavy as three men and it couldn't jump well.

➡ _____

13 다음 중 주어진 문장의 밑줄 친 부분과 쓰임이 같은 것은?

It was exciting to feed a sea bird.

① They went out to see what was going on.
② She has many friends to talk with.
③ We made a cake to make her happy.
④ It is dangerous to swim in this lake.
⑤ To win the contest, Julia did everything she could.

14 다음 세 사람의 공부 시간을 읽고 형용사 long을 사용하여 세 사람의 공부 시간을 비교하는 문장의 빈칸을 채우시오.

> **Clara:** I study four hours a day.
>
> **Smith:** I study three hours a day.
>
> **Zach:** I study two hours a day.

➡ Smith doesn't study _____ _____
_____ Clara. Clara studies _____
_____ _____ _____ Zach.

15 다음 중 어법상 바르지 <u>않은</u> 것은?

① It is necessary to respect other cultures.

② The cheetah runs as fast as a car.

③ She is as tall as her mother.

④ It is amusing that he makes so many jokes.

⑤ Have so much food as you want.

16 다음 중 빈칸에 들어갈 말이 바르게 짝지어진 것은?

> • To train children to be polite is important.
>
> = (A)_____ is important (B)_____ children to be polite.
>
> • Please send me the e-mail as soon as possible.
>
> = Please send me the e-mail as soon as (C)_____.

① That – train – you do

② That – to train – you can

③ It – train – you can

④ It – to train – you do

⑤ It – to train – you can

17 주어진 어구를 활용하여 다음 우리말을 영어로 쓰시오.

> 그의 말을 듣는 것은 중요해. 그의 의견은 너의 의견만큼 중요하기 때문이야.
>
> (It / what he says / It's because / opinion)

➡ _____

_____

[18~25] 다음 글을 읽고 물음에 답하시오.

> Date/Time: July 8th / 2:35 p.m.
> Notes: Today was my first day in Africa. I took lots of pictures of elephants. This morning, I found an elephant group by a small water hole. ① I saw a baby elephant drinking water beside her mother. Her eyes were as bright as stars. ② I gave her a name, Stella. ③ The elephants stood around Stella and made a thick wall. ____(A)____ them, Stella was safe.
> Date/Time: July 12th / 7:20 p.m.
> Notes: Around sunset, I heard a strange sound. ④ I followed the sound and found Stella crying next to her mom. ⑤ She was lying dead and Stella was alone. (a)It is dangerous to stay alone in such a wild area. What's more, it was going to be dark soon. Elephants can't see well at night. So Stella could easily be attacked. I called the elephant shelter and asked for help. I decided to stay by her ____(B)____ the rescue team came.

18 ①~⑤ 중 주어진 문장이 들어가기에 가장 적절한 곳은?

> Around noon, I saw a group of lions approaching Stella.

①　　　②　　　③　　　④　　　⑤

19 다음 중 빈칸 (A)에 들어갈 말로 가장 적절한 것은?

① Despite　　　② Instead of

③ Thanks to　　　④ In spite of

⑤ Apart from

20 다음 중 글의 흐름상 빈칸 (B)에 들어갈 말로 가장 적절한 것은?

① if   ② because   ③ or

④ until   ⑤ since

21 다음 중 밑줄 친 (a)와 쓰임이 같은 것은?

① It is under your bed.

② It was fun to play with the dogs.

③ It is a rocket.

④ It was quite dark outside.

⑤ It can't be true.

22 다음은 글쓴이가 코끼리 보호소에 전화한 내용이다. 글의 내용에 맞게 빈칸에 알맞은 말을 쓰시오.

> A: Hi. This is _____ _____ _____.
>
> How can I help you?
>
> B: Hello. I'm calling you because of a baby elephant. She is _____ now.
>
> A: Oh, it is dangerous _____ _____ _____ in the wild.
>
> B: Yes. It's going to be _____ soon, so I'm very worried about her.

23 Which is NOT true about the passage?

① The writer saw a group of elephant on the first day in Africa.

② Stella was drinking water next to her mother.

③ Stella's eyes shone brightly like stars.

④ The elephant group saved the baby elephant by making a thick wall.

⑤ Stella's mom was dead because she was attacked by lions.

24 What did the writer see in the elephant group? Answer in English with eight words.

➡ _____

25 다음은 글쓴이와 통화한 코끼리 보호소 직원의 말이다. 원급 비교와 주어진 단어를 이용하여 영어로 쓰시오.

> 우리가 가능한 한 빨리 그곳에 갈게요.
>
> (be there / soon)

➡ _____

Lesson 7

Art around Us

 의사소통 기능

- 구체적인 종류나 장르 묻기
  A: **What kind of** music are you going to play?
  B: I'm going to play rock music.
- 둘 중에 더 좋아하는 것 말하기
  A: There are two kinds of *Mona Lisas*. Which do you prefer?
  B: I **prefer** Botero's *Mona Lisa* **to** da Vinci's.

 언어 형식

- 사역동사
  It will **make** you **wonder** about the painting more.
- 간접의문문
  Do you know **where Icarus is**?

Words & Expressions

Key Words

- **artist**[ɑ́:rtist] 명 예술가, 미술가
- **artwork**[ɑ́rtwərk] 명 예술 작품
- **brush**[brʌʃ] 명 붓
- **canvas**[kǽnvəs] 명 화폭, 캔버스
- **classical**[klǽsikəl] 형 클래식의
- **comedy**[kɑ́mədi] 명 희극, 코미디
- **despite**[dispáit] 전 ~에도 불구하고
- **detail**[ditéil] 명 세부 사항
- **direct**[dirékt] 동 ~로 향하다, 겨냥하다
- **direction**[dirékʃən] 명 방향
- **exhibit**[igzíbit] 동 전시하다
- **feather**[féðər] 명 깃털
- **flat**[flæt] 형 납작한
- **frog**[frɔ:g] 명 개구리
- **hip-hop**[híphɑp] 명 (음악) 힙합
- **landscape**[lǽndskèip] 명 풍경
- **maze**[meiz] 명 미로
- **melt**[melt] 동 녹다
- **modern**[mɑ́dərn] 형 현대의
- **myth**[miθ] 명 신화
- **notice**[nóutis] 동 ~을 알아차리다
- **novel**[nɑ́vəl] 명 소설
- **novelist**[nɑ́vəlist] 명 소설가
- **pop**[pɑp] 명 팝 음악
- **prefer**[prifə́:r] 동 더 좋아하다
- **prince**[prins] 명 왕자
- **produce**[prədjú:s] 동 생산하다
- **production**[prədʌ́kʃən] 명 생산
- **promise**[prɑ́mis] 동 약속하다
- **queen**[kwi:n] 명 왕비, 여왕
- **real**[rí:əl] 형 진짜의, 현실적인
- **rock**[rɑk] 명 록 음악
- **seaside**[sísaid] 명 해변, 바닷가
- **since**[sins] 접 ~ 때문에, ~이므로
- **stick**[stik] 동 (몸의 일부를) 밀다, 내밀다
- **teen**[ti:n] 명 십 대
- **tourist**[túərist] 명 관광객
- **tragedy**[trǽdʒədi] 명 비극
- **version**[vɔ́:rʒən] 명 (어떤 것의) 변형
- **wax**[wæks] 명 밀랍, 왁스
- **wing**[wiŋ] 명 날개
- **wonder**[wʌ́ndər] 동 궁금해하다

Key Expressions

- **glance at** ~을 힐끗 보다
- **loot at** ~을 보다
- **move on** ~로 이동하다, 넘어가다
- **prefer A to B** A를 B보다 더 좋아하다
- **right away** 즉시, 바로
- **soap bubble** 비눗방울
- **stay away from** ~을 가까이하지 않다
- **take a look** ~을 보다

Word Power

※ 서로 반대되는 뜻을 가진 어휘

□ **ancient** 고대의 ↔ **modern** 현대의

□ **noticed** 알아차려진 ↔ **unnoticed** 눈에 띄지 않는

□ **melt** 녹다 ↔ **freeze** 얼다

□ **comedy** 희극 ↔ **tragedy** 비극

□ **ask** 묻다 ↔ **answer** 대답하다

□ **cheap** 싼 ↔ **expensive** 비싼

□ **prince** 왕자 ↔ **princess** 공주

□ **direct** 직접적인 ↔ **indirect** 간접적인

□ **king** 왕 ↔ **queen** 왕비, 여왕

□ **produce** 생산하다 ↔ **consume** 소비하다

□ **real** 진짜의 ↔ **fake** 가짜의

□ **entire** 전체의 ↔ **partial** 일부의

English Dictionary

□ **artist** 예술가
→ someone who produces art
예술을 만들어 내는 사람

□ **canvas** 화폭, 캔버스
→ a piece of thick cloth used by artists for painting on, usually with oil paints, or the painting itself
보통 유성 물감으로 그 위에 그림을 그리기 위해, 또는 그림 자체를 위해 미술가에 의해 사용되는 두꺼운 천 조각

□ **detail** 세부 사항
→ a single piece of some information of fact about something
무언가에 관한 사실에 대한 하나의 정보

□ **direction** 방향
→ the way something or someone moves, faces, or is aimed
무언가 또는 누군가가 움직이거나 마주하거나 또는 목표로 하는 길

□ **feather** 깃털
→ one of the light soft things that cover a bird's body
새의 몸을 덮고 있는 가볍고 부드러운 것들 중 하나

□ **landscape** 풍경
→ an area of countryside, especially in relation to its appearance
특히 외관과 관련된 시골 지역

□ **melt** 녹다
→ to change from a solid to a liquid by applying heat
열을 가함으로써 고체에서 액체로 변하다

□ **myth** 신화
→ an ancient story, especially one invented in order to explain natural or historical events
특히 자연적이거나 역사적인 사건을 설명하기 위해 만들어진 고대의 이야기

□ **notice** 알아차리다
→ to see or become conscious of something or someone
무언가 또는 어떤 사람을 보거나 의식하게 되다

□ **seaside** 해변, 바닷가
→ an area that is close to the sea
바다에 가까운 지역

□ **stick** 내밀다
→ to put it in a position where other people can see a part of your body
다른 사람들이 당신의 신체의 일부를 볼 수 있는 자리에 놓다

□ **tragedy** 비극
→ a very sad event, especially one involving death
특히 죽음과 관련된 매우 슬픈 사건

□ **wing** 날개
→ one of the parts of a bird's or insect's body that it uses for flying
날기 위해 사용하는 새나 곤충의 신체 부분 중의 하나

□ **wonder** 궁금해하다
→ to want to know more about something because it interests you
당신에게 흥미를 불러일으키기 때문에 어떤 것에 대해 더 알고 싶어지다

01 다음 짝지어진 단어의 관계가 같도록 빈칸에 알맞은 말을 쓰시오.

> increase : decrease = _____ : freeze

02 다음 영영풀이가 가리키는 것을 고르시오.

> an ancient story, especially one invented in order to explain natural or historical events

① myth
② article
③ novel
④ essay
⑤ poem

03 다음 중 밑줄 친 부분의 뜻풀이가 바르지 <u>않은</u> 것은?

① He doesn't use a <u>brush</u> when he draws.
붓
② My boss will tell you about the <u>details</u>.
세부 사항
③ I like to watch the <u>comedy</u> show on Sundays. 희극
④ Our attention <u>directed</u> to the result of the race. 향했다
⑤ Jane looks young and beautiful <u>despite</u> her age. ~ 때문에

04 다음 우리말에 맞게 빈칸에 알맞은 말을 쓰시오.

(1) 우리는 멈춰서 그 가게를 보았다.
➡ We stopped and _____ a look at the store.
(2) 그녀는 버스 정류장에서 나를 힐끗 보았다.
➡ She _____ at me at the bus station.
(3) 나는 종종 미술 작품을 보러 박물관에 간다.
➡ I often go to the museum to see _____.
(4) 아이들이 비눗방울을 가지고 놀고 있다.
➡ The kids are playing with _____ _____.

05 다음 문장의 빈칸에 들어갈 말을 〈보기〉에서 골라 쓰시오.

> ┤ 보기 ├
> wings / details / wax / myth / landscape

(1) A tiger and a bear appear in the _____ of Dangun.
(2) I looked down on the peaceful _____ from the hill.
(3) My boss will tell you about the _____.
(4) They made _____ dolls of many actors.
(5) Airplanes have _____ like birds.

06 다음 주어진 문장의 밑줄 친 notice와 같은 의미로 쓰인 것은?

> I didn't <u>notice</u> the mistakes in this movie.

① I didn't <u>notice</u> whether she was there or not.
② This <u>notice</u> was on my front door.
③ We received the <u>notice</u> two weeks ago.
④ All rules cannot be changed without any <u>notice</u>.
⑤ Will you post up a <u>notice</u> on the board?

01 다음 짝지어진 단어의 관계가 같도록 빈칸에 알맞은 말을 쓰시오.

> king : queen = prince : _____

02 다음 우리말에 맞게 빈칸에 알맞은 말을 쓰시오.

(1) 산꼭대기 위의 눈은 절대 녹지 않는다.
➡ The snow on the top of the mountain never _____.

(2) 나는 당신을 나의 전시회에 초대하고 싶어요.
➡ I'd like to invite you to my _____.

(3) 어떤 새들은 다채로운 깃털을 갖고 있다.
➡ Some birds have colorful _____.

03  다음 문장의 빈칸에 들어갈 말을 〈보기〉에서 골라 쓰시오.

┌─ 보기 ├─
notice / landscape / seaside / promise / stick
└─

(1) From the hill, she looked down on the beautiful _____.

(2) I didn't _____ that Ted was there.

(3) Don't _____ your arm out of the car window.

(4) My dad _____d to buy me new shoes.

(5) We are going on a picnic at the _____ this Sunday.

04 다음 우리말을 주어진 단어를 이용하여 영작하시오.

(1) 나는 그가 왜 나를 그의 파티에 초대했는지 궁금하다. (invite)
➡ _____

(2) 새 자동차의 생산이 다음 달에 시작될 것이다. (car, start)
➡ _____

(3) 처음에 아무도 나를 알아차리지 못했다. (nobody)
➡ _____

05 다음 영영풀이가 가리키는 말을 쓰시오.

> to change from a solid to a liquid by applying heat

➡ _____ .

06 다음 우리말과 일치하도록 주어진 단어를 모두 배열하여 영작하시오.

(1) 폭풍우 치는 동안 창문 가까이 가지 마라.
(during / stay / a storm / windows / from / away)
➡ _____

(2) 제가 당신의 영화표를 봐도 될까요?
(take / movie / I / at / your / may / look / a / ticket)
➡ _____

(3) 나는 경찰에 바로 신고했다.
(police / right / called / I / away / the)
➡ _____

Conversation

1 구체적인 종류나 장르 묻기

> **A** What kind of music are you going to play? 어떤 종류의 음악을 연주할 거니?
>
> **B** I'm going to play rock music. 나는 록 음악을 연주할 거야.

■ "What kind of ~?"는 어떤 대상의 종류나 유형에 대해서 구체적으로 묻고자 할 때 사용된다. 예를 들어, 어떤 식당에서 먹을 수 있는 음식의 종류가 무엇인지 궁금할 때 "What kind of food does the restaurant serve?"와 같이 물을 수 있다.

구체적인 종류나 장르 묻기

- What sort of traditional food do you like? 어떤 종류의 전통 음식을 좋아하니?
- What type of person is the new math teacher? 새로 오신 수학 선생님은 어떤 사람인가요?
- To which category does this game belong? 이 게임은 어느 범주에 속하나요?

핵심 Check

1. 다음 우리말과 일치하도록 빈칸에 알맞은 말을 쓰시오.

   (1) **A:** ＿＿＿＿＿ ＿＿＿＿＿ ＿＿＿＿＿ ＿＿＿＿＿ do you like? (어떤 종류의 콘서트를 좋아하니?)

      B: I like a rock concert. (나는 록 콘서트를 좋아해.)

   (2) **A:** What sort of ＿＿＿＿ ＿＿＿＿ ＿＿＿＿ ＿＿＿＿ ＿＿＿＿?

      (어떤 종류의 영화를 보고 싶니?)

      B: I want to see a comedy movie. (나는 코미디 영화를 보고 싶어.)

   (3) **A:** What ＿＿＿＿ of person is the new English teacher? (새로 오신 영어 선생님은 어떤 분이니?)

      B: She is so kind and humorous. (그 선생님은 매우 친절하고 유머가 풍부하셔.)

② 둘 중에 더 좋아하는 것 말하기

A There are two kinds of *Mona Lisas*. Which do you prefer?

두 종류의 모나리자가 있어. 어느 것을 더 좋아하니?

B I prefer Botero's *Mona Lisa* to da Vinci's. 나는 다 빈치의 모나리자보다 보테로의 모나리자를 더 좋아해.

■ "I prefer A to B."는 두 가지 비교되는 사람이나 사물 등에 대하여 자신이 어떤 것을 더 좋아하는지를 표현할 때 사용된다. 예를 들어, 책을 읽는 것보다 영화 보는 것을 더 좋아한다는 것을 표현하고자 할 때는 "I prefer watching movies to reading books."와 같이 말할 수 있다.

둘 중에 더 좋아하는 것 말하기

- I like watching music videos better than listening to music.
  나는 음악을 듣는 것보다 음악 비디오를 보는 것을 더 좋아한다.

- I prefer taking a taxi to the station if possible. 나는 가능하면 역에 택시 타고 가는 것을 더 좋아한다.

- I think sending text messages is better than talking on the phone.
  나는 문자 메시지를 보내는 것이 전화로 이야기하는 것보다 더 낫다고 생각한다.

핵심 Check

2. 다음 우리말과 일치하도록 빈칸에 알맞은 말을 쓰시오.

(1) **A:** _____ _____ _____ _____, listening to music or reading books?

(음악 듣는 것과 책을 읽는 것 중에 어느 것을 더 좋아하니?)

B: I prefer listening to music to reading books. (나는 책을 읽는 것보다 음악 듣는 것을 더 좋아해.)

(2) **A:** Which do you prefer, taking photos or drawing pictures?

(사진 찍는 것과 그림 그리는 것 중에 어느 것을 더 좋아하니?)

B: I prefer _____ _____ to _____ _____.

(나는 그림을 그리는 것보다 사진 찍는 것을 더 좋아해.)

(3) **A:** Which do you prefer, dogs or cats? (개와 고양이 중에 어느 것을 더 좋아하니?)

B: _____ _____ _____ _____ _____. (나는 고양이보다 개를 더 좋아해.)

Listen & Talk 1-B

W: (*ringing*) Hello, Steve.

M: Hi, Anna. We're meeting at the arts festival tomorrow at 1:30, right?

W: Right. ❶What kind of performance do you want to watch first?

M: I want to watch the hip-hop dance performance first.

W: ❷Sounds good. It's at 2 p.m. at the ❸gym, right?

M: Yeah, and ❹how about watching the play, *Romeo and Juliet*, at 4 p.m.?

W: Oh, the ❺one at the Main Hall near the gym? Sure!

W: (전화벨 소리) 안녕, Steve.

M: 안녕, Anna. 우리 내일 1시 30분에 예술 축제에서 만나는 거 맞지?

W: 맞아. 먼저 어떤 종류의 공연을 보고 싶어?

M: 난 힙합 댄스 공연을 먼저 보고 싶어.

W: 좋은 생각이야. 체육관에서 오후 2시에 하는 거 맞지?

M: 응, 그리고 오후 4시에 '로미오와 줄리엣' 연극을 보는 건 어때?

W: 아, 체육관 근처 대강당에서 하는 연극 말이지? 좋아!

❶ 구체적인 종류를 묻는 질문으로 'What sort of performance do you want to watch first?'로 바꾸어 쓸 수 있다.
❷ (That) sounds good. = Good idea.
❸ gym: 체육관
❹ 제안하는 표현으로 What about ~? = Why don't we ~? = Let's ~. 구문으로 바꾸어 쓸 수 있다.
❺ one은 play를 가리킨다.

Check(√) True or False

(1) Anna and Steve are going to visit the arts festival tomorrow. T ☐ F ☐

(2) Anna prefers watching the play to the hip-hop dance performance. T ☐ F ☐

Communication

M: Hi, we are planning a school festival, so we want to ❶find out students' favorite types of performances. ❷May I ask you a few questions?

W: Sure.

M: What kind of performance do you like best?

W: I like music performances best.

M: Okay. Then, which do you prefer, rock or hip-hop?

W: I ❸prefer rock to hip-hop.

M: Who's your favorite musician?

W: ❹My favorite musician is TJ.

M: Great. Thank you for your answers.

M: 안녕하세요, 저희는 학교 축제를 계획 중이고, 그래서 학생들이 어떤 종류의 공연을 좋아하는지 알고 싶습니다. 몇 가지 질문을 해도 될까요?

W: 물론이죠.

M: 어떤 종류의 공연을 가장 좋아하나요?

W: 저는 음악 공연을 가장 좋아해요.

M: 알겠습니다. 그러면 록과 힙합 중 어느 것을 더 좋아하나요?

W: 저는 힙합보다 록을 더 좋아해요.

M: 가장 좋아하는 뮤지션은 누구인가요?

W: 제가 가장 좋아하는 뮤지션은 TJ입니다.

M: 좋습니다. 답변해 주셔서 감사합니다.

❶ find out: ~을 알아내다
❷ 부탁을 나타내는 표현으로 'Can I ask you a few questions?'로 바꾸어 쓸 수 있다.
❸ prefer A to B: A를 B보다 더 좋아하다
❹ I love TJ. 또는 I like TJ best.로 바꾸어 쓸 수 있다.

Check(√) True or False

(3) The boy is asking some questions to prepare a school festival. T ☐ F ☐

(4) The girl likes rock more than hip-hop. T ☐ F ☐

Listen & Talk 1 A-1

W: Brian, is your band going to play at the Teen Music Festival?

M: Yes, we're practicing ❶almost every day.

W: ❷What kind of music are you going to play ❸this year?

M: Rock music. We'll play songs from the nineties.

❶ almost: 거의
❷ 'What sort of music are you going to play this year?'로 바꾸어 쓸 수 있다.
❸ this year: 올해

Listen & Talk 1 A-2

W: ❶Can you help me? I don't know how to paint clean lines.

M: What kind of ❷brush were you using?

W: This round brush.

M: When you paint lines, a ❸flat brush is better. Try this one.

W: Okay, thank you.

❶ 도움을 요청하는 표현으로 'Can you give me your hand?' = 'Would you help me?' 등으로 바꾸어 쓸 수 있다.
❷ brush: 붓
❸ flat: 납작한

Listen & Talk 2 A-1

M: What are you reading, Jina?

W: The ❶novel, *Life of Pi*. ❷It's a story of a boy and a tiger.

M: ❷It's a great book. I've seen the movie of ❷ it, too. I prefer the movie to the novel.

W: Why do you like ❷it better?

M: The ❸scenes are very beautiful. And the tiger ❹looks so ❺real.

❶ novel: 소설
❷ It[it]은 모두 *Life of Pi*를 가리킨다.
❸ scene: 장면
❹ look+형용사: ~처럼 보이다
❺ real: 진짜의 (↔ fake: 가짜의)

Listen & Talk 2 A-2

W: ❶Have you listened to Jane's new song, *Girl Friend*?

M: Yeah, ❷it's really cool. The guitar part is great.

W: ❸There is also a dance version of the song on the album.

M: I've listened to ❹it, but I prefer the guitar version to the dance version. ❺It matches her voice better.

❶ 현재완료(have+p.p) 구문으로 경험을 묻고 있다.
❷ it은 Jane's new song, *Girl Friend*를 가리킨다.
❸ There is+단수 명사: ~가 있다
❹ it은 a dance version을 가리킨다.
❺ It은 the guitar version을 가리킨다.

Listen & Talk 2 B

W: I saw an interesting painting in an art book. ❶Look at this.

M: Wow, it looks like da Vinci's *Mona Lisa*.

W: ❷Actually, it's *Mona Lisa* by Fernando Botero. Which do you prefer?

M: I prefer da Vinci's to Botero's. Da Vinci's *Mona Lisa* has an interesting smile. ❸How about you?

W: Well, I prefer Botero's to da Vinci's. His *Mona Lisa* is cute, and ❹it looks ❺modern.

❶ look at: ~을 보다
❷ actually: 사실은, 실제로
❸ How about you? = What about you?: 너는 어때?
❹ Botero's *Mona Lisa*를 가리킨다.
❺ modern: 현대적인

Wrap Up 1

M: Can you help me? I want to buy a guitar.

W: ❶There are various kinds of guitars. What kind of music do you want to play?

M: I want to play pop songs.

W: Then you should get a classical guitar.

M: Okay, I will take a classical guitar.

❶ There are+복수 명사

● 다음 우리말과 일치하도록 빈칸에 알맞은 말을 쓰시오.

Listen & Talk 1 A-1

W: Brian, is your band _____ _____ _____ at the Teen Music Festival?

M: Yes, we're practicing _____ _____ _____.

W: _____ _____ _____ _____ are you going to play this year?

M: Rock music. We'll _____ _____ from the nineties.

Listen & Talk 1 A-2

W: Can you help me? I don't know _____ _____ _____ _____ _____.

M: _____ _____ _____ _____ were you using?

W: This round brush.

M: When you paint lines, a _____ brush is _____. _____ this one.

W: Okay, thank you.

Listen & Talk 1 B

W: (ringing) Hello, Steve.

M: Hi, Anna. We're _____ at the arts festival tomorrow at 1:30, _____?

W: Right. What kind of performance _____ _____ _____ _____ _____ _____?

M: I _____ _____ watch the hip-hop dance performance first.

W: _____ good. It's at 2 p.m. at the gym, _____?

M: Yeah, and how about _____ _____ _____, *Romeo and Juliet*, at 4 p.m.?

W: Oh, _____ _____ at the Main Hall near the gym? Sure!

Listen & Talk 2 A-1

M: What are you reading, Jina?

W: The novel, *Life of Pi*. It's _____ _____ of a boy and a tiger.

M: It's a great book. I've seen the movie _____ _____, too. I _____ the movie _____ the novel.

W: Why do you _____ it _____?

M: The _____ are very beautiful. And the tiger looks so _____.

해석

W: Brian, 너희 밴드는 '십 대 음악 축제'에서 연주할 거야?
M: 응, 우리는 거의 매일 연습하고 있어.
W: 너희는 올해 어떤 종류의 음악을 연주하려고 해?
M: 록 음악. 우리는 90년대 곡들을 연주할 거야.

W: 나 좀 도와줄래? 나는 선을 깔끔하게 그리는 방법을 모르겠어.
M: 어떤 종류의 붓을 사용하고 있었니?
W: 이 둥근 붓이야.
M: 선을 그릴 때는 납작한 붓이 더 나아. 이것을 써 봐.
W: 알았어, 고마워.

W: (전화벨 소리) 안녕, Steve.
M: 안녕, Anna. 우리 내일 1시 30분에 예술 축제에서 만나는 거 맞지?
W: 맞아. 먼저 어떤 종류의 공연을 보고 싶어?
M: 난 힙합 댄스 공연을 먼저 보고 싶어.
W: 좋은 생각이야. 체육관에서 오후 2시에 하는 거 맞지?
M: 응, 그리고 오후 4시에 '로미오와 줄리엣' 연극을 보는 건 어때?
W: 아, 체육관 근처 대강당에서 하는 연극 말이지? 좋아!

M: 지나야, 너 무엇을 읽고 있니?
W: '파이 이야기'라는 소설이야. 한 소년과 호랑이에 대한 이야기이지.
M: 훌륭한 책이야. 나는 그것을 영화로도 봤어. 나는 소설보다는 영화가 더 좋아.
W: 왜 영화가 더 좋은데?
M: 장면이 매우 아름다워. 그리고 호랑이가 매우 진짜같이 보이거든.

Listen & Talk 2 A-2

W: _____ you _____ to Jane's new song, *Girl Friend*?

M: Yeah, it's really _____. The guitar _____ is great.

W: There is also a _____ _____ of the song on the album.

M: I've listened to it, but _____ _____ _____ _____ _____ to the dance version. It _____ her voice better.

Listen & Talk 2 B

W: I saw an _____ _____ in an art book. Look at this.

M: Wow, it _____ _____ da Vinci's *Mona Lisa*.

W: Actually, it's *Mona Lisa* by Fernando Botero. _____ _____ _____ _____?

M: I _____ da Vinci's _____ Botero's. Da Vinci's *Mona Lisa* has an interesting smile. _____ _____ _____?

W: Well, I _____ Botero's _____ da Vinci's. His *Mona Lisa* is cute, and it looks _____.

Communication

M: Hi, we are planning a school festival, _____ we want to _____ _____ students' favorite types of performances. _____ I _____ you a few questions?

W: Sure.

M: _____ _____ _____ _____ do you like best?

W: I like music performances best.

M: Okay. Then, which _____ you _____, rock or hip-hop?

W: I _____ _____ _____ _____.

M: Who's your _____ _____?

W: My favorite musician is TJ.

M: Great. _____ you _____ your answers.

Wrap Up 1

M: _____ you _____ me? I want to buy a guitar.

W: There are _____ _____ of guitars. _____ _____ _____ _____ do you want to play?

M: I _____ _____ play pop songs.

W: Then you _____ _____ a classical guitar.

M: Okay, I will take a classical guitar.

해석

W: 너는 Jane의 새 노래인 '여자 친구'를 들어 봤니?

M: 응, 정말 멋져. 기타 부분이 굉장하지.

W: 앨범에는 그 노래의 댄스 버전도 있어.

M: 나는 그것을 들었는데 댄스 버전보다는 기타 버전이 더 좋아. 그 버전이 그녀의 목소리와 더 잘 어울리거든.

W: 나 미술 책에서 흥미로운 그림을 봤어. 이것 봐.

M: 와, 그것은 다빈치의 '모나리자'처럼 보이는데.

W: 사실 이 그림은 페르난도 보테로의 '모나리자'야. 넌 어느 것이 더 마음에 드니?

M: 나는 보테로의 그림보다 다빈치의 모나리자가 더 좋아. 다빈치의 '모나리자'에는 흥미로운 미소가 있어. 너는 어때?

W: 음, 나는 다빈치의 모나리자보다는 보테로의 모나리자가 더 좋아. 그의 '모나리자'는 귀엽고 현대적으로 보여.

M: 안녕하세요, 저희는 학교 축제를 계획 중이고, 그래서 학생들이 어떤 종류의 공연을 좋아하는지 알고 싶습니다. 몇 가지 질문을 해도 될까요?

W: 물론이죠.

M: 어떤 종류의 공연을 가장 좋아하나요?

W: 저는 음악 공연을 가장 좋아해요.

M: 알겠습니다. 그러면 록과 힙합 중 어떤 것을 더 좋아하나요?

W: 저는 힙합보다 록을 더 좋아해요.

M: 가장 좋아하는 뮤지션은 누구인가요?

W: 제가 가장 좋아하는 뮤지션은 TJ입니다.

M: 좋습니다. 답변해 주셔서 감사합니다.

M: 저 좀 도와주시겠어요? 저는 기타를 하나 사고 싶어요.

W: 다양한 종류의 기타가 있어요. 어떤 종류의 음악을 연주하고 싶으신가요?

M: 저는 팝송을 연주하려고 해요.

W: 그럼 클래식 기타를 사셔야 해요.

M: 알겠습니다, 클래식 기타로 살게요.

[01~02] 다음 대화를 읽고 물음에 답하시오.

Sora: (A)Can you help me? I don't know how to paint clean lines.

Mike: _____ (B) _____

Sora: This round brush.

Mike: When you paint lines, a flat brush is better. Try this one.

Sora: Okay, thank you.

---

01 위 대화의 밑줄 친 (A)와 바꾸어 쓸 수 있는 것을 <u>모두</u> 고르시오.

① Can you give me a hand? ② Do you need any help?

③ What can I do for you? ④ Would you do me a favor?

⑤ Can I give you a hand?

02 위 대화의 빈칸 (B)에 들어갈 말을 <보기>에 주어진 단어를 배열하여 완성하시오.

> ┤ 보기 ├
>
> of / brush / you / what / using / were / kind

➡ _____

[03~04] 다음 대화를 읽고 물음에 답하시오.

Minsu: What are you reading, Jina?

Jina: The novel, *Life of Pi*. It's a story of a boy and a tiger.

Minsu: It's a great book. I've seen the movie of (A)it, too. I prefer the movie to the novel.

Jina: Why do you like (B)it better?

Minsu: The scenes are very beautiful. And the tiger looks so real.

---

03 위 대화의 밑줄 친 (A)와 (B)의 it이 각각 가리키는 것을 찾아 쓰시오.

(A) _____ (B) _____

04 위 대화의 내용과 일치하지 <u>않는</u> 것은?

① Jina is reading *Life of Pi*.

② *Life of Pi* is the novel about a boy and a tiger.

③ Minsu has seen the movie of *Life of Pi*.

④ Minsu likes the novel more than the movie.

⑤ The scenes are very beautiful in the movie.

01 다음 대화의 내용과 일치하지 <u>않는</u> 것은?

> Susan: Brian, is your band going to play at the Teen Music Festival?
>
> Brian: Yes, we're practicing almost every day.
>
> Susan: What kind of music are you going to play this year?
>
> Brian: Rock music. We'll play songs from the nineties.

① Brian의 밴드는 '십 대 음악 축제'에서 연주할 것이다.

② Brian의 밴드는 거의 매일 연습하고 있다.

③ Brian의 밴드는 올해 록 음악을 연주할 것이다.

④ Brian의 밴드는 90년대 곡들을 연주할 것이다.

⑤ Brian의 밴드는 90분 동안 연주할 것이다.

[02~03] 다음 대화를 읽고 물음에 답하시오.

> Sue: Have you listened to Jane's new song, *Girl Friend*?
>
> Tony: Yeah, (A)it's really cool. The guitar part is great.
>
> Sue: There is also a dance version of the song on the album.
>
> Tony: I've listened to (B)it, but I prefer the guitar version to the dance version. (C) It matches her voice better.

서답형

02 위 대화의 밑줄 친 (A)~(C)의 it이 가리키는 것을 각각 찾아 쓰시오.

(A) _____

(B) _____

(C) _____

03 위 대화의 내용과 일치하지 <u>않는</u> 것은?

① Jane released her new song, *Girl Friend*.

② Tony likes the guitar part of *Girl Friend*.

③ There are both a dance version and the guitar version of *Girl Friend* on the album.

④ Tony thought that Jane's voice matches the dance version.

⑤ Tony likes the guitar version more than the dance version.

04 다음 대화를 읽고 대답할 수 <u>없는</u> 질문은?

> Anna: (*ringing*) Hello, Steve.
>
> Steve: Hi, Anna. We're meeting at the arts festival tomorrow at 1:30, right?
>
> Anna: Right. What kind of performance do you want to watch first?
>
> Steve: I want to watch the hip-hop dance performance first.
>
> Anna: Sounds good. It's at 2 p.m. at the gym, right?
>
> Steve: Yeah, and how about watching the play, *Romeo and Juliet*, at 4 p.m.?
>
> Anna: Oh, the one at the Main Hall near the gym? Sure!

① What is Anna going to do with Steve tomorrow?

② What kind of performance does Steve want to watch first?

③ When is the hip-hop dance performance?

④ Where can Anna and Steve watch the play, *Romeo and Juliet*?

⑤ Why does Steve suggest watching the play, *Romeo and Juliet*?

서답형

05 다음 대화의 내용과 일치하도록 주어진 표를 완성하시오.

> Mina: I saw an interesting painting in an art book. Look at this.
> Jack: Wow, it looks like da Vinci's *Mona Lisa*.
> Mina: Actually, it's *Mona Lisa* by Fernando Botero. Which do you prefer?
> Jack: I prefer da Vinci's to Botero's. Da Vinci's *Mona Lisa* has an interesting smile. How about you?
> Mina: Well, I prefer Botero's to da Vinci's. His *Mona Lisa* is cute, and it looks modern.

Title	*Mona Lisa*	
Painter	Leonardo da Vinci	Fernando Botero
Who prefers	(A)	(B)
opinion	(C)	(D)

(A) _____ (B) _____

(C) _____

(D) _____

[06~08] 다음 대화를 읽고 물음에 답하시오.

> Jason: Hi, we are planning a school festival, so we want to find out students' favorite types of performances. (A) May I ask you a few questions?
> Emily: Sure.
> Jason: What kind of performance do you like best?
> Emily: I like music performances best.

> Jason: Okay. Then, (B)어느 것을 더 좋아하나요, rock or hip-hop?
> Emily: I prefer rock to hip-hop.
> Jason: Who's your favorite musician?
> Emily: My favorite musician is TJ.
> Jason: Great. Thank you for your answers.

06 위 대화의 밑줄 친 (A)와 바꾸어 쓸 수 있는 것은?

① Do you have any questions?
② Do you want to ask any questions?
③ Would you answer a few questions?
④ How can I ask a few questions of you?
⑤ Did you answer a few questions?

서답형

07 위 대화의 밑줄 친 (B)의 우리말을 4단어를 사용하여 영작하시오.

➡ _____

서답형

08 What kind of music does Emily like better?

➡ _____

서답형

09 다음 주어진 문장 뒤에 이어지는 대화가 자연스럽게 이어지도록 순서대로 배열하시오.

> Can you help me? I want to buy a guitar.

> (A) Okay, I will take a classical guitar.
> (B) I want to play pop songs.
> (C) There are various kinds of guitars. What kind of music do you want to play?
> (D) Then you should get a classical guitar.

➡ _____

01 다음 대화의 빈칸 (A)~(C)에 들어갈 알맞은 대답을 〈보기〉에서 찾아 쓰시오.

> Jason: Hi, we are planning a school festival, so we want to find out students' favorite types of performances. May I ask you a few questions?
> Emily: Sure.
> Jason: What kind of performance do you like best?
> Emily: (A)_____
> Jason: Okay. Then, which do you prefer, rock or hip-hop?
> Emily: (B)_____
> Jason: Who's your favorite musician?
> Emily: (C)_____
> Jason: Great. Thank you for your answers.

> ┤ 보기 ├
> ⓐ My favorite musician is TJ.
> ⓑ I like music performances best.
> ⓒ I prefer rock to hip-hop.

(A) _____ (B) _____ (C) _____

[02~03] 다음 대화를 읽고 물음에 답하시오.

> Sue: Have you listened to Jane's new song, *Girl Friend*?
> Tony: Yeah, it's really cool. The guitar part is great.
> Sue: There is also a dance version of the song on the album.
> Tony: I've listened to it, but I prefer the guitar version to the dance version. It matches her voice better.

02 What song have Tony and Sue listened to in Jane's album?

➡ _____

03 Why does Tony prefer the guitar version to the dance version?

➡ _____

_____

[04~06] 다음 대화를 읽고 물음에 답하시오.

> Minsu: What are you reading, Jina?
> Jina: The novel, *Life of Pi*. It's a story of a boy and a tiger.
> Minsu: It's a great book. I've seen the movie of it, too. (A)나는 소설보다는 영화가 더 좋아. (prefer)
> Jina: Why do you like it better?
> Minsu: The scenes are very beautiful. And the tiger looks so real.

04 위 대화의 밑줄 친 (A)의 우리말을 주어진 단어를 사용하여 영작하시오.

➡ _____

05 What is the novel, *Life of Pi*, about?

➡ _____

06 Why does Minsu prefer the movie to the novel?

➡ _____

_____

Grammar

① 사역동사

> • He **made** me **do** the laundry. 그는 내가 빨래를 하도록 시켰다.
> • Alicia **had** her son **park** her car. Alicia는 그녀의 아들이 그녀의 차를 주차하게 했다.

■ 사역동사는 문장의 주어가 목적어에게 어떠한 행동을 하도록 시키는 동사로 make, have, let 등이 이에 속한다.

• Gloria **let** me **go** home early. Gloria는 내가 집에 일찍 가도록 허락해 주었다.

• Paul **had** my sister **sing** in front of many people. Paul은 내 여동생이 많은 사람들 앞에서 노래하게 했다.

• They **make** us **do** our best. 그들은 우리가 최선을 다하게 만든다.

■ 사역동사는 5형식에 속하여 목적격 보어를 갖는데, 사역동사의 목적격 보어는 동사원형의 형태를 취하며, '~에게 …하게 하다'라고 해석하는 것에 유의한다.

• The teacher **made** us **find** the dog. 선생님은 우리가 그 개를 찾도록 시키셨다.

• She **had** me **do** the job instead of her. 그녀는 그녀 대신에 내가 그 일을 하도록 시켰다.

• The sisters **made** me buy the car. 그 자매들은 내가 그 차를 사게 했다.

• I **had** my sister **fix** dinner. 나는 내 여동생이 저녁 식사를 차리게 했다.

■ 준사역동사에 해당하는 help는 목적격 보어로 to부정사나 동사원형 형태를 취한다.

• We **helped** the man **stand[to stand]** on his own. 우리는 그 남자가 혼자 힘으로 설 수 있도록 도왔다.

핵심 Check

1. 다음 우리말과 일치하도록 빈칸에 알맞은 말을 쓰시오.

(1) Mike는 내가 그의 가방을 지켜보게 했다.

➡ Mike had _____ _____ his bag.

(2) 나는 그가 내 스마트폰을 사용하게 한다.

➡ I let _____ _____ my smartphone.

(3) 엄마는 아빠가 일찍 집에 오게 하셨다.

➡ My mom made _____ _____ _____ home early.

② 간접의문문

- Do you know **who he is**? 너는 그가 누구인지 아니?
- I wonder **what her name is**. 나는 그녀의 이름이 무엇인지 궁금해.

■ 의문문이 문장 내에서 주어, 목적어, 보어 역할을 할 때 이를 간접의문문이라고 한다. 간접의문문의 어순은 '의문사+주어+동사'임에 유의한다.

- I don't know **how you came here**. 나는 네가 어떻게 이곳에 왔는지 모르겠어.
- He doesn't remember **what her name is**. 그는 그녀의 이름이 무엇인지 기억하지 못한다.
- Jane wants to know **where her mother is**. Jane은 그녀의 엄마가 어디에 있는지 알고 싶다.

■ 의문사가 주어로 쓰인 경우 의문사가 동시에 주어 역할을 하므로 의문사 뒤에 동사가 바로 이어서 나올 수 있다.

- Do you know **who invented the light bulb**? 누가 전구를 발명했는지 아니?
- Can you tell me **what made her upset**? 무엇이 그녀를 화나게 했는지 말해줄 수 있니?

■ think, believe, guess, imagine, suppose 등과 같은 동사가 주절에 있을 경우 간접의문문의 의문사를 문장 맨 앞으로 배치한다.

- Do you think what it is? (✗)

  What do you think **it is**? (○) 너는 그것이 무엇이라고 생각하니?

- Do you guess who he is? (✗)

  Who do you guess **he is**? (○) 너는 그가 누구라고 생각하는 거야?

■ 의문사가 없는 경우 간접의문문의 어순은 'if/whether+주어+동사'로 쓴다.

- Can you tell me? + Is he hungry?
  → Can you tell me **if[whether] he is hungry**? 그가 배가 고픈지 내게 말해줄래?
- I wonder **whether Kevin wants to come**. Kevin이 오기를 원하는지 궁금하다.
- I want to know **whether they will accept the job**. 그들이 그 일을 받아들일지 알고 싶어.

핵심 Check

2. 다음 두 문장을 하나의 문장으로 연결할 때 빈칸에 알맞은 말을 쓰시오.

(1) Do you know? Who is she?

➡ Do you know _____ _____ _____?

(2) Can you tell me? Why do you study English?

➡ Can you tell me _____ _____ _____ English?

(3) I wonder. Where did you go yesterday?

➡ I wonder _____ _____ _____ yesterday.

01 다음 문장에서 어법상 <u>어색한</u> 부분을 바르게 고쳐 쓰시오.

(1) My teacher made me to read this book.

_____ ➡ _____

(2) I wonder how was the weather yesterday.

_____ ➡ _____

(3) My father let me buying the laptop computer.

_____ ➡ _____

(4) I didn't know who were you at first.

_____ ➡ _____

02 다음 두 문장을 간접의문문을 이용하여 하나의 문장으로 쓰시오.

(1) Oliver wanted to ask. Was she satisfied with his service?

➡ _____

(2) Can you tell me? Where are we going?

➡ _____

(3) I'd like to know. What do you do during your free time?

➡ _____

(4) I wonder. How often do you water the plant?

➡ _____

03 주어진 어구를 바르게 배열하여 다음 우리말을 영어로 쓰시오. 필요하다면 어형을 바꾸시오.

(1) 그 상사는 그가 사무실에 머무르게 시켰다.

(the office / make / stay / him / in / the boss)

➡ _____

(2) 너는 네 친구가 네 자전거를 빌려가도록 허락했니?

(bicycle / did / your / you / borrow / let / friend / your)

➡ _____

(3) 우리는 그가 밀짚모자를 쓰게 했어요.

(have / wear / we / him / a straw hat)

➡ _____

(4) 제가 답을 보게 해 주세요.

(the answer / me / please / see / let)

➡ _____

01 다음 빈칸에 들어갈 말로 적절하지 <u>않은</u> 것은?

> Mary _____ us play the computer game.

① made　　② saw　　③ let
④ had　　⑤ wanted

02 다음 우리말을 영어로 바르게 옮긴 것은?

> 나는 그 남자가 내 차를 세차하게 만들었다.

① I wanted the man to wash my car.
② I wondered whether the man washed my car.
③ I made the man wash my car.
④ I asked the man to wash my car.
⑤ I saw the man wash my car.

03 다음 중 빈칸에 들어갈 수 <u>없는</u> 말은?

> Who do you _____ has this car?

① guess　　② imagine　　③ think
④ wonder　　⑤ suppose

04 다음 중 빈칸에 들어갈 단어 'do'의 형태가 <u>다른</u> 하나는?

① Julie made me _____ my best.
② Clara saw me _____ aerobics.
③ They let me _____ the flowers.
④ Paul had me _____ some research.
⑤ Jane allowed me _____ the cooking with her brother.

05 다음 빈칸에 알맞은 말을 쓰시오.

> 그들은 내가 이곳에 일찍 오게 했습니다.
> ➡ They made me _____ here early.

06 다음 우리말을 영어로 옮길 때 다섯 번째로 오는 단어를 쓰시오.

> 나는 네가 이곳에 언제 도착할 것인지 궁금해.

➡ _____

07 다음 중 어법상 올바른 문장의 개수는?

> ⓐ Susan had them finish the homework until that night.
> ⓑ I want to know when will they call me again.
> ⓒ My brother let me wearing this new T-shirt.
> ⓓ Tell me who told you the secret.
> ⓔ Could you tell me what Jason is doing in his room?

① 1개　　② 2개　　③ 3개
④ 4개　　⑤ 5개

08 다음 중 빈칸에 들어갈 말로 가장 적절한 것은?

> I wonder. Why is he running?
> = I wonder _____.

① why he running
② whether he is running
③ why he is running
④ why is he running
⑤ whether he running

09 주어진 단어를 활용하여 다음 우리말을 영어로 쓰시오.

> 너는 그 창문을 누가 깼다고 생각하니?
> (suppose / break)

➡ _____

10 다음 중 밑줄 친 부분이 어색한 것은?

① Can you tell me <u>where he is from</u>?
② Do you know <u>who Hanguel made</u>?
③ I wonder <u>how often you visit your grandparents</u>.
④ Tell me <u>when she sent the email to me</u>.
⑤ Do you understand <u>what he is trying to say</u>?

11 다음 중 빈칸에 들어갈 말이 바르게 짝지어진 것은?

> • Mr. Davidson made the children _____ their hands before dinner.
> • Tell me _____ while your parents are not at home.

① to wash – who do you take care of
② to wash – who you will take care of
③ wash – who will take care of you
④ wash – whom you take care of
⑤ washing – whom you take care of

12 주어진 어구를 바르게 배열하여 대화를 완성하시오.

> A: My teacher made me do my paper again.
> B: _____
> (do you think / you / why / made / she / it / again / do)

13 주어진 단어를 활용하여 다음 우리말을 영어로 쓰시오.

> 나는 그가 내 시계를 고치게 했어.
> (make / repair)

➡ _____

14 다음 우리말을 영어로 옮길 때 다섯 번째로 오는 단어는?

> 지금 몇 시라고 생각하세요?

① time   ② you   ③ it
④ think   ⑤ is

15 다음 빈칸에 들어갈 말로 적절하지 <u>않은</u> 것은?

> Did you _____ them study together for the exam?

① have   ② make   ③ let
④ allow   ⑤ help

16 다음 빈칸에 들어갈 말로 가장 적절한 것은?

> A: Do you know _____ now?
> B: Oh, she is making some cookies in the kitchen.

① what is Molly doing
② what Molly doing
③ what Molly is doing
④ Molly is doing what
⑤ Molly is doing

17 다음 빈칸에 들어갈 말로 가장 적절한 것은?

> Lily always makes him _____.

① laughing   ② to laugh   ③ laugh
④ laughs   ⑤ to laughing

18 다음 빈칸에 공통으로 들어갈 말로 가장 적절한 것은?

> - Karl _____ her son a tennis player.
> - Jina _____ me some delicious cookies.
> - He _____ us jump the rope.
> - June _____ the paper robot very well.

① had   ② let   ③ went

④ made   ⑤ wanted

19 다음 중 영어로 옮긴 것이 바르지 <u>않은</u> 것은?

① 나는 그 아이들이 벽에 페인트칠을 하도록 허락했다.
    → I let the children paint on the wall.

② 누가 올 것이라고 생각해?
    → Who do you think will come?

③ 우리 선생님은 가끔 우리에게 무엇을 하라고 시키시니?
    → What does our teacher sometimes make us do?

④ 나는 그가 그녀에게서 무엇을 빌렸는지 몰라요.
    → I don't know what he borrowed from her.

⑤ 누가 그 건물을 지었다고 생각하니?
    → Who do you guess the building built?

20 다음 빈칸에 들어갈 말로 가장 적절한 것은?

> A: I'd like to know _____.
> B: I'm in the 8th grade.

① where you are now

② which grade are you

③ which grade you are in

④ who you are

⑤ which you are in the grade

21 빈칸에 들어갈 말로 가장 적절한 것은?

> Did you _____ the students ride the bikes?

① want   ② force   ③ allow

④ have   ⑤ enable

22 주어진 단어를 활용하여 빈칸에 알맞은 말을 쓰시오. (7단어)

> **Jason:** I would like to know _____.
> (what / do / when / free)
> **Kelly:** I write songs when I am free.

➡ _____

23 다음 중 어법상 어색한 것은?

① He made me stand on the street for an hour.

② They helped me to finish the project very well.

③ Do you think who you are?

④ Tell me when your birthday is.

⑤ Julian had her say sorry again.

24 주어진 문장과 같은 의미의 문장은?

> Mom tells me to do something.

① Mom enables me to do something.

② Mom makes me do something.

③ Mom sees me do something.

④ Mom thinks I do something.

⑤ Mom wants to know when I do something.

25 다음 두 문장을 하나의 문장으로 쓰시오.

> I want to know. Did she like the present?

➡ _____

01 주어진 단어를 활용하여 다음 우리말을 영어로 바르게 옮기시오.

> 엄마는 나와 내 여동생이 집을 청소하게 시키셨다.
> (make, clean)

➡ _____

02 주어진 단어를 활용하여 다음 우리말을 영어로 쓰시오.

> 누가 그 돈을 훔쳤다고 생각하니?
> (think / steal)

➡ _____

03 주어진 단어를 바르게 배열하여 다음 우리말을 영어로 쓰시오.

> 그들이 언제 너를 집에 가게 했는지 말해 줄 수 있니? (home / can / go / tell / when / you / me / they / you / let)

➡ _____

04 다음 빈칸에 알맞은 말을 쓰시오.

(1) 아빠는 내가 그의 차를 운전하게 허락하신다.
  ➡ My father lets _____ _____
  _____ _____ .

(2) Jane은 그가 자기에게 물 한 잔을 가져오게 했다.
  ➡ Jane had _____ _____ _____
  a glass of water.

(3) 그녀는 내가 그녀를 쳐다보게 만들었다.
  ➡ She made _____ _____ _____
  her.

05 주어진 단어를 활용하여 다음 문장과 같은 의미의 문장을 쓰시오.

> Brad forced me to accept the job.
> (make)

➡ _____

06 〈보기〉와 같이 다음 두 문장을 하나의 문장으로 쓰시오.

> ┤ 보기 ├
> Can you tell me? Who is she?
> ➡ Can you tell me who she is?

(1) I don't know. Where does he live?
  ➡ _____

(2) Do you guess? How old is he?
  ➡ _____

(3) Can you tell me? Why were you absent from school?
  ➡ _____

(4) I want to know. When did you meet him for the first time?
  ➡ _____
  _____

(5) Do you think? When does the concert start?
  ➡ _____

(6) Do you imagine? Why is the baby crying?
  ➡ _____

(7) Do you know? Was Charley sleeping at that time?
  ➡ _____
  _____

07 주어진 단어를 활용하여 다음 우리말을 영어로 쓰시오.

> 나는 나의 사촌이 숙제하는 것을 도와줬습니다.
> (help / his)

➡ _____

08 주어진 단어를 어법이나 내용에 맞게 빈칸에 쓰시오.

> ┌─ 보기 ─┐
> take / publish / report / work / play

(1) Don't let the children _____ with matches.

(2) Do you know who _____ these books last year?

(3) Julia made the professional photographer _____ pictures of her.

(4) The boss had the employees _____ harder.

(5) What do you think the scientist _____ _____ tomorrow?

09 다음 상황을 읽고 빈칸에 알맞은 말을 쓰시오.

> Andy: How much are the oranges?
> Paul: How many oranges do you want to buy?

➡ Andy wants to know how much _____ _____. So Paul asks Andy _____.

10 주어진 단어를 활용하여 다음 우리말을 영어로 쓰시오.

> 여자는 남자가 물을 마시게 한다.
> (the woman / the man / let)

➡ _____

11 주어진 단어를 바르게 배열하여 다음 우리말을 영어로 쓰시오. 필요하다면 어형을 변환하시오.

> 그 정장은 나를 멋지게 보이도록 만들어.
> (fancy / the suit / look / make / me)

➡ _____

12 주어진 단어를 활용하여 다음 대화를 영어로 쓰시오.

> A: 그 영화가 어땠다고 생각하니? (how / think / be)
> B: It was so boring. 그것은 나를 졸리게 만들었어. (make / feel)

A: _____

B: _____

13 다음 우리말을 영어로 쓰시오.

> 어제 그 차를 누가 운전했는지 아니?

➡ _____

14 다음 중 어법상 틀린 것을 바르게 고쳐 올바른 문장으로 다시 쓰시오.

(1) Can you tell me when did she write this book?

➡ _____

(2) You can lead a horse to water, but you can't make him to drink.

➡ _____

(3) I wonder that he is full or not.

➡ _____

The More You See, The More You Know

Welcome to the World Art Museum tour. When you go to an art
museum, how much time do you spend looking at each painting?
Many visitors glance at one painting for only a few seconds
before they move on. But you might miss the important details of
paintings since it is hard to notice them right away.

Today, we'll look at two paintings closely and I'll help you see
interesting details.

Look at this painting first. The seaside landscape is so peaceful and
beautiful, isn't it? The title of this painting is *Landscape with the Fall
of Icarus*. So, can you see where Icarus is? Do you see two legs that
are sticking out of the water near the ship? This is Icarus in the famous
myth in Greece. In the myth, Icarus' father made wings for him with
feathers and wax and told him to stay away from the sun.

detail 세부 사항	
since ~ 때문에	
notice ~을 알아차리다	
glance at ~을 힐끗 보다	
right away 즉시, 바로	
seaside 해변, 바닷가	
landscape 풍경	
stick 내밀다	
myth 신화	
wing 날개	
feather 깃털	
wax 밀랍	
stay away from ~을 가까이 하지 않다	

확인문제

● 다음 문장이 본문의 내용과 일치하면 T, 일치하지 않으면 F를 쓰시오.

1 It is enough to spend a few minutes looking at a painting. ☐

2 It is hard to notice the important details of paintings right away. ☐

3 We can see peaceful and beautiful landscape in the first painting. ☐

4 Icarus is waving his hands in the painting. ☐

5 Icarus made his wings without any help. ☐

However, Icarus didn't listen. He <u>flew</u> too close to the sun. So, the
fly–flew–flown

wax melted and he fell into the water. Now, look at the entire painting

again. <u>Despite</u> the tragedy of Icarus, people are going on with their
전치사(~에도 불구하고)

<u>everyday</u> activities. Does the painting still <u>look peaceful</u>?
일상의   감각동사+형용사: 평화스럽게 보이다

<u>What do you think the artist is trying to tell us?</u>
간접의문문: think, imagine, guess 등이 동사로 쓰인 문장에서 간접의문문의 의문사를 문장 맨 앞으로 보냄

Now, let's <u>move on to</u> the next painting. Do you see the artist <u>behind</u>
~으로 옮겨가다   ~ 뒤에

the large canvas? He is Diego Velázquez, and he actually painted this

picture. <u>Who do you think he is painting?</u> Take a quick look. The
Do you think? + Who is he painting?

young princess <u>seems to</u> be the main person because she is in the center
~인 것처럼 보이다

of the painting. But the title of the painting is *The Maids of Honour*.

Then, is the artist drawing the two women <u>beside</u> the princess? Take
~ 옆에 있는

a close look. It will <u>make you wonder</u> about the painting more. <u>Try to</u>
앞 문장 'Take a close look.'을 가리킴   사역동사+목적어+동사원형: 목적어가 ~하게 하다   ~하려고 애쓰다

<u>see which direction the artist is looking at.</u> Can you see the king and
Try to see. + Which direction is the artist looking at?

the queen <u>in the mirror</u> <u>in the background of the painting</u>? <u>Who do you</u>
형용사구   the mirror를 수식하는 형용사구   = Do you think? +

<u>think he is painting now?</u>
Who is he painting now?

melt 녹다

despite ~에도 불구하고

tragedy 비극

artist 예술가, 미술가

canvas 화폭, 캔버스

wonder 궁금해하다

direction 방향

take a look 보다

beside ~옆에

background 배경

 확인문제

● 다음 문장이 본문의 내용과 일치하면 T, 일치하지 <u>않으면</u> F를 쓰시오.

1 Icarus followed what his father had said. ☐

2 Icarus fell into the water because the wax melted. ☐

3 Diego Velázquez is in the painting. ☐

4 There are two women beside the princess. ☐

5 There is a mirror in the background of the painting. ☐

6 Diego Velázquez drew himself in the mirror of the painting. ☐

Reading 교과서 확인학습 A

● 우리말을 참고하여 빈칸에 알맞은 말을 쓰시오.

1 _____ _____ the World Art Museum tour.

2 _____ you _____ _____ an art museum, _____ _____ _____ do you spend _____ at each painting?

3 Many visitors _____ _____ one painting _____ only _____ _____ seconds before they move _____.

4 But you _____ _____ the important details of paintings _____ it is hard _____ _____ _____ right away.

5 Today, we'll _____ _____ two paintings _____ and I'll _____ _____ _____ interesting details.

6 Look _____ this painting _____.

7 The _____ _____ is so _____ and beautiful, _____ _____?

8 The _____ of this painting _____ *Landscape with the Fall of Icarus.*

9 So, can you see _____ _____ _____?

10 Do you see two legs that _____ _____ _____ _____ _____ _____ near the ship?

11 This is Icarus _____ _____ _____ _____ in Greece.

12 In the myth, Icarus' father _____ _____ with feathers and wax and told him _____ _____ _____ the sun.

13 _____, Icarus didn't _____.

14 He _____ _____ _____ to the sun.

15 So, the wax _____ and he _____ _____ the water.

1 세계 미술관(the World Art Museum)에 오신 것을 환영합니다.

2 미술관에 갈 때 여러분은 각각의 그림을 보는 데 얼마나 많은 시간을 보내나요?

3 많은 방문객들은 이동하기 전에 하나의 그림을 몇 초간만 힐끗 봅니다.

4 하지만 그림의 중요한 세부 사항들을 즉시 알아채는 것은 어렵기 때문에 여러분은 그것들을 놓칠 수 있습니다.

5 오늘 우리는 두 개의 그림을 자세히 살펴볼 것이고, 여러분이 흥미로운 세부 사항들을 볼 수 있도록 제가 도와드리겠습니다.

6 먼저 이 그림을 보세요.

7 바닷가 풍경이 매우 평화롭고 아름답죠, 그렇지 않나요?

8 이 그림의 제목은 '추락하는 이카루스가 있는 풍경'입니다.

9 그러면 이카루스가 어디에 있는지 보이나요?

10 배 근처에 물 밖으로 나와 있는 두 다리가 보이죠?

11 이것이 그리스의 유명한 신화에 나오는 이카루스입니다.

12 신화에서 이카루스의 아버지는 그를 위해 깃털과 밀랍으로 날개를 만들어 주었고 그에게 태양을 가까이 하지 말라고 말했습니다.

13 하지만 이카루스는 듣지 않았습니다.

14 그는 태양에 너무 가깝게 날았습니다.

15 그래서 밀랍이 녹았고 그는 물에 빠졌습니다.

16 Now, look _____ the _____ painting again.

17 _____ the tragedy of Icarus, people are _____ _____ _____ their everyday activities.

18 Does the painting _____ _____ _____ ?

19 _____ _____ _____ _____ the artist is trying to tell us?

20 Now, let's _____ _____ _____ the next painting.

21 Do you _____ the artist _____ the large canvas?

22 He is Diego Velázquez, and he _____ _____ this picture.

23 _____ _____ _____ _____ _____ painting?

24 _____ a quick look.

25 The young princess _____ _____ _____ the main person _____ she is in the center of the painting.

26 But the _____ of the _____ is *The Maids of Honour*.

27 Then, is the artist _____ the two women _____ the princess?

28 _____ a close look.

29 It will _____ _____ _____ about the painting more.

30 Try to see _____ _____ _____ _____ _____ looking at.

31 Can you _____ the king and the queen _____ _____ _____ in the _____ of the painting?

32 _____ _____ _____ _____ _____ _____ painting now?

16 이제, 그림 전체를 다시 보세요.

17 이카루스의 비극에도 불구하고 사람들은 일상의 활동을 계속하고 있습니다.

18 그림이 어진히 평화로워 보이나요?

19 화가가 우리에게 무엇을 말하려 한다고 생각하나요?

20 이제, 다음 그림으로 넘어갑시다.

21 커다란 캔버스 뒤에 있는 화가가 보이나요?

22 그는 Diego Velázquez이고, 그가 실제로 이 그림을 그렸습니다.

23 그가 누구를 그리고 있다고 생각하나요?

24 재빨리 봅시다.

25 어린 공주가 그림의 중앙에 있기 때문에 주인공처럼 보입니다.

26 하지만 그림의 제목은 '시녀들'입니다.

27 그렇다면 화가는 공주 옆에 있는 두 여인을 그리고 있나요?

28 자세히 보세요.

29 그림에 대해 더 궁금해하게 될 겁니다.

30 화가가 바라보고 있는 방향을 보려고 노력해 보세요.

31 그림의 배경에 있는 거울 속 왕과 왕비가 보이나요?

32 이제 여러분은 그가 누구를 그리고 있다고 생각하나요?

● 우리말을 참고하여 본문을 영작하시오.

1 세계 미술관(the World Art Museum)에 오신 것을 환영합니다.

➡ _____

2 미술관에 갈 때 여러분은 각각의 그림을 보는 데 얼마나 많은 시간을 보내나요?

➡ _____

3 많은 방문객들은 이동하기 전에 하나의 그림을 몇 초간만 힐끗 봅니다.

➡ _____

4 하지만 그림의 중요한 세부 사항들을 즉시 알아채는 것은 어렵기 때문에 여러분들은 그것들을 놓칠 수 있습니다.

➡ _____

5 오늘 우리는 두 개의 그림을 자세히 살펴볼 것이고, 여러분이 흥미로운 세부 사항들을 볼 수 있도록 제가 도와드리겠습니다.

➡ _____

6 먼저 이 그림을 보세요.

➡ _____

7 바닷가 풍경이 매우 평화롭고 아름답죠, 그렇지 않나요?

➡ _____

8 이 그림의 제목은 '추락하는 이카루스가 있는 풍경'입니다.

➡ _____

9 그러면 이카루스가 어디에 있는지 보이나요?

➡ _____

10 배 근처에 물 밖으로 나와 있는 두 다리가 보이죠?

➡ _____

11 이것이 그리스의 유명한 신화에 나오는 이카루스입니다.

➡ _____

12 신화에서 이카루스의 아버지는 그를 위해 깃털과 밀랍으로 날개를 만들어 주었고 그에게 태양을 가까이 하지 말라고 말했습니다.

➡ _____

➡ _____

13 하지만 이카루스는 듣지 않았습니다.

➡ _____

14 그는 태양에 너무 가깝게 날았습니다.

➡ _____

15 그래서 밀랍이 녹았고 그는 물에 빠졌습니다.

➡ _____

16 이제, 그림 전체를 다시 보세요.

➡ _____

17 이카루스의 비극에도 불구하고 사람들은 일상의 활동을 계속하고 있습니다.

➡ _____

18 그림이 여전히 평화로워 보이나요?

➡ _____

19 화가가 우리에게 무엇을 말하려 한다고 생각하나요?

➡ _____

20 이제, 다음 그림으로 넘어갑시다.

➡ _____

21 커다란 캔버스 뒤에 있는 화가가 보이나요?

➡ _____

22 그는 Diego Velázquez이고, 그가 실제로 이 그림을 그렸습니다.

➡ _____

23 그가 누구를 그리고 있다고 생각하나요?

➡ _____

24 재빨리 봅시다.

➡ _____

25 어린 공주가 그림의 중앙에 있기 때문에 주인공처럼 보입니다.

➡ _____

26 하지만 그림의 제목은 '시녀들'입니다.

➡ _____

27 그렇다면 화가는 공주 옆에 있는 두 여인을 그리고 있나요?

➡ _____

28 자세히 보세요.

➡ _____

29 그림에 대해 더 궁금해하게 될 겁니다.

➡ _____

30 화가가 바라보고 있는 방향을 보려고 노력해 보세요.

➡ _____

31 그림의 배경에 있는 거울 속 왕과 왕비가 보이나요?

➡ _____

32 이제 여러분은 그가 누구를 그리고 있다고 생각하나요?

➡ _____

[01~04] 다음 글을 읽고 물음에 답하시오.

Welcome to the World Art Museum tour. When you go to an art museum, how much time do you spend looking at each painting? Many visitors glance at one painting for only a few seconds before they move on. But you might miss the important details of paintings (A)since it is hard (B)to notice them right away. Today, we'll look at two paintings closely and I'll help you see interesting details.

01 다음 중 밑줄 친 (A)를 대신하여 쓰일 수 있는 것은?

① because ② when ③ if
④ because of ⑤ while

서답형

02 다음과 같이 풀이되는 단어를 위 글에서 찾아 쓰시오.

> to see or become conscious of something or someone

➡ _____

중요

03 다음 중 밑줄 친 (B)와 쓰임이 같은 것은?

① They hoped to meet again someday.
② Are you happy to see me again?
③ It is necessary to keep your promise.
④ Is there anything to drink?
⑤ His hobby is to make something.

서답형

04 According to the writer, how many paintings will we look at closely? Answer in English with a full sentence.

➡ _____

[05~10] 다음 글을 읽고 물음에 답하시오.

Look at this painting first. The seaside landscape is so peaceful and beautiful, isn't it? The title of this painting is *Landscape with the Fall of Icarus*. So, _____(A)_____? Do you see two legs that are sticking out of the water near the ship? This is Icarus in the famous myth in Greece. ① In the myth, Icarus' father made wings for him with feathers and wax and told him to stay away from the sun. ② He flew too close to the sun. ③ So, the wax melted and he fell into the water. ④ Now, look at the entire painting again. ⑤ _____(B)_____ the tragedy of Icarus, people are going on with their everyday activities. Does the painting still look peaceful? What do you think the artist is trying to tell us?

서답형

05 다음 두 문장을 하나의 문장으로 연결하여 빈칸 (A)에 알맞게 쓰시오.

> • Can you see?
> • Where is Icarus?

➡ _____

06 다음 중 빈칸 (B)에 들어갈 말로 가장 적절한 것은?

① In spite of ② Due to
③ In addition to ④ Thanks to
⑤ Along with

서답형

07 다음 중 주어진 문장이 들어가기에 가장 적절한 곳은?

> However, Icarus didn't listen.

①　　②　　③　　④　　⑤

08 위 글을 읽고 다음 질문에 완전한 문장의 영어로 답하시오.

Q: What is the title of the painting?

➡ _____

09 첫 번째 그림에서 찾아볼 수 없는 것은?

① peaceful landscape
② people doing their everyday activities
③ Icarus flying to the sun
④ a ship on the water
⑤ two legs sticking out of the water

10 위 글의 내용과 일치하지 않는 것은?

① The landscape of the first painting looks peaceful and beautiful.
② We can see only two legs of Icarus in the painting.
③ Icarus can be seen near the ship in the painting.
④ Icarus made his wings by himself.
⑤ Icarus flew close to the sun and fell into water.

[11~15] 다음 글을 읽고 물음에 답하시오.

Now, let's move on to the next painting. Do you see the artist behind the large canvas? He is Diego Velázquez, and he actually painted this picture. Who do you think he is painting? Take a quick look. ⓐ어린 공주가 그림의 중앙에 있기 때문에 주인공처럼 보입니다. But the title of the painting is *The Maids of Honour*. Then, is the artist drawing the two women beside the princess? Take a close look. It will make you ___(A)___ about the painting more. Try to see which direction the artist is looking at. Can you see the king and the queen in the mirror in the background of the painting? Who do you think he is (B)painting now?

11 단어 'wonder'를 어법에 맞게 빈칸 (A)에 쓰시오.

➡ _____

12 다음 중 밑줄 친 (B)와 쓰임이 같은 것은?

① Are you interested in writing a poem?
② His job is delivering mails.
③ Jason was doing his laundry.
④ Mina enjoyed watching movies with me.
⑤ David didn't mind asking about it.

13 위 글의 밑줄 친 우리말 ⓐ를 주어진 어휘를 이용하여 18 단어로 영작하시오. (the young princess로 시작할 것.)

the young princess, the painting, the main person, the center, because, be

➡ _____
_____

14 Where can we find the artist of the next painting? Answer in English with a full sentence. Use the word 'him,'

➡ _____

15 다음 중 위 글을 읽고 답할 수 없는 질문은?

① What is the name of the artist of the second painting?
② What makes the young princess seem to be the main person?
③ What is the title of the painting?
④ How many women are there beside the princess?
⑤ How large is the painting?

[16~18] 다음 글을 읽고 물음에 답하시오.

Welcome to the World Art Museum tour. When you go to an art museum, (A)[how many / how much] time do you spend looking at each painting? Many visitors glance at one painting for only a few seconds before they move on. But you might miss the important details of paintings since it is hard to notice (B)[it / them] right away. Today, we'll look at two paintings closely and I'll help you (C)[seeing / to see] interesting details.

16 (A)~(C)에서 어법상 옳은 것끼리 바르게 짝지은 것은?

① how much – them – seeing
② how much – them – to see
③ how many – it – to see
④ how many – it – seeing
⑤ how many – them – to see

서답형

17 According to the writer, how long does it take many visitors to see one painting? Answer in English with a full sentence. Use the words 'it', 'them' and 'to.'

➡ _____

18 다음 중 위 글 다음에 이어질 내용으로 가장 적절한 것은?

① the problem of the museum tour
② a request for donating good paintings
③ how to see the details of paintings
④ bad behaviors of people in the museum
⑤ how to be friendly with the curator

[19~23] 다음 글을 읽고 물음에 답하시오.

Look at this painting first. The seaside landscape is so peaceful and beautiful, ①isn't it? The title of this painting is *Landscape with the Fall of Icarus*. So, can you see ②where is Icarus?
(A) So, the wax melted and he fell into the water. Now, look at the entire painting again. Despite the tragedy of Icarus, people are going on with their everyday activities.
(B) In the myth, Icarus' father made wings ③for him with feathers and wax and told him ④to stay away from the sun. _____ⓐ_____, Icarus didn't listen. He flew too close to the sun.
(C) Do you see two legs that ⑤are sticking out of the water near the ship? This is Icarus in the famous myth in Greece.

Does the painting still look peaceful? What do you think the artist is trying to tell us?

19 다음 중 빈칸 ⓐ에 들어갈 말로 가장 적절한 것은?

① Moreover   ② Therefore
③ However   ④ For example
⑤ Thus

20 자연스러운 내용이 되도록 (A)~(C)를 바르게 나열한 것은?

① (A) – (B) – (C)   ② (B) – (A) – (C)
③ (B) – (C) – (A)   ④ (C) – (A) – (B)
⑤ (C) – (B) – (A)

21 ①~⑤ 중 어법상 바르지 <u>않은</u> 것은?

①   ②   ③   ④   ⑤

22 Which is NOT true about Icarus?

① He is in the famous myth in Greece.

② His father made wings for him.

③ He had wings made of feathers and wax.

④ He flew close to the sun.

⑤ He listened to his father very well.

서답형

23 According to the passage, what did Icarus' father tell Icarus? Answer in English with a full sentence.

➡ _____

[24~25] 다음 글을 읽고 물음에 답하시오.

Today, I went to the Amazing Art exhibition. At the exhibition, I saw many interesting pieces of art. Among them, I liked the piece called *Moon Tree*. It was made by French artist, David Myriam. Interestingly, sand was used in this painting. I like it because a tree in the moon makes me ____(A)____ . Now I know that anything can be used to make art. Anything is possible!

24 다음 중 빈칸 (A)에 들어갈 말로 적절한 것은?

① feels calm   ② feel calmly

③ feel calm   ④ feeling calm

⑤ feeling calmly

중요

25 Which is NOT true about the passage?

① There were many interesting pieces of art at the Amazing Art exhibition.

② What the writer liked was *Moon Tree*.

③ *Moon Tree* was made by David Myriam.

④ David Myriam used a tree in his painting.

⑤ David Myriam is French.

[26~28] 다음 글을 읽고 물음에 답하시오.

Now, let's move on to the next painting. Do you see the artist behind the large canvas? He is Diego Velázquez, and he actually painted this picture. Who do you ____(A)____ he is painting? Take a quick look. The young princess seems to be the main person because she is in the center of the painting. But the title of the painting is *The Maids of Honour*. Then, is the artist drawing the two women beside the princess? Take a close look. It will make you wonder about the painting more. Try to see which direction the artist is looking at. Can you see the king and the queen in the mirror in the background of the painting? Who do you think he is painting now?

26 다음 중 빈칸 (A)에 들어갈 말로 적절하지 않은 것은?

① think   ② guess   ③ believe

④ know   ⑤ imagine

서답형

27 According to the passage, who is in the middle of the painting? Answer in English with a full sentence.

➡ _____

중요

28 위 글의 내용과 일치하지 않는 것은?

① Diego Velázquez drew *The Maids of Hornour*.

② Diego Velázquez doesn't appear in the painting.

③ Both the king and the queen can be found in the painting.

④ There are two women beside the princess in the painting.

⑤ A mirror was drawn in the background of the painting.

[01~03] 다음 글을 읽고 물음에 답하시오.

Welcome to the World Art Museum tour. (A) When you go to an art museum, how much time do you spend looking at each painting? Many visitors glance at one painting for only a few seconds before they move on. But you might miss the important details of paintings since it is hard to notice (B)them right away. Today, we'll look at two paintings closely and (C)여러분이 흥미로운 세부 사항들을 볼 수 있도록 제가 도와드리겠습니다.

01 다음은 밑줄 친 (A)와 같은 의미의 문장이다. 빈칸을 알맞게 채우시오.

I wonder _____ when you go to an art museum.

➡ _____

02 위 글의 밑줄 친 (B)가 의미하는 것을 위 글에서 찾아 쓰시오.

➡ _____

03 주어진 단어를 활용하여 밑줄 친 우리말 (C)를 영어로 쓰시오.

(help / see)

➡ _____

[04~08] 다음 글을 읽고 물음에 답하시오.

Look at this painting first. The seaside landscape is so peaceful and beautiful, isn't it? The title of this painting is *Landscape with the Fall of Icarus*. So, can you see where Icarus is? Do you see two legs that are sticking out of the water near the ship? This is Icarus in the famous myth in Greece.

In the myth, Icarus' father made wings for him with feathers and wax and told him to stay away from the sun. However, Icarus didn't listen. He flew too close to the sun. So, the wax melted and he fell into the water. Now, look at the entire painting again. Despite the tragedy of Icarus, people are going on with their everyday activities. Does the painting still look peaceful?

_____ (A)

04 다음 두 문장을 하나의 문장으로 만들어 빈칸 (A)에 쓰시오.

• Do you think?
• What is the artist trying to tell us?

➡ _____

05 다음은 화가가 위 그림을 통해 말하려는 것이다. 빈칸에 적절한 말을 위 글에서 찾아 쓰시오.

The artist is trying to tell us that we do not know other people's _____.

➡ _____

06 What did Icarus' father make for Icarus? Answer in English with five words.

➡ _____

07 위 글의 내용에 맞게 빈칸에 알맞은 말을 쓰시오.

A: What made the wax _____?
B: Flying too close to the sun made it so.

➡ _____

08 다음은 '추락하는 이카루스가 있는 풍경'을 감상하고 있는 두 학생의 대화이다. 빈칸에 알맞은 말을 쓰시오.

> **A:** Can you tell me _____? I can't find him.
> **B:** Oh, he is near the ship.
> **A:** The two legs that _____? Is that him?
> **B:** Yes, he is.

➡ _____, _____

[09~13] 다음 글을 읽고 물음에 답하시오.

Now, let's move on to the next painting. Do you see the artist behind the large canvas? He is Diego Velázquez, and he (A)actual painted this picture. Who do you think he is painting? Take a quick look. The young princess seems to be the main person because she is in the center of the painting. But the title of the painting is *The Maids of Honour*. Then, is the artist drawing the two women beside the princess? Take a close look. (B)It will make you wonder about the painting more. Try to see which direction the artist is looking at. Can you see the king and the queen in the mirror in the background of the painting? Who do you think he is painting now?

09 밑줄 친 (A)를 알맞은 형으로 고치시오.

➡ _____

10 Who painted the picture, *The Maids of Honour*? Answer in English with a full sentence.

➡ _____

11 밑줄 친 (B)가 의미하는 것을 우리말로 쓰시오.

➡ _____

12 Who are the people in the mirror in the background of the painting? Answer in English with a full sentence.

➡ _____

13 위 글의 표현을 이용하여 다음 우리말을 영어로 쓰시오.

> 나는 누가 실제로 이 그림을 그렸는지 궁금해.

➡ _____

[14~15] 다음 글을 읽고 물음에 답하시오.

Today, I went to the Amazing Art exhibition. At the exhibition, I saw many interesting pieces of art. Among them, I liked the piece called *Moon Tree*. It was made by French artist, David Myriam. Interestingly, sand was used in this painting. I like it because a tree in the moon makes me feel calm. Now I know that anything can be used to make art. Anything is possible!

14 위 글의 내용에 맞게 빈칸에 알맞은 말을 쓰시오.

> **A:** Do you know _____ in this painting?
> **B:** Yes, I do. He used sand.

15 Write the reason why the writer likes *Moon Tree*. Use the word 'because.'

➡ _____
_____

해석

Listen & Talk

M: What are you reading, Sally?

W: I'm reading *The Maze Runner*. It's about boys who are put in a maze.
　　　　　　　　　　　　　　= The Maze Runner　　　주격 관계대명사

M: It's a great story. I've seen the movie of it, too. I prefer the novel to the
　　　　　　　　　　현재완료　　　　　　　　　　　prefer A to B: B보다 더 A가 좋다

movie.

W: Why do you like it better?
　　　　　　　= the novel

M: The novel has various stories. But the movie didn't show some important

parts of the story.

구문해설　• maze: 미로　• novel: 소설

M: Sally, 너는 무엇을 읽고 있니?

W: 나는 '미로를 달리는 사람'을 읽고 있어. 미로에 갇힌 소년들에 관한 내용이야.

M: 그건 대단한 이야기이지. 나는 그것을 영화로도 봤어. 나는 영화보다는 소설이 더 좋아.

W: 왜 소설이 더 좋은데?

M: 소설에는 다양한 이야기가 담겨 있어. 하지만 영화에서는 이야기의 중요한 몇 부분이 나오지 않았어.

Grammar in Real Life

1. Princess, please let me in.
　　　　　　　　　let A in: A를 들어가게 하다
2. Who are you?

3. The princess promised me, "If you help me, I'll let you enter the palace and
　　　　　　　　　　　　　　　　　　　　사역동사+목적어+동사원형: 목적어가 ~하게 하다

be my friend."
(let you) be my friend
4. Come here. I'll have people serve you some cookies and tea.
　　　　　　　　　　사역동사　　4형식 동사(~에게 …을 내어주다)
5. No! Never let him in. I don't like him.
　　　　　　부정 명령문
6. Don't worry, Frog. I'll make the princess keep her promise.
　　　　　　　　　　　　사역동사+목적어+동사원형: 목적어가 ~하게 하다

구문해설　• promise: 약속하다　• enter: ~로 들어가다　• serve: ~을 내어주다

• keep one's promise: ~의 약속을 지키다

1. 공주님, 저를 들어가게 해 주세요.
2. 그대는 누군가?
3. 공주님은 제게 "네가 날 도와준다면, 나는 너를 궁전에 들어오게 하고 내 친구가 되게 해 주겠어."라고 약속하셨어요.
4. 이쪽으로 오게. 내가 사람들을 시켜 자네에게 과자와 차를 가져다 주게 하겠네.
5. 안 돼요! 그를 들어오게 하지 마세요. 저는 그를 좋아하지 않아요.
6. 걱정 말게, 개구리. 나는 공주가 그녀의 약속을 지키게 하겠네.

Think and Write C

Today, I went to the Amazing Art exhibition. At the exhibition, I saw many

interesting pieces of art. Among them, I liked the piece called *Moon Tree*. It
흥미를 유발하는　　　　　　many interesting pieces of art　　= which was called
was made by French artist, David Myriam. Interestingly, sand was used in this
　　　　　　　　　　　　　　　　　　　　　　　　　　　　　　수동태

painting. I like it because a tree in the moon makes me feel calm. Now I know
　　　　　　　　　　이유를 나타내는 접속사　　　　　　　　사역동사+목적어+동사원형

that anything can be used to make art. Anything is possible!
명사절을 이끄는 접속사　　　　　부사적 용법

구문해설　• exhibition: 전시회　• interesting: 흥미로운　• called: ~라고 불리는

• be made by: ~에 의해 만들어지다　• calm: 고요한

오늘 나는 놀라운 미술 전시회에 갔다. 전시회에서, 나는 많은 흥미로운 미술 작품들을 보았다. 그 중에서, 나는 *Moon Tree*라고 불리는 작품이 좋았다. 그것은 프랑스 미술가 David Myriam에 의해 만들어졌다. 흥미롭게도, 모래가 이 미술품에 사용되었다. 달 속에 있는 나무 한 그루가 내 마음을 고요하게 만들기 때문에 나는 그것이 좋다. 이제 나는 어떠한 것이든 미술을 만들기 위해 사용될 수 있다는 사실을 안다. 무엇이든 가능하다!

영역별 핵심문제

01 다음 짝지어진 단어의 관계가 같도록 빈칸에 알맞은 말을 쓰시오.

> prince: princess = comedy : _____

02 다음 영영풀이가 가리키는 것을 고르시오.

> a very sad event, especially one involving death

① comedy   ② artwork   ③ detail
④ tear   ⑤ tragedy

03 다음 중 밑줄 친 부분의 뜻풀이가 바르지 <u>않은</u> 것은?

① Some birds have colorful <u>feathers</u>. 깃털
② I will <u>exhibit</u> my pictures someday. 전시하다
③ <u>Frogs</u> sleep during winter. 개구리
④ We need <u>flat</u> ground to build a house. 울퉁불퉁한
⑤ I looked down on the peaceful <u>landscape</u> from the hill. 풍경

04 다음 우리말에 맞게 빈칸에 알맞은 말을 쓰시오.

(1) 이탈리아에는 항상 많은 관광객들이 있다.
➡ There are always many _____ in Italy.
(2) 네 친구에게 혀를 내밀지 마라.
➡ Don't _____ your tongue at your friend.
(3) Tom은 정말 소설가를 만나고 싶어 한다.
➡ Tom really wants to meet the _____.

05 다음 우리말에 맞게 주어진 단어를 사용하여 영작하시오.

(1) 나는 시보다 소설을 더 좋아한다. (prefer)
➡ _____
(2) 우리 가족은 해변으로 여행갈 것이다.
(trip, take, seaside)
➡ _____
(3) 그 전쟁은 전 세계에 비극이었다. (whole)
➡ _____

06 다음 주어진 문장의 밑줄 친 stick과 같은 의미로 쓰인 것은?

> Don't <u>stick</u> your head out of the window.

① Did your brother <u>stick</u> a stamp on the letter?
② Would you <u>stick</u> your arms out of your sleeves?
③ Brian is using a <u>stick</u> to find something.
④ Will you <u>stick</u> a note on the door?
⑤ He is striking the tree with a <u>stick</u>.

07 다음 문장에 공통으로 들어갈 말을 고르시오.

> • We need to _____ our attention to our mistakes.
> • Can you _____ me to Seoul Station?
> • Is there a _____ flight to San Francisco?

① direct   ② prefer
③ melt   ④ notice
⑤ promise

[08~09] 다음 대화를 읽고 물음에 답하시오.

> Jean: (A) What are you reading, Sally?
>
> Sally: (B) I'm reading *The Maze Runner*. It's about boys who are put in a maze.
>
> Jean: (C) It's a great story. I've seen the movie of it, too. I prefer the novel to the movie.
>
> Sally: (D) Why do you like it better?
>
> Jean: (E) But the movie didn't show some important parts of the story.

08 위 대화의 (A)~(E) 중 주어진 문장이 들어가기에 적절한 곳은?

> The novel has various stories.

① (A) ② (B) ③ (C) ④ (D) ⑤ (E)

09 위 대화의 내용과 일치하지 <u>않는</u> 것은?

① Sally is reading *The Maze Runner*.
② *The Maze Runner* is about boys who are put in a maze.
③ Jean saw the movie of *The Maze Runner* with Sally.
④ Jean prefers the novel to the movie because the novel has various stories.
⑤ Jean thinks that the movie missed some important parts of the story.

[10~11] 다음 대화를 읽고 물음에 답하시오.

> Anna: (*ringing*) Hello, Steve.
>
> Steve: Hi, Anna. We're meeting at the arts festival tomorrow at 1:30, right?
>
> Anna: Right. _____ (A)
>
> Steve: I want to watch the hip-hop dance performance first.
>
> Anna: Sounds good. It's at 2 p.m. at the gym, right?
>
> Steve: Yeah, and how about watching the play, *Romeo and Juliet*, at 4 p.m.?
>
> Anna: Oh, the one at the Main Hall near the gym? Sure!

10 위 대화의 빈칸 (A)에 들어갈 말을 〈보기〉에 주어진 단어를 모두 배열하여 완성하시오.

> ┤ 보기 ├
>
> kind / do / to / of / watch / you / what / performance / want / first

➡ _____

11 위 대화의 내용과 일치하지 <u>않는</u> 것은?

① Anna와 Steve는 내일 1시 30분에 예술 축제에서 만나기로 했다.
② Steve는 먼저 힙합 댄스 공연을 보고 싶어 한다.
③ 힙합 댄스 공연은 체육관에서 2시에 열린다.
④ '로미오와 줄리엣' 연극이 오후 4시에 공연된다.
⑤ Anna와 Steve는 연극을 보기 위해 대강당에서 체육관으로 이동할 것이다.

12 다음 짝지어진 대화가 <u>어색한</u> 것은?

① A: What kind of music do you like most?
   B: I love hip-hop.
② A: There are two kinds of guitars. Which do you prefer?
   B: I prefer the classic guitar.
③ A: What kind of brush were you using?
   B: I don't know how to paint clean lines.
④ A: I prefer the movie to the novel.
   B: Why do you like it better?
⑤ A: What kind of movie do you like?
   B: I like horror movies.

[13~14] 다음 대화를 읽고 물음에 답하시오.

> Minsu: What are you reading, Jina? (A)
> Jina: The novel, *Life of Pi*. It's a story of a boy and a tiger. (B)
> Minsu: It's a great book. I've seen the movie of it, too. (C)
> Jina: Why do you like it better? (D)
> Minsu: The scenes are very beautiful. And the tiger looks so real. (E)

13 위 대화의 (A)~(E) 중 주어진 문장이 들어가기에 적절한 곳은?

> I prefer the movie to the novel.

① (A)   ② (B)   ③ (C)   ④ (D)   ⑤ (E)

14 위 대화를 읽고 대답할 수 <u>없는</u> 것은?

① What is Jina doing now?
② What is *Life of Pi* about?
③ Which one does Minsu prefer, the novel or the movie?
④ How does the tiger look in the movie?
⑤ When did Minsu see the movie?

[15~16] 다음 대화를 읽고 물음에 답하시오.

> Sora: Can you help me? I don't know how to paint clean lines.
> Mike: What kind of brush were you using?
> Sora: This round brush.
> Mike: When you paint lines, a flat brush is better. Try this one.
> Sora: Okay, thank you.

15 What's the matter with Sora?

➡ _____

16 After talking with Mike, what will Sora use to paint lines?

➡ _____

17 다음 우리말을 영어로 바르게 옮긴 것은?

> 누가 너를 이 파티에 초대했는지 말해 줘.

① Tell me who you invited to this party.
② Tell me whom you will invite to this party.
③ Tell me who invited you to this party.
④ I wonder how you were invited to this party.
⑤ I wonder whom you came with.

18 다음 빈칸에 공통으로 들어갈 말로 적절한 것은?

> • _____ he comes late, there will be no food.
> • Do you want to know _____ Jane swims every Sunday?

① that   ② who   ③ what
④ whether   ⑤ if

19 다음 중 어법상 <u>틀린</u> 것은?

① Kelly made me do her homework.
② Julia wondered who brought the book.
③ Jerry asked me what I ate for lunch.
④ Olivia let him to use her computer.
⑤ Tell me whether Tom is tired now.

20 주어진 단어를 활용하여 다음 우리말을 영어로 쓰시오.

> 그녀가 지금 어디에 있다고 생각하시나요?
> (think / where)

➡ _____

21 다음 우리말을 영어로 쓸 때 세 번째 오는 단어와 일곱 번째 오는 단어를 바르게 묶은 것은?

> 당신이 내게 이 꽃을 보내도록 누가 시켰는지 궁금해요.

① wonder – made   ② who – me
③ who – send   ④ made – this
⑤ made – flower

22 다음 두 문장을 하나의 문장으로 바르게 쓴 것은?

> Can you tell me? Who kicked the ball?

① Can you tell me who the ball kicked?
② Can you tell me if who kicked the ball?
③ Can you tell me who kicked the ball?
④ Can you tell me who is kicking the ball?
⑤ Can you tell me who the ball is kicking?

23 다음 중 빈칸에 들어갈 말로 적절하지 않은 것은?

> Thomson _____ us carry the boxes.

① had   ② made   ③ helped
④ let   ⑤ told

24 다음 빈칸에 알맞은 말을 쓰시오. 한 칸에 하나의 단어만 쓰시오.

> 나는 그들이 집안일을 하는 것을 돕습니다.
> ➡ I _____ them _____ the chores.
> * chore: 집안일

25 다음 중 어법상 올바른 문장의 개수는?

> ⓐ Can you tell me who are you talking with?
> ⓑ Their parents always have them to go to school early in the morning.
> ⓒ I want to know what they are doing now.
> ⓓ Can you tell me what does Jason do for a living?
> ⓔ May I ask that you have brothers or sisters?

① 1개   ② 2개   ③ 3개   ④ 4개   ⑤ 5개

26 주어진 단어를 활용하여 다음 우리말을 영어로 쓰시오.

> 그 괴물은 아이들이 비명을 지르게 했다.
> (monster, make, scream)

➡ _____

27 간접의문문을 이용하여 다음 두 문장을 하나의 문장으로 쓰시오.

(1) I didn't hear. What did you say?
➡ _____

(2) I'd like to know. Are you friends with Jina?
➡ _____

28 다음 중 빈칸에 들어갈 말로 적절한 것을 모두 고르시오.

> May I ask _____ Brady is here?

① whether   ② if   ③ where
④ what   ⑤ who

Reading

[29~33] 다음 글을 읽고 물음에 답하시오.

Look at this painting first. The seaside landscape is so peaceful and beautiful, isn't it? The title of this painting is *Landscape with the Fall of Icarus*. So, can you see where Icarus is? Do you see two legs that are sticking out of the water near the ship? This is Icarus in the famous myth in Greece. In the myth, Icarus' father made wings for ①him with feathers and wax and told ②him to stay away from the sun. However, Icarus didn't listen to ③him. ④He flew too close to the sun. So, the wax melted and ⑤he fell into the water. Now, look at the entire painting again. Despite the tragedy of Icarus, people are going on with their everyday activities. (A)Does the painting still look peaceful? What do you think the artist is trying to tell us?

29 위 글의 밑줄 친 ①~⑤ 중 지칭하는 바가 다른 하나는?

①   ②   ③   ④   ⑤

30 What were Icarus' wings made of? Use the word 'they.'

➡ _____

31 다음 중 위 글의 내용과 일치하지 <u>않는</u> 것은?

① You can see the seaside landscape in the painting.
② There is a story behind the painting.
③ Icarus' father made Icarus wings.
④ Icarus didn't listen to what his father said.
⑤ Icarus flew close to the sun without wings.

32 위 글의 밑줄 친 (A)를 어법에 맞게 다음 빈칸에 쓰시오.

I wonder _____ .

➡ _____

33 다음과 같이 풀이되는 단어를 위 글에서 찾아 쓰시오.

a very sad event, especially one involving death

➡ _____

[34~36] 다음 글을 읽고 물음에 답하시오.

Welcome to the World Art Museum tour. When you go to an art museum, how much time do you spend (A)[looking / to look] at each painting? Many visitors glance at one painting for only (B)[a few / a little] seconds before they move on. But you might miss the important details of paintings since ⓐit is hard to notice them right away. Today, we'll look at two paintings (C)[close / closely] and I'll help you see interesting details.

34 (A)~(C)에서 어법상 옳은 것을 고르시오.

(A) _____ (B) _____ (C) _____

35 What is the problem with taking only several seconds to look at a painting? Answer in English with a full sentence.

➡ _____

36 다음 중 밑줄 친 ⓐ와 쓰임이 같은 것은?

① It was cold yesterday morning.
② It is still bright outside.
③ It was difficult to tell you all of my secrets.
④ It hurt my feeling.
⑤ It is going up the tree.

[01~02] 다음 대화를 읽고 물음에 답하시오.

Sue: Have you (A)listened to Jane's new song, *Girl Friend*?

Tony: Yeah, it's really cool. The guitar part is great.

Sue: There is also a dance version (B)of the song (C)on the album.

Tony: I've listened to it, but I prefer the guitar version (D)than the dance version. It matches her voice (E)better.

출제율 90%

01 위 대화의 (A)~(E) 중 어법상 어색한 것을 찾아 바르게 고치시오.

➡ _____

출제율 95%

02 위 대화를 읽고 대답할 수 없는 것은?

① What are Sue and Tony talking about?

② What does Tony think about Jane's new song, *Girl Friend*?

③ How many versions of *Girl Friend* are there on the album?

④ Why does Tony like the guitar version more than the dance version?

⑤ What does Tony think about the dance version of *Girl Friend*?

[03~05] 다음 대화를 읽고 물음에 답하시오.

Jason: Hi, we are planning a school festival, so we want to find out students' favorite types of performances. May I ask you a few questions?

Emily: Sure.

Jason: _____ (A)

Emily: I like music performances best.

Jason: Okay. Then, which do you prefer, rock or hip-hop?

Emily: I prefer rock to hip-hop.

Jason: (B)Who's your favorite musician? (which, like)

Emily: My favorite musician is TJ.

Jason: Great. Thank you for your answers.

출제율 95%

03 위 대화의 빈칸 (A)에 들어갈 말을 〈보기〉에 주어진 단어를 모두 배열하여 완성하시오.

┌─── 보기 ────┐
of / you / what / best / like / do / kind / performance
└──────────┘

➡ _____

출제율 85%

04 위 대화의 밑줄 친 (B)를 주어진 단어를 사용하여 의미가 같도록 다시 쓰시오.

➡ _____

출제율 100%

05 위 대화의 내용과 일치하지 않는 것을 고르시오.

① Jason은 학교 축제를 계획하고 있다.

② Jason은 학생들이 가장 선호하는 공연의 종류에 대해 알아보고 있다.

③ Emily는 음악 공연을 가장 좋아한다.

④ Emily는 힙합 공연을 록 공연보다 더 좋아한다.

⑤ Emily가 가장 좋아하는 음악가는 TJ이다.

[06~07] 다음 대화를 읽고 물음에 답하시오.

Anna: (*ringing*) Hello, Steve.

Steve: Hi, Anna. We're meeting at the arts festival tomorrow at 1:30, right?

Anna: Right. What kind of ___ⓐ___ do you want to watch first?

Steve: I want to watch the hip-hop dance performance first.

Anna: Sounds good. It's at 2 p.m. at the gym, right?

Steve: Yeah, and how about watching the play, *Romeo and Juliet*, at 4 p.m.?

Anna: Oh, the one at the Main Hall near the gym? Sure!

06 위 대화의 빈칸 ⓐ에 들어갈 적절한 말을 대화에서 찾아 쓰시오.

➡ _____

07 다음 대화의 내용과 일치하도록 빈칸을 완성하시오.

<Arts Festival Schedule>		
Performance	Time	Place
Dance: hip-hop	(A)	(B)
(C) : *Romeo and Juliet*	4:00 p.m	(D)

(A) _____ (B) _____

(C) _____ (D) _____

[08~09] 다음 대화를 읽고 물음에 답하시오.

Mina: I saw an interesting painting in an art book. Look at this. (A)

Jack: Wow, it looks like da Vinci's *Mona Lisa*. (B)

Mina: Actually, it's *Mona Lisa* by Fernando Botero. Which do you prefer? (C)

Jack: I prefer da Vinci's to Botero's. Da Vinci's *Mona Lisa* has an interesting smile. (D)

Mina: Well, I prefer Botero's to da Vinci's. His *Mona Lisa* is cute, and it looks modern. (E)

08 위 대화의 (A)~(E) 중 다음 주어진 문장이 들어가기에 적절한 곳은?

How about you?

① (A) ② (B) ③ (C) ④ (D) ⑤ (E)

09 위 대화를 읽고 대답할 수 <u>없는</u> 것은?

① What did Mina see in the art book?

② Which *Mona Lisa* does Jack prefer?

③ What does Jack think about da Vinci's *Mona Lisa*?

④ Why does Mina like Botero's *Mona Lisa*?

⑤ Why does Botero's *Mona Lisa* look modern?

10 다음 대화가 자연스럽게 이어지도록 순서대로 배열하시오.

(A) The scenes are very beautiful. And the tiger looks so real.

(B) The novel, *Life of Pi*. It's a story of a boy and a tiger.

(C) What are you reading, Jina?

(D) Why do you like it better?

(E) It's a great book. I've seen the movie of it, too. I prefer the movie to the novel.

➡ _____

11 다음 우리말을 영어로 바르게 옮긴 것은?

누가 너에게 그 비밀을 말해 줬는지 궁금해.

① I wonder who the secret you told.

② I wonder whom did you tell the secret.

③ I wonder who told you the secret.

④ I want to know who you told the secret.

⑤ Tell me who you want to tell the secret.

12 다음 빈칸에 들어갈 말이 바르게 짝지어진 것은?

> • They made us _____ by their house.
> • The teacher had students _____ softball.

① to drop – to play
② dropped – playing
③ dropped – played
④ drop – play
⑤ dropping – playing

13 다음 빈칸에 알맞은 말을 쓰시오.

> I don't know. What did you wear for the Halloween party?
> = I don't know _____
> for the Halloween party.

14 다음 빈칸에 들어갈 말로 적절하지 <u>않은</u> 것은?

> I _____ my sister set the table.

① had   ② made   ③ let
④ helped   ⑤ wanted

15 다음 중 어법상 바르지 <u>않은</u> 것은?

① Do you know what the teacher made us do?
② I wonder whether Jessy is sad or happy.
③ Please let her knows what he likes.
④ Can you tell me who let you go out at night?
⑤ Terry asks me if there was something to drink.

16 다음 빈칸에 들어갈 말이 바르게 짝지어진 것은?

> A: Can you tell me what kind of fruit _____?
> B: I like tomato most.

① you like least   ② you like most
③ you used to like   ④ do you like most
⑤ did you like

17 주어진 단어를 활용하여 다음 우리말을 영어로 쓰시오.

> 나의 부모님은 주말마다 내가 늦잠을 자도록 허락하신다. (let / late / on weekends)

➡ _____

[18~20] 다음 글을 읽고 물음에 답하시오.

Now, let's move on to the next painting. Do you see the artist behind the large canvas? ① He is Diego Velázquez, and he actually painted this picture. ② Who do you think he is painting? Take a quick look. ③ The young princess seems to be the main person because she is in the center of the painting. ④ Then, is the artist drawing the two women beside the princess? Take a close look. ⑤ It will make you wonder about the painting more. Try to see which direction the artist is looking at. Can you see the king and the queen in the mirror in the background of the painting? Who do you think he is painting now?

18 ①~⑤ 중 다음 주어진 문장이 들어가기에 가장 적절한 곳은?

> But the title of the painting is *The Maids of Honour.*

①   ②   ③   ④   ⑤

19 다음 중 위 글을 읽고 답할 수 있는 것은? *출제율 95%*

① Why did Diego Velázquez paint the picture?
② When did Diego Velázquez paint the picture?
③ How many maids are there in the picture?
④ Where did Diego Velázquez paint the picture?
⑤ How often did Diego Velázquez meet the king to paint the picture?

20 다음 중 위 그림에서 찾을 수 없는 것은? *출제율 95%*

① an artist who painted the picture
② a young prince between two women
③ the young princess in the middle of the painting
④ the mirror in the background
⑤ the king and the queen

[21~22] 다음 글을 읽고 물음에 답하시오.

This is Icarus in the famous myth in Greece. In the myth, Icarus' father made wings for him with feathers and wax and told him to stay away from the sun. However, Icarus didn't listen. He flew too close to the sun.   (A) , the wax melted and he fell into the water. Now, look at the entire painting again. Despite the tragedy of Icarus, people are going on with their everyday activities. Does the painting still look peaceful? What do you think the artist is trying to tell us?

21 다음 중 빈칸 (A)에 들어갈 말로 알맞은 것은? *출제율 90%*

① So   ② But
③ Though   ④ Still
⑤ Instead

22 위 글에 대한 다음 질문을 완성하시오. *출제율 95%*

> A: Can you tell me _____?
> (이카루스에게 무슨 일이 생겼는지 말해 줄래?)
> B: He flew too close to the sun and the wax of his wings melted.

[23~24] 다음 글을 읽고 물음에 답하시오.

Amazing Sand Art
Today, I went to the Amazing Art exhibition. At the exhibition, I saw many interesting pieces of art. Among them, I liked the piece called *Moon Tree*. It was made by French artist, David Myriam. Interestingly, sand was used in this painting. I like it because a tree in the moon makes me feel calm. Now I know that anything can be used to make art. Anything is possible!

23 위 글의 표현을 활용하여 다음 우리말을 영어로 쓰시오. *출제율 85%*

> 나는 네가 많은 흥미로운 예술 작품들을 보았는지 궁금해.

➡ _____

24 Which is NOT true about the passage? *출제율 100%*

① The writer went to an art exhibition.
② There were many interesting pieces of art at the Amazing Art exhibition.
③ *Moon Tree* was made by David Myriam.
④ David Myriam made *Moon Tree* by using paint.
⑤ The writer realized anything can be used to make art.

[01~03] 다음 대화를 읽고 물음에 답하시오.

Anna: (ringing) Hello, Steve.

Steve: Hi, Anna. We're meeting at the arts festival tomorrow at 1:30, right?

Anna: Right. What kind of performance do you want to watch first?

Steve: I want to watch the hip-hop dance performance first.

Anna: Sounds good. It's at 2 p.m. at the gym, right?

Steve: Yeah, and how about watching the play, *Romeo and Juliet*, at 4 p.m.?

Anna: Oh, the one at the Main Hall near the gym? Sure!

01 What festival will Anna and Steve go to?

➡ _____

02 중요 Where will Anna and Steve watch the hip-hop dance performance?

➡ _____

03 What time and where is *Romeo and Juliet*?

➡ _____

04 중요 간접의문문을 이용하여 다음 두 문장을 하나의 문장으로 쓰시오.

(1) Tell me. Where does Maria live?

➡ _____

(2) I wonder. Are you married?

➡ _____

(3) May I ask? Is he alone?

➡ _____

(4) Can you tell me? Who drove your car?

➡ _____

05 주어진 단어를 바르게 배열하여 다음 우리말을 영어로 쓰시오.

어떤 것도 내가 나의 마음을 바꾸도록 하지는 못할 거야.
(my mind / change / make / nothing / me / will)

➡ _____

06 다음 빈칸에 알맞은 말을 쓰시오.

누가 그 문을 열었는지 궁금해.
➡ I wonder _____.

07 중요 괄호 안의 말을 바르게 배열하여 대화를 완성하시오.

A: I want (how many / read / last year / know / to / books / you).

B: I read about 10 books.

➡ _____

[08~12] 다음 글을 읽고 물음에 답하시오.

Look at this painting first. The seaside landscape is so peaceful and beautiful, isn't it? The title of this painting is *Landscape with the Fall of Icarus*. So, can you see where Icarus is? Do you see two legs that are sticking out of the water near the ship? This is Icarus in the famous myth in Greece. In the myth, Icarus' father made wings for him with feathers and wax and told him to stay away from the sun. However, Icarus didn't listen. He flew too close to the sun. So, the wax __(A)__ and he __(B)__ the water. Now, look at the entire painting again. Despite the tragedy of Icarus, people are going on with their everyday activities. Does the painting still look peaceful? ⓐ화가가 우리에게 무엇을 말하려 한다고 생각하나요?(think, try)

08 위 글의 빈칸 (A)와 (B)에 알맞은 말을 쓰시오.

(A) _____ (B) _____

09 주어진 단어를 활용하여 밑줄 친 우리말 ⓐ를 영어로 쓰시오.

➡ _____

10 위 글의 내용에 맞게 빈칸에 알맞은 말을 쓰시오.

> A: Where is Icarus?
> B: He is _____ _____ _____. You can see his legs _____ _____ _____ _____.

11 주어진 단어를 활용하여 다음 우리말을 영어로 쓰시오.

> 그는 그의 아들이 태양에서 멀리 떨어지게 하지 못했다. (make / stay)

➡ _____

12 위 글의 내용에 맞게 빈칸에 알맞은 말을 쓰시오.

> Q: What happened to Icarus?
> A: He _____ too _____ to the sun and the _____ of his wings _____.

[13~14] 다음 글을 읽고 물음에 답하시오.

Now, let's move __ⓐ__ to the next painting. Do you see the artist behind the large canvas?

(A) The young princess seems to be the main person because she is in the center of the painting.

(B) It will make you wonder about the painting more. Try to see which direction the artist is looking at.

(C) But the title of the painting is *The Maids of Honour*. Then, is the artist drawing the two women beside the princess? Take a close look.

(D) He is Diego Velázquez, and he actually painted this picture. Who do you think he is painting? Take a quick look.

Can you see the king and the queen in the mirror __ⓑ__ the background of the painting? Who do you think he is painting now?

13 자연스러운 글이 되도록 (A)~(D)를 바르게 나열하시오.

➡ _____

14 위 글의 빈칸 ⓐ와 ⓑ에 알맞은 말을 쓰시오.

ⓐ _____ ⓑ _____

01 다음 대화의 내용과 일치하도록 Mina의 일기를 완성하시오.

> Mina: I saw an interesting painting in an art book. Look at this.
> Jack: Wow, it looks like da Vinci's *Mona Lisa*.
> Mina: Actually, it's *Mona Lisa* by Fernando Botero. Which do you prefer?
> Jack: I prefer da Vinci's to Botero's. Da Vinci's *Mona Lisa* has an interesting smile. How about you?
> Mina: Well, I prefer Botero's to da Vinci's. His *Mona Lisa* is cute, and it looks modern.

> Mon, Oct 14th, 2019
> Today, I saw an interesting painting in an art book. It looked like da Vinci's *Mona Lisa*, but it was *Mona Lisa* by Fernando Botero. Between them, Jack preferred (A) _____ _____ to (B)_____, because of (C)_____ on da Vinci's *Mona Lisa*. However, I like (D)_____ much more because his *Mona Lisa* is cute and it looks modern.

02 다음 설문 조사표를 보고 대화를 완성하시오.

> Museum Survey   Name: Clark
> 01 What grade are you in?   ☐ 7th grade   ☑ 8th grade   ☐ 9th grade
> 02 How often do you go to a museum?
> ☐ once a month   ☑ twice a month   ☐ once a year   ☐ others: _____
> 03 What kind of museum do you like to go to?
> ☑ art museum   ☐ history museum   ☐ others: _____
> 04 How long do you usually spend time in the museum?
> ☐ about an hour   ☑ about two hours   ☐ about three hours   ☐ about four hours

> Q: I would like to know _____.
> A: I am in the 8th grade.
> Q: May I ask _____?
> A: I go to a museum twice a month.
> Q: I wonder _____.
> A: I like to go to the art museum.
> Q: Would you mind telling me _____?
> A: Certainly not. I usually spend about two hours in the museum.

단원별 모의고사

01 다음 문장에 공통으로 들어갈 말을 고르시오.

- Tom, _____ your teeth clean.
- I didn't need the _____ anymore.
- This _____ was worn out.

① produce
② stick
③ wax
④ flat
⑤ brush

02 다음 문장의 빈칸에 들어갈 말을 <보기>에서 골라 쓰시오.

┌──── 보기 ├────┐
tourist / wonder / direction / melt / despite
└─────────────┘

(1) _____ the butter over low heat.
(2) _____ the bad weather, we went on a picnic at a beach.
(3) A foreign _____ asked me to take her picture.
(4) Everyone in the photo is looking in the same _____ .
(5) I _____ why she did that.

[03~05] 다음 대화를 읽고 물음에 답하시오.

M: (A)Can you help me? (hand) I want to buy a guitar.
W: There are various kinds of guitars. (B)어떤 종류의 음악을 연주하고 싶으신가요?
M: I want to play pop songs.
W: Then you should get a classical guitar.
M: Okay, I will take a classical guitar.

03 위 대화의 밑줄 친 (A)를 주어진 단어를 사용하여 의미가 같도록 쓰시오.

➡ _____

04 위 대화의 밑줄 친 우리말 (B)를 영작하시오.

➡ _____

05 위 대화에서 나타난 두 사람의 관계로 적절한 것은?

① student – teacher
② tourist – guide
③ customer – clerk
④ patient – doctor
⑤ interviewee – interviewer

[06~07] 다음 대화를 읽고 물음에 답하시오.

Jason: Hi, we are planning a school festival, so we want to find out students' favorite types of performances. May I ask you (A)[a few / few] questions?
Emily: Sure.
Jason: What kind of performance do you like (B)[more / most]?
Emily: I like music performances best.
Jason: Okay. Then, which do you prefer, rock (C)[and / or] hip-hop?
Emily: I prefer rock to hip-hop.
Jason: Who's your favorite musician?
Emily: My favorite musician is TJ.
Jason: Great. Thank you for your answers.

06 위 대화의 (A)~(C)에 들어갈 말로 바르게 짝지어진 것은?

① a few – more – and
② a few – most – or
③ a few – most – and
④ few – most – or
⑤ few – more – and

07 위 대화를 읽고 대답할 수 <u>없는</u> 것은?

① What does Jason want Emily to do?
② What kind of performance does Emily like best?
③ What kind of music does Emily like?
④ Who is Emily's favorite musician?
⑤ Why does Emily like TJ most?

[08~09] 다음 대화를 읽고 물음에 답하시오.

Mina: I saw an (A)<u>interesting</u> painting in an art book. Look (B)<u>at</u> this.
Jack: Wow, it looks like da Vinci's *Mona Lisa*.
Mina: Actually, it's *Mona Lisa* by Fernando Botero. (C)<u>How do you prefer?</u>
Jack: I prefer da Vinci's (D)<u>to</u> Botero's. Da Vinci's *Mona Lisa* has an interesting smile. How (E)<u>about</u> you?
Mina: Well, I prefer Botero's to da Vinci's. His *Mona Lisa* is cute, and it looks modern.

08 위 대화의 밑줄 친 (A)~(E) 중 어색한 것을 찾아 바르게 고치시오.

➡ _____

09 위 대화의 내용과 일치하지 <u>않는</u> 것은?

① Mina는 미술책에서 페르난도 보테로의 '모나리자'를 보았다.
② Jack은 보테로의 '모나리자'보다 다빈치의 '모나리자'를 더 좋아한다.
③ Jack은 다빈치의 '모나리자'에 흥미로운 미소가 있다고 생각한다.
④ Mina는 다빈치의 '모나리자'보다는 보테로의 '모나리자'를 더 좋아한다.
⑤ Mina는 다빈치의 '모나리자'가 귀엽고 현대적이라고 생각한다.

[10~12] 다음 대화를 읽고 물음에 답하시오.

Susan: Brian, is your band going to play at the Teen Music Festival?
Brian: Yes, we're practicing (A)<u>almost</u> every day.
Susan: (B)<u>너희는 올해 어떤 종류의 음악을 연주하려고 하니?</u>
Brian: Rock music. We'll play songs from the (C)<u>ninety</u>.

10 위 대화의 밑줄 친 (A)와 같은 뜻의 단어를 쓰시오.

➡ _____

11 위 대화의 밑줄 친 (B)의 우리말을 영작하시오.

➡ _____

12 위 대화의 밑줄 친 (C)를 알맞은 형으로 고치시오.

➡ _____

13 다음 빈칸에 들어갈 말로 가장 적절한 것은?

Rapunzel's mom _____ in the tower.

① makes Rapunzel staying
② made herself to stay
③ made Rapunzel stayed
④ made herself staying
⑤ made Rapunzel stay

14 주어진 단어를 활용하여 다음 우리말을 7 단어로 이루어진 한 문장으로 쓰시오.

좋은 음악은 네가 기분이 더 좋아지도록 만들 것이다. (make / feel)

➡ _____

15 다음 빈칸에 들어갈 말로 적절하지 <u>않은</u> 것은?

> Do you know _____ ?

① who called you last night
② when the Morisons will arrive
③ where they are going to meet
④ how the word is spelled
⑤ what Tom made upset

16 간접의문문을 이용하여 다음 두 문장을 하나의 문장으로 쓰시오.

(1) Do you remember? Where did you find this bag?

➡ _____

(2) Can you tell me? Why does Kelly want to become a dancer?

➡ _____

17 다음 중 어법상 바르지 <u>않은</u> 것은?

① She made their dreams come true.
② Would you mind telling me who pushed you?
③ I want you to tell me when you will start the project.
④ Do you know who the lights turned off?
⑤ I had the man fix my chair.

[18~21] 다음 글을 읽고 물음에 답하시오.

Look at this painting first. The seaside landscape is so peaceful and beautiful, isn't it? The title of this painting is *Landscape with the Fall of Icarus*. So, can you see where Icarus is? Do you see two legs that are sticking out of the water near the ship? This is Icarus in the famous myth in Greece. In the myth, Icarus' father made wings for him with feathers and wax and told him to stay away ___(A)___ the sun. However, Icarus didn't listen. He flew too close to the sun. So, the wax melted and he fell into the water. Now, look at the entire painting again. Despite the tragedy of Icarus, people are going on with their everyday activities. Does the painting still look peaceful? What do you think the artist is trying to tell us?

18 다음 중 빈칸 (A)에 들어갈 말과 같은 말이 들어가는 것은?

① I want you to listen _____ my words.
② Do you take good care _____ your plants?
③ Many people suffer _____ headache.
④ Turn _____ the lights when you go out.
⑤ She will be satisfied _____ your presents.

19 When Icarus fell into the water, what were the other people in the painting doing? Answer in English with a full sentence.

➡ _____

20 다음 중 위 글의 내용과 일치하지 <u>않는</u> 것은?

① Icarus flew too close to the sun.
② Icarus' legs are sticking out of the ship.
③ Icarus' father wanted his son not to fly close to the sun.
④ Icarus' wings were made by his father.
⑤ People in the painting didn't care about the tragedy of Icarus.

21 위 글의 내용에 맞게 다음 대화의 빈칸을 채우시오.

> A: I would like to know _____.
>
> B: Oh, that's because he flew too close to the sun.

➡ _____

[22~25] 다음 글을 읽고 물음에 답하시오.

Now, let's move on to the next painting. Do you see the artist behind the large canvas? He is Diego Velázquez, and he actually painted this picture. _____(A)_____ Take a quick look. The young princess seems to be the main person ①because she is in the center of the painting. But the title of the painting is *The Maids of Honour*. Then, is the artist ②drawing the two women ③beside the princess? Take a close look. It will make you ④wonder about the painting more. Try to see which direction ⑤is the artist looking at. Can you see the king and the queen in the mirror in the background of the painting? _____(B)_____

22 (A)와 (B)에 공통으로 들어갈 말로 가장 적절한 것은?

① When do you think he drew this painting?
② Who do you imagine he is painting?
③ How do you guess he is painting?
④ Do you know where he is painting?
⑤ What made him paint?

23 위 글의 ①~⑤ 중 어법상 바르지 않은 것은?

①   ②   ③   ④   ⑤

24 다음과 같이 풀이되는 단어를 위 글에서 찾아 쓰시오.

> a piece of thick cloth used by artists for painting on

➡ _____

25 Which is NOT true about the artist who painted *The Maids of Honour*?

① His name is Diego Velázquez.
② He drew the young princess in the painting.
③ The king and the queen appear in the painting.
④ He drew himself behind the large canvas.
⑤ He drew the king and the queen in front of the princess.

Lesson 8

Changes Ahead

의사소통 기능

- 상대방의 의견 묻기
  A: What do you think about the present?
  B: I think it's really touching.

- 상대방의 의견과 같거나 다름을 표현하기
  A: I think it's great that many people see my posts.
  B: I'm (not) with you on that.

언어 형식

- so ~ that ... can't
  We were **so** tired **that** we **could not** go out.

- 현재[과거]분사
  The seafood **fried** rice was amazing.

Words & Expressions

Key Words

- **agree**[əɡríː] 동 동의하다
- **bakery**[béikəri] 명 빵집, 제과점
- **balance**[bǽləns] 동 균형을 잡다
- **counter**[káuntər] 명 계산대, 판매대
- **creative**[kriéitiv] 형 창의적인
- **debate**[dibéit] 명 토론, 논의
- **deliver**[dilívər] 동 전달하다, 배달하다
- **dependence**[dipéndəns] 명 의존, 의지
- **donate**[dóuneit] 동 기부하다
- **downtown**[dauntaun] 형 시내의
- **effect**[ifékt] 명 효과
- **elderly**[éldərli] 형 나이가 지긋한
- **experience**[ikspíəriəns] 명 경험
- **fry**[frai] 동 튀기다
- **guesthouse**[gesthaus] 명 (여행자 등의) 숙소, 여관
- **guidebook**[gaidbuk] 명 (여행) 안내서
- **handwritten**[hǽndrìtn] 형 손으로 쓴
- **hundred**[hʌ́ndrəd] 명 백, 100
- **importance**[impɔ́ːrtəns] 명 중요함
- **local**[lóukəl] 형 지역의, 현지의 명 주민, 현지인
- **machine**[məʃíːn] 명 기계
- **memory stick** 소형 메모리 카드
- **mixture**[míkstʃər] 명 혼합물, 혼합
- **moment**[móumənt] 명 순간
- **nearby**[nìərbái] 부 근처에
- **opinion**[əpínjən] 명 의견
- **post**[poust] 동 (웹 사이트에 정보, 사진을) 올리다
- **presence**[prézns] 명 존재
- **price**[prais] 명 가격
- **remain**[riméin] 동 남아 있다, 남다
- **scared**[skɛərd] 형 무서워하는, 겁먹은
- **side**[said] 명 면, 측면
- **smartphone** 스마트폰
- **sugar-free**[ʃúɡərfrìː] 형 무가당의
- **suggest**[səɡdʒést] 동 제안하다
- **surprise**[sərpráiz] 동 놀라게 하다
- **technology**[teknálədʒi] 명 (과학) 기술
- **thought**[θɔːt] 명 생각
- **trendy**[tréhdi] 형 최신 유행의
- **wisely**[wáizli] 부 현명하게

Key Expressions

- **be busy -ing** ~하느라 바쁘다
- **can't wait to** ~하기를 기대하다
- **even though** 비록 ~할지라도
- **fall asleep** 잠들다
- **get attention** 주목을 받다
- **get lost** 길을 잃다
- **keep -ing** 계속해서 ~하다
- **pay for** 대금을 지불하다
- **throw away** ~을 버리다
- **rely on** ~에 의존하다

Word Power

※ 서로 반대되는 뜻을 가진 어휘

- □ **agree** 동의하다 ↔ **disagree** 반대하다
- □ **heavy** 무거운 ↔ **right** 가벼운
- □ **balanced** 균형 잡힌 ↔ **imbalanced** 불균형의
- □ **near** 가까운 ↔ **far** 먼, 멀리 떨어진
- □ **important** 중요한 ↔ **unimportant** 중요하지 않은

- □ **dependence** 의존, 의지 ↔ **independence** 독립
- □ **wisely** 현명하게 ↔ **stupidly** 어리석게도
- □ **useful** 유용한 ↔ **useless** 쓸모없는
- □ **present** 있는, 출석한 ↔ **absent** 부재의, 결석한
- □ **succeed** 성공하다 ↔ **fail** 실패하다

English Dictionary

- □ **bakery** 빵집, 제과점
  - → a place where bread and cakes are made or sold
  - 빵과 케이크를 만들거나 파는 곳

- □ **balance** 균형을 잡다
  - → to be in a steady position without falling to one side
  - 한쪽으로 치우치지 않고 한결같은 자세를 취하다

- □ **downtown** 시내의, 도심지의
  - → relating to or located in the center of a town or city
  - 마을이나 도시의 중심에 위치하거나 연관된

- □ **experience** 경험
  - → knowledge or skill that you gain from doing a job or activity
  - 당신이 어떤 일이나 활동을 하며 얻은 지식 또는 기술

- □ **fry** 튀기다
  - → to cook something in hot oil
  - 뜨거운 기름으로 무언가를 요리하다

- □ **guesthouse** (여행자 등의) 숙소, 여관
  - → a private house where people can pay to stay and have meals
  - 사람들이 머무르고 식사하기 위해 돈을 지불할 수 있는 사적인 집

- □ **guidebook** (여행) 안내서
  - → a book of directions and information for travelers
  - 여행자들을 위한 지침 또는 정보에 대한 책

- □ **local** 지역의, 현지의
  - → relating to the particular area you live in
  - 당신이 살고 있는 특정 지역과 관련된

- □ **moment** 순간
  - → a particular point in time
  - 시간상의 특정 시점

- □ **post** (웹사이트에 정보, 사진을) 올리다
  - → to put a message or computer document on the Internet
  - 인터넷에 메시지 또는 컴퓨터 서류를 올리다

- □ **remain** 남아 있다, 남다
  - → to continue to exist or be left after others have gone
  - 다른 사람들이 가버린 후 계속 존재하거나 남겨져 있다

- □ **suggest** 제안하다
  - → to tell someone your ideas about what they should do, where they should go, etc.
  - 누군가에게 그들이 해야 하는 것, 그들이 가야 하는 곳 등에 대해 당신의 생각을 말하다

- □ **technology** (과학) 기술
  - → new machines, equipment, and ways of doing things that are based on modern scientific knowledge
  - 현대의 과학적 지식을 바탕으로 한 무언가를 하는 새로운 기계, 장비 방법

- □ **wisely** 현명하게
  - → in a way that show experience, knowledge, and good judgment
  - 경험, 지식, 그리고 좋은 판단을 보여주는 방식으로

서답형
01 다음 짝지어진 단어의 관계가 같도록 빈칸에 알맞은 말을 쓰시오.

> appear : disappear = agree : _____

02 다음 영영풀이가 가리키는 것을 고르시오.

> to tell someone your ideas about what they should do, where they should go, etc.

① remain ② suggest
③ donate ④ deliver
⑤ agree

중요
03 다음 중 밑줄 친 부분의 뜻풀이가 바르지 <u>않은</u> 것은?

① My sister is standing at the <u>counter</u>. 계산대
② James opened his new office near the <u>downtown</u>. 시내
③ I <u>agree</u>, but I'd like to listen to your reasons. 동의하다
④ How about offering your seat to an <u>elderly</u> person? 나이가 지긋한
⑤ <u>Pour</u> the <u>mixture</u> into the frying pan. 완료

서답형
04 다음 우리말에 맞게 빈칸에 알맞은 말을 쓰시오.

(1) 우리 부모님은 매년 돈을 기부하신다.
➡ My parents _____ money every year.
(2) 우리는 지역 신문에 우리의 차를 광고했다.
➡ We advertised our car in the _____ newspaper.
(3) 이 손을 쓸 필요가 없는 기기는 음성 명령으로 전화가 걸린다.
➡ This _____ device lets me make calls by voice commands.

서답형
05 다음 우리말에 맞게 주어진 단어를 사용하여 영작하시오.

(1) 우리는 환경의 중요성을 알아야만 한다.
(should, environment)
➡ _____
(2) 나는 일과 놀이 사이에 균형을 잡으려고 노력한다.
(try, work)
➡ _____
(3) 내 남동생은 시애틀 시내에서 일한다.
(Seattle, in)
➡ _____

06 다음 주어진 문장의 밑줄 친 post와 같은 의미로 쓰인 것은?

> Would you <u>post</u> these advertisements on Sam's website?

① He has held the <u>post</u> for three years.
② You can <u>post</u> your suggestions on the board.
③ Tom will send the documents to you by <u>post</u>.
④ Was there any <u>post</u> to me?
⑤ I'm sorry that I forgot to <u>post</u> the letter.

01 다음 짝지어진 단어의 관계가 같도록 빈칸에 알맞은 말을 쓰시오.

> balanced : imbalanced =
> important : _____

02 다음 문장의 빈칸에 들어갈 말을 〈보기〉에서 골라 쓰시오.

> ─┤ 보기 ├─
> get attention / throw away / rely on /
> fall asleep / even though

(1) Don't _____ _____ trash on the street.

(2) I used to _____ _____ my own judgement.

(3) Why do you want to _____ _____ from people?

(4) _____ _____ Emma is young, she is wise enough to handle the problems.

(5) I can't _____ _____ because of noise from the upper floor.

03 다음 우리말에 맞게 주어진 단어를 사용하여 영작하시오.

(1) 네 시간을 현명하게 써라. (spend)
➡ _____

(2) 우리는 이 사진들을 인터넷에 게시할 것이다. (will, these)
➡ _____

(3) 그 직업은 약간의 창의적인 상상력을 필요로 한다. (some, job)
➡ _____

04 다음 영영풀이가 가리키는 것을 쓰시오.

> a place where bread and cakes are made or sold

➡ _____

05 다음 주어진 우리말과 일치하도록 주어진 단어를 모두 배열하여 영작하시오.

(1) 몇몇 과학자들은 무가당 음료가 치아에 나쁘다고 말한다. (sugar-free / some / are / bad / your / for / teeth / say / scientists / drinks)
➡ _____
_____

(2) 그 어린 소녀는 소년의 존재에 수줍어했다. (little / presence / felt / boy's / the / shy / the / girl / in)
➡ _____

(3) 나의 반 친구들이 나를 위한 깜짝 파티를 열었다. (me / my / for / a / threw / party / classmates / surprise)
➡ _____

(4) 내 새 드레스에 대해 어떻게 생각하니? (about / my / new / do / dress / what / you / think)
➡ _____

(5) 그 여행은 내 인생에서 가장 흥미진진한 순간 중의 하나였다. (one / moments / the trip / my life / exciting / was / the most / in / of)
➡ _____
_____

Conversation

① 상대방의 의견 묻기

A What do you think about the present? 그 선물에 대해 어떻게 생각하니?

B I think it's really touching. 나는 그것이 정말 감동적이라고 생각해.

■ "What do you think about ~?"은 어떤 일이나 사건, 사물, 사람들에 대하여 상대방의 의견을 물을 때 사용한다. 예를 들어, 상대방에게 자신의 새로운 머리 스타일에 대한 의견을 물을 때는 "What do you think about my new hair style?"과 같이 말할 수 있다.

상대방의 의견 묻기

- How do you feel about my study plan? 내 공부 계획에 대해 어떻게 생각하세요?
- What would you like to say about smartphones? 스마트폰에 대해 무슨 말을 하고 싶으세요?
- What is your opinion on extreme sports? 극한 스포츠에 대해 어떻게 생각하세요?

핵심 Check

1. 다음 주어진 우리말과 일치하도록 빈칸을 완성하시오.

(1) **A:** _____ _____ _____ _____ _____ the School Rooftop Farm?
(학교 옥상 농장에 대해 어떻게 생각하니?)

B: I think it's cool. It can give us _____ _____ and make our school _____.
(나는 좋다고 생각해. 이것은 우리에게 신선한 야채들을 제공해 줄 수 있고 우리 학교를 더 푸르게 만들어 줄 수 있어.)

(2) **A:** How _____ _____ _____ _____ the Sharing Library?
(공유 도서관에 대해 어떻게 생각하니?)

B: _____ _____ _____ _____. It can be a great way to read various kinds of books _____ _____. (나는 좋다고 생각해. 이것은 무료로 다양한 종류의 책들을 읽을 수 있는 훌륭한 방식일 수 있어.)

(3) **A:** _____ your opinion on the Donation Walk? (기부 걷기에 대해 어떻게 생각하니?)

B: I think it's great. It can help people _____ _____ and make us _____, too. (나는 매우 좋다고 생각해. 어려움에 처한 사람들을 도울 수 있고 또한 우리를 건강하게 만들어 줄 수 있어.)

2 상대방의 의견과 같거나 다름을 표현하기

A I think it's great that many people see my posts.

나는 많은 사람들이 내 게시물들을 보는 것이 정말 좋다고 생각해.

B I'm (not) with you on that. 나도 그렇게 생각해. / 나는 그 점에 있어서 너랑 생각이 달라.

■ "I'm (not) with you on that."은 어떤 특정 이슈나 사안에 대하여 상대방의 의견에 동의하거나 이의를 나타낼 때 사용한다.

상대방의 의견에 동의를 나타낼 때

- I think so, too. 나도 그렇게 생각해.
- I believe so, too. 나도 그렇게 믿어.
- I agree with you. 당신의 의견에 동의해요.
- I see it that way, too. 나도 그렇게 생각해.

상대방의 의견에 이의를 나타낼 때

- I don't think so. 나는 그렇게 생각하지 않아.
- I don't believe so. 난 그렇게 믿지 않아.
- I don't agree with you. 저는 당신에게 동의하지 않아요.
- I disagree with you. 난 당신의 의견에 동의하지 않아요.

핵심 Check

2. 다음 주어진 우리말과 일치하도록 빈칸을 완성하시오.

(1) **A:** I think taking _____ classes is better than taking _____ classes.

(나는 온라인 수업들을 듣는 것이 오프라인 수업들을 듣는 것보다 더 낫다고 생각해.)

B: I'm _____ you _____ that. I can watch the lessons any time.

(나도 그렇게 생각해. 나는 언제든지 수업들을 볼 수가 있어.)

C: _____ _____ _____ _____. I can't focus well outside of the classroom. (나는 그렇게 생각하지 않아. 나는 교실 밖에서는 잘 집중할 수 없어.)

(2) **A:** I think watching movies at home is better than watching them at a _____.

(나는 집에서 영화를 보는 것이 극장에서 보는 것보다 더 낫다고 생각해.)

B: I'm _____ _____ _____ on that. I can't enjoy the large screen and the sound _____. (나는 그렇게 생각하지 않아. 나는 큰 화면과 음향 효과를 즐길 수 없어.)

Listen and Talk 1-B

Tony: Hey, Julie! ❶Have you heard about the *Quiz & Rice* game?

Julie: Yeah, isn't it the one that ❷donates rice when you get a right answer?

Tony: Yeah, ❸what do you think about the game?

Julie: I think ❹it's a creative game. ❺You can have fun and help out hungry people. Have you played ❹it yet?

Tony: No, but I'm going to ❻try ❹it out this weekend.

Tony: 저기, Julie! 너 '퀴즈와 쌀'이라는 게임에 대해 들어 봤니?
Julie: 응, 정답을 맞히면 쌀을 기부하는 게임 아니야?
Tony: 맞아. 넌 그 게임에 대해 어떻게 생각하니?
Julie: 난 그것이 창의적인 게임이라고 생각해. 재미있게 놀면서 배고픈 사람들을 도울 수 있잖아. 너 그거 이미 해 봤니?
Tony: 아니, 하지만 이번 주말에 해 보려고 해.

❶ 현재완료 시제를 사용하여 경험을 묻고 있다.

❷ donate: 기부하다

❸ 상대방의 의견을 묻는 표현으로 What's your opinion on that game?으로 바꾸어 쓸 수 있다.

❹ it은 모두 '퀴즈와 쌀'이라는 게임을 가리킨다.

❺ help out: ~을 돕다

❻ 이어동사의 목적어가 인칭대명사일 때는 목적어는 동사와 부사 사이에 위치한다.

Check(√) True or False

(1) People who play the *Quiz & Rice* game can donate money when they get the right answer.　T ☐ F ☐

(2) Tony is going to try out the *Quiz & Rice* game this weekend.　T ☐ F ☐

 Listen and Talk 2-B

Emma: Excuse me. ❶Can you help me ❷order with this machine?

Tom: Sure. First, ❸press the Hot Dog button and choose your hot dog and drink.

Emma: Okay. How do I ❹pay for my order?

Tom: Touch the Done button at the bottom and ❹pay for them.

Emma: Wow, it's so simple. This machine is much faster than ordering at the counter.

Tom: ❺I'm with you on that. It really saves a lot of time when there's a long line.

Emma: 실례합니다. 제가 이 기계로 주문하는 것을 좀 도와주실 수 있나요?
Tom: 물론이죠. 먼저 '핫도그' 버튼을 누르시고, 드시고 싶은 핫도그와 음료를 고르세요.
Emma: 알겠습니다. 주문한 것에 대한 지불은 어떻게 하나요?
Tom: 맨 아래에 있는 '완료' 버튼을 누르시고 그것들에 대해 지불하세요.
Emma: 와, 정말 간단하네요. 이 기계가 계산대에서 주문하는 것보다 훨씬 더 빨라요.
Tom: 저도 그렇게 생각해요. 줄이 길 때, 그것은 정말 많은 시간을 절약해 줘요.

❶ 도움을 요청하는 구문으로 'Can you tell me how to order with this machine?'으로 바꾸어 쓸 수 있다.

❷ order: 주문하다

❸ 동사로 시작하는 명령문으로 이어지는 동사 choose와 병렬 구조이다.

❹ pay for: 지불하다

❺ 상대방의 의견에 동의하는 표현으로 'I agree with you.'로 바꾸어 쓸 수 있다.

Check(√) True or False

(3) Emma used to order hot dogs with this machine.　T ☐ F ☐

(4) Tom disagrees with Emma's opinion about saving lots of time with the machine.　T ☐ F ☐

Listen and Talk 1 A-1

Jane: Look, Dad. This is Mom's birthday gift.

Dad: Oh, you're giving her a memory stick?

Jane: Yeah, I've made a family video clip for Mom and saved ❶it on this stick. ❷What do you think about the present?

Dad: I think ❸it's really ❹touching. She'll love ❸it.

❶ it은 a family video clip을 가리킨다.
❷ 상대방의 의견을 묻는 표현으로 'How do you feel about the present?'로 바꾸어 쓸 수 있다.
❸ it은 the present를 가리킨다.
❹ touching: 감동적인

Listen and Talk 1 A-2

Mike: Jenny, ❶what do you think about the new online comic *Scary Night*?

Jenny: I didn't like ❷it. I thought ❷it had too many sound ❸effects.

Mike: Really? I thought ❹they made the story more interesting.

Jenny: Not me. I couldn't focus because I was too ❺scared.

❶ 상대방의 의견을 묻는 표현으로 'What's your opinion on the new online comic *Scary Night*?'으로 바꾸어 물어볼 수 있다.
❷ it은 모두 the new online comic *Scary Night*을 가리킨다.
❸ effect: 효과
❹ they는 sound effects를 가리킨다.
❺ scared: 겁먹은

Listen and Talk 2 A-1

Jack: Sally, did you watch *Super Voice's* Top 10 finalists yesterday?

Sally: Yeah. They all sang much better than before.

Jack: Yeah, they did. I think this singing contest helps them ❶get closer to their dreams.

Sally: ❷I'm with you on that. I ❸can't wait to watch their next performances.

❶ help의 목적보어로 원형부정사가 이어졌다.
❷ 상대방의 의견에 동의하는 표현으로 'I think so, too.'라고 바꾸어 말할 수 있다.
❸ can't wait to: ∼하기를 기대하다

Listen & Talk 2 A-2

Steve: Hey, Lisa. I've got ❶over a hundred comments on my SNS ❷posts.

Lisa: Oh, I wouldn't feel ❸comfortable to ❹share my posts with so many people.

Steve: Really? I think it's great that a lot of people see my posts.

Lisa: ❺I'm not with you on that. I only want to share my posts with my close friends.

❶ over a hundred comments: 100개 이상의 댓글
❷ post: (명) 게시물, (동) 게시하다
❸ comfortable: 편안한
❹ share: 공유하다
❺ 상대방의 의견에 이의를 나타내는 표현으로 'I disagree with you.' 또는 'I don't think so, too.'로 바꾸어 말할 수 있다.

Communication

Sujin: Now, we will start the three-minute ❶debate. Today's first topic is fast fashion. What do you think about ❷it? Please, begin, James.

James: I think fast fashion is good. We can wear ❸trendy clothes at a cheaper price.

Wendy: I'm not with you on that. ❷It makes us spend too much money and ❹throw away clothes too often.

Sujin: It looks like the two of you have different opinions on the first topic. Now, let's ❺move on to the second topic.

❶ debate: 토론
❷ it은 fast fashion을 가리킨다.
❸ trendy: 최신의
❹ throw away: 버리다
❺ move on to: ∼로 넘어가다

● 다음 우리말과 일치하도록 빈칸에 알맞은 말을 쓰시오.

Listen & Talk 1 A-1

Jane: Look, Dad. This is Mom's birthday gift.

Dad: Oh, you're giving her a _____ _____?

Jane: Yeah, I've made a family video clip for Mom and _____ it on this stick. What do you _____ about the _____?

Dad: I think it's really _____. She'll love it.

Listen & Talk 1 A-2

Mike: Jenny, _____ _____ _____ _____ _____ the new online comic *Scary Night*?

Jenny: I didn't like it. I thought it had too many _____ _____.

Mike: Really? I thought they made the story more _____.

Jenny: Not me. I couldn't focus because I was too _____.

Listen & Talk 1 B

Tony: Hey, Julie! Have you _____ about the *Quiz & Rice* game?

Julie: Yeah, isn't it the one that _____ rice when you get a right answer?

Tony: Yeah, _____ do you think about the game?

Julie: I think it's a _____ game. You can _____ _____ and _____ _____ hungry people. Have you played it yet?

Tony: No, but I'm going to _____ it _____ this weekend.

Listen & Talk 2 A-1

Jack: Sally, did you watch *Super Voice's* Top 10 finalists yesterday?

Sally: Yeah. They all sang much _____ _____ _____.

Jack: Yeah, they did. I think this singing contest helps them _____ _____ to their dreams.

Sally: I'm _____ _____ _____ _____. I can't _____ _____ _____ their next performances.

Jane: 보세요, 아빠. 이거 엄마의 생신 선물이에요.

Dad: 오, 너는 엄마에게 막대 기억 장치 (메모리 스틱)를 준다는 거지?

Jane: 네, 엄마를 위한 가족 동영상을 만들어서, 그것을 이 막대 기억 장치에 저장했어요. 이 선물에 대해 어떻게 생각하세요?

Dad: 정말 감동적인 것 같구나. 엄마가 그걸 정말 좋아할 거 같아.

Mike: Jenny, 너는 새로운 온라인 만화 '무서운 밤'에 대해 어떻게 생각하니?

Jenny: 난 그거 별로였어. 거기에 음향 효과가 너무 많다고 생각했어.

Mike: 정말? 나는 그것이 이야기를 더욱 흥미진진하게 만들어 준다고 생각했는데.

Jenny: 난 아니야. 난 너무 무서워서 집중할 수가 없었거든.

Tony: 저기, Julie! 너 '퀴즈와 쌀'이라는 게임에 대해 들어봤어?

Julie: 응, 정답을 맞히면 쌀을 기부하는 게임 아니야?

Tony: 맞아, 넌 그 게임에 대해 어떻게 생각하니?

Julie: 난 그것이 창의적인 게임이라고 생각해. 재미있게 놀면서 배고픈 사람들을 도울 수 있잖아. 너 그거 이미 해 봤니?

Tony: 아니, 하지만 이번 주말에 해 보려고 해.

Jack: Sally, 너 어제 '슈퍼 보이스'의 상위 10위 결정전을 봤니?

Sally: 응. 그들은 모두 전보다 훨씬 더 노래를 잘 불렀어.

Jack: 맞아, 그랬어. 나는 이 노래 경연 대회가 그들이 자신의 꿈에 더 가까워지도록 도와준다고 생각해.

Sally: 나도 그 말에 동의해. 그들의 다음 공연을 보는 것이 너무 기다려진다.

Listen & Talk 2 A-2

Steve: Hey, Lisa. I've got over a hundred _____ on my SNS posts.

Lisa: Oh, I wouldn't feel _____ to share my posts with so many people.

Steve: Really? I think it's great _____ a lot of people see my _____.

Lisa: I'm _____ _____ _____ _____ _____. I only want to _____ my posts with my close friends.

Listen & Talk 2 B

Emma: Excuse me. Can you _____ me _____ with this machine?

Tom: Sure. First, _____ the Hot Dog button and choose your hot dog and drink.

Emma: Okay. _____ do I _____ _____ _____ _____?

Tom: Touch the Done button at the _____ and _____ for them.

Emma: Wow, it's so _____. This machine is much faster than ordering at the _____.

Tom: I'm _____ _____ on that. It really _____ a lot of _____ when there's a long _____.

Communication

Sujin: Now, we will start the three-minute _____. Today's first topic is fast fashion. _____ do you _____ about it? Please, begin, James.

James: I think fast fashion is good. We can wear _____ clothes at a cheaper _____.

Wendy: I'm not with you _____ _____. It makes us spend too much money and _____ _____ clothes too often.

Sujin: It looks like the two of you have different _____ on the first topic. Now, let's _____ _____ to the second topic.

Wrap Up 1

Alex: I've just finished _____ _____ _____ for Leon, Mom. _____ _____ _____ _____ _____ _____ _____?

Mom: Oh, the title "LOST CAT" in big letters at the top is easy to see.

Alex: Yeah, I did it to _____ _____. How about these photos _____ the title?

Mom: Hmm... the _____ on the _____ doesn't show Leon's face well.

Alex: Okay, I'll _____ the photo.

Mom: Oh, I _____ we can _____ Leon.

Steve: 저기, Lisa. 나 내 SNS 게시물들에 100개가 넘는 댓글을 받았어.

Lisa: 아, 나는 내 게시물들을 너무 많은 사람들과 공유하는 게 편하지 않을 거야.

Steve: 정말? 나는 많은 사람들이 내 게시물들을 보는 게 정말 좋다고 생각해.

Lisa: 나는 그 점에 있어서 너랑 생각이 달라. 나는 그냥 가까운 친구들하고만 내 게시물들을 공유하고 싶어.

Emma: 실례합니다. 제가 이 기계로 주문하는 것을 좀 도와주실 수 있나요?

Tom: 물론이죠. 먼저 '핫도그' 버튼을 누르고, 드시고 싶은 핫도그와 음료를 고르세요.

Emma: 알겠습니다. 주문한 것에 대한 지불을 어떻게 하나요?

Tom: 맨 아래에 있는 '완료' 버튼을 누르시고 그것들에 대해 지불하세요.

Emma: 와, 정말 간단하네요. 이 기계가 계산대에서 주문하는 것보다 훨씬 더 빨라요.

Tom: 저도 그렇게 생각해요. 줄이 길 때, 그것은 정말 많은 시간을 절약해 줘요.

Sujin: 자, 3분 토론을 시작하겠습니다. 오늘의 첫 번째 주제는 '패스트 패션'입니다. 여러분들은 그것에 대해 어떻게 생각하십니까? 시작해 주세요, James.

James: 저는 '패스트 패션'이 좋다고 생각합니다. 우리는 보다 저렴한 가격으로 최신 유행의 옷들을 입을 수 있습니다.

Wendy: 저는 그 의견에 동의하지 않습니다. 그것은 우리가 너무 많은 돈을 쓰고 너무 자주 옷을 버리게 합니다.

Sujin: 첫 번째 주제에 대해서는 두 사람이 다른 의견을 갖고 있는 것 같습니다. 이제 두 번째 주제로 넘어가 보도록 하겠습니다.

Alex: 엄마, Leon을 위한 인터넷 게시물 만드는 걸 막 끝냈어요. 이것에 대해 어떻게 생각하세요?

Mom: 오, 맨 위에 큰 글자로 된 제목 "LOST CAT"이 잘 보이는구나.

Alex: 네, 주목을 끌기 위해 그렇게 했어요. 제목 밑에 있는 이 사진들은 어때요?

Mom: 흠… 오른쪽에 있는 사진에서 Leon의 얼굴이 잘 보이지 않아.

Alex: 알겠어요, 그 사진을 바꿀게요.

Mom: 오, 우리가 Leon을 찾을 수 있으면 좋겠구나.

[01~02] 다음 대화를 읽고 물음에 답하시오.

> **Tony:** Hey, Julie! Have you ⓐheard about the *Quiz & Rice* game?
>
> **Julie:** Yeah, isn't it the one that ⓑdonates rice when you get a right answer?
>
> **Tony:** Yeah, what do you think about the game?
>
> **Julie:** I think it's a ⓒcreative game. You can have fun and ⓓhelp out hungry people. Have you played it yet?
>
> **Tony:** No, but I'm going to ⓔtry out it this weekend.

01 위 대화의 밑줄 친 ⓐ~ⓔ 중 어법상 어색한 것을 찾아 바르게 고치시오.

➡ _____

02 위 대화의 내용과 일치하지 <u>않는</u> 것은?

① '퀴즈와 쌀' 게임은 정답을 맞히면 쌀을 기부하는 게임이다.
② Julie는 '퀴즈와 쌀' 게임이 창의적인 게임이라고 생각한다.
③ '퀴즈와 쌀' 게임은 재미있게 놀면서 배고픈 사람들을 도울 수 있다.
④ Tony는 이번 주말에 '퀴즈와 쌀' 게임을 해보려고 한다.
⑤ Julie는 '퀴즈와 쌀' 게임을 하며 많은 쌀을 기부하였다.

[03~04] 다음 대화를 읽고 물음에 답하시오.

> **Jack:** Sally, did you watch *Super Voice's* Top 10 finalists yesterday?
>
> **Sally:** Yeah. They all sang much better than before.
>
> **Jack:** Yeah, they did. I think this singing contest helps them get closer to their dreams.
>
> **Sally:** I'm with you on that. (A)I can't wait to watch their next performances.

03 위 대화의 밑줄 친 (A)에서 나타난 Sally의 의도로 알맞은 것은?

① 일정 설명하기　② 기대감 표현하기
③ 긴장감 묘사하기　④ 불만 표현하기
⑤ 만족 표현하기

04 What does Jack think about this singing contest?

➡ _____

[01~03] 다음 대화를 읽고 물음에 답하시오.

> Jane: Look, Dad. This is Mom's birthday gift.
>
> Dad: Oh, you're giving her a memory stick?
>
> Jane: Yeah, I've made a family video clip for Mom and saved (A)it on this stick.
> _____ⓐ_____
>
> Dad: I think (B)it's really touching. She'll love it.

01 위 대화의 빈칸 ⓐ에 들어갈 말을 〈보기〉에 주어진 단어를 모두 배열하여 영작하시오.

> ┌ 보기 ┐
> about / do / the / think /
> present / you / what

➡ _____

02 위 대화의 (A)와 (B)의 it이 가리키는 것을 각각 쓰시오.

(A) _____ (B) _____

03 위 대화의 내용과 일치하지 <u>않는</u> 것은?

① Jane은 엄마의 생일 선물로 가족 동영상을 만들었다.
② Jane은 가족 동영상을 메모리 칩에 담았다.
③ 아빠는 Jane의 선물이 매우 감동적이라고 생각한다.
④ 아빠는 엄마가 Jane의 선물을 매우 좋아할 것이라고 생각한다.
⑤ 아빠는 Jane의 가족 동영상을 본 후 감동 받았다.

[04~05] 다음 대화를 읽고 물음에 답하시오.

> Tony: (A) Hey, Julie! Have you heard about the *Quiz & Rice* game?
>
> Julie: (B) Yeah, isn't it the one that donates rice when you get a right answer?
>
> Tony: (C) Yeah, what do you think about the game?
>
> Julie: (D) You can have fun and help out hungry people. Have you played it yet?
>
> Tony: (E) No, but I'm going to try it out this weekend.

04 위 대화의 (A)~(E) 중 주어진 문장이 들어가기에 알맞은 곳은?

> I think it's a creative game.

① (A)   ② (B)   ③ (C)   ④ (D)   ⑤ (E)

05 위 대화를 읽고 대답할 수 <u>없는</u> 것은?

① What is the *Quiz & Rice* game?
② When can you donate the rice, playing the *Quiz & Rice* game?
③ What is Julie's opinion about the *Quiz & Rice* game?
④ When will Tony try out the *Quiz & Rice* game?
⑤ How much rice is Tony going to donate to hungry people?

06 다음 대화가 자연스럽게 이어지도록 순서대로 배열하시오.

> (A) Really? I thought they made the story more interesting.
> (B) I didn't like it. I thought it had too many sound effects.
> (C) What do you think about the new online comic *Scary Night*?
> (D) Not me. I couldn't focus because I was too scared.

➡ _____

[07~09] 다음 대화를 읽고 물음에 답하시오.

Emma: Excuse me. ⓐCan you help me order with this machine?

Tom: Sure. First, press the Hot Dog button and choose your hot dog and drink.

Emma: Okay. How do I pay for my order?

Tom: Touch the Done button at the bottom and pay for them.

Emma: Wow, it's so simple. This machine is ____(A)____ faster than ordering at the counter.

Tom: I'm with you on that. It really saves a lot of time when there's a long line.

07 위 대화의 빈칸 (A)에 들어가기에 <u>어색한</u> 것은?

① much   ② far   ③ even

④ a lot   ⑤ very

08 위 대화의 밑줄 친 ⓐ와 같은 의미를 나타내는 것을 <u>모두</u> 고르시오.

① Do you need any help to order with this machine?

② Can you give me your hand to order with this machine?

③ Can I order with this machine?

④ How can I help you?

⑤ Would you mind helping me order with this machine?

서답형

09 다음 도표를 보고 빈칸을 완성하시오.

<How to order your food here>

Step	What to do
1	Press the Hot Dog button.
2	(A)
3	Touch the Done button.
4	(B)

(A) _____

(B) _____

[10~11] 다음 대화를 읽고 물음에 답하시오.

Alex: I've just finished (A)[to make / making] the posting for Leon, Mom. What do you think about it?

Mom: Oh, the title "LOST CAT" in big letters at the top (B)[is / are] easy to see.

Alex: Yeah, I did it to get (C)[attentive / attention]. How about these photos below the title?

Mom: Hmm... the one on the right doesn't show Leon's face well.

Alex: Okay, I'll change the photo.

Mom: Oh, I hope we can find Leon.

10 위 대화의 괄호 (A)~(C)에 들어갈 말로 알맞게 짝지어진 것은?

① to make – is – attentive

② to make – are – attention

③ making – is – attention

④ making – are – attentive

⑤ making – is – attentive

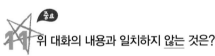

11 위 대화의 내용과 일치하지 <u>않는</u> 것은?

① Alex는 잃어버린 Leon을 찾기 위해 게시물을 만들었다.

② 게시물 맨 위에 큰 글자로 된 "LOST CAT"이 잘 보인다.

③ 게시물 오른쪽에 있는 사진에서 Leon의 얼굴이 잘 보이지 않는다.

④ Alex는 제목 밑에 있는 사진들을 모두 바꿀 것이다.

⑤ 엄마는 Leon을 찾기늘 희망한다.

[01~03] 다음 대화를 읽고 물음에 답하시오.

> Jane: Look, Dad. This is Mom's birthday gift.
> Dad: Oh, you're giving her a memory stick?
> Jane: Yeah, I've made a family video clip for Mom and saved it on this stick. What do you think about the present?
> Dad: I think it's really touching. She'll love it.

01 What is Jane talking about with her dad?

➡ _____

_____

02 What will Jane give her mom as a birthday gift?

➡ _____

_____

03 What did Jane save on the memory stick?

➡ _____

04 다음 대화의 내용과 일치하도록 Jenny의 일기를 완성하시오.

> Mike: Jenny, what do you think about the new online comic *Scary Night*?
> Jenny: I didn't like it. I thought it had too many sound effects.
> Mike: Really? I thought they made the story more interesting.
> Jenny: Not me. I couldn't focus because I was too scared.

↓

> Mon, Dec 2nd, 2019
> Today, I talked about the new online comic *Scary Night* with Mike. Actually, I didn't like it because of (A)_____ _____ _____ _____. I was so (B)_____ that I couldn't focus on the story. On the other hand, Mike told me that (C)_____ _____ _____ made the story more interesting.

[05~06] 다음 대화를 읽고 물음에 답하시오.

> Tony: Hey, Julie! Have you heard about the *Quiz & Rice* game?
> Julie: Yeah, isn't it the one that donates rice when you get a right answer?
> Tony: Yeah, (A)넌 그 게임에 대해 어떻게 생각하니?
> Julie: I think it's a creative game. You can have fun and help out hungry people. Have you played it yet?
> Tony: No, but I'm going to try it out this weekend.

05 위 대화의 밑줄 친 (A)의 우리말을 영작하시오.

➡ _____

06 위 대화의 내용과 일치하도록 빈칸을 완성하시오.

> <Try the *Quiz & Rice* game!>
> Get the (A)_____ answer and (B)_____ rice. Not only you can have fun but also (C)_____ _____ _____ _____.

교과서

Grammar

1 so ~ that ... can't

> • He is **so** tired **that** he **can't** finish his homework. 그는 너무 피곤해서 숙제를 끝낼 수 없다.
> • I am **so** sad **that** I **can't** stay here. 나는 너무 슬퍼서 이곳에 머물 수 없어.

■ 'so+형용사/부사+that+주어+can't+동사원형'은 '너무 ~해서 …할 수 없다'는 의미로, 형용사나 부사가 that절의 원인이 되고, that절은 그 결과를 이끈다. 'too+형용사/부사+to V'로 바꾸어 쓸 수 있다.

　• Jimmy is **so** weak **that** he **can't** lift it.
　　= Jimmy is **too** weak **to** lift it. Jimmy는 너무 약해서 그것을 들 수 없다.

　• She was **so** busy **that** she **couldn't** talk with us.
　　= She was **too** busy **to** talk with us. 그녀는 너무 바빠서 우리와 이야기할 수 없었다.

　• Patrick was **so** upset **that** he **couldn't** go to the party.
　　= Patrick was **too** upset **to** go to the party. Patrick은 너무 화가 나서 파티에 갈 수 없었다.

■ '아주 ~해서 …할 수 있다'는 의미를 나타낼 때에는 'so+형용사/부사+that+주어+can+동사원형'을 쓰고, 이는 '형용사/부사+enough+to부정사'와 같다.

　• The man is **so** kind **that** he can help you. 그 남자는 아주 친절해서 너를 도울 수 있어.
　　= The man is kind **enough to** help you.

　• Julie was **so** happy **that** she could invite anyone. Julie는 아주 행복해서 누구든 초대할 수 있었다.
　　= Julie was happy **enough to** invite anyone.

　• Amelia is **so** wise **that** she can give us advice. Amelia는 아주 현명해서 우리에게 조언을 해 줄 수 있다.
　　= Amelia is wise **enough to** give us advice.

핵심 Check

1. 다음 우리말과 같도록 빈칸에 알맞은 말을 쓰시오.

　(1) 너는 너무 어려서 일을 할 수 없어.

　　➡ You are ＿＿＿＿ ＿＿＿＿ ＿＿＿＿ you ＿＿＿＿ ＿＿＿＿.

　　➡ You are ＿＿＿＿ ＿＿＿＿ ＿＿＿＿ ＿＿＿＿.

　(2) 그는 너무 피곤해서 저녁을 먹을 수 없었다.

　　➡ He was ＿＿＿＿ ＿＿＿＿ ＿＿＿＿ he ＿＿＿＿ have dinner.

　　➡ He was ＿＿＿＿ ＿＿＿＿ ＿＿＿＿ have dinner.

② 명사를 수식하는 현재분사와 과거분사

> • Look at the **sleeping** baby. 잠자고 있는 아이를 보아라.
>
> • Is this a **baked** potato? 이것은 구워진 감자인가요?

■ 분사는 Ving 형태를 취하는 현재분사와, p.p. 형태를 취하는 과거분사로 나뉘며, 모두 명사를 수식하거나 설명하는 형용사 역할을 한다. 현재분사는 '~하는'이라는 의미로 주로 해석되어 능동이나 진행의 의미를 나타내고, 과거분사는 '~된'이라는 의미로 해석되어 수동이나 완료의 의미를 나타낸다.

  • I saw a **crying** baby. 나는 우는 아기를 봤어.

  • The **disappointing** result made me sad. 그 실망스러운 결과는 나를 슬프게 했다.

■ 분사가 단독으로 명사를 수식할 때에는 일반적으로 명사 앞에서 수식하지만, 분사가 다른 어구와 함께 명사를 수식할 때에는 명사 뒤에서 수식한다.

  • Do you see the children **playing** together? 함께 놀고 있는 아이들이 보이세요?

  • Kevin found a letter **written** on his note. Kevin은 자신의 노트 위에 쓰여진 편지를 발견했다.

  • People **living** in the town felt happy. 그 마을에 사는 사람들은 행복했다.

■ '사역동사(have, make)+목적어+과거분사', '지각동사+목적어+과거분사', 'help(또는 get)+목적어+과거분사'는 목적어와 목적보어의 관계가 수동인 경우 쓰인다.

  • Jason **has** the man **repair** his car. Jason은 그 남자가 자신의 차를 수리하게 한다.

  = Jason **has** his car **repaired** by the man. Jason은 그의 차가 그 남자에 의해 수리되게 한다.

■ 'Ving'로 형태가 같은 현재분사와 동명사의 차이를 구별하자. 현재분사는 '~하는', '~하는 중인'이라고 해석되고, 동명사는 '~하는 것'이라고 해석되거나 'V를 용도로 하는 명사'로 해석된다.

  • There is a **sleeping** baby. 잠자는 아기가 있다.

  • Did you find your **sleeping bag**? 너의 침낭을 찾았니? (잠자는 데 쓰이는 가방 – 침낭)

핵심 Check

2. 다음 주어진 동사를 어법에 맞게 빈칸에 쓰시오.

　(1) 노래 부르는 그 소녀를 보았니?

　　➡ Did you see the ＿＿＿＿ girl?

　(2) 나는 John에 의해 쓰여진 책을 읽었어.

　　➡ I read the book ＿＿＿＿ by John. (write)

　(3) 무언가를 쓰고 있는 저 소녀를 아니?

　　➡ Do you know the girl ＿＿＿＿ something? (write)

01 다음 문장에서 어법상 어색한 부분을 바르게 고치시오.

(1) The shirt is so big to wear.

_____ ➡ _____

(2) She was so old that she can't drive safely.

_____ ➡ _____

(3) I watched the excited bowling game on TV.

_____ ➡ _____

(4) Who is the boy thrown a ball?

_____ ➡ _____

02 주어진 단어를 어법에 맞게 빈칸에 쓰시오.

(1) He came too late _____ _____ part in the race. (take)

(2) I smelled something _____ in the kitchen. (burn)

(3) The rose is beautiful enough _____ _____ many people.
(attract)

(4) A girl _____ Jiho called you an hour ago. (name)

(5) The _____ robot is really expensive. (talk)

03 주어진 어구를 바르게 배열하여 다음 우리말을 영어로 쓰시오. 필요하다면 단어를 추가하시오.

(1) Olivia는 너무 추워서 잠들 수 없었다.
(asleep / Olivia / cold / felt / fall / that / she / couldn't)
➡ _____

(2) 그 집은 살기에 충분히 따뜻해.
(in / the house / warm / is / live / enough)
➡ _____

(3) 나는 떨어지는 낙엽을 보았어. (the / falling / I / leaves / looked at)
➡ _____

(4) 관객은 게임이나 연극을 지켜보는 사람이다.
(a game or a play / a spectator / watching / someone / is)
➡ _____

01 다음 중 빈칸에 들어갈 말로 가장 적절한 것은?

> Blair was too tired _____ the movie.

① watching   ② to watching
③ watched   ④ to watch
⑤ watch

02 다음 빈칸에 들어갈 말이 바르게 짝지어진 것은?

> • The girl _____ a book is my sister.
> • There was a _____ window.

① read – breaking   ② read – broken
③ reading – broken   ④ read – break
⑤ reading – break

03 다음 중 주어진 문장과 같은 의미의 문장으로 가장 적절한 것은?

> She is too young to get married.

① She is too young that she can't get married.
② She is so young that she can't get married.
③ She is so young that she can get married.
④ She is young enough to get married.
⑤ She is too young that she can get married.

서답형

04 다음 빈칸에 알맞은 말을 일곱 단어로 쓰시오.

> I can't drink the milk. It is too hot.
> = The milk _____.

05 다음 중 어법상 바르지 않은 것은?

> ①The injured man was ②taken to a hospital. But he ③arrived too ④late ⑤to getting proper treatment.

①   ②   ③   ④   ⑤

06 다음 중 주어진 문장의 밑줄 친 부분과 쓰임이 다른 하나는?

> Playing the violin is very fun.

① Are you interested in baking bread?
② Making a film was not that easy.
③ It was a very embarrassing moment.
④ Julie really enjoyed playing soccer.
⑤ His hobby is flying a drone.

07 다음 빈칸에 들어갈 말을 바르게 짝지은 것은?

> The wall was _____ high _____ over.

① too – to climbing
② too – that we can't climb
③ so – that we can't climb
④ so – to climb
⑤ so – that we couldn't climb

서답형

08 주어진 단어를 활용하여 다음 우리말을 지시에 맞게 영어로 쓰시오.

> 이 지갑은 너무 커서 내 주머니에 넣을 수 없었어. (wallet / pocket / big)

(1) to부정사를 사용하여 10단어로
➡ _____

(2) that절을 사용하여 13단어로
➡ _____
_____

09 다음 우리말을 영어로 바르게 표현한 것은?

> 그 목걸이는 너무 비싸서 살 수 없어.

① The necklace is expensive enough to buy.
② It is an expensive necklace to buy.
③ The necklace is too expensive to buying.
④ The necklace is so expensive that we can't buy it.
⑤ It is expensive to buy the necklace.

10 다음 중 문장의 전환이 바르지 <u>않은</u> 것은?

① 나는 그 상자를 들 만큼 충분히 힘이 세.
  → I am strong enough to lift the box.
② 그는 너무 뚱뚱해서 오랫동안 걸을 수 없었다.
  → He was too fat to walk for a long time.
③ 그녀는 어제 머리카락을 잘랐다.
  → She had her hair cut yesterday.
④ 우리는 우리의 사진이 찍히도록 했다.
  → We had our picture taking.
⑤ Jamie는 너무 아파서 학교에 갈 수 없었다.
  → Jamie was so sick that he couldn't go to school.

11 다음 중 어법상 <u>틀린</u> 문장은?

① I wonder who the man talking with her is.
② The weather was too hot to go out.
③ She is talented enough to be a singer.
④ They were so scared that they couldn't say a word.
⑤ The movie was so moved that we wanted to watch it again.

서답형
12 주어진 단어를 활용하여 다음 우리말을 일곱 단어로 이루어진 한 문장의 영어로 쓰시오.

> 우리는 낙엽 위를 걷는 것을 좋아합니다.
> (like / on / fall / leaves)

➡ _____

중요
13 다음 빈칸에 들어갈 말로 알맞은 것을 고르시오.

> A: Did you hear what Karen was saying?
> B: No, I was _____ what she was saying.

① close enough to hear
② too far away hear
③ so far away to hear
④ too far away to hear
⑤ too close to hear

14 다음 중 빈칸에 들어갈 말로 적절하지 <u>않은</u> 것은? (2개)

> We _____ the house painted.

① saw   ② wanted   ③ got
④ had   ⑤ appeared

서답형
15 다음 문장을 영어로 옮길 때 표시된 곳에 들어가는 단어를 차례대로 쓰시오.

> 그는 너무 게을러서 그 일을 할 수 없어.
> ➡ _____ _____ ★ _____
>   _____ _____ ★ _____
>   _____ _____

➡ _____

서답형
16 다음 빈칸에 알맞은 말을 쓰시오.

> 저 춤추는 소년은 누구니?
> ➡ Who is that _____ _____?

중요

17 다음 중 서로 의미가 같지 <u>않은</u> 문장은?

① Charlie was too sick to go on a picnic.

= Charlie was so sick that he couldn't go on a picnic.

② I had my room cleaned by my brother.

= I had my brother clean my room.

③ Dick is tall enough to play basketball well.

= Dick is so tall that he can play basketball well.

④ I can't play with you because I am very busy.

= I am too busy to play with you.

⑤ Jimmy was too nervous to say hello.

= Jimmy was so nervous that he could say hello.

18 다음 중 빈칸에 들어갈 말이 바르게 짝지어진 것은?

• I am _____ to attend the meeting. So I have to wait outside.

• Tom was _____ buy the car. But he didn't buy it.

① late enough – so rich that he can

② late enough – too rich to

③ too late – so rich that he could

④ too late – enough rich to

⑤ too late – so rich that he couldn't

서답형

19 주어진 단어를 활용하여 다음 문장을 영어로 쓰시오.

그는 그 날아오는 공을 쳤다.
(hit / fly)

➡ _____

서답형

20 다음 빈칸에 알맞은 말을 쓰시오.

그 잠자는 고양이는 너무 귀여워서 나는 그것에서 눈을 뗄 수 없다.

➡ The _____ cat is _____ _____ _____ _____ take my eyes off it.

21 다음 빈칸에 들어갈 말로 가장 적절한 것은?

나는 구운 생선을 좋아해.

➡ I like _____ fish.

① baking   ② bake   ③ bakes

④ baked   ⑤ being baked

중요

22 다음 중 어법상 바르지 <u>않은</u> 것은?

① I was too tired to go out.

② She looked at their smiling faces.

③ I was boring with the movie.

④ Mindy was so happy that she hugged everyone.

⑤ The scaring film was interesting.

서답형

23 주어진 단어를 바르게 배열하여 다음 우리말을 영어로 쓰시오. 세 개의 단어를 적절히 변형하시오.

그 놀라운 소식은 나를 흥분되게 만들었다.
(excite / surprise / make / news / me)

➡ The _____.

서답형

24 다음 빈칸에 들어갈 알맞은 말을 쓰시오.

The train was so fast that we couldn't catch it.

= The train was _____ _____ for us _____ _____.

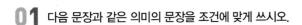

01 다음 문장과 같은 의미의 문장을 조건에 맞게 쓰시오.

> Nobody could move the table. It was too heavy.

(1) to부정사를 사용하여 한 문장으로

⇒ _____

(2) that절을 사용하여 한 문장으로

⇒ _____

_____

02 주어진 단어를 어법에 맞게 활용하여 다음 우리말을 다섯 단어로 이루어진 한 문장의 영어로 쓰시오.

> 그 부서진 의자를 내게 보여줘. (break)

⇒ _____

03 주어진 단어를 활용하여 다음 우리말을 영어로 쓰시오.

> 그녀의 가족은 너무 가난해서 그 집을 살 수 없었다.
> (so / they / buy)

⇒ _____

_____

04 다음 문장과 같은 의미가 되도록 빈칸에 알맞은 말을 쓰시오.

> My brother can't stay home alone because he is so young.
> = My brother is _____ _____ _____ _____ home alone.
> = My brother is _____ _____ _____ _____ _____ home alone.

05 다음 주어진 단어를 어법에 맞게 빈칸에 쓰시오.

> hit / excite / play / amaze / repair

(1) The girl _____ badminton is my sister.
(2) I have an _____ story to tell you.
(3) We had the car _____ by Potter and Parker.
(4) Jina is an _____ basketball player.
(5) Did you see the building _____ by a dump truck?

06 다음 두 문장의 해석을 쓰고 밑줄 친 부분의 어법상 차이를 설명하시오.

> (1) Jane likes sliced cheese.
> (2) Jane likes slicing cheese.

(1) 해석: _____
(2) 해석: _____
(3) 어법상 차이: _____

_____

_____

07 접속사 that을 활용하여 다음 두 문장을 하나의 문장으로 표현하시오.

> The room is very small. You can't invite all the friends to your party.

⇒ _____

_____

08 다음 빈칸에 알맞은 말을 쓰시오.

> 나는 숨겨진 보물을 찾으려는 중이야.
> ➡ I am trying to find _____ treasure.

09 접속사 that을 이용하여 다음 주어진 문장과 같은 의미의 문장을 쓰시오.

> The news is too good to be true.

➡ _____

10 주어진 단어를 바르게 배열하여 다음 우리말을 영어로 쓰시오.

> 산타클로스는 너무 자주 전화기를 확인해서 일에 집중할 수가 없다.
> (focus / Santa Claus / often / can't / on / his work / he / his phone / that / checks / so)

➡ _____
_____

11 다음 대화의 빈칸에 주어진 단어를 어법에 맞게 쓰시오.

> A: Maria makes me so _____(annoy) that I don't want her to be around me.
> B: But she is our guest. You should be nice to her during the _____(remain) days.

12 다음 우리말을 조건에 맞게 영어로 쓰시오.

> 나는 너무 피곤해서 눈을 뜰 수 없었다.

(1) to부정사를 사용하여 한 문장으로

➡ _____

(2) that절을 사용하여 한 문장으로

➡ _____

13 다음 문장과 같은 의미의 문장을 쓰시오.

(1) Daisy was too nervous to speak in front of many people.

➡ _____
_____

(2) Christopher is so tall that he can be a model.

➡ _____

(3) Jamie is too scared to be alone at home.

➡ _____

(4) Amelia was rich enough to throw a big party for her friend.

➡ _____
_____

14 주어진 단어를 활용하여 다음 우리말을 영어로 쓰시오.

> 그것은 신나는 게임처럼 들리는구나.
> (it / like / excite)

➡ _____

15 다음 문장과 같은 의미의 문장을 조건에 맞게 쓰시오.

> He can't sleep because he has much work.

(1) to부정사를 사용하여 한 문장으로

➡ _____

(2) that절을 사용하여 한 문장으로

➡ _____

My Tech-Free Trip Story

Last summer, my father suggested a surprising event: a family trip
without smartphones! He said, "I hate to see you sitting together and
only looking at your smartphones." My sister and I explained the need
for smartphones, but he kept saying that we could not fully enjoy
the trip with them. So we started a technology-free trip to a new city,
Barcelona, Spain.

Our first day was terrible. On the way to our guesthouse around Plaza
Reial, we got lost in downtown Barcelona. Dad was busy looking at
the map and asking for directions with a few Spanish words he got
from a tour guidebook. Even though our guesthouse was right next to
the Plaza, it took us about two hours to get there. We were so tired that
we could not go out for dinner. I went to bed but couldn't fall asleep
because I was worried about what would happen the next day.

After looking around Gaudi's Park Guell, we decided to have seafood
fried rice for lunch. However, we didn't know which restaurant to go
to.

suggest 제안하다
surprise 놀라게 하다
technology (과학) 기술
keep -ing 계속해서 ~하다
guesthouse (여행자 등의) 숙소, 여관
get lost 길을 잃다
downtown 시내의, 도심지의
be busy -ing ~하느라 바쁘다
guidebook (여행) 안내서
even though 비록 ~할지라도
fall asleep 잠들다
fry 튀기다

 확인문제

● 다음 문장이 본문의 내용과 일치하면 T, 일치하지 않으면 F를 쓰시오.

1 The writer's father proposed a trip without smartphones. ⬜

2 Not only the writer but also his sister explained the need for smartphones. ⬜

3 They got lost in Plaza Reial. ⬜

4 Dad didn't know Spanish words at all. ⬜

We needed help, so Mom went up to an elderly lady and tried to ask for directions to a popular seafood restaurant.

Luckily, she seemed to understand Mom's few Spanish words. She took us to a small local restaurant nearby. The seafood fried rice was amazing. I really wanted to take pictures of the food and post them on my blog. But without my phone, I just decided to enjoy the moment.

During the remaining days, we relied more and more on the locals. We were able to meet and talk with various people on the streets, in the bakeries, and in the parks. They were always kind enough to show us different sides of Barcelona with a smile. Also, our family talked a lot with each other. We spent much of our time together on the Spanish train, on the bus, and at the restaurants.

Our technology-free trip was a new and different experience. Before the trip, I was so dependent on my smartphone that I couldn't do anything without it. But now I see that I can enjoy the moment without it. From the experience, I have learned the importance of a balanced use of the smartphone. So, next time, would I travel without a smartphone? Probably not. But I will try to use it more wisely.

elderly 나이가 지긋한
nearby 근처에
local 현지의, 지역의; 주민
post (웹사이트에 정보나 사진을) 올리다
moment 순간
remain 남아 있다, 남다
rely on ~에 의존하다
various 다양한
bakery 빵집, 제과점
experience 경험
dependent 의존적인
importance 중요함
balance 균형을 잡다

📎 **확인문제**

● 다음 문장이 본문의 내용과 일치하면 T, 일치하지 않으면 F를 쓰시오.

1 They found a local seafood restaurant with a help from an elderly woman. ☐

2 The writer posted the pictures of the food on his blog. ☐

3 As the writer didn't have his smartphone, he didn't know how to enjoy the moment. ☐

4 As time goes by, they became independent from the locals. ☐

5 The writer learned how to use his smartphone wisely after the trip. ☐

● 우리말을 참고하여 빈칸에 알맞은 말을 쓰시오.

1 Last summer, my father _____ a _____ event: a family trip _____ smartphones!

2 He said, "I hate _____ _____ you _____ together and only _____ _____ your smartphones."

3 My sister and I _____ the need for smartphones, but he _____ _____ _____ we could not fully enjoy the trip with them.

4 So we _____ a technology-free trip _____ a new city, Barcelona, Spain.

5 Our first day was _____.

6 _____ _____ _____ _____ our guesthouse around Plaza Reial, we _____ _____ in downtown Barcelona.

7 Dad _____ _____ _____ at the map and _____ for directions _____ a few Spanish words he got _____ a tour guidebook.

8 _____ _____ our guesthouse was _____ _____ _____ the Plaza, _____ took us about two hours _____ _____ there.

9 We _____ _____ _____ _____ we could not go out for dinner.

10 I went to bed but couldn't _____ _____ because I was _____ about _____ _____ _____ the next day.

11 _____ looking around Gaudi's Park Guell, we decided _____ _____ seafood _____ rice for lunch.

12 However, we didn't know _____ _____ _____ _____ _____.

13 We needed help, so Mom _____ _____ _____ an elderly lady and _____ _____ _____ for directions to a popular seafood restaurant.

1 지난여름, 아빠가 깜짝 놀랄 만한 이벤트로 스마트폰 없는 가족 여행을 제안하셨다!

2 아빠는 "나는 우리 가족이 함께 앉아서 각자의 스마트폰만 보고 있는 걸 보는 게 참 싫구나."라고 말씀하셨다.

3 여동생과 내가 스마트폰이 필요하다고 설명했지만, 아빠는 스마트폰이 있으면 여행을 충분히 즐길 수 없을 거라고 계속해서 말씀하셨다.

4 그래서 우리는 새로운 도시인 스페인의 바르셀로나로 '첨단 과학 기술 없는 여행'을 시작했다.

5 우리의 첫째 날은 엉망이었다.

6 레이알 광장 주변에 있는 여행자 숙소로 가는 길에 우리는 바르셀로나 시내에서 길을 잃었다.

7 아빠는 지도를 보며 여행안내 책자에서 배운 스페인어 몇 마디로 길을 묻느라 분주하셨다.

8 우리의 숙소가 광장 바로 옆에 있었음에도 불구하고, 우리가 그곳에 도착하는 데는 거의 두 시간이 걸렸다.

9 우리는 너무 피곤해서 저녁을 먹으러 나갈 수가 없었다.

10 나는 잠자리에 들었지만 내일 무슨 일이 일어날지 걱정이 되어서 잠들 수가 없었다.

11 가우디가 지은 구엘 공원을 둘러본 후, 우리는 점심으로 해산물 볶음밥을 먹기로 했다.

12 그러나 우리는 어떤 식당으로 가야 할지 몰랐다.

13 우리는 도움이 필요해서, 엄마가 한 노부인에게 가서 인기 있는 해산물 식당으로 가는 길을 물어보려고 애쓰셨다.

14 Luckily, she seemed _____ _____ Mom's few Spanish _____.

15 She _____ _____ to a small local restaurant _____.

16 The seafood _____ _____ was _____.

17 I really wanted to _____ _____ _____ the food and post _____ on my blog.

18 But _____ my phone, I just decided _____ _____ the moment.

19 During the _____ days, we _____ more and more _____ the locals.

20 We _____ _____ _____ _____ and talk with various people on the streets, in the bakeries, and in the parks.

21 They were always _____ _____ _____ _____ us different sides of Barcelona with a smile.

22 Also, our family _____ a lot _____ each other.

23 We spent _____ _____ _____ _____ _____ on the Spanish train, on the bus, and at the restaurants.

24 Our technology-free trip was a _____ _____ _____ experience.

25 Before the trip, I was _____ _____ _____ my smartphone _____ I couldn't do anything without it.

26 But now I see _____ I can enjoy the moment _____ _____.

27 _____ the experience, I _____ _____ the importance of a _____ _____ of the smartphone.

28 So, next time, _____ _____ _____ without a smartphone?

29 Probably not. But I will _____ _____ _____ more wisely.

14 운이 좋게도 그녀는 몇 마디 안 되는 엄마의 스페인어를 이해하는 듯했다.

15 그녀는 우리를 근처에 있는 작은 현지 식당으로 데려다 주었다.

16 그 해산물 볶음밥은 놀랍도록 맛있었다.

17 나는 음식 사진을 찍어 그것을 내 블로그에 올리고 싶은 마음이 정말 간절했다.

18 그러나 스마트폰이 없었기 때문에 나는 그냥 그 순간을 즐기기로 했다.

19 (여행의) 남아 있는 날들 동안, 우리는 점점 더 현지 사람들에게 의존하게 되었다.

20 우리는 거리에서, 빵집에서, 공원에서 다양한 사람들을 만나 이야기할 수 있었다.

21 그들은 항상 웃으면서 너무나 친절히도 바르셀로나의 다양한 면을 우리에게 보여 주었다.

22 또한 우리 가족은 서로 많은 대화를 나누었다.

23 우리는 스페인의 기차에서, 버스에서, 그리고 식당에서 많은 시간을 함께 보냈다.

24 우리의 '첨단 과학 기술 없는' 여행은 새롭고 색다른 경험이었다.

25 여행 전에 나는 내 스마트폰에 너무 의존해서 그것 없이는 아무것도 할 수 없었다.

26 하지만 지금은 내가 스마트폰 없이도 그 순간을 즐길 수 있음을 알고 있다.

27 그 경험을 통해, 나는 스마트폰을 균형 있게 사용하는 것이 중요함을 배우게 되었다.

28 그러면, 다음번에 나는 스마트폰 없이 여행을 하게 될까?

29 아마도 그렇지는 않을 것이다. 하지만 나는 그것을 좀 더 현명하게 사용하기 위해 노력할 것이다.

● 우리말을 참고하여 본문을 영작하시오.

1 지난여름, 아빠가 깜짝 놀랄 만한 이벤트로 스마트폰 없는 가족 여행을 제안하셨다!

➡ _____

2 아빠는 "나는 우리 가족이 함께 앉아서 각자의 스마트폰만 보고 있는 걸 보는 게 참 싫구나."라고 말씀하셨다.

➡ _____

3 여동생과 내가 스마트폰이 필요하다고 설명했지만, 아빠는 스마트폰이 있으면 여행을 충분히 즐길 수 없을 거라고 계속해서 말씀하셨다.

➡ _____

4 그래서 우리는 새로운 도시인 스페인의 바르셀로나로 '첨단 과학 기술 없는 여행'을 시작했다.

➡ _____

5 우리의 첫째 날은 엉망이었다.

➡ _____

6 레이알 광장 주변에 있는 여행자 숙소로 가는 길에 우리는 바르셀로나 시내에서 길을 잃었다.

➡ _____

7 아빠는 지도를 보며 여행안내 책자에서 배운 스페인어 몇 마디로 길을 묻느라 분주하셨다.

➡ _____

8 우리의 숙소가 광장 바로 옆에 있었음에도 불구하고, 우리가 그곳에 도착하는 데는 거의 두 시간이 걸렸다.

➡ _____

9 우리는 너무 피곤해서 저녁을 먹으러 나갈 수가 없었다.

➡ _____

10 나는 잠자리에 들었지만 내일 무슨 일이 일어날지 걱정이 되어서 잠들 수가 없었다.

➡ _____

11 가우디가 지은 구엘 공원을 둘러본 후, 우리는 점심으로 해산물 볶음밥을 먹기로 했다.

➡ _____

12 그러나 우리는 어떤 식당으로 가야 할지 몰랐다.

➡ _____

13 우리는 도움이 필요해서, 엄마가 한 노부인에게 가서 인기 있는 해산물 식당으로 가는 길을 물어보려고 애쓰셨다.

➡ _____

14 운이 좋게도 그녀는 몇 마디 안 되는 엄마의 스페인어를 이해하는 듯했다.

➡ _____

15 그녀는 우리를 근처에 있는 작은 현지 식당으로 데려다 주었다.

➡ _____

16 그 해산물 볶음밥은 놀랍도록 맛있었다.

➡ _____

17 나는 음식 사진을 찍어 그것을 내 블로그에 올리고 싶은 마음이 정말 간절했다.

➡ _____

18 그러나 스마트폰이 없었기 때문에 나는 그냥 그 순간을 즐기기로 했다.

➡ _____

19 (여행의) 남아 있는 날들 동안, 우리는 점점 더 현지 사람들에게 의존하게 되었다.

➡ _____

20 우리는 거리에서, 빵집에서, 공원에서 다양한 사람들을 만나 이야기할 수 있었다.

➡ _____

21 그들은 항상 웃으면서 너무나 친절히도 바르셀로나의 다양한 면을 우리에게 보여 주었다.

➡ _____

22 또한 우리 가족은 서로 많은 대화를 나누었다.

➡ _____

23 우리는 스페인의 기차에서, 버스에서, 그리고 식당에서 많은 시간을 함께 보냈다.

➡ _____

24 우리의 '첨단 과학 기술 없는' 여행은 새롭고 색다른 경험이었다.

➡ _____

25 여행 전에 나는 내 스마트폰에 너무 의존해서 그것 없이는 아무것도 할 수 없었다.

➡ _____

26 하지만 지금은 내가 스마트폰 없이도 그 순간을 즐길 수 있음을 알고 있다.

➡ _____

27 그 경험을 통해, 나는 스마트폰을 균형 있게 사용하는 것이 중요함을 배우게 되었다.

➡ _____

28 그러면, 다음번에 나는 스마트폰 없이 여행을 하게 될까?

➡ _____

29 아마도 그렇지는 않을 것이다. 하지만 나는 그것을 좀 더 현명하게 사용하기 위해 노력할 것이다.

➡ _____

[01~04] 다음 글을 읽고 물음에 답하시오.

Last summer, my father suggested a surprising event: a family trip without smartphones! He said, "I hate to see you sitting together and only looking at your smartphones." My sister and I explained the need for smartphones, ___(A)___ he kept ___(B)___ that we could not fully enjoy the trip with them. So we started a technology-free trip to a new city, Barcelona, Spain.

01 다음 중 빈칸 (A)에 들어갈 말로 가장 적절한 것은?

① for   ② but   ③ while
④ if   ⑤ unless

서답형
02 동사 say를 어법에 맞게 빈칸 (B)에 쓰시오.

➡ _____

서답형
03 Where did they go for a family trip? Answer in English with five words.

➡ _____

 중요
04 다음 중 글의 내용과 일치하지 않는 것은?

① The writer's father suggested an event which was surprising.
② The writer's father wanted to have a family trip.
③ The writer explained the need for smartphones with his sister.
④ The writer's father wanted to enjoy the trip without smartphones.
⑤ The writer's father didn't want to see the writer and his sister sitting together.

[05~07] 다음 글을 읽고 물음에 답하시오.

Our first day was terrible. ①On the way to our guesthouse around Plaza Reial, we ②got lost in downtown Barcelona. Dad ③was busy looking at the map and asking for directions with a few Spanish words he got from a tour guidebook. Even though our guesthouse was ④right next to the Plaza, it took us about two hours to get there. We were so tired that we could not go out for dinner. I went to bed but ⑤couldn't fall asleep because I was worried about what would happen the next day.

05 다음 중 밑줄 친 ①~⑤의 의미로 알맞지 않은 것은?

① ~로 가는 길에
② 길을 잃었다
③ 지도를 보느라 바빴다
④ 광장 오른쪽에
⑤ 잠들 수 없었다

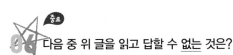 중요
06 다음 중 위 글을 읽고 답할 수 없는 것은?

① Where was the writer's guesthouse?
② Where did the writer's dad get a few Spanish words?
③ How long did it take to get to the guesthouse?
④ Why couldn't they go out for dinner?
⑤ How big was the Plaza Reial?

서답형
07 According to the writer, how was their first day of the trip? Answer in English with three words.

➡ _____

[08~10] 다음 글을 읽고 물음에 답하시오.

After looking around Gaudi's Park Guell, we decided to have seafood fried rice for lunch. ①   (A)   , we didn't know which restaurant to go to. ② We needed help, so Mom went up to an elderly lady and tried to ask for directions to a popular seafood restaurant. ③ She took us to a small local restaurant nearby. ④ The seafood fried rice was amazing. ⑤ I really wanted to take pictures of the food and post them on my blog. But without my phone, I just decided to enjoy the moment.

08 다음 중 빈칸 (A)에 들어갈 말로 적절한 것은?

① Therefore
② Moreover
③ However
④ Instead
⑤ For example

09 위 글의 ①~⑤ 중 주어진 문장이 들어가기에 가장 적절한 곳은?

Luckily, she seemed to understand Mom's few Spanish words.

①   ②   ③   ④   ⑤

10 다음 중 글의 내용을 잘못 이해한 사람은?

① Jason: They looked around the Gaudi's Park Guell before having lunch.
② Claire: They had to decide which restaurant to go to.
③ Brady: Thanks to the elderly lady, they could eat what they wanted to.
④ Amy: The writer made up his mind to enjoy the moment.
⑤ Frank: I am looking forward to seeing the writer's blog to see pictures of the food.

[11~13] 다음 글을 읽고 물음에 답하시오.

During the remaining days, we relied more and more on the locals. We were able to meet and talk with various people on the streets, in the bakeries, and in the parks. They were always kind enough to show us different sides of Barcelona with a smile. Also, our family talked a lot with each other. We spent much of our time together on the Spanish train, on the bus, and at the restaurants.

Our technology-free trip was a new and different experience. Before the trip, I was so dependent on my smartphone that I couldn't do anything without it. But now I see that I can enjoy the moment without it. From the experience, I have learned the importance of a balanced use of the smartphone. So, next time, would I travel without a smartphone? Probably not. But I will try to use it more wisely.

서답형

11 다음과 같이 풀이되는 말을 위 글에서 찾아 쓰시오.

to be in a steady position without falling to one side

서답형 ➡ _____

12 What did the writer learn from the trip?

➡ _____

13 다음 중 위 글의 내용과 일치하는 것은?

① They didn't depend on the locals.
② They were too busy to talk with various people.
③ They had a technology-free trip.
④ The writer wasn't interested in the smartphone before the trip.
⑤ The writer doesn't want to use his smartphone any more.

[14~18]. 다음 글을 읽고 물음에 답하시오.

Last summer, my father suggested a surprising event: a family trip without smartphones! He said, "I hate to see you sitting together and only (A)[look / looking] at your smartphones." My sister and I explained the need for smartphones, but he kept saying that we could not fully enjoy the trip with them. So we started a technology-free trip to a new city, Barcelona, Spain.

Our first day was terrible. On the way to our guesthouse around Plaza Reial, we (B)[lost / got lost] in downtown Barcelona. Dad was busy looking at the map and asking for directions with a few Spanish words he got from a tour guidebook. Even though our guesthouse was right next to the Plaza, it took us about two hours (C)[getting / to get] (D)there. We were so tired that we could not go out for dinner. I went to bed but couldn't fall asleep because I was worried about what would happen the next day.

14 다음 괄호 (A)~(C)에서 어법상 옳은 것을 바르게 짝지은 것은?

① look – lost – getting
② look – got lost – to get
③ look – lost – to get
④ looking – got lost – to get
⑤ looking – lost – getting

서답형

15 밑줄 친 (D)가 가리키는 것을 위 글에서 찾아 쓰시오.

➡ _____

서답형

16 What surprising event did the writer's dad suggest last summer? Answer in English.

➡ _____

17 다음 중 글쓴이가 여행 중 느낀 감정으로 가장 적절한 것은?

① excited and lively
② worried and lonely
③ anxious and tired
④ tired but pleased
⑤ embarrassed and upset

18 다음 중 위 글을 읽고 답할 수 없는 것은?

① When did the writer's father suggest the event?
② What did the writer's father hate to see?
③ Where did they have their dinner?
④ Why couldn't the writer fall asleep?
⑤ Where is Barcelona?

[19~21] 다음 글을 읽고 물음에 답하시오.

After looking around Gaudi's Park Guell, we decided to have seafood fried rice for lunch.
(A) The seafood fried rice was amazing. I really wanted to take pictures of the food and post them on my blog. But without my phone, I just decided to enjoy the moment.
(B) Luckily, she seemed to understand Mom's few Spanish words. She took us to a small local restaurant nearby.
(C) However, we didn't know which restaurant to go to. We needed help, so Mom went up to an elderly lady and tried to ask for directions to a popular seafood restaurant.

19 자연스러운 글이 되도록 (A)~(C)를 바르게 배열한 것은?

① (A) - (B) - (C) ② (B) - (A) - (C)
③ (B) - (C) - (A) ④ (C) - (A) - (B)
⑤ (C) - (B) - (A)

서답형

20 What did the writer want to do with a smartphone at the restaurant? Answer in English with a full sentence.

➡ _____

_____

21 다음 중 위 글의 내용과 일치하는 것은?

① The writer's family wanted to have seafood fried rice for dinner.

② The writer thought Gaudi's Park Guell was amazing.

③ The writer took many pictures of the food.

④ The writer went up to an elderly lady and asked for directions.

⑤ The elderly lady took the family to a seafood restaurant.

[22~26] 다음 글을 읽고 물음에 답하시오.

During the remaining days, we relied more and more on the locals. We were able to meet and talk with various people on the streets, in the bakeries, and in the parks. They were always kind enough to show us different sides of Barcelona with a smile. Also, our family talked a lot with each other. We spent much of our time together on the Spanish train, on the bus, and at the restaurants.

Our technology-free trip was a new and different experience. Before the trip, I was so dependent on my smartphone that I couldn't do anything without it. But now I see that I can enjoy the moment without it. From (A) the experience, I have learned the importance of a balanced use of the smartphone. So, next time, would I travel without a smartphone? Probably not. But I will try to use it more wisely.

서답형

22 밑줄 친 (A)가 의미하는 것을 위 글에서 찾아 쓰시오.

➡ _____

중요

23 다음 중 글쓴이가 여행 중 한 일이 <u>아닌</u> 것은?

① depending on the locals

② meeting a number of people

③ talking with many people in the parks

④ showing people different sides of Barcelona

⑤ spending much time with his family

24 다음 중 위 글에서 반의어를 찾을 수 <u>없는</u> 것은?

① independent   ② same

③ sensibly   ④ old

⑤ less

중요

25 Choose the one which is <u>NOT</u> true.

① The writer's family depended upon the local people.

② Thanks to the locals, the writer's family could see different sides of the city.

③ The writer used to be dependent on his smartphone.

④ The trip was an unfamiliar experience to the writer.

⑤ The writer hopes to travel without a smartphone someday.

서답형

26 What will the writer try to do when he goes on a trip next time? Answer in English with nine words.

➡ _____

[01~06] 다음 글을 읽고 물음에 답하시오.

Last summer, my father suggested a surprising event: a family trip without smartphones! He said, "I hate to see you sitting together and only looking at your smartphones." My sister and I explained the need for smartphones, but he kept saying that we could not fully enjoy the trip with them. So we started a technology-free trip to a new city, Barcelona, Spain.

Our first day was terrible. On the way to our guesthouse around Plaza Reial, we got lost in downtown Barcelona. Dad was busy looking at the map and asking for directions with a few Spanish words he got from a tour guidebook. Even though our guesthouse was right next to the Plaza, it took us about two hours to get there. (A)We were so tired that we could not go out for dinner. I went to bed but couldn't fall asleep because I was worried about what would happen the next day.

01 According to the passage, what is a technology-free trip? Answer in English.

➡ _____

02 What did the writer do when he heard his father's suggestion? Answer in English and use the word 'with.'

➡ _____

_____

03 to부정사를 활용하여 밑줄 친 (A)와 같은 의미의 문장을 쓰시오.

➡ _____

04 According to the passage, where did the writer's dad get a few Spanish words from? Answer in English, using 'them.'

➡ _____

05 다음은 가족 여행을 제안한 아버지의 말이다. 글의 내용에 맞게 빈칸에 알맞은 말을 쓰시오.

Dad: In order to fully _____ _____ _____ , we should travel _____ _____ .

06 Where was the family's guesthouse?

➡ _____

[07~10] 다음 글을 읽고 물음에 답하시오.

After looking around Gaudi's Park Guell, we decided to have seafood fried rice for lunch. However, we didn't know which restaurant to go to. We ①needed help, so Mom went up to an elderly lady and tried ②to ask for directions to a popular seafood restaurant. Luckily, she seemed ③to understand Mom's few Spanish words. She took us to a small local restaurant nearby. The seafood fried rice was ④amazing. I really wanted to take pictures of the food and post (A)them on my blog. But ⑤with my phone, I just decided to enjoy the moment.

07 Write the reason why the family needed help. Use the phrase 'It's because.'

➡ _____

_____

08 다음은 여행을 다녀온 글쓴이가 친구에게 한 말이다. 글의 내용에 맞게 빈칸에 알맞은 말을 쓰시오.

> We didn't know where we should go to have lunch, but an elderly lady was kind _____ _____ _____ us to a small local restaurant nearby.

09 밑줄 친 (A)가 가리키는 것을 위 글에서 찾아 쓰시오.

➡ _____

10 위 글의 ①~⑤ 중 글의 흐름에 맞지 <u>않은</u> 것을 골라 바르게 고치시오.

➡ _____

[11~15] 다음 글을 읽고 물음에 답하시오.

During the remaining days, we relied more and more on the locals. We were able to meet and talk with various people on the streets, in the bakeries, and in the parks. They were always kind enough to show us different sides of Barcelona with a smile. Also, our family talked a lot with each other. We spent much of our time together on the Spanish train, on the bus, and at the restaurants.

Our technology-free trip was a new and different experience. Before the trip, I was so dependent on my smartphone that I couldn't do anything without it. But now I see that I can enjoy the moment without it. From the experience, I have learned the importance of a __(A)__ use of the smartphone. So, next time, would I travel without a smartphone? (B)Probably not. But I will try to use it more wisely.

11 주어진 단어를 어법에 맞게 빈칸 (A)에 쓰시오.

> balance

➡ _____

12 위 글의 내용에 맞게 빈칸에 알맞은 말을 쓰시오.

> The family not only _____ _____ _____ with various people in Barcelona but also _____ _____ _____ with each other.

13 다음 대화의 빈칸에 알맞은 말을 쓰시오.

> A: Was the technology-free trip a familiar experience to the writer?
> B: _____, _____ _____. It _____ _____ _____ _____ _____ to the writer.

14 다음은 밑줄 친 (B)의 의미이다. 빈칸에 알맞은 말을 쓰시오.

> Probably I wouldn't _____ _____ _____ _____ next time, but I will try to use it more wisely.

15 According to the passage, who did the writer's family depend on during the remaining days? Answer in English with five words.

➡ _____

Read and Think

Technology-Free Trip to Barcelona
_{~이 없는}

Last summer, I had a new and different experience: a family trip without smartphones.

Troubles

- On the first day, we got lost <u>on our way</u> to the guesthouse.
  _{특정한 날 앞에 전치사 on} _{~로 가는 길에}
- I couldn't take pictures of the food and post <u>them</u> on my blog.
  _{pictures of the food}

Joys

- I enjoyed the places and the people <u>around</u> me.
  _{~의 주위에 있는}
- I talked a lot with my family <u>all the time</u> and everywhere.
  _{언제든, 항상}

Changes after the Trip

- My thoughts on <u>using</u> a smartphone
  _{동명사}

Before: I couldn't do anything without it.

Now: I understand the importance of a balanced use of it.

_{구문해설} · technology-free: 첨단 과학 기술이 없는 · get lost: 길을 잃다 · thought: 생각
· importance: 중요성 · balanced: 균형 잡힌

해석

바르셀로나로의 첨단 과학 기술 없는 여행
지난여름, 나는 새롭고 색다른 경험으로 '스마트폰 없는 가족 여행'을 갔다.

· 힘들었던 점
– 첫째 날, 우리는 숙소로 가는 도중에 길을 잃었다.
– 나는 음식 사진을 찍어 블로그에 올릴 수 없었다.

· 좋았던 점
– 나는 내 주위에 있는 장소들과 사람들을 즐겼다.
– 나는 가족들과 언제 어디서든 많은 대화를 나누었다.

· 여행 후 달라진 점
– 스마트폰 사용에 대한 나의 생각
이전: 나는 그것 없이는 아무것도 할 수 없었다.
지금: 나는 그것을 균형 있게 사용하는 것이 중요함을 이해한다.

Grammar in Real Life B

1. Wash one apple under <u>running</u> water and cut it into small pieces.
   _{현재분사(흐르는)}
2. Cook the cut apple pieces with brown sugar on low heat.
   _{과거분사(잘린 사과 조각)}
3. Add salt, milk, and a beaten egg <u>to make</u> the egg mixture.
   _{to부정사의 부사적 용법(~하기 위해서)}
4. Roll the bread out and put the <u>cooked</u> apple <u>filling</u> on it.
   _{과거분사(조리된)} _{(음식의) 소, 속}
5. Put the rolled bread in the egg mixture and <u>take it out</u> quickly. Then bake it for 3 minutes.
   _{take out it (X)}
6. Decorate a dish with the bread rolls and the remaining apple filling.

_{구문해설} · piece: 조각 · low: 낮은 · mixture: 혼합물 · roll out: 밀어 펴다 · decorate: 장식하다

1. 사과 한 개를 흐르는 물에 씻어 작은 조각으로 자르세요.
2. 잘라진 사과 조각들을 갈색 설탕과 함께 약한 불에서 조리세요.
3. 계란 혼합물을 만들기 위해 소금, 우유, 그리고 휘저은 계란을 더하세요.
4. 식빵을 얇게 밀어서 펴고 그 위에 조리된 사과 소를 올리세요.
5. 돌돌 말은 빵을 계란 혼합물에 넣었다가 빠르게 꺼내세요. 그러고 나서 그것을 3분간 구우세요.
6. 돌돌 말은 빵과 남아 있는 사과 소로 접시를 장식하세요.

영역별 핵심문제

Words & Expressions

01 다음 짝지어진 단어의 관계가 같도록 빈칸에 알맞은 말을 쓰시오.

> live : die = _____ : absent

02 다음 영영풀이가 가리키는 것을 쓰시오.

> to cook something in hot oil

➡ _____

03 다음 중 밑줄 친 부분의 뜻풀이가 바르지 <u>않은</u> 것은?

① Have you tried <u>sugar-free</u> juice? 무가당의
② I was <u>scared</u> after watching the horror movie. 겁먹은
③ I <u>suggest</u> to him that he should take a walk every day. 설득하다
④ The <u>debate</u> was highly emotional at times. 토론
⑤ I studied the beneficial <u>effects</u> of exercise. 효과

04 다음 우리말에 맞게 빈칸에 알맞은 말을 쓰시오.

(1) 나는 캐나다를 방문하는 것이 너무 기다려져!
➡ I can't _____ _____ visit Canada.

(2) 너는 너 자신을 믿고 계속 나아가야 한다.
➡ You should believe in yourself and _____ _____.

(3) 신용카드로 그것을 지불할 수 있을까요?
➡ Can I _____ _____ it with a credit card?

05 다음 문장에 공통으로 들어갈 말을 고르시오.

> • It is important for you to _____ various things and learn from failure.
> • We _____ these problems at some time in our lives.
> • To get the position as the manager, you should have skills and _____.

① deliver   ② donate   ③ post
④ experience ⑤ surprise

06 다음 문장의 빈칸에 들어갈 말을 〈보기〉에서 골라 쓰시오.

> ─┤ 보기 ├─
> importance / thought / side / effect / scared

(1) I want you to realize the _____ of working hard.
(2) I was surprised when I saw the serious _____ of the situation.
(3) I don't like acting without _____.
(4) My younger sister was _____ and began to cry.
(5) Weather has an _____ on our moods.

07 다음 주어진 문장의 밑줄 친 counter와 다른 의미로 쓰인 것은?

> Pay for this at the <u>counter</u>, please.

① Many people are lined up at the ticket <u>counter</u>.
② My father is standing behind the <u>counter</u>.
③ Would you put things up on the <u>counter</u>?
④ You can keep your valuables at the <u>counter</u>.
⑤ We read the <u>counter</u> proposal written from different point of view.

Conversation

[08~10] 다음 대화를 읽고 물음에 답하시오.

> Mike: Jenny, what do you think about the new online comic *Scary Night*?
>
> Jenny: I didn't like it. I thought it had too many sound effects.
>
> Mike: Really? I thought they made the story more interesting.
>
> Jenny: Not me. I couldn't focus because I was too (A)scared.

08 위 대화의 밑줄 친 (A)와 바꾸어 쓸 수 있는 것은?

① terrified
② terrific
③ brilliant
④ pleased
⑤ satisfied

09 What did Mike think about the sound effects in *Scary Night*?

➡ _____

10 How did Jenny feel when she was watching *Scary Night*?

➡ _____

[11~12] 다음 대화를 읽고 물음에 답하시오.

> Steve: Hey, Lisa. I've got over a hundred comments on my SNS posts.
>
> Lisa: Oh, I wouldn't feel comfortable to share my posts with so many people.
>
> Steve: Really? I think it's great that a lot of people see my posts.
>
> Lisa: (A)I'm not with you on that. I only want to share my posts with my close friends.

11 위 대화의 밑줄 친 (A)의 의도와 다른 것은?

① I don't think so.
② I don't believe so.
③ I don't agree with you.
④ I disagree with you.
⑤ I see it that way, too.

12 위 대화의 내용과 일치하지 않는 것은?

① Steve는 그의 SNS 게시물들에 100개가 넘는 댓글을 받았다.
② Lisa는 게시물 공유에 관해 Steve와 같은 의견을 갖고 있다.
③ Steve는 많은 사람들이 그의 게시물들을 보는 것을 좋아한다.
④ Lisa는 가까운 친구들하고만 그녀의 게시물을 공유하고 싶어 한다.
⑤ Lisa는 너무 많은 사람들과 게시물들을 공유하는 것이 편하지 않다.

[13~14] 다음 대화를 읽고 물음에 답하시오.

> Sujin: Now, we will start the three-minute debate. Today's first topic is fast fashion. (A) What do you think about it? Please, begin, James.
>
> James: (B) I think fast fashion is good. We can wear trendy clothes at a cheaper price.
>
> Wendy: (C) It makes us spend too much money and throw away clothes too often.
>
> Sujin: (D) It looks like the two of you have different opinions on the first topic. (E) Now, let's move on to the second topic.

13 위 대화의 (A)~(E) 중 주어진 문장이 들어가기에 알맞은 곳은?

> I'm not with you on that.

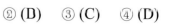 ① (A) ② (B) ③ (C) ④ (D) ⑤ (E)

14 위 대화를 읽고 대답할 수 <u>없는</u> 것은?

① What are students doing now?

② What is the first topic of the debate?

③ What does James think about the fast fashion?

④ Why doesn't Wendy like the fast fashion?

⑤ What did Wendy throw away too often?

Grammar

15 다음 중 빈칸에 들어갈 말로 가장 적절한 것은?

> My dad had his shoes _____.

① to shine   ② shining

③ shined   ④ to shining

⑤ shine

16 다음 중 빈칸에 들어갈 말로 적절하지 <u>않은</u> 것은?

> You look so _____ that I can't help looking at you.

① lovely   ② nice   ③ pretty

④ beautifully   ⑤ cool

17 다음 빈칸에 들어갈 말이 바르게 짝지어진 것은?

> • I am too _____ to find any mistakes in your essay.
> • The shop offers _____ prices.

① careful – discounting

② careless – discounting

③ careless – discounted

④ carelessly – discount

⑤ carelessly – discounted

18 주어진 단어를 활용하여 다음 우리말을 11 단어로 이루어진 한 문장의 영어로 쓰시오.

> 나의 방은 너무 더러워서 내 친구들을 초대할 수 없어. (so / invite)

➡ _____

19 다음 중 어법상 바르지 <u>않은</u> 것은?

① He had his wallet stolen.

② Jane was so mad that he couldn't say a word.

③ The computer game looked boring.

④ You are not kind enough taking care of my plants.

⑤ Tom is too talkative to listen to his friends.

20 다음 중 우리말을 영어로 바르게 옮기지 <u>않은</u> 것은?

① 나는 너무 바빠서 지금 당장 너와 이야기할 수 없어.

= I am too busy to talk with you right now.

② Katherine은 너무 배불러서 음식을 더 먹을 수 없었다.

= Katherine was so full that she couldn't eat more food.

③ 땅 위에 떨어진 오렌지들을 봐!

= Look at the oranges fallen on the ground!

④ 나는 혼자 여행을 할 만큼 충분히 건강해.

= I am healthy enough to take a trip alone.

⑤ 그녀는 그 결과에 만족하는 것처럼 보였어.

= She looked satisfying with the result.

21 다음 중 주어진 문장의 밑줄 친 부분과 쓰임이 다른 하나는?

> Did you see the <u>swimming</u> pool?

① Kevin was not interested in <u>playing</u> soccer.
② My hobby is <u>taking</u> pictures.
③ The boys are <u>riding</u> bikes together.
④ They enjoyed <u>cooking</u> with her.
⑤ Dana focused on <u>studying</u> English.

22 다음 빈칸에 들어갈 말로 가장 적절한 것은?

> I am _____ make a decision by myself.

① too old that
② so old to
③ enough old to
④ old enough
⑤ so old that I can

23 다음 중 빈칸에 들어갈 단어 use의 형태가 다른 하나는?

① I found her _____ my pen.
② The boy _____ your computer is my son.
③ David is _____ the copy machine.
④ They bought a _____ car.
⑤ She isn't good at _____ the tool.

24 주어진 단어를 활용하여 다음 우리말을 영어로 쓰시오.

> 나는 너무 화가 나서 그 소식을 들을 수 없었어.
> (too / upset)

➡ _____

[25~29] 다음 글을 읽고 물음에 답하시오.

Last summer, my father suggested ① <u>a surprising event</u>: a family trip without smartphones! He said, "I hate to see you sitting together and ②<u>only looking at</u> your smartphones." My sister and I explained the need for smartphones, but he kept saying that we could not fully enjoy the trip ③<u>without them</u>. So we started a technology-free trip to a new city, Barcelona, Spain.

Our first day was terrible. On the way to our guesthouse around Plaza Reial, we ④<u>got lost</u> in downtown Barcelona. Dad was busy looking at the map and asking for directions with a few Spanish words he got from a tour guidebook. __(A)__ our guesthouse was right next to the Plaza, it (B)<u>took</u> us about two hours to get there. We were so tired that we ⑤<u>could not go out</u> for dinner. I went to bed but couldn't fall asleep because I was worried about what would happen the next day.

25 다음 중 빈칸 (A)에 들어갈 말로 가장 적절한 것은?

① Unless ② Because ③ Although
④ When ⑤ If

26 위 글의 밑줄 친 ①~⑤ 중 글의 흐름상 적절하지 <u>않은</u> 것은?

① ② ③ ④ ⑤

27 다음 중 밑줄 친 (B)와 같은 의미로 쓰인 것은?

① A girl took us to our room.

② Take this to the hotel for me.

③ Grace took the grey jacket.

④ The journey took half an hour.

⑤ He took a bus to get there.

28 위 글의 내용에 맞게 다음 질문의 답변을 완성하시오.

Q: Why did the writer's dad suggest a family trip without smartphones?

➡ Because _____

_____.

29 다음 중 위 글의 내용과 일치하지 <u>않는</u> 것은?

① Barcelona was a new city to the family.

② The guesthouse was next to Plaza Reial.

③ The writer's father spoke a few Spanish words to ask for directions.

④ The writer was busy looking at the map.

⑤ The writer was too worried to fall asleep.

[30~32] 다음 글을 읽고 물음에 답하시오.

After looking around Gaudi's Park Guell, we decided to have seafood ①fried rice for lunch. However, we didn't know ②which restaurant to go to. We needed help, so Mom went up to an elderly lady and tried to ask for directions to a popular seafood restaurant. Luckily, she seemed ③to understand Mom's few Spanish words. She took us to a small local restaurant nearby. The seafood fried rice was ④amazing. I really wanted to take pictures of the food and ⑤posted them on my blog. But without my phone, I just decided to enjoy the moment.

30 위 글의 ①~⑤ 중 어법상 바르지 <u>않은</u> 것을 골라 바르게 고쳐 쓰시오.

➡ _____

31 다음 중 위 글의 내용과 일치하지 <u>않는</u> 것은?

After we looked around Gaudi's Park Guell, we ①wanted to eat seafood fried rice. Because ②Mom could speak a few Spanish words, she asked ③an elderly lady where we should go. She took us ④to a local restaurant far from the park. Even though the food was amazing, I ⑤couldn't take pictures of it.

①   ②   ③   ④   ⑤

32 다음 중 위 글을 읽고 답할 수 <u>없는</u> 것은?

① What did they decide to do after looking around Gaudi's Park Guell?

② How did they get to the restaurant?

③ Why did the writer's mom go up to the elderly lady?

④ How was the seafood fried rice at the restaurant?

⑤ How popular was the seafood restaurant?

[01~02] 다음 대화를 읽고 물음에 답하시오.

Mike: Jenny, what do you think about the new online comic *Scary Night*?

Jenny: I didn't like (A)it. I thought it had too many sound effects.

Mike: Really? I thought (B)they made the story more interesting.

Jenny: Not me. I couldn't focus because I was too scared.

출제율 90%

01 위 대화의 (A)it과 (B)they가 가리키는 것을 각각 찾아 쓰시오.

(A) _____

(B) _____

출제율 95%

02 위 대화의 내용과 일치하지 <u>않는</u> 것은?

① *Scary Night* is a new online comic.

② Jenny didn't like *Scary Night* because of lots of sound effects.

③ Mike was with Jenny on *Scary Night*.

④ Mike liked *Scary Night* because many sound effects made the story more interesting.

⑤ Jenny was so scared that she couldn't focus on *Scary Night*.

[03~05] 다음 대화를 읽고 물음에 답하시오.

Tony: Hey, Julie! Have you heard about the *Quiz & Rice* game?

Julie: Yeah, isn't it the one that donates rice when you get a right answer?

Tony: Yeah, what do you think about the game?

Julie: I think it's a creative game. You can have fun and help out hungry people. Have you played it yet?

Tony: No, but I'm going to try it out this weekend.

출제율 90%

03 What can you donate when you get the right answer in the *Quiz & Rice* game?

➡ _____

출제율 85%

04 What does Julie think about the *Quiz & Rice* game?

➡ _____

출제율 95%

05 When will Tony try out the *Quiz & Rice* game?

➡ _____

[06~07] 다음 대화를 읽고 물음에 답하시오.

Jack: Sally, did you watch *Super Voice's* Top 10 finalists yesterday?

Sally: Yeah. They all sang much better than before.

Jack: Yeah, they did. I think this singing contest helps them get closer to their dreams.

Sally: _____ (A) _____ (B)I can't wait to watch their next performances.

출제율 100%

06 위 대화의 빈칸 (A)에 들어갈 말로 나머지와 의도가 <u>다른</u> 것은?

① I'm with you on that.

② I think so, too.

③ I see it that way, too.

④ I agree with you.

⑤ I disagree with you.

07 위 대화의 밑줄 친 (B)와 의미가 같도록 forward를 사용하여 다시 쓰시오.

➡ _____

_____

[08~10] 다음 대화를 읽고 물음에 답하시오.

Sujin: Now, we will start the three-minute debate. Today's first topic is fast fashion. What do you think about it? Please, begin, James.

James: I think fast fashion is good. We can wear trendy clothes at a cheaper price.

Wendy: I'm not with you on that. It makes us spend too much money and throw away clothes too often.

Sujin: It looks like the two of you have different opinions on the first topic. Now, let's move on to the second topic.

출제율 90%

08 What are students debating now?

➡ _____

출제율 95%

09 Why does James think that fast fashion is good?

➡ _____

_____

출제율 90%

10 What does Wendy think about fast fashion?

➡ _____

_____

출제율 100%

11 다음 중 빈칸에 들어갈 말이 바르게 짝지어진 것은?

- Claire was _____ worried to do her homework.
- The stick is light _____ to float on water.
- Thank you for your _____ gift.

① so – that – amazed
② so – that – amaze
③ so – enough – amazing
④ too – enough – amazing
⑤ too – enough – amazed

출제율 95%

12 다음 중 어법상 바르지 <u>않은</u> 것은?

David runs ①too ②fast ③that no one ④can catch ⑤him.

①　　②　　③　　④　　⑤

출제율 90%

13 주어진 단어를 바르게 배열하여 다음 우리말을 영어로 쓰시오. 필요하다면 단어의 형태를 변형하시오.

그 걷고 있는 로봇은 내가 가장 좋아하는 장난감이야.

(toy / walk / favorite / robot / the / my / is)

➡ _____

출제율 95%

14 다음 중 밑줄 친 부분의 쓰임이 같은 것끼리 바르게 묶은 것은?

> ⓐ Can you see the girl <u>wearing</u> a cap?
> ⓑ We are curious about <u>making</u> the cookies.
> ⓒ Are you still doing the <u>boring</u> game?
> ⓓ George's hobby is <u>playing</u> chess.

① ⓐ-ⓓ, ⓑ-ⓒ   ② ⓐ-ⓒ, ⓑ-ⓓ
③ ⓐ-ⓑ-ⓒ, ⓓ   ④ ⓑ-ⓒ-ⓓ, ⓐ
⑤ ⓐ-ⓑ-ⓓ, ⓒ

출제율 100%

15 다음 중 어법상 바르지 <u>않은</u> 것은?

① The news made him disappointed.
② I am too angry to forgive you right now.
③ Mike was so full that he couldn't eat the dessert.
④ Chris kept the door closed.
⑤ We had the tree plant in the garden.

출제율 95%

16 다음 빈칸에 알맞은 말을 다섯 단어로 쓰시오.

> Molly was too busy to take care of her children.
> = Molly was _____ take care of her children.

출제율 85%

17 동사 write를 어법에 맞게 빈칸에 쓰시오.

> • My cousin is the boy _____ something on his note.
> • Did you see a letter _____ in Korean?

[18~21] 다음 글을 읽고 물음에 답하시오.

During the remaining days, we relied more and more on the locals.
(A) Also, our family talked a lot with each other.
(B) They were always kind enough to show us different sides of Barcelona with a smile.
(C) We were able to meet and talk with various people on the streets, in the bakeries, and in the parks.
We spent much of our time together on the Spanish train, on the bus, and at the restaurants.

Our technology-free trip was a new and different experience. Before the trip, I was so dependent on my smartphone that I couldn't do anything without it. But now I see that I can enjoy the moment without it. From the experience, I have learned the importance of a balanced use of the smartphone. So, next time, would I travel without a smartphone? Probably not. But I will try to use it more wisely.

출제율 90%

18 자연스러운 글이 되도록 (A)~(C)를 바르게 배열하시오.

➡ _____

출제율 95%

19 다음 중 위 글의 내용과 일치하는 것은?

① The family took the trip without relying on the locals.
② The writer was independent enough to do something without his smartphone before the trip.
③ The writer understands that he can enjoy moments without a smartphone.
④ The writer looks forward to going on another trip without his smartphone.
⑤ There's nothing that the writer learned from the trip

20 출제율 90%

According to the passage, where did the family meet and talk with the locals? Answer in English with a full sentence.

➡ _____

_____

21 출제율 100%

다음 중 위 글을 읽고 찾아볼 수 없는 것은?

① the writer's family talking with each other
② the writer's family getting on the bus
③ the writer's family talking with the locals at the restaurant
④ the writer's family meeting people in the parks
⑤ the locals showing the family different sides of Barcelona

[22~25] 다음 글을 읽고 물음에 답하시오.

　Wash one apple under ①running water and cut it into small pieces. Cook the ②cutting apple pieces with brown sugar on low heat. Add salt, milk, and a beaten egg to make the egg mixture. Roll the bread out and put the ③cooked apple filling on it. Put the ④rolled bread in the egg mixture and take it out quickly. Then bake it __(A)__ 3 minutes. Decorate a dish with the bread rolls and the ⑤remaining apple filling.

22 출제율 90%

다음 중 빈칸 (A)에 들어갈 말로 가장 적절한 것은?

① at　　　② in　　　③ for
④ about　　⑤ to

23 출제율 95%

위 글의 밑줄 친 ①~⑤ 중 어법상 바르지 않은 것은?

①　　　②　　　③　　　④　　　⑤

24 출제율 100%

다음 중 위 글의 내용을 잘못 이해한 사람은?

① 은주: 가장 먼저 사과를 씻어야 해.
② 준휘: 계란 혼합물을 만들려면 소금, 우유, 그리고 계란이 필요하네.
③ 재영: 식빵을 얇게 밀어서 펴야 해.
④ 혜준: 식빵 위에 올린 사과 소는 조리할 필요가 없어.
⑤ 서현: 남아 있는 사과 소로 접시를 장식해야 해.

25 출제율 95%

다음 중 위 글을 읽고 답할 수 없는 것은?

① What did we have to do with the apple after washing it?
② What sugar do we have to use?
③ What do we have to prepare to make the dish?
④ What do we decorate the dish with?
⑤ How long do we have to cook the cut apple pieces?

[01~03] 다음 대화를 읽고 물음에 답하시오.

Steve: Hey, Lisa. I've got over a hundred comments on my SNS posts.

Lisa: Oh, I wouldn't feel comfortable to share my posts with so many people.

Steve: Really? I think it's great that a lot of people see my posts.

Lisa: _____(A)_____ I only want to share my posts with my close friends.

01 위 대화의 빈칸 (A)에 들어갈 말을 <보기>에 주어진 단어들을 모두 배열하여 영작하시오.

┌─ 보기 ─┐
with / that / I'm / you / not / on
└────┘

➡ _____

02 What does Steve think about sharing his posts with many people?

➡ _____

03 With whom does Lisa want to share her posts?

➡ _____

04 다음 대화가 자연스럽게 이어지도록 순서대로 배열하시오.

(A) I think it's really touching. She'll love it.
(B) Oh, you're giving her a memory stick?
(C) Look, Dad. This is Mom's birthday gift.
(D) Yeah, I've made a family video clip for Mom and saved it on this stick. What do you think about the present?

➡ _____

05 다음 주어진 단어를 어법에 맞게 빈칸에 쓰시오.

Angela said _____ words to me. So I was _____. (encourage)

06 다음 우리말 의미에 맞게 빈칸에 알맞은 말을 쓰시오.

(1) 그 젊은 주자들은 응원하는 군중 옆을 지나갔다.
➡ The young runners passed by the _____ crowd.

(2) 그 요리사는 얇게 잘린 양파를 차가운 물에 넣었다.
➡ The chef put the _____ onions in cold water.

07 주어진 어구를 활용하여 다음 우리말을 조건에 맞게 영어로 쓰시오.

그녀는 선반 꼭대기에 닿을 만큼 키가 커.
(reach, the top shelf)

(1) to부정사를 활용하여 한 문장으로
➡ _____

(2) that절을 활용하여 한 문장으로
➡ _____

08 주어진 단어를 활용하여 다음 대화의 빈칸에 알맞은 말을 쓰시오.

A: Do you know why the dog didn't bark at a stranger?
B: I think _____.
(hungry / that)

➡ _____

[09~11] 다음 글을 읽고 물음에 답하시오.

Our first day was terrible. On the way to our guesthouse around Plaza Reial, we got lost in downtown Barcelona. Dad was busy looking at the map and asking for directions with a few Spanish words he got from a tour guidebook. Even though our guesthouse was right next to the Plaza, it took us about two hours to get there. We were so tired that we could not go out for dinner. I went to bed but couldn't fall asleep because I was worried about what would happen the next day.

09 How did the writer's dad ask for directions? Answer in English with a full sentence.

➡ _____

_____

10 Why couldn't the writer fall asleep? Use the word 'because.'

➡ _____

_____

11 Where did they get lost? Answer in English with a full sentence.

➡ _____

[12~14] 다음 글을 읽고 물음에 답하시오.

It is my 15th birthday today. Last night, I was so excited that I couldn't sleep well. However, my birthday started badly. I woke up too late to have my birthday breakfast. All day, I felt so sleepy that I couldn't focus during class. I was sad because nothing was going right. But something unexpected happened. My classmates threw a surprise party for me. (A)I was too moved to say anything. It was a wonderful day.　※ I=Jesse

12 to부정사를 활용하여 다음 물음에 답하시오.

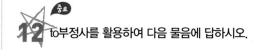

Q: Why couldn't Jesse focus during class?

➡ _____

13 How did Jesse feel when his classmates threw a surprise party for him? Answer in English with three words.

➡ _____

14 that절을 활용하여 밑줄 친 (A)와 같은 의미의 문장을 쓰시오.

➡ _____

01 다음 대화의 내용과 일치하도록 Mina의 일기를 완성하시오.

Alex: I've just finished making the posting for Leon, Mom. What do you think about it?

Mom: Oh, the title "LOST CAT" in big letters at the top is easy to see.

Alex: Yeah, I did it to get attention. How about these photos below the title?

Mom: Hmm··· the one on the right doesn't show Leon's face well.

Alex: Okay, I'll change the photo.

Mom: Oh, I hope we can find Leon.

Alex made the posting to (A)_____ his lost cat, Leon. He wrote the title "LOST CAT" in (B)_____ at the top to get attention. He added (C)_____ below the title on the posting. His mom wanted to change the one on the right because (D)_____. His mom wished to find Leon soon.

02 다음 주어진 문장과 같은 의미의 문장을 쓰시오.

(1) The man was so shocked that he couldn't say anything.

➡ _____

(2) The book was so difficult that it couldn't be read easily.

➡ _____

(3) The dog was so hungry that he couldn't bark at a stranger.

➡ _____

(4) She was so frightened that she couldn't phone us.

➡ _____

단원별 모의고사

01 다음 문장에 공통으로 들어갈 말을 고르시오.

> • I would like to listen to your _____s on this issue.
> • Have you ever _____ about becoming a lawyer?
> • I _____ that you were afraid of trying something new.

① suggest ② remain ③ presence
④ post ⑤ thought

02 다음 우리말에 맞게 빈칸에 알맞은 말을 쓰시오.

(1) 나의 아버지는 멀리 떨어져 계시지만, 나의 마음은 항상 그와 함께 있다.

➡ _____ _____ my father is far away, my heart is always with him.

(2) 그는 그녀의 관심을 얻기 위해 노력했다.

➡ He tried to _____ her _____.

03 다음 문장의 빈칸에 들어갈 말을 〈보기〉에서 골라 쓰시오.

┌ 보기 ┐
elderly / handwritten / guidebook /
local / guesthouse
└────────────────────────┘

(1) I brought this _____ to get some information about China.

(2) Jessica felt touched when she got the _____ letters from her daughter.

(3) I decided to stay at the _____ for three days.

(4) How about offering your seat to the _____ lady?

(5) Have you ever visited that restaurant serving organic and _____ food?

04 다음 우리말을 주어진 단어를 이용하여 영작하시오.

(1) 나는 내 방을 청소하느라 바빴다.
(cleaning, was)

➡ _____

(2) 나는 커피 한 잔을 마신 후 잠이 들 수 없었다.
(aslccp, drinking)

➡ _____

(3) 젊은 사람들은 기술에 너무 많이 의존한다.
(rely, much, young)

➡ _____

[05~06] 다음 대화를 읽고 물음에 답하시오.

> Emma: Excuse me. Can you help me order with this machine?
> Tom: Sure. First, press the Hot Dog button and choose your hot dog and drink.
> Emma: Okay. How do I pay for my order?
> Tom: Touch the Done button at the bottom and pay for them.
> Emma: Wow, it's so simple. This machine is much faster than ordering at the counter.
> Tom: I'm with you on that. It really saves a lot of time when there's a long line.

05 Which button should Emma touch before paying for the order?

➡ _____

06 What does Tom think about the machine?

➡ _____
  _____

[07~09] 다음 대화를 읽고 물음에 답하시오.

> Sujin: Now, we will start the three-minute debate. Today's first topic is fast fashion. What do you think about it? Please, begin, James.
>
> James: I think fast fashion is good. We can wear trendy clothes at a ⓐcheaper price.
>
> Wendy: I'm not ⓑwith you on that. It makes us spend too much money and ⓒthrows away clothes too often.
>
> Sujin: It ⓓlooks like the two of you have different opinions on the first topic. Now, let's ⓔmove on to the second topic.

07 위 대화에서 다음 주어진 영영풀이가 나타내는 말을 찾아 쓰시오.

> an argument or a discussion expressing different opinions

➡ _____

08 위 대화의 밑줄 친 ⓐ~ⓔ 중 어법상 어색한 것을 찾아 바르게 고치시오.

➡ _____

09 위 대화의 내용과 일치하지 않는 것은?

① Students are debating the pros and cons of fast fashion.
② James thinks that fast fashion is good because trendy clothes are available at a cheaper price.
③ Wendy has the same opinion as James about the fast fashion.
④ Wendy thinks that trendy clothes make us waste much money.
⑤ Wendy insists that fast fashion is bad because it makes us throw away clothes too often.

[10~11] 다음 대화를 읽고 물음에 답하시오.

> Emma: Excuse me. Can you help me order with this machine?
>
> Tom: (A) Sure. First, press the Hot Dog button and choose your hot dog and drink.
>
> Emma: (B) Okay. How do I pay for my order?
>
> Tom: (C) Touch the Done button at the bottom and pay for them.
>
> Emma: (D) Wow, it's so simple. This machine is much faster than ordering at the counter.
>
> Tom: (E) It really saves a lot of time when there's a long line.

10 위 대화의 (A)~(E) 중 주어진 문장이 들어가기에 알맞은 곳은?

> I'm with you on that.

① (A) ② (B) ③ (C) ④ (D) ⑤ (E)

11 위 대화의 내용과 일치하지 않는 것은?

① Emma는 기계로 주문을 하려고 한다.
② Emma는 먼저 '핫도그' 버튼을 누르고 먹고 싶은 핫도그와 음료를 골라야 한다.
③ Emma는 맨 아래의 '완료' 버튼을 누르고 결제할 수 있다.
④ 기계에서 주문하는 것이 계산대에서 주문하는 것보다 훨씬 더 빠르다.
⑤ 줄이 길 때, 계산대에서 주문하면 많은 시간을 절약할 수 있다.

12 다음 우리말과 일치하도록 주어진 단어를 모두 배열하여 영작하시오.

> 나는 온라인 쇼핑이 상점에서 쇼핑하는 것보다 낫다고 생각해.
> (shopping / think / is / better / shopping / at / the stores / I / online / than)

➡ _____

_____

13 주어진 단어를 활용하여 다음 우리말을 영어로 쓰시오.

> 그녀는 그 충격적인 소식에 실망할 거야.
> (will / shock / disappoint / with)

➡ _____

14 다음 문장과 같은 의미의 문장을 <u>모두</u> 고르시오.

> You can't eat the soup because it is very hot.

① The soup is too hot for you to eat.
② The soup is hot enough to eat.
③ The soup is so hot that you can eat it.
④ The soup is too hot that you can't eat it.
⑤ The soup is so hot that you can't eat it.

15 다음 중 어법상 바르지 <u>않은</u> 것은?

① There are many excited people in the hall.
② Did you find your broken camera?
③ The movie is interesting enough to watch several times.
④ They were so busy that they can't have lunch.
⑤ The book is too difficult to understand.

[16~19] 다음 글을 읽고 물음에 답하시오.

After looking around Gaudi's Park Guell, we decided to have seafood fried rice for lunch. However, we didn't know which restaurant to go to. We needed help, so Mom went up to an (a)elderly lady and tried to ask for directions to a popular seafood restaurant. Luckily, she seemed to understand Mom's few Spanish words. She took us to a small local restaurant nearby. The seafood fried rice was amazing. I really wanted to take pictures of the food and (b)post them on my blog. But without my phone, I just decided to enjoy the (c)moment.

During the remaining days, we relied more and more on the locals. We were able to meet and talk with various people on the streets, in the (d)bakeries, and in the parks. They were always kind enough to show us different sides of Barcelona with a smile. Also, our family talked a lot with each other. We spent much of our time together on the Spanish train, on the bus, and at the restaurants.

16 다음 중 (a)~(d)를 풀이한 말에 해당하지 <u>않는</u> 것은?

① a particular point in time
② to put a message or computer document on the Internet
③ old or aging
④ a book of directions and information for travelers
⑤ a building where bread is baked or sold

17 다음 중 위 글을 읽고 답할 수 <u>없는</u> 것은?

① What did they do before they decided to have lunch?
② Why did they need help?
③ Who took them to a small restaurant?
④ How was the seafood fried rice?
⑤ How far was it from Park Guell to the restaurant?

18 Where did the family spend their time together during the trip? Answer in English with a full sentence.

➡ _____

_____

19 How did the locals act toward the family? Answer in English with a full sentence.

➡ _____

_____

[20~22] 다음 글을 읽고 물음에 답하시오.

It is my 15th birthday today. Last night, I was so excited that I couldn't sleep well. ___(A)___ , my birthday started badly. I woke up too late to have my birthday breakfast. All day, I felt so sleepy that I couldn't focus during class. I was sad because nothing was going right. But something unexpected happened. My classmates threw a surprise party for me. I was so moved that I couldn't say anything. It was a wonderful day.

20 다음 중 빈칸 (A)에 들어갈 말로 가장 적절한 것은?

① Therefore
② Besides
③ However
④ Luckily
⑤ On the other hand

21 위 글의 내용에 맞게 빈칸에 알맞은 말을 쓰시오.

A: Jesse, did you have your birthday breakfast?
B: No. I woke up _____ _____ _____ _____ _____ have my birthday breakfast.

22 다음 중 위 글의 내용과 일치하지 않는 것은?

① The writer wrote this story on his birthday.
② The writer was too excited to sleep well.
③ The writer felt sleepy all day long.
④ The surprise party made the writer feel moved.
⑤ The writer knew that there would be a surprise party for him.

23 자연스러운 글이 되도록 (A)~(C)를 바르게 나열한 것은?

Our technology-free trip was a new and different experience.
(A) But now I see that I can enjoy the moment without it. From the experience, I have learned the importance of a balanced use of the smartphone.
(B) Before the trip, I was so dependent on my smartphone that I couldn't do anything without it.
(C) So, next time, would I travel without a smartphone? Probably not. But I will try to use it more wisely.

① (A)–(C)–(B)
② (B)–(A)–(C)
③ (B)–(C)–(A)
④ (C)–(A)–(B)
⑤ (C)–(B)–(A)

Special

The Stone

Words & Expressions

Key Words

- **arrive** [əráiv] 동 도착하다
- **bear** [bɛər] 동 (새끼를) 낳다
- **beard** [biərd] 명 수염
- **cart** [kaːrt] 명 수레, 우마차
- **cow** [kau] 명 소, 암소
- **decide** [disáid] 동 결심하다, 결정하다
- **delight** [diláit] 명 기쁨
- **destroy** [distrɔ́i] 동 파괴하다, 없애다
- **dwarf** [dwɔːrf] 명 난쟁이
- **explain** [ikspéin] 동 설명하다
- **field** [fiːld] 명 들판, 밭
- **free** [friː] 동 빼내다, 풀어 주다 형 자유로운
- **glad** [glæd] 형 기쁜
- **grandchild** [grǽndtʃàild] 명 손주

- **ground** [graund] 명 땅, 지면
- **hand** [hænd] 동 건네주다
- **log** [lɔg] 명 통나무
- **magic** [mǽdʒik] 형 마술의
- **nothing** [nʌ́θiŋ] 대 아무것도 아닌 것
- **reward** [riwɔ́ːrd] 명 보상, 보답
- **season** [síːzn] 명 계절
- **stone** [stoun] 명 돌
- **tooth** [tuːθ] 명 이, 치아
- **trouble** [trʌbl] 명 문제
- **unless** [ənlés] 접 ~하지 않는 한
- **warn** [wɔːrn] 동 경고하다
- **wife** [waif] 명 아내, 부인

Key Expressions

- **be proud of** ~을 자랑스러워하다
- **change into** ~으로 바꾸다
- **far from** ~에서 멀리
- **get rid of** ~을 없애다
- **give birth** 출산하다, 새끼를 낳다
- **go away** 떠나가다
- **go by** 흐르다, 지나가다

- **keep ~ from -ing** ~가 …하지 못하게 하다
- **keep -ing** 계속 ~하다
- **look forward to** ~을 기대하다, ~을 고대하다
- **on one's way to** ~로 가는 길에
- **throw away** ~을 버리다
- **try to** ~하려고 노력하다
- **worry about** ~에 대해 걱정하다

Word Power

※ 서로 반대되는 뜻을 가진 어휘

- arrive 도착하다 ↔ depart 출발하다, 떠나다
- delight 기쁨 ↔ grief 슬픔
- destroy 파괴하다 ↔ construct 건설하다
- wife 아내 ↔ husband 남편
- sick 아픈 ↔ healthy 건강한
- old 늙은 ↔ young 젊은

- dwarf 난쟁이 ↔ giant 거인
- slow 느린 ↔ fast 빠른
- if ~한다면 ↔ unless ~하지 않으면
- proud 자랑스러운 ↔ shameful 부끄러운
- nothing 아무것도 아닌 것 ↔ everything 모든 것
- far from ~에서 멀리 ↔ close to ~에 가까이

English Dictionary

- **arrive** 도착하다
  → to get to a place, especially at the end of a journey
  어떤 장소, 특히 여행의 끝에 다다르다

- **bear** (아이나 새끼를) 낳다
  → to give birth to a child
  아이를 낳다

- **beard** 수염
  → hair that grows on the chin and cheeks of a man's face
  남자 얼굴의 턱과 뺨에 자라는 털

- **cart** 수레, 우마차
  → a vehicle with two or four wheels that is pulled by a horse and used for carrying loads
  말이 끌고 짐을 나르기 위해 사용되는 두 개 또는 네 개의 바퀴가 있는 수송 수단

- **destroy** 파괴하다
  → to damage something so badly that it no longer exists, works, etc.
  무언가를 매우 심하게 손상시켜 더 이상 존재하거나 작동하지 않게 하다

- **free** 빼내다, 풀어 주다
  → to remove something that is unpleasant or not wanted from somebody/something
  누군가나 무언가로부터 불쾌하거나 원하지 않는 무언가를 제거하다

- **grandchild** 손주
  → a child of your son or daughter
  당신의 아들이나 딸의 아이

- **hand** 건네주다
  → to pass or give something to somebody
  누군가에게 무언가를 전달하거나 주다

- **log** 통나무
  → a thick piece of wood that is cut from or has fallen from a tree
  나무에서 떨어졌거나 베어진 두꺼운 나무 조각

- **reward** 보상
  → a thing that you are given because you have done something good, worked hard, etc.
  당신이 무언가 잘했거나 열심히 일을 했기 때문에 당신에게 주어진 것

- **warn** 경고하다
  → to tell somebody about something, especially something dangerous or unpleasant that is likely to happen, so that they can avoid it
  누군가에게 특히 일어나기 쉬운 위험하거나 불쾌한 무언가에 대해 그들이 그것을 피할 수 있도록 이야기하다

- **wife** 아내, 부인
  → the woman that somebody is married to
  누군가와 결혼한 여성

Reading

The Stone

One day, Maibon was driving down the road on his horse and cart when he saw an old man. The old man looked very sick. Maibon began to worry about growing old. Later that day, he saw a dwarf, Doli, in the field. He was trying to get his leg out from under a log. Maibon pulled the log away and freed the dwarf. "You'll have your reward. What do you want?" "I've heard that you have magic stones that can keep a man young. I want one." "Oh, you humans have it all wrong. Those stones don't make you young again. They only keep you from getting older." "Just as good!" Doli tried to explain the problem with the stones, but Maibon didn't listen. So Doli handed him a magic stone and went away.

After a few days, Maibon saw that his beard didn't grow at all. He became happy, but his wife, Modrona, got upset. "The eggs don't change into chickens!" "Oh, the season's slow, that's all." But she was not happy. "The cow doesn't give birth!" Maibon, then, told her about the stone, and she got very angry and told him to throw it away. He didn't want to, but he listened to his wife and threw the stone out the window.

(학습 주석)
- when — 시간을 이끄는 부사절 접속사
- began — to부정사와 동명사를 모두 목적어로 취하는 동사
- growing — 동명사
- Later that day — 그날 늦게
- Doli — 동격
- trying to — ~하려고 애쓰다
- from under — ~ 아래에서
- that — 명사절 접속사(+완전한 문장)
- that — 주격 관계대명사
- one — = a stone
- you — 동격
- have it all wrong — 잘못 알고 있다
- make — 5형식 동사(make+목적어+목적격보어)
- handed — 4형식 동사(hand+간접목적어+직접목적어)
- a few — 몇몇의(셀 수 있는 명사 수식)
- saw — 알았다
- his wife와 Modrona는 동격
- told — to부정사를 목적격 보어로 취하는 동사
- it — the stone
- to — = to throw it away

어휘
cart 수레, 우마차
worry about ~에 대해 걱정하다
dwarf 난쟁이
field 들판
log 통나무
free 빼내다, 풀어 주다
reward 보상, 보답
keep ~ from Ving ~가 V하지 못하게 하다
go away 떠나가다
not ~ at all 전혀 ~ 않다
change into ~으로 바뀌다
give birth 새끼를 낳다
throw away 버리다

📎 **확인문제**

● 다음 문장이 본문의 내용과 일치하면 T, 일치하지 <u>않으면</u> F를 쓰시오.

1 Maibon helped the old man who looked sick. ☐

2 Maibon wanted a magic stone from the dwarf as a reward. ☐

3 Maibon understood that the magic stone could keep him from getting older. ☐

4 Maibon's wife didn't like the stone. ☐

However, the next morning, he found the stone <u>sitting</u> by the window!
현재분사(목적보어)

Maibon was worried about the animals, but he <u>was glad that</u> he was
that 이하가 기뻤다

still young. Now Maibon's baby was having trouble. No tooth was seen

in his mouth. His wife <u>told him to throw</u> away the stone and this time,
tell+목적어+to부정사: 목적어가 V하도록 말하다

Maibon put the stone under the ground. But, the next day, the stone

came back! Time went by and nothing grew or changed. Maibon began

to worry. "There's nothing <u>to look</u> forward to, nothing <u>to show</u> for
to부정사의 형용사적 용법(nothing 수식)   to부정사의 형용사적 용법(nothing 수식)

my work." Maibon tried to destroy the stone, but it <u>kept coming</u> back.
keep Ving: 계속해서 V하다

Maibon <u>decided</u> to throw away the stone far from his house. On his
to부정사를 목적어로 취하는 동사

way to the field, he saw the dwarf. Maibon got angry with him. "Why

didn't you warn me about the stone?" "I tried <u>to</u>, but you wouldn't
= to warn you about the stone

listen." Doli explained <u>that</u> Maibon couldn't get rid of the stone <u>unless</u>
명사절 접속사(+완전한 문장)

he really wanted to. "I want no more of it. <u>Whatever</u> may happen, <u>let</u>
= if he really didn't want to   복합관계대명사   사역동사+목적어+동사원형

it happen!" Doli told him to throw the stone onto the ground and go

back home. Maibon did <u>as</u> Doli said. When he arrived home, Modrona
접속사(~하는 대로)

told him the good news — the eggs changed into chickens and the cow

bore her baby. And Maibon laughed <u>with delight</u> when he saw the first
bear-bore-born   기뻐서

tooth in his baby's mouth. Maibon, Modrona and their children and

grandchildren lived for many years. Maibon <u>was proud of</u> his white
~을 자랑스러워했다

hair and long beard.

nothing 아무것도 아닌 것

destroy 파괴하다, 없애다

go by 흐르다, 지나가다

warn 경고하다

unless ~하지 않는 한

bear 새끼를 낳다

grandchild 손주

get rid of ~을 없애다

 **확인문제**

● 다음 문장이 본문의 내용과 일치하면 T, 일치하지 <u>않으면</u> F를 쓰시오.

1 Doli forgot to warn about the stone. ☐

2 Doli told Maibon to throw the stone onto the ground and went home. ☐

3 As soon as Maibon arrived home, he got the good news. ☐

● 우리말을 참고하여 빈칸에 알맞은 말을 쓰시오.

1 One day, Maibon was _____ _____ the road on his horse and cart _____ he saw an old man.

2 The old man _____ very _____. Maibon began _____ _____ _____ growing old.

3 _____ _____ _____, he saw a dwarf, Doli, in the field.

4 IIe was trying _____ _____ his leg _____ _____ under a log.

5 Maibon _____ the log _____ and _____ the dwarf.

6 "You'll have your _____. What do you want?"

7 "I've heard that you have magic stones _____ can keep a man _____. I want one."

8 "Oh, you humans have _____ _____ _____. Those stones don't make you _____ _____. They only _____ you _____ getting older."

9 "Just as good!" Doli tried _____ _____ the problem with the stones, but Maibon didn't _____.

10 So Doli _____ _____ a magic stone and went away.

11 After _____ _____ days, Maibon saw that his beard didn't _____ _____ _____.

12 He _____ happy, but his wife, Modrona, _____ _____.

13 The eggs don't _____ _____ chickens!" "Oh, the season's _____, that's all."

14 But she was not happy. "The cow doesn't _____ _____!" Maibon, then, told her about the stone, and she _____ very _____ and told him _____ _____ _____ _____.

15 He didn't want to, but he _____ _____ his wife and _____ the stone _____ the window.

16 However, the next morning, he _____ the stone _____ by the window!

1 어느 날, Maibon이 한 노인을 보았을 때, 그는 마차를 타고 길을 내려가고 있던 중이었다.

2 그 노인은 매우 아파 보였다. Maibon은 늙어 가는 것이 걱정되기 시작했다.

3 그날 오후, 그는 들판에서 Doli 라는 난쟁이를 보았다.

4 그는 통나무 아래에 깔린 그의 다리를 빼내려고 하고 있었다.

5 Maibon은 통나무를 잡아당겨서 난쟁이를 풀어주었다.

6 "너는 보상을 받게 될 거야. 원하는게 뭐니?"

7 "나는 네가 사람의 젊음을 유지해 주는 마법의 돌들을 가지고 있다고 들었어. 나는 그것을 원해."

8 "오, 너희 인간들은 잘못 알고 있어. 그 돌들은 너희들이 다시 젊어지게 해 주지 않아. 단지 더 늙지 않게 막아 줄 뿐이라고."

9 "그것대로 좋아!" Doli는 그 돌에 관한 문제를 설명하려고 했지만, Maibon은 듣지 않았다.

10 그래서 Doli는 그에게 마법의 돌을 건네고는 가버렸다.

11 며칠이 지나서, Maibon은 그의 수염이 전혀 자라지 않았음을 알았다.

12 그는 행복해졌지만, 그의 아내 Modrona는 화가 났다.

13 "달걀이 닭이 되지 않아요!" "아, 시기가 더딘 거예요. 그 뿐이에요."

14 하지만 그녀는 탐탁해하지 않았다. "소가 새끼를 낳지 않아요!" 그때 Maibon은 그 돌에 대해 그녀에게 이야기를 했고 그녀는 매우 화를 내며 그에게 그것을 버리라고 말했다.

15 그는 원하지 않았지만, 아내의 말을 듣고 창밖으로 돌을 던졌다.

16 그러나 다음날 아침 그는 창가에 그 돌이 있는 것을 발견했다!

17 Maibon was _____ _____ the animals, but he was _____ _____ he was still young.

18 Now Maibon's baby was _____ _____. No tooth was _____ in his mouth.

19 His wife told him _____ _____ _____ the stone and this time, Maibon _____ the stone _____ the ground.

20 But, the next day, the stone _____ _____! Time _____ _____ and nothing _____ or _____.

21 Maibon began _____ _____. "There's _____ _____ _____ _____ _____, nothing to show for my work."

22 Maibon tried _____ _____ the stone, but it kept _____ _____.

23 Maibon decided _____ _____ _____ the stone _____ _____ his house.

24 _____ his way _____ the field, he saw the dwarf. Maibon _____ _____ with him.

25 "Why _____ _____ _____ me about the stone?"

26 "I tried to, but you wouldn't _____."

27 Doli _____ that Maibon couldn't _____ _____ _____ the stone _____ he really wanted to.

28 "I want _____ _____ _____ it. _____ may happen, _____ it _____!"

29 Doli told him _____ _____ the stone _____ the ground and go back home.

30 Maibon _____ as Doli _____. When he _____ home, Modrona told him the good news — the eggs _____ _____ chickens and the cow _____ her baby.

31 And Maibon _____ _____ _____ when he saw the first tooth in his baby's mouth.

32 Maibon, Modrona and their children and grandchildren _____ _____ many years.

33 Maibon _____ _____ _____ his white hair and long beard.

17 Maibon은 동물들이 걱정되긴 했지만, 자신이 여전히 젊어서 기뻤다.

18 이제 Maibon의 아기에게 문제가 생겼다. 아기의 입에서 이가 보이지 않았다.

19 그의 아내는 그에게 그 돌을 버리라고 말했고 Maibon은 이번엔 그 돌을 땅속에 묻었다.

20 그런데 그 다음날 그 돌은 다시 돌아왔다! 시간이 흘렀고 어떤 것도 자라거나 변하지 않았다.

21 Maibon은 걱정이 되기 시작했다. "기대할 것도 내 일의 결과를 보여 줄 것도 아무것도 없어."

22 Maibon은 그 돌을 없애려고 노력했지만 돌은 계속 되돌아왔다.

23 Maibon은 그 돌을 그의 집에서 멀리 떨어진 곳에 버리기로 결심했다.

24 그는 들판으로 가는 길에 난쟁이를 보았다. Maibon은 그에게 화를 냈다.

25 "너는 왜 내게 그 돌에 대해 경고하지 않았어?"

26 "나는 하려고 했지만, 너는 들으려 하지 않았어."

27 Doli는 Maibon이 진심으로 원하지 않는 한 그 돌을 없앨 수 없다고 설명했다.

28 "나는 그것을 더 이상 원하지 않아. 무슨 일이 있어도 일어나게 해!"

29 Doli는 그에게 그 돌을 땅에 던지고 집으로 돌아가라고 말했다.

30 Maibon은 Doli가 말한 대로 했다. 그가 집에 도착했을 때, Modrona는 그에게 달걀이 닭이 되고 소가 새끼를 낳았다는 좋은 소식을 말해 주었다.

31 그리고 Maibon은 아기의 입에 첫 이가 난 것을 보고 기뻐서 웃었다.

32 Maibon과 Modrona, 그리고 그들의 자녀들과 손주들은 오랫동안 살았다.

33 Maibon은 그의 흰 머리와 긴 수염을 자랑스러워했다.

● 우리말을 참고하여 본문을 영작하시오.

1 어느 날, Maibon이 한 노인을 보았을 때, 그는 마차를 타고 길을 내려가고 있던 중이었다.
➡ _____

2 그 노인은 매우 아파 보였다. Maibon은 늙어 가는 것이 걱정되기 시작했다.
➡ _____

3 그날 오후, 그는 들판에서 Doli라는 난쟁이를 보았다.
➡ _____

4 그는 통나무 아래에 깔린 그의 다리를 빼내려고 하고 있었다.
➡ _____

5 Maibon은 통나무를 잡아당겨서 난쟁이를 풀어 주었다.
➡ _____

6 "너는 보상을 받게 될 거야. 원하는 게 뭐니?"
➡ _____

7 "나는 네가 사람의 젊음을 유지해 주는 마법의 돌들을 가지고 있다고 들었어. 나는 그것을 원해."
➡ _____

8 오, 너희 인간들은 잘못 알고 있어. 그 돌들은 너희들이 다시 젊어지게 해 주지 않아. 단지 더 늙지 않게 막아 줄 뿐이라고."
➡ _____
_____

9 "그것대로 좋아!" Doli는 그 돌에 관한 문제를 설명하려고 했지만, Maibon은 듣지 않았다.
➡ _____

10 그래서 Doli는 그에게 마법의 돌을 건네고는 가버렸다.
➡ _____

11 며칠이 지나서, Maibon은 그의 수염이 전혀 자라지 않았음을 알았다.
➡ _____

12 그는 행복해졌지만, 그의 아내 Modrona는 화가 났다.
➡ _____

13 "달걀이 닭이 되지 않아요!" "아, 시기가 더딘 거예요. 그 뿐이에요."
➡ _____

14 하지만 그녀는 탐탁해하지 않았다. "소가 새끼를 낳지 않아요!" 그때 Maibon은 그 돌에 대해 그녀에게 이야기를 했고 그녀는 매우 화를 내며 그에게 그것을 버리라고 말했다.
➡ _____
_____

15 그는 원하지 않았지만, 아내의 말을 듣고 창밖으로 돌을 던졌다.
➡ _____

16 그러나 다음날 아침 그는 창가에 그 돌이 있는 것을 발견했다!
➡ _____

17 Maibon은 동물들이 걱정되긴 했지만, 자신이 여전히 젊어서 기뻤다.

➡ _____

18 이제 Maibon의 아기에게 문제가 생겼다. 아기의 입에서 이가 보이지 않았다.

➡ _____

19 그의 아내는 그에게 그 돌을 버리라고 말했고 Maibon은 이번엔 그 돌을 땅속에 묻었다.

➡ _____

20 그런데 그 다음날 그 돌은 다시 돌아왔다! 시간이 흘렀고 어떤 것도 자라거나 변하지 않았다.

➡ _____

21 Maibon은 걱정이 되기 시작했다. "기대할 것도 내 일의 결과를 보여 줄 것도 아무것도 없어."

➡ _____

22 Maibon은 그 돌을 없애려고 노력했지만 돌은 계속 되돌아왔다.

➡ _____

23 Maibon은 그 돌을 그의 집에서 멀리 떨어진 곳에 버리기로 결심했다.

➡ _____

24 그는 들판으로 가는 길에 난쟁이를 보았다. Maibon은 그에게 화를 냈다.

➡ _____

25 "너는 왜 내게 그 돌에 대해 경고하지 않았어?"

➡ _____

26 "나는 하려고 했지만, 너는 들으려 하지 않았어."

➡ _____

27 Doli는 Maibon이 진심으로 원하지 않는 한 그 돌을 없앨 수 없다고 설명했다.

➡ _____

28 "나는 그것을 더 이상 원하지 않아. 무슨 일이 있어도 일어나게 해!"

➡ _____

29 Doli는 그에게 그 돌을 땅에 던지고 집으로 돌아가라고 말했다.

➡ _____

30 Maibon은 Doli가 말한 대로 했다. 그가 집에 도착했을 때, Modrona는 그에게 달걀이 닭이 되고 소가 새끼를 낳았다는 좋은 소식을 말해 주었다.

➡ _____

_____

31 그리고 Maibon은 아기의 입에 첫 이가 난 것을 보고 기뻐서 웃었다.

➡ _____

32 Maibon과 Modrona, 그리고 그들의 자녀들과 손주들은 오랫동안 살았다.

➡ _____

33 Maibon은 그의 흰 머리와 긴 수염을 자랑스러워했다.

➡ _____

01 다음 주어진 우리말과 의미가 같도록 빈칸을 완성하시오.

(1) 그녀는 아들을 낳았고 그를 Tony라고 불렀다.

➡ She _____ a son and called him Tony.

(2) 수염이 있는 그 남자는 내가 가장 좋아하는 배우이다.

➡ The man with a _____ is my favorite actor.

(3) 농부들은 들판에서 쌀을 재배한다.

➡ Farmers grow rice in the _____.

(4) 내 친구의 집은 통나무로 만들어졌다.

➡ My friend's house is made of _____.

02 다음 문장의 빈칸에 들어갈 말을 〈보기〉에서 골라 알맞은 형태로 쓰시오.

┌─── 보기 ───┐
throw away / change into /
worry about / go by / go away
└────────────┘

(1) I hope this year _____ _____ quickly.

(2) She _____ _____ without saying goodbye yesterday.

(3) _____ _____ garbage in the trash can.

(4) Parents always _____ _____ their children's safety.

(5) It can _____ _____ different types of clothes.

03 다음 우리말을 주어진 단어를 사용하여 영작하시오.

(1) 나는 나의 나쁜 습관들을 없애기 위해 노력한다. (try, rid)

➡ _____

(2) 나의 선생님은 우리가 학교에서 휴대폰을 사용하지 못하게 하신다. (cell, keeps)

➡ _____
_____

(3) 나의 이모는 귀여운 아기를 낳았다. (cute, gave)

➡ _____

04 주어진 단어를 이용하여 우리말을 영어로 옮기시오.

(1) 그들은 우리에게 그 컴퓨터를 사용하지 말라고 말했다. (tell)

➡ _____

(2) 나는 이번 주말에 삼촌을 방문할 계획이야. (plan)

➡ _____

05 다음 문장을 능동태는 수동태로, 수동태는 능동태로 전환하시오.

(1) David repaired my car yesterday.

➡ _____

(2) The man on the street was hit by a car.

➡ _____

One day, Maibon was driving down the road on his horse and cart when he saw an old man. The old man looked very sick. Maibon began to worry about growing old.

(A) Maibon pulled the log away and freed the dwarf. "You'll have your reward. What do you want?"

(B) "Just as good!" Doli tried to explain the problem with the stones, but Maibon didn't listen.

(C) "I've heard that you have magic stones that can keep a man young. I want ⓐone."

(D) Later that day, he saw a dwarf, Doli, in the field. He was trying to get his leg out from under a log.

(E) "Oh, you humans have it all wrong. Those stones don't make you young again. They only keep you from getting older."

So Doli handed him a magic stone and went away.

06 자연스러운 글이 되도록 (A)~(E)를 바르게 배열하시오.

➡ _____

07 How did the old man look? Answer in English with a full sentence.

➡ _____

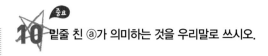

08 What did Maibon worry about? Answer in English with five words.

➡ _____

09 What is the name of the dwarf?

➡ _____

10 밑줄 친 ⓐ가 의미하는 것을 우리말로 쓰시오.

➡ _____

[11~13] 다음 글을 읽고, 물음에 답하시오.

After a few days, Maibon saw that his beard didn't grow at all. He became happy, but his wife, Modrona, got upset. "The eggs don't change into chickens!" "Oh, the season's slow, that's all." But she was not happy. "The cow doesn't give birth!" Maibon, then, told her about the stone, and she got very angry and told him to throw it away. (A)He didn't want to, but he listened to his wife and threw the stone out the window. However, the next morning, he found the stone sitting by the window! Maibon was worried about the animals, but he was glad that he was still young.

11 Who is Modrona?

➡ _____

12 밑줄 친 문장 (A)를 생략된 말을 보충하여 다시 쓰시오.

➡ _____

13 After throwing away the stone, what did Maibon find the next morning?

➡ _____

출제율 95%

01 다음 밑줄 친 단어의 뜻이 바르지 <u>않은</u> 것은?

① The best student will receive a <u>reward</u>.
보상

② <u>Unless</u> you buy a ticket, you can't enter this museum. ~하지 않으면

③ We sometimes have <u>trouble</u> with our friends. 문제

④ Teachers <u>warned</u> us not to cheat on the tcst. 경고했다

⑤ The police decided to <u>free</u> the man. 자유로운

출제율 90%

02 다음 문장의 빈칸에 공통으로 들어갈 말로 적절한 것은?

- Mike couldn't _____ the pain caused by the disease.
- Stephanie was not able to _____ children anymore.
- Mike was as strong as the _____ when he was young.

① bear   ② free   ③ hand
④ stand   ⑤ reward

출제율 100%

03 다음 문장의 빈칸에 들어갈 말을 〈보기〉에서 골라 적절한 형태로 쓰시오.

┌─ 보기 ─┐
reward / trouble / warn / glad / hand

(1) My aunt _____ed me not to leave my cousin alone.

(2) Would you _____ the salt to me?

(3) You won't get any _____s as long as you don't do chore.

(4) My heart is full of _____.

(5) I'm _____ that you have come here.

출제율 95%

04 다음 영영풀이가 나타내는 말을 고르시오.

hair that grows on the chin and cheeks of a man's face

① beard   ② delight
③ log   ④ field
⑤ cart

출제율 90%

05 다음 우리말을 주어진 단어를 사용하여 영작하시오.

(1) 나는 이 의자가 필요 없어. 그것을 버리자.
(away, let)

➡ _____

(2) 내 고향은 서울로부터 멀지 않아요.
(far, hometown)

➡ _____

(3) 나는 홍콩 방문을 기대하고 있다.
(forward, visiting)

➡ _____

(4) 나는 학교 가는 길에, 외국인을 만났다.
(way, on)

➡ _____

(5) 해가 갈수록, 일이 더 어려워진다. (go, as)

➡ _____

출제율 100%

06 다음 중 어법상 바르지 <u>않은</u> 것은?

① Tell me how she is doing.

② The boy crying over there is my brother.

③ Did you know that they would come here?

④ They made her so angrily.

⑤ We made you do your best.

07 다음 두 문장을 하나의 문장으로 쓰시오.

> • Paul met a woman.
> • She knew Ann's best friend.

➡ _____

08 다음 빈칸에 들어갈 말로 알맞지 <u>않은</u> 것은?

> Brandy's parents _____ her go to the party.

① helped ② made ③ told
④ had ⑤ let

09 다음 중 밑줄 친 부분의 쓰임이 <u>다른</u> 하나는?

① They need <u>to do</u> something special.
② Did you decide <u>to go</u> to the field trip?
③ I would like <u>to throw</u> a party for you.
④ They have nothing <u>to tell</u> you.
⑤ Do you want <u>to give</u> her a present?

10 다음 중 주어진 문장의 밑줄 친 부분과 쓰임이 <u>다른</u> 하나는?

> Did you hear <u>that</u> Michael made her cry?

① I thought <u>that</u> he needed to hear what others said.
② Is it true <u>that</u> Ms. James is our homeroom teacher?
③ The fact <u>that</u> she helped us doesn't change.
④ Don't say <u>that</u> you can't do it.
⑤ The letter <u>that</u> he sent to you is on the table.

11 주어진 단어를 활용하여 다음 우리말을 여섯 단어로 이루어진 한 문장으로 쓰시오.

> 그녀는 그녀의 삶에 관하여 계속 말했다.
> (keep / talk)

➡ _____

12 다음 주어진 동사를 어법에 맞게 빈칸에 쓰시오.

(1) 마실 무언가를 주세요. (drink)
➡ Please give me something _____
_____.

(2) 너에게 할 말이 있어. (say)
➡ I have something _____ _____
to you.

13 다음 우리말에 맞게 빈칸에 알맞은 말을 쓰시오.

(1) 그녀는 나에게 두 송이의 꽃을 건넸다.
➡ She _____ _____ _____.
(2) 한 선생님은 우리에게 피자를 사 주셨다.
➡ Mr. Han _____ _____ _____.

[14~20] 다음 글을 읽고, 물음에 답하시오.

One day, Maibon was driving down the road on his horse and cart when he saw an old man. ① The old man looked very sick. Maibon began to worry about growing old. ② Later that day, he saw a dwarf, Doli, in the field. ③ Maibon pulled the log away and freed the dwarf. ④ "You'll have your reward. What do you want?" "I've heard that you have magic stones that can keep a man young. I want one." ⑤ "Oh, you humans have it all wrong. Those stones don't make you young again. They only keep you from getting older." "Just as good!" Doli tried to explain the problem with the stones, but Maibon didn't listen. So Doli handed him a magic stone and went away.

14 출제율 95%

다음 중 주어진 문장이 들어가기에 가장 적절한 곳은?

He was trying to get his leg out from under a log.

①   ②   ③   ④   ⑤

15 출제율 100%

다음 중 위 글을 읽고 답할 수 <u>없는</u> 것은?

① Where did Maibon see Doli?
② What did Maibon do for Doli?
③ What did Maibon want from Doli?
④ How many stones did Doli give Maibon?
⑤ Why did Doli go to the field?

16 출제율 85%

What did Doli do after he gave a stone to Maibon? Answer in English.

➡ _____

17 출제율 90%

What was Maibon doing when he saw an old man? Answer in English.

➡ _____

18 출제율 95%

다음 중 위 글의 내용과 일치하지 <u>않는</u> 것은?

① Maibon met a dwarf on the same day that he saw an old man.
② Maibon came to worry about growing old because of an old man.
③ The name of a dwarf is Doli.
④ Maibon wanted to give reward to the dwarf.
⑤ There was a problem with the magic stone.

19 출제율 85%

다음 물음에 알맞은 답을 하시오.

Q: Does the stone make people young?
A: _____, _____
_____.

20 출제율 95%

What did Doli try to explain? Answer in English with a full sentence.

➡ _____

[21~28] 다음 글을 읽고, 물음에 답하시오.

After a few days, Maibon saw that his beard didn't grow at all. He became happy, but his wife, Modrona, got upset. "The eggs don't change into chickens!" "Oh, the season's slow, that's all." But she was not happy. "The cow doesn't give birth!" Maibon, then, told her about the stone, and she got very angry and told him to throw it away. He didn't want to, but he listened to his wife and threw the stone out the window. ___(A)___, the next morning, he found the stone sitting ___(B)___ the window! Maibon was worried about the animals, but he was glad that he was still young.

Now Maibon's baby was having trouble. No tooth was seen in his mouth. His wife told him to throw away the stone and this time, Maibon put the stone under the ground. But, the next day, the stone came back! Time went ___(C)___ and nothing grew or changed. Maibon began to worry. "There's nothing to look forward to, nothing to show for my work." Maibon tried to destroy the stone, but it kept ___(D)___.

출제율 90%

21 다음 중 빈칸 (A)에 들어갈 말로 가장 적절한 것은?

① Therefore   ② However
③ Luckily   ④ For example
⑤ In contrast

출제율 95%

22 다음 빈칸 (B)와 (C)에 공통으로 들어갈 말로 적절한 것은?

① on   ② to   ③ by
④ in   ⑤ for

출제율 85%

23 위 글의 빈칸 (D)에 들어갈 말을 위 글에서 찾아 어법에 맞게 쓰시오.

➡ _____

출제율 100%

24 Which are NOT true about the passage? Select all.

① The cow didn't give birth because of the stone.
② As his wife said, Maibon threw the stone away.
③ Although his baby had a trouble, Maibon didn't throw the stone away.
④ As nothing grew and changed, Maibon began to worry.
⑤ When Maibon tried to throw the stone away for the second time, he threw it out the window.

출제율 95%

25 What trouble did Maibon's baby have?

➡ _____

출제율 90%

26 Why did Maibon begin to worry? Answer in English with a full sentence.

➡ _____

출제율 90%

27 Write the reason why Maibon was glad even though he was worried about the animals. Use the phrase 'it's because.'

➡ _____

출제율 90%

28 주어진 어구를 바르게 배열하여 위 글의 내용에 맞게 답변을 완성하시오.

> **A:** Did Maibon succeed in destroying the stone?
> **B:** _____
> (tried to / failed / it / he / he / no / but / to / destroy)

[29~35] 다음 글을 읽고 물음에 답하시오.

Maibon decided ___(A)___ away the stone far from his house. On ①his way to the field, he saw the dwarf. Maibon got angry with ②him. "Why didn't you warn me about the stone?" "I tried to, but you wouldn't listen." Doli explained that Maibon couldn't get rid of the stone unless ③he really wanted to. "I want no more of it. Whatever may happen, let it ___(B)___ !" Doli told ④him to throw the stone onto the ground and go back home. Maibon did as Doli said. When ⑤he arrived home, Modrona told him the good news — the eggs changed into chickens and the cow bore her baby. And Maibon laughed with delight when he saw the first tooth in his baby's mouth. Maibon, Modrona and their children and grandchildren lived for many years. Maibon was proud of his white hair and long beard.

출제율 90%

29 다음 중 빈칸 (A)와 (B)에 들어갈 말이 바르게 짝지어진 것은?

① throwing – happen
② throwing – to happen
③ throw – happen
④ to throw – happened
⑤ to throw – happen

출제율 100%

30 위 글의 ①~⑤ 중 지칭하는 것이 다른 하나는?

① ② ③ ④ ⑤

출제율 95%

31 다음 중 Maibon의 감정 변화로 가장 적절한 것은?

① upset → sad
② angry → lonely
③ happy → scared
④ angry → delighted
⑤ pleased → relieved

출제율 85%

32 What did Doli tell Maibon to do? Answer in English with a full sentence.

➡ _____

출제율 90%

33 Why couldn't Maibon get rid of the stone? Use the word 'because.' (6 words)

➡ _____

출제율 95%

34 위 글의 내용에 맞게 다음 물음에 완전한 문장의 영어로 답하시오.

Q: Why did Maibon laugh with delight at home?

A: _____

출제율 90%

35 What was Maibon proud of?

➡ _____

중간 + 기말
적중100 plus
영어 기출문제집

영어 중 2

비상 | 김진완

Best Collection

내용문의 중등영어발전소 적중100 편집부 TEL 070-7707-0457

INSIGHT
on the textbook

교과서 파헤치기

영어 기출 문제집
적중 100 plus
2학기 전과정

영어 중 **2**

비상 | 김진완

INSIGHT
on the textbook
교과서 파헤치기

※ 다음 영어를 우리말로 쓰시오.

01 avoid _____

02 suggestion _____

03 upset _____

04 worry _____

05 contact _____

06 advice _____

07 fight _____

08 haircut _____

09 alone _____

10 stuff _____

11 hurt _____

12 messy _____

13 wise _____

14 share _____

15 lunch break _____

16 repeat _____

17 matter _____

18 yell _____

19 since _____

20 mean _____

21 hate _____

22 stand _____

23 limit _____

24 explain _____

25 advise _____

26 yet _____

27 pack _____

28 difficult _____

29 forgive _____

30 elementary _____

31 fear _____

32 reason _____

33 solve _____

34 line _____

35 focus on _____

36 wake up _____

37 stay up late _____

38 gain weight _____

39 on purpose _____

40 shut down _____

41 work out _____

42 in the end _____

43 point out _____

※ 다음 우리말을 영어로 쓰시오.

01	거울	
02	초보의, 초급의	
03	공유하다, 나누다	
04	어려운	
05	반복하다	
06	소리치다	
07	접촉, 닿음	
08	조언하다, 충고하다	
09	문제	
10	싸다, 꾸리다	
11	싸우다	
12	점심시간	
13	이발, 머리 깎기	
14	물건	
15	다치게 하다	
16	참다, 견디다	
17	피하다	
18	한계, 제한	
19	아직	
20	치통	
21	제안	

22	홀로, 혼자	
23	걱정하다; 걱정	
24	어질러진, 더러운	
25	속상한, 마음이 상한	
26	이유, 까닭	
27	싫어하다	
28	(연극, 영화의) 대사	
29	조언	
30	용서하다	
31	설명하다	
32	두려움, 공포	
33	현명한	
34	풀다, 해결하다	
35	결국, 마침내	
36	~에 집중하다	
37	(기계가) 멈추다	
38	체중이 늘다	
39	좋다가 나쁘다가 하는	
40	늦게까지 자지 않고 있다	
41	고의로	
42	자명종을 맞추다	
43	잠에서 깨다	

※ 다음 영영풀이에 알맞은 단어를 <보기>에서 골라 쓴 후, 우리말 뜻을 쓰시오.

1 _____ : dirty and/or untidy: _____

2 _____ : to dislike something very much: _____

3 _____ : a pain in one of your teeth: _____

4 _____ : the state of touching something: _____

5 _____ : the act of someone cutting your hair: _____

6 _____ : the words spoken by an actor in a play or film/movie: _____

7 _____ : to say or write something again or more than once: _____

8 _____ : to have or use something at the same time as somebody else: _____

9 _____ : an idea or a plan that you mention for somebody else to think about: _____

10 _____ : the bad feeling that you have when you are in danger: _____

11 _____ : to keep away from somebody/something; to try not to do something: _____

12 _____ : in or connected with the first stages of a course of study: _____

13 _____ : to cause physical pain to somebody/yourself; to injure somebody/ yourself: _____

14 _____ : to shout loudly, for example because you are angry, excited, frightened or in pain: _____

15 _____ : an opinion or a suggestion about what somebody should do in a particular situation: _____

16 _____ : to stop feeling angry with somebody who has done something to harm, annoy or upset you: _____

보기			
forgive	advice	toothache	contact
line	messy	hurt	elementary
hate	yell	repeat	share
fear	suggestion	avoid	haircut

Step1

※ 다음 우리말과 일치하도록 빈칸에 알맞은 말을 쓰시오.

Listen & Talk 1-A-1

M: You don't _____ so _____ today. What's the _____?

W: I _____ my _____ _____ T-shirt. But I _____ grape juice on it.

M: Oh, no. _____ you _____ your sister?

W: No, _____ _____. I don't know _____ _____ _____.

Listen & Talk 1-A-2

Sora: David, you _____ _____ today. _____ _____ _____ _____?

David: I _____ _____ _____ but it's too short. I look _____.

Sora: _____ _____ your hat and _____ _____ _____.
(*pause*) Oh, it _____ _____.

David: Really? I guess I'm just _____ _____ _____ it yet.

Listen & Talk 1-B

Jane: You _____ _____. What's _____ _____?

Mike: _____ _____ _____ _____ _____ _____ _____. I'm so hungry.

Jane: Oh, that's _____ _____. We still have two more hours _____ _____ _____.

Mike: Our school should have a _____ _____. Then, we _____ _____ a quick breakfast or snacks.

Jane: I _____ _____, _____. _____ can we _____ that _____?

Mike: We _____ _____ it on the _____ board.

Listen & Talk 2 A-1

Sujin: I don't know _____ _____ _____ _____ in math. Can you _____ _____ _____ _____?

Jake: _____ do you _____ for tests?

Sujin: I just _____ _____ _____ _____ problems.

Jake: Well, don't _____ everything. I think you _____ _____ _____ the _____ you _____ _____.

M: 너 오늘은 별로 행복해 보이지가 않네. 무슨 일 있어?

W: 언니가 가장 좋아하는 티셔츠를 입었어. 그런데 거기에 포도 주스를 쏟았지 뭐야.

M: 오, 저런. 너희 언니에게 말했어?

W: 아니, 아직. 내가 뭘 해야 할지 모르겠어.

Sora: David, 너 오늘 침울해 보여. 무슨 일 있어?

David: 머리를 잘랐는데 너무 짧아. 우스꽝스럽게 보여.

Sora: 모자를 벗으면 내가 한 번 볼게. 오, 괜찮아 보이는데.

David: 정말? 난 아직 익숙해지지 않은 것 같아.

Jane: 너 피곤해 보인다. 무슨 일 있어?

Mike: 오늘 아침에 밥을 못 먹었어. 너무 배가 고파.

Jane: 오, 안됐다. 점심시간까지 아직 두 시간도 더 남았는데.

Mike: 우리 학교도 매점이 있어야 돼. 그러면 간단히 아침이나 간식을 먹을 수 있잖아.

Jane: 내 생각도 그래. 어떻게 하면 우리가 그 제안을 할 수 있을까?

Mike: 우리는 이걸 제안 게시판에 올릴 수 있어.

Sujin: 수학을 더 잘하는 방법을 모르겠어. 나에게 조언을 좀 해 줄래?

Jake: 시험을 목표로 어떻게 공부해?

Sujin: 난 그냥 많은 문제를 풀어 봐.

Jake: 글쎄, 전부 풀지 마. 내 생각엔 네가 틀린 문제들에 집중해야 할 것 같아.

Listen & Talk 2 A-2

Emily: I _____ _____ _____ _____ again. I just can't _____ _____ in the morning.

Tom: Do you _____ _____ _____?

Emily: Yeah, but I _____ _____ _____ and go back to sleep.

Tom: I _____ _____ _____ put it _____ _____ your bed. _____ _____, you'll have to _____ _____ _____ _____.

Review 1

Eric: Ms. Morris, I just can't _____ _____ _____ _____. _____ _____ _____ _____ _____?

Ms. Morris: Well, _____ _____ _____ _____ _____ a special program? When you _____ a time _____, the computer _____ _____ at that time.

Eric: Oh, that's _____ _____ _____.

Ms. Morris: And _____ _____ _____ _____ _____ _____ the computer _____ _____ your room and _____ the living room.

Eric: _____ _____ I _____. Thank you _____ _____ _____, Ms. Morris.

Communication

Solomon: Hello, you're _____ _____ _____.

Amy: Hi, Solomon. I'm Amy.

Solomon: Hi, Amy. _____ _____ _____?

Amy: I hate _____ my room _____ my little sister. She uses my _____ _____ _____ _____ me first. _____ _____ _____ I _____?

Solomon: Hmm.... I think you should _____ _____. And you should also _____ _____ _____ with your sister.

Amy: Oh, _____ _____ _____. _____ _____ the advice.

※ 다음 우리말에 맞도록 대화를 영어로 쓰시오.

Listen & Talk 1-A-1

M: _____

W: _____

M: _____

W: _____

해석

M: 너 오늘은 별로 행복해 보이지가 않네. 무슨 일 있어?

W: 언니가 가장 좋아하는 티셔츠를 입었어. 그런데 거기에 포도 주스를 쏟았지 뭐야.

M: 오, 저런. 너희 언니에게 말했어?

W: 아니, 아직. 내가 뭘 해야 할지 모르겠어.

Listen & Talk 1-A-2

Sora: _____

David: _____

Sora: _____

David: _____

Sora: David, 너 오늘 침울해 보여. 무슨 일 있어?

David: 머리를 잘랐는데 너무 짧아. 우스꽝스럽게 보여.

Sora: 모자를 벗으면 내가 한 번 볼게. 오, 괜찮아 보이는데.

David: 정말? 난 아직 익숙해지지 않은 것 같아.

Listen & Talk 1-B

Jane: _____

Mike: _____

Jane: _____

Mike: _____

Jane: _____

Mike: _____

Jane: 너 피곤해 보인다. 무슨 일 있어?

Mike: 오늘 아침에 밥을 못 먹었어. 너무 배가 고파.

Jane: 오, 안됐다. 점심시간까지 아직 두 시간도 더 남았는데.

Mike: 우리 학교도 매점이 있어야 돼. 그러면 간단히 아침이나 간식을 먹을 수 있잖아.

Jane: 내 생각도 그래. 어떻게 하면 우리가 그 제안을 할 수 있을까?

Mike: 우리는 이걸 제안 게시판에 올릴 수 있어.

Listen & Talk 2 A-1

Sujin: _____

Jake: _____

Sujin: _____

Jake: _____

Sujin: 수학을 더 잘하는 방법을 모르겠어. 나에게 조언을 좀 해 줄래?

Jake: 시험을 목표로 어떻게 공부해?

Sujin: 난 그냥 많은 문제를 풀어 봐.

Jake: 글쎄, 전부 풀지 마. 내 생각엔 네가 틀린 문제들에 집중해야 할 것 같아.

Listen & Talk 2 A-2

Emily: _____

Tom: _____

Emily: _____

Tom: _____

Emily: 나 또 수업에 늦었어. 난 정말 아침에 못 일어나겠어.
Tom: 자명종은 맞춰 두는 거야?
Emily: 응, 그렇지만 자명종을 끄고 다시 잠들게 돼.
Tom: 내 생각엔 자명종을 침대에서 멀리 떨어진 곳에 두어야 할 것 같아. 그러면 침대에서 일어날 수밖에 없을 거야.

Review 1

Eric: _____

Ms. Morris: _____

_____

Eric: _____

Ms. Morris: _____

_____

Eric: _____

Eric: Morris 선생님, 저 컴퓨터 게임하는 것을 멈출 수가 없어요. 제가 어떻게 해야 할까요?
Mr. Morris: 음, 특별한 프로그램을 써 보는 게 어떨까? 네가 시간 제한을 정해 두면 컴퓨터가 그 시간에 맞춰 종료돼.
Eric: 오, 좋은 생각이네요.
Mr. Morris: 그리고 내 생각엔 컴퓨터를 네 방에서 거실로 옮겨 두어야 할 것 같아.
Eric: 제 생각에도 그래야 할 것 같아요. Morris 선생님, 조언해 주셔서 감사합니다.

Communication

Solomon: _____

Amy: _____

Solomon: _____

Amy: _____

_____

Solomon: _____

_____

Amy: _____

Solomon: 안녕하세요, (방송에) 연결되었습니다.
Amy: 안녕하세요, Solomon. 전 Amy라고 해요.
Solomon: 안녕하세요, Amy. 무슨 일 있어요?
Amy: 전 여동생이랑 제 방을 같이 쓰는 게 싫어요. 그 애는 제게 먼저 물어보지도 않고 제 물건을 쓰거든요. 제가 어떻게 해야 할까요?
Solomon: 흠.... 제 생각엔 당신의 기분을 여동생에게 말해야 할 것 같아요. 그리고 여동생과 몇 가지 규칙을 만들어 봐요.
Amy: 오, 그렇게 할게요. 조언 감사해요.

※ 다음 우리말과 일치하도록 빈칸에 알맞은 것을 골라 쓰시오.

1 Bella is 15 years _____ this year and _____ days her feelings are _____ up and _____.
    A. these   B. down   C. old   D. going

2 Today, she _____ _____.
    A. down   B. looks

3 _____ listen to Bella's _____ and _____ out why.
    A. find   B. let's   C. feelings

Day 1

4 Anger: _____ a day! I can't believe Jenny _____ _____ Bella _____ the school play.
    A. at   B. what   C. after   D. yelled

5 Sadness: Well, that's _____ Bella _____ her _____ on stage.
    A. forgot   B. because   C. lines

6 Anger: Jenny pointed _____ the mistake _____ Bella _____.
    A. made   B. out   C. that

7 How _____ she do that _____ _____ of everyone?
    A. front   B. could   C. in

8 Joy: But I'm _____ Jenny did not _____ to _____ Bella.
    A. hurt   B. mean   C. sure

9 They _____ _____ best friends _____ elementary school. Remember?
    A. since   B. been   C. have

10 Anger: That's _____ I'm _____.
    A. saying   B. what

11 A true friend would _____ _____ Bella _____ like that.
    A. put   B. never   C. down

12 Fear: I'm worried _____ they are not _____ to friends anymore.
    A. going   B. that   C. be

13 Joy: Come on, Fear. _____ go too _____. We'll _____.
    A. don't   B. far   C. see

Day 2

14 Anger: I can't _____ Jenny. She didn't _____ a _____ to Bella.
    A. word   B. forgive   C. say

15 Fear: Jenny didn't _____ _____ _____ her.
    A. at   B. even   C. look

---

1 Bella는 올해 15세이고 요즘 그 애의 기분은 좋다가 안 좋다가 한다.

2 오늘 그 애는 우울해 보인다.

3 Bella의 감정에 귀 기울여 보고 그 이유를 알아보자.

Day 1

4 Anger: 정말 끔찍한 하루야! 학교 연극이 끝난 후 Jenny가 Bella에게 소리를 지르다니 믿을 수가 없어.

5 Sadness: 글쎄, 그건 Bella가 무대에서 그녀의 대사를 잊어버렸기 때문이잖아.

6 Anger: Jenny는 Bella가 저지른 실수를 지적했잖아.

7 어떻게 모든 사람 앞에서 그렇게 할 수가 있니?

8 Joy: 하지만 난 Jenny가 Bella에게 상처를 주려고 했던 건 아니었다고 확신해.

9 그들은 초등학교 때부터 가장 친한 친구였잖아. 기억하지?

10 Anger: 내 말이 바로 그거야.

11 진정한 친구라면 절대로 그런 식으로 Bella를 깎아내리지 않을 거야.

12 Fear: 나는 그들이 더 이상 친구로 지내지 않을까봐 걱정돼.

13 Joy: 자, Fear. 너무 극단적으로 생각하지 마. 곧 알게 되겠지.

Day 2

14 Anger: 난 Jenny를 용서할 수 없어. 그 애는 Bella에게 한마디도 말을 안 했어.

15 Fear: Jenny는 심지어 Bella를 쳐다 보지도 않았어.

16 Jenny _____ _____ _____ this cold before.

    A. never   B. has   C. been

17 Sadness: Bella ate _____ _____ lunch today. Poor Bella!

    A. during   B. alone

18 Joy: Jenny is Bella's _____ _____.

    A. friend   B. best

19 I'm sure there is a _____ that we don't _____ _____.

    A. about   B. reason   C. know

20 Anger: I can't _____ this _____ _____.

    A. any   B. stand   C. longer

21 Bella should just _____ and _____ her _____ her feelings.

    A. about   B. tell   C. go

22 Fear: I don't _____ Bella _____ be _____ again.

    A. to   B. hurt   C. want

23 She should _____ it _____.

    A. go   B. let

24 Joy: They are good friends. They will _____ it _____.

    A. out   B. work

Day 3

25 Joy: Whew! I'm _____ happy _____ they are _____ again.

    A. that   B. talking   C. so

26 Anger: Yeah, Bella _____ to Jenny and _____ to _____ first.

    A. talked   B. went   C. her

27 Joy: Jenny didn't _____ Bella _____ _____.

    A. on   B. avoid   C. purpose

28 Sadness: Yeah, Jenny _____ know a _____ to _____ sorry.

    A. say   B. way   C. didn't

29 Fear: I hope Bella _____ have _____ _____ problems like this.

    A. any   B. doesn't   C. more

30 Joy: Me, _____. But problems are _____ of growing _____.

    A. part   B. too   C. up

31 Just _____ this time, Bella will _____ the problems, solve them, and become _____ in the _____.

    A. face   B. like   C. end   D. wiser

---

16 Jenny가 전에 이렇게 차가웠던 적이 없었어.

17 Sadness: Bella는 오늘 점심시간에 혼자 밥을 먹었잖아. 가엾은 Bella!

18 Joy: Jenny는 Bella의 가장 친한 친구야.

19 나는 우리가 모르는 어떤 이유가 있다고 확신해.

20 Anger: 나는 더 이상 이 상황을 못 참아.

21 Bella는 일단 가서 Jenny에게 자신의 감정을 말해야 해.

22 Fear: 나는 Bella가 또다시 상처 받는 걸 원하지 않아.

23 그 애는 그냥 내버려 두어야 해.

24 Joy: 그 애들은 좋은 친구야. 그 애들이 잘 해낼 거야.

Day 3

25 Joy: 휴! 나는 그 애들이 다시 이야기하게 되어 무척 기뻐.

26 Anger: 그래, Bella가 Jenny에게 가서 그 애에게 먼저 말을 걸었지.

27 Joy: Jenny는 일부러 Bella를 피한 게 아니었어.

28 Sadness: 맞아, Jenny는 사과하는 방법을 몰랐던 거야.

29 Fear: 나는 Bella에게 이번과 같은 문제가 더 이상 없기를 바라.

30 Joy: 나도 그래. 하지만 문제들은 성장의 일부야.

31 이번과 꼭 마찬가지로 Bella는 문제들에 직면하게 될 거고, 그것들을 해결할 거고, 그리고 결국 더 현명해질 거야.

Step2

※ 다음 우리말과 일치하도록 빈칸에 알맞은 말을 쓰시오.

1 Bella is 15 _____ _____ this year and _____ _____ her feelings are _____ _____ _____ _____ .

2 Today, she _____ _____ .

3 _____ _____ _____ Bella's _____ and _____ _____ _____ .

Day 1

4 Anger: _____ _____ _____ ! I can't believe Jenny _____ _____ Bella _____ the school play.

5 Sadness: Well, that's _____ Bella _____ her _____ _____ .

6 Anger: Jenny _____ _____ the mistake _____ _____ _____ .

7 How _____ she do that _____ _____ _____ everyone?

8 Joy: But I'm _____ Jenny _____ _____ _____ _____ Bella.

9 They _____ _____ best friends _____ _____ _____ . Remember?

10 Anger: That's _____ I'm _____ .

11 A true friend _____ _____ _____ Bella _____ like that.

12 Fear: I'm worried _____ they are _____ _____ _____ _____ _____ .

13 Joy: Come on, Fear. _____ _____ _____ _____ _____ . We'll _____ .

Day 2

14 Anger: I _____ _____ Jenny. She _____ _____ _____ _____ to Bella.

15 Fear: Jenny _____ _____ _____ _____ _____ her.

---

1 Bella는 올해 15세이고 요즘 그 애의 기분은 좋다가 안 좋다가 한다.

2 오늘 그 애는 우울해 보인다.

3 Bella의 감정에 귀 기울여 보고 그 이유를 알아보자.

Day 1

4 Anger: 정말 끔찍한 하루야! 학교 연극이 끝난 후 Jenny가 Bella에게 소리를 지르다니 믿을 수가 없어.

5 Sadness: 글쎄, 그건 Bella가 무대에서 그녀의 대사를 잊어버렸기 때문이잖아.

6 Anger: Jenny는 Bella가 저지른 실수를 지적했잖아.

7 어떻게 모든 사람 앞에서 그렇게 할 수가 있니?

8 Joy: 하지만 난 Jenny가 Bella에게 상처를 주려고 했던 건 아니었다고 확신해.

9 그들은 초등학교 때부터 가장 친한 친구였잖아. 기억하지?

10 Anger: 내 말이 바로 그거야.

11 진정한 친구라면 절대로 그런 식으로 Bella를 깎아내리지 않을 거야.

12 Fear: 나는 그들이 더 이상 친구로 지내지 않을까봐 걱정돼.

13 Joy: 자, Fear. 너무 극단적으로 생각하지 마. 곧 알게 되겠지.

Day 2

14 Anger: 난 Jenny를 용서할 수 없어. 그 애는 Bella에게 한마디도 말을 안 했어.

15 Fear: Jenny는 심지어 Bella를 쳐다 보지도 않았어.

16 Jenny _____ _____ _____ this cold before.

17 Sadness: Bella _____ _____ _____ lunch today. Poor Bella!

18 Joy: Jenny is _____ _____ _____ .

19 I'm sure there is a _____ _____ _____ _____ _____ _____ .

20 Anger: I _____ _____ this _____ _____ .

21 Bella should just _____ and _____ her _____ her feelings.

22 Fear: I don't _____ Bella _____ _____ _____ again.

23 She _____ _____ _____ _____ .

24 Joy: They are good friends. They will _____ _____ .

Day 3

25 Joy: Whew! I'm so happy _____ they _____ _____ again.

26 Anger: Yeah, Bella _____ _____ Jenny and _____ _____ first.

27 Joy: Jenny _____ _____ Bella _____ _____ .

28 Sadness: Yeah, Jenny didn't know _____ _____ _____ _____ _____ .

29 Fear: I hope Bella doesn't have _____ _____ _____ _____ this.

30 Joy: _____ , _____ . But problems are _____ _____ _____ _____ .

31 _____ _____ this time, Bella will _____ the problems, _____ _____ , and become _____ in the _____ .

---

16 Jenny가 전에 이렇게 차가웠던 적이 없었어.

17 Sadness: Bella는 오늘 점심시간에 혼자 밥을 먹었잖아. 가엾은 Bella!

18 Joy: Jenny는 Bella의 가장 친한 친구야.

19 나는 우리가 모르는 어떤 이유가 있다고 확신해.

20 Anger: 나는 더 이상 이 상황을 못 참아.

21 Bella는 일단 가서 Jenny에게 자신의 감정을 말해야 해.

22 Fear: 나는 Bella가 또다시 상처 받는 걸 원하지 않아.

23 그 애는 그냥 내버려 두어야 해.

24 Joy: 그 애들은 좋은 친구야. 그 애들이 잘 해낼 거야.

Day 3

25 Joy: 휴! 나는 그 애들이 다시 이야기하게 되어 무척 기뻐.

26 Anger: 그래, Bella가 Jenny에게 가서 그 애에게 먼저 말을 걸었지.

27 Joy: Jenny는 일부러 Bella를 피한 게 아니었어.

28 Sadness: 맞아, Jenny는 사과하는 방법을 몰랐던 거야.

29 Fear: 나는 Bella에게 이번과 같은 문제가 더 이상 없기를 바라.

30 Joy: 나도 그래. 하지만 문제들은 성장의 일부야.

31 이번과 꼭 마찬가지로 Bella는 문제들에 직면하게 될 거고, 그것들을 해결할 거고, 그리고 결국 더 현명해질 거야.

※ 다음 문장을 우리말로 쓰시오.

1 Bella is 15 years old this year and these days her feelings are going up and down.

➡ _____

2 Today, she looks down.

➡ _____

3 Let's listen to Bella's feelings and find out why.

➡ _____

4 Anger: What a day! I can't believe Jenny yelled at Bella after the school play.

➡ _____

5 Sadness: Well, that's because Bella forgot her lines on stage.

➡ _____

6 Anger: Jenny pointed out the mistake that Bella made.

➡ _____

7 How could she do that in front of everyone?

➡ _____

8 Joy: But I'm sure Jenny did not mean to hurt Bella.

➡ _____

9 They have been best friends since elementary school. Remember?

➡ _____

10 Anger: That's what I'm saying.

➡ _____

11 A true friend would never put Bella down like that.

➡ _____

12 Fear: I'm worried that they are not going to be friends anymore.

➡ _____

13 Joy: Come on, Fear. Don't go too far. We'll see.

➡ _____

14 Anger: I can't forgive Jenny. She didn't say a word to Bella.

➡ _____

15 Fear: Jenny didn't even look at her.

➡ _____

16 Jenny has never been this cold before.

➡ _____

17 Sadness: Bella ate alone during lunch today. Poor Bella!

➡ _____

18 Joy: Jenny is Bella's best friend.

➡ _____

19 I'm sure there is a reason that we don't know about.

➡ _____

20 Anger: I can't stand this any longer.

➡ _____

21 Bella should just go and tell her about her feelings.

➡ _____

22 Fear: I don't want Bella to be hurt again.

➡ _____

23 She should let it go.

➡ _____

24 Joy: They are good friends. They will work it out.

➡ _____

25 Joy: Whew! I'm so happy that they are talking again.

➡ _____

26 Anger: Yeah, Bella went to Jenny and talked to her first.

➡ _____

27 Joy: Jenny didn't avoid Bella on purpose.

➡ _____

28 Sadness: Yeah, Jenny didn't know a way to say sorry.

➡ _____

29 Fear: I hope Bella doesn't have any more problems like this.

➡ _____

30 Joy: Me, too. But problems are part of growing up.

➡ _____

31 Just like this time, Bella will face the problems, solve them, and become wiser in the end.

➡ _____

Step4

※ 다음 괄호 안의 단어들을 우리말에 맞도록 바르게 배열하시오.

1 (is / Bella / years / 15 / old / year / this / and / days / these / feelings / her / going / are / down. / and / up)
➡ _____
_____

2 (she / today, / down. / looks)
➡ _____

3 (listen / let's / Bella's / to / and / feelings / why. / out / find)
➡ _____

4 (a / what / day! // can't / I / Jenny / believe / at / yelled / Bella / the / play. / school / after)
➡ Anger: _____
_____

5 (that's / well, / Bella / because / forgot / lines / her / stage. / on)
➡ Sadness: _____

6 (pointed / Jenny / the / out / that / mistake / made. / Bella)
➡ Anger: _____

7 (could / how / do / she / that / front / in / everyone? / of)
➡ _____

8 (I'm / but / Jenny / sure / not / did / to / mean / Bella. / hurt)
➡ Joy: _____

9 (have / they / been / friends / best / school. / elementary / since // remember?)
➡ _____

10 (what / that's / saying. / I'm)
➡ Anger: _____

11 (true / a / would / friend / put / never / Bella / that. / like / down)
➡ _____

12 (worried / I'm / they / that / not / are / to / going / anymore. / friends / be)
➡ Fear: _____

13 (on, / come / Fear. // go / don't / far. / too // see. / we'll)
➡ Joy: _____

14 (can't / I / Jenny. / forgive // didn't / she / word / a / say / Bella. / to)
➡ Anger: _____

15 (didn't / Jenny / look / even / her. / at)
➡ Fear: _____

1 Bella는 올해 15세이고 요즘 그 애의 기분은 좋다가 안 좋다가 한다.

2 오늘 그 애는 우울해 보인다.

3 Bella의 감정에 귀 기울여 보고 그 이유를 알아보자.

Day **1**

4 Anger: 정말 끔찍한 하루야! 학교 연극이 끝난 후 Jenny가 Bella에게 소리를 지르다니 믿을 수가 없어.

5 Sadness: 글쎄, 그건 Bella가 무대에서 그녀의 대사를 잊어버렸기 때문이잖아.

6 Anger: Jenny는 Bella가 저지른 실수를 지적했잖아.

7 어떻게 모든 사람 앞에서 그렇게 할 수가 있니?

8 Joy: 하지만 난 Jenny가 Bella에게 상처를 주려고 했던 건 아니었다고 확신해.

9 그들은 초등학교 때부터 가장 친한 친구였잖아. 기억하지?

10 Anger: 내 말이 바로 그거야.

11 진정한 친구라면 절대로 그런 식으로 Bella를 깎아내리지 않을 거야.

12 Fear: 나는 그들이 더 이상 친구로 지내지 않을까봐 걱정돼.

13 Joy: 자, Fear. 너무 극단적으로 생각하지 마. 곧 알게 되겠지.

Day **2**

14 Anger: 난 Jenny를 용서할 수 없어. 그 애는 Bella에게 한마디도 말을 안 했어.

15 Fear: Jenny는 심지어 Bella를 쳐다 보지도 않았어.

16 (has / Jenny / been / never / before. / cold / this)

➡ _____

17 (ate / Bella / during / alone / today. / lunch // Bella! / poor)

➡ Sadness: _____

18 (is / Jenny / friend. / best / Bella's)

➡ Joy: _____

19 (sure / I'm / is / there / reason / a / that / don't / we / about. / know)

➡ _____

20 (can't / I / this / stand / longer. / any)

➡ Anger: _____

21 (should / Bella / go / just / and / her / tell / about / feelings. / her)

➡ _____

22 (don't / I / want / to / Bella / again. / hurt / be)

➡ Fear: _____

23 (should / she / go. / it / let)

➡ _____

24 (are / they / friends. / good // will / they / out. / it / work)

➡ Joy: _____

25 (I'm / whew! / so / that / happy / they / again. / talking / are)

➡ Joy: _____

26 (Bella / yeah, / to / went / Jenny / and / first. / her / to / talked)

➡ Anger: _____

27 (didn't / Jenny / avoid / purpose. / on / Bella)

➡ Joy: _____

28 (Jenny / yeah, / know / didn't / way / a / sorry. / say / to)

➡ Sadness: _____

29 (hope / I / doesn't / Bella / any / have / problems / this. / like / more)

➡ Fear: _____

30 (too. / me, // problems / but / part / are / up. / growing / of)

➡ Joy: _____

31 (like / just / time, / this / Bella / face / will / problems, / the / them, / solve / become / and / wiser / end. / the / in)

➡ _____
_____

16 Jenny가 전에 이렇게 차가웠던 적이 없었어.

17 Sadness: Bella는 오늘 점심시간에 혼자 밥을 먹었잖아. 가엾은 Bella!

18 Joy: Jenny는 Bella의 가장 친한 친구야.

19 나는 우리가 모르는 어떤 이유가 있다고 확신해.

20 Anger: 나는 더 이상 이 상황을 못 참아.

21 Bella는 일단 가서 Jenny에게 자신의 감정을 말해야 해.

22 Fear: 나는 Bella가 또다시 상처받는 걸 원하지 않아.

23 그 애는 그냥 내버려 두어야 해.

24 Joy: 그 애들은 좋은 친구야. 그 애들이 잘 해낼 거야.

Day 3

25 Joy: 휴! 나는 그 애들이 다시 이야기하게 되어 무척 기뻐.

26 Anger: 그래, Bella가 Jenny에게 가서 그 애에게 먼저 말을 걸었지.

27 Joy: Jenny는 일부러 Bella를 피한 게 아니었어.

28 Sadness: 맞아, Jenny는 사과하는 방법을 몰랐던 거야.

29 Fear: 나는 Bella에게 이번과 같은 문제가 더 이상 없기를 바라.

30 Joy: 나도 그래. 하지만 문제들은 성장의 일부야.

31 이번과 꼭 마찬가지로 Bella는 문제들에 직면하게 될 거고, 그것들을 해결할 거고, 그리고 결국 더 현명해질 거야.

※ 다음 우리말을 영어로 쓰시오.

1 Bella는 올해 15세이고 요즘 그 애의 기분은 좋다가 안 좋다가 한다.

➡ _____

2 오늘 그 애는 우울해 보인다.

➡ _____

3 Bella의 감정에 귀 기울여 보고 그 이유를 알아보자.

➡ _____

4 Anger: 정말 끔찍한 하루야! 학교 연극이 끝난 후 Jenny가 Bella에게 소리를 지르다니 믿을 수가 없어.

➡ _____

5 Sadness: 글쎄, 그건 Bella가 무대에서 그녀의 대사를 잊어버렸기 때문이잖아.

➡ _____

6 Anger: Jenny는 Bella가 저지른 실수를 지적했잖아.

➡ _____

7 어떻게 모든 사람 앞에서 그렇게 할 수가 있니?

➡ _____

8 Joy: 하지만 난 Jenny가 Bella에게 상처를 주려고 했던 건 아니었다고 확신해.

➡ _____

9 그들은 초등학교 때부터 가장 친한 친구였잖아. 기억하지?

➡ _____

10 Anger: 내 말이 바로 그거야.

➡ _____

11 진정한 친구라면 절대로 그런 식으로 Bella를 깎아내리지 않을 거야.

➡ _____

12 Fear: 나는 그들이 더 이상 친구로 지내지 않을까봐 걱정돼.

➡ _____

13 Joy: 자, Fear. 너무 극단적으로 생각하지 마. 곧 알게 되겠지.

➡ _____

14 Anger: 난 Jenny를 용서할 수 없어. 그 애는 Bella에게 한마디도 말을 안 했어.

➡ _____

15 Fear: Jenny는 심지어 Bella를 쳐다보지도 않았어.

➡ _____

16 ▶ Jenny가 전에 이렇게 차가웠던 적이 없었어.

➡ _____

17 ▶ Sadness: Bella는 오늘 점심시간에 혼자 밥을 먹었잖아. 가엾은 Bella!

➡ _____

18 ▶ Joy: Jenny는 Bella의 가장 친한 친구야.

➡ _____

19 ▶ 나는 우리가 모르는 어떤 이유가 있다고 확신해.

➡ _____

20 ▶ Anger: 나는 더 이상 이 상황을 못 참아.

➡ _____

21 ▶ Bella는 일단 가서 Jenny에게 자신의 감정을 말해야 해.

➡ _____

22 ▶ Fear: 나는 Bella가 또다시 상처받는 걸 원하지 않아.

➡ _____

23 ▶ 그 애는 그냥 내버려 두어야 해.

➡ _____

24 ▶ Joy: 그 애들은 좋은 친구야. 그 애들이 잘 해낼 거야.

➡ _____

25 ▶ Joy: 휴! 나는 그 애들이 다시 이야기하게 되어 무척 기뻐.

➡ _____

26 ▶ Anger: 그래, Bella가 Jenny에게 가서 그 애에게 먼저 말을 걸었지.

➡ _____

27 ▶ Joy: Jenny는 일부러 Bella를 피한 게 아니었어.

➡ _____

28 ▶ Sadness: 맞아, Jenny는 사과하는 방법을 몰랐던 거야.

➡ _____

29 ▶ Fear: 나는 Bella에게 이번과 같은 문제가 더 이상 없기를 바라.

➡ _____

30 ▶ Joy: 나도 그래. 하지만 문제들은 성장의 일부야.

➡ _____

31 ▶ 이번과 꼭 마찬가지로 Bella는 문제들에 직면하게 될 거고, 그것들을 해결할 거고, 그리고 결국 더 현명해질 거야.

➡ _____

※ 다음 우리말과 일치하도록 빈칸에 알맞은 말을 쓰시오.

Wrap up 1

1. Mr. Jones: Daisy, you're _____ _____.

2. Daisy: I'm really sorry, Mr. Jones. I _____ _____ _____ again _____ _____.

3. Mr. Jones: Well, I think you _____ _____ _____ go to bed _____.

4. You _____ _____ _____ your bag the night before, so you can _____ _____ in the morning.

5. Daisy: Okay, Mr. Jones. I'll _____ _____ _____.

Read & Think

1. Bella: Jenny, I was _____ _____ you _____ _____ my mistake _____ _____ _____ _____.

2. But I'm sure you didn't _____ _____ _____ my feelings.

3. Jenny: I'm so sorry, Bella. _____ _____ _____ _____ to me first.

Think & Write

1. Dear _____ _____,

2. I _____ _____ _____ you a problem that I _____.

3. I'm _____ _____ my terrible _____ _____.

4. I _____ _____ this problem _____ _____ _____ _____.

5. I want to _____ _____ in math.

6. But when I _____ _____ _____ math, I just _____ _____ _____ it.

7. I don't know _____ _____ _____.

8. I _____ _____ _____ a good night's sleep _____ _____ this worry.

9. Can you _____ my worries _____?

1. Mr. Jones: Daisy, 너 또 지각이구나.
2. Daisy: Jones 선생님, 정말 죄송해요. 어젯밤에 또 늦게까지 자지 않고 깨어 있었어요.
3. Mr. Jones: 음, 내 생각엔 넌 더 일찍 잠자리에 들려고 노력해야 할 것 같구나.
4. 또 전날 밤에 가방을 싸 둔다면 아침에 시간을 절약할 수 있어.
5. Daisy: 알겠어요, Jones 선생님. 조언해 주신 것을 해 볼게요.

1. Bella: Jenny야, 네가 다른 사람들 앞에서 내 잘못을 지적했을 때 화가 났어.
2. 그렇지만 난 네가 내게 상처를 주려고 일부러 그런 게 아니라고 믿어.
3. Jenny: Bella야, 미안해. 먼저 내게 와 줘서 고마워.

1. 걱정 인형에게,
2. 나는 너에게 내가 가진 문제를 말하고 싶어.
3. 나는 나의 끔찍한 수학 성적이 걱정돼.
4. 나는 작년부터 이 문제를 가지고 있어.
5. 나는 수학을 더 잘하고 싶어.
6. 하지만 내가 수학을 공부하려고 하면, 나는 단지 그것에 집중할 수 없어.
7. 나는 무엇을 해야 할지 모르겠어.
8. 이 걱정 때문에 밤에 잠도 잘 못자.
9. 내 걱정을 없애 줄 수 있겠니?

※ 다음 우리말을 영어로 쓰시오.

Wrap up 1

1. Mr. Jones: Daisy, 너 또 지각이구나.
   ➡ _____

2. Daisy: Jones 선생님, 정말 죄송해요. 어젯밤에 또 늦게까지 자지 않고 깨어 있었어요.
   ➡ _____

3. Mr. Jones: 음, 내 생각엔 넌 더 일찍 잠자리에 들려고 노력해야 할 것 같구나.
   ➡ _____

4. 또 전날 밤에 가방을 싸 둔다면 아침에 시간을 절약할 수 있어.
   ➡ _____

5. Daisy: 알겠어요, Jones 선생님. 조언해 주신 것을 해 볼게요.
   ➡ _____

Read & Think

1. Bella: Jenny야, 네가 다른 사람들 앞에서 내 잘못을 지적했을 때 화가 났었어.
   ➡ _____

2. 그렇지만 난 네가 내게 상처를 주려고 일부러 그런 게 아니라고 믿어.
   ➡ _____

3. Jenny: Bella야, 미안해. 먼저 내게 와 줘서 고마워.
   ➡ _____

Think & Write

1. 걱정 인형에게,
   ➡ _____

2. 나는 너에게 내가 가진 문제를 말하고 싶어.
   ➡ _____

3. 나는 나의 끔찍한 수학 성적이 걱정 돼.
   ➡ _____

4. 나는 작년부터 이 문제를 가지고 있어.
   ➡ _____

5. 나는 수학을 더 잘하고 싶어.
   ➡ _____

6. 하지만 내가 수학을 공부하려고 하면, 나는 단지 그것에 집중할 수 없어.
   ➡ _____

7. 나는 무엇을 해야 할지 모르겠어.
   ➡ _____

8. 이 걱정 때문에 밤에 잠도 잘 못자.
   ➡ _____

9. 내 걱정을 없애 줄 수 있겠니?
   ➡ _____

※ 다음 영어를 우리말로 쓰시오.

01 blind

02 dead

03 seem

04 attract

05 careless

06 throughout

07 curious

08 sense

09 dangerous

10 huge

11 thick

12 appear

13 ginger

14 feed

15 attack

16 shelter

17 rescue

18 giant

19 restless

20 tongue

21 friendship

22 trunk

23 strength

24 tail

25 humorous

26 insect

27 allow

28 unbelievably

29 whale

30 lifeless

31 approach

32 probably

33 female

34 adventurous

35 thanks to

36 keep one's eyes on

37 be born

38 care for

39 tell the difference

40 millions of

41 become part of

42 give a presentation

43 next to

※ 다음 우리말을 영어로 쓰시오.

01 거대한	
02 나타나다	
03 구조	
04 궁금한, 호기심이 많은	
05 죽은	
06 모험심이 강한	
07 허락하다	
08 돌고래	
09 우정	
10 뱀	
11 위험한	
12 다가가다, 다가오다	
13 생강	
14 죽은, 생명이 없는	
15 공격하다	
16 구멍	
17 부주의한	
18 감각	
19 재미있는, 유머러스한	
20 ~ 동안, ~ 내내	
21 암컷의	

22 혀	
23 (종이) 한 장	
24 곤충	
25 언어	
26 가만히 못 있는	
27 믿을 수 없을 정도로	
28 힘	
29 눈 먼, 맹인인	
30 먹이를 주다	
31 보호소	
32 끌다, ~을 끌어당기다	
33 두꺼운	
34 (코끼리의) 코	
35 ~ 덕분에	
36 ~ 옆에	
37 ~을 돌보다	
38 ~의 일원이 되다	
39 수백만의	
40 발표하다	
41 태어나다	
42 ~에서 눈을 떼지 않다	
43 차이를 구별하다	

※ 다음 영영풀이에 알맞은 단어를 <보기>에서 골라 쓴 후, 우리말 뜻을 쓰시오.

1　_____ : no longer alive: _____

2　_____ : the long nose of an elephant: _____

3　_____ : not able to see: _____

4　_____ : having a strong desire to know about something: _____

5　_____ : to give food to a person or an animal: _____

6　_____ : not afraid to do new and dangerous or exciting things: _____

7　_____ : to come near to somebody/something in distance or time: _____

8　_____ : the feeling or relationship that friends have; the state of being friends: _____

9　_____ : any small creature with six legs and a body divided into three parts: _____

10　_____ : a very large animal that lives in the ocean and looks like a very large fish: _____

11　_____ : to save somebody/something from a dangerous or harmful situation: _____

12　_____ : a structure built to give protection, especially from the weather or from attack: _____

13　_____ : the soft part in the mouth that moves around, used for tasting, swallowing, speaking, etc.: _____

14　_____ : to let somebody/something do something; to let something happen or be done: _____

15　_____ : not giving enough attention and thought to what you are doing, so that you make mistakes: _____

16　_____ : the part that sticks out and can be moved at the back of the body of a bird, an animal or a fish: _____

allow	feed	tongue	approach
blind	careless	trunk	friendship
tail	shelter	rescue	whale
curious	dead	insect	adventurous

※ 다음 우리말과 일치하도록 빈칸에 알맞은 말을 쓰시오.

Listen & Talk 1 A-1

Ryan: Judy, did you _____ a _____ for your science project?

Judy: Not yet. _____ _____ you, Ryan?

Ryan: _____ _____ _____ _____ _____. So I'm _____
_____ _____ the project on that.

Judy: That's an _____ _____!

Ryan: Judy, 너 과학 과제로 할 주제 골랐어?
Judy: 아직. 너는 어때, Ryan?
Ryan: 나는 날씨 변화가 궁금하거든. 그래서 난 그것에 관한 과제를 하려고 생각 중이야.
Judy: 주제가 흥미로운걸!

Listen & Talk 1 A-2

Jane: _____ _____ this picture of a _____ flower.

Tom: Wow, it is _____ _____ a person.

Jane: Yeah. I'm really _____ _____ this flower. It also _____
here that the flower _____ very _____, but _____ love
the smell.

Tom: Hmm, I _____ _____.

Jane: 이 커다란 꽃 사진을 봐.
Tom: 와, 사람보다 더 크네.
Jane: 그래. 나는 이 꽃이 정말 궁금해. 또 여기에 나와 있는데 그 꽃은 냄새가 매우 고약하지만 벌레들은 그 냄새를 좋아한대.
Tom: 흠, 이유가 궁금하다.

Listen & Talk 1 B

Clare: Do you think we can _____ _____ with lions, Todd?

Todd: No, Clare. I _____ _____ _____.

Clare: Well, I _____ a video clip about _____ _____ two men
_____ a lion.

Todd: Really? I'm _____ _____ the story. Can you tell me more?

Clare: The two men _____ a baby lion and _____ her _____
into the _____. When the men and the lion met _____
_____ _____, she remembered them.

Todd: Wow, that's so _____.

Clare: 우리가 사자와 친구가 될 수 있을 거라고 생각해, Todd?
Todd: 아니, Clare. 난 그렇게 생각하지 않아.
Clare: 음, 나 두 남자와 사자 사이의 우정에 대한 동영상을 봤어.
Todd: 정말? 그 이야기가 궁금해. 더 얘기해 줄 수 있어?
Clare: 두 남자가 아기 사자를 길러서 야생으로 돌려보냈대. 일 년 후에 그 남자들과 사자가 만났을 때, 그 사자는 그들을 기억했다는 거야.
Todd: 와, 정말 감동적이구나.

Listen & Talk 2 A-1

Dylan: _____ _____ this picture, Mina. We got a new _____
yesterday. He's only _____ _____ old.

Mina: Oh, Dylan, he's _____ _____!

Dylan: Yeah. He's _____ _____ _____ my hand now, but he'll
get _____ _____ in a _____ _____.

Mina: Wow, puppies _____ very quickly.

Dylan: 이 사진 좀 봐, 미나야. 우리 어제 새 강아지를 데리고 왔어. 그 강아지는 2주밖에 안 됐어.
Mina: 오, Dylan, 걔 너무 조그맣다!
Dylan: 맞아. 그 애는 지금 내 손만큼 작지만, 몇 달 뒤에는 훨씬 더 커질 거야.
Mina: 와, 강아지들은 정말 빨리 크네.

Listen & Talk 2 A-2

Kelly: George, that red house _____ _____ is my _____ house.

George: Wow, the tree _____ the house is _____ _____.

Kelly: Actually, that tree is _____ _____ _____ _____, thirteen years old.

George: _____ do you _____ that, Kelly?

Kelly: My grandfather _____ the tree in 2004 when I _____ _____.

Kelly: George, 저기에 있는 빨간 집이 우리 할아버지와 할머니 댁이야.

George: 와, 집 옆에 있는 나무가 굉장히 크네.

Kelly: 사실, 저 나무의 나이는 나랑 같아서 수령이 13년 되었어.

George: 그걸 어떻게 알아, Kelly?

Kelly: 할아버지께서 내가 태어난 해인 2004년에 그 나무를 심으셨거든.

Listen & Talk 2 B

Toby: Hi, I'm Toby. I'm _____ to _____ _____ _____ about the blue whale. It's _____ _____ sea animal in the world. _____ _____ is it? Well, it's about 30m long. That means it's _____ _____ a basketball court. _____ _____ _____ is that its tongue is _____ _____ _____ an elephant! Surprising, _____ _____?

Toby: 안녕하세요, 저는 Toby입니다. 저는 흰긴수염고래에 대해서 발표를 하려고 해요 그 고래는 세상에서 가장 큰 바다 동물이에요. 얼마나 크냐고요? 음, 길이가 30미터 정도 돼요. 그 말은 그 고래가 농구 경기장보다 길다는 뜻이에요. 또 다른 흥미로운 점은 그 고래의 혀가 코끼리만큼 무겁다는 거예요! 놀랍죠, 그렇지 않나요?

Communication

Emily: Hello, Dr. Watson. Can you _____ _____ about your study?

Dr. Watson: I study animals that lived _____ _____ _____.

Emily: Oh, I'm _____ _____ those animals. Were there _____ interesting ones?

Dr. Watson: Yes, there were _____. This is the _____ kangaroo. It lived in Australia. It was _____ _____ _____ three men and it _____ _____ well.

Emily: That's _____!

Emily: 안녕하세요, Watson 박사님. 박사님의 연구에 대해 이야기해 주시겠어요?

Dr Watson: 전 수백만 년 전에 살았던 동물들을 연구합니다.

Emily: 오, 전 그 동물들이 궁금해요. 흥미로운 동물들이 있었나요?

Dr Watson:네, 많이 있었죠. 이 동물은 '자이언트 캥거루'입니다. 호주에서 살았어요. 사람 세 명만큼 무거웠고, 잘 뛰지 못했어요.

Emily: 그거 정말 놀랍군요!

※ 다음 우리말에 맞도록 대화를 영어로 쓰시오.

해석

Listen & Talk 1 A-1

Ryan: _____

Judy: _____

Ryan: _____

_____

Judy: _____

Ryan: Judy, 너 과학 과제로 할 주제 골랐어?
Judy: 아직. 너는 어때, Ryan?
Ryan: 나는 날씨 변화가 궁금하거든. 그래서 난 그것에 관한 과제를 하려고 생각 중이야.
Judy: 주제가 흥미로운걸!

Listen & Talk 1 A-2

Jane: _____

Tom: _____

Jane: _____

_____

Tom: _____

Jane: 이 커다란 꽃 사진을 봐.
Tom: 와, 사람보다 더 크네.
Jane: 그래. 나는 이 꽃이 정말 궁금해. 또 여기에 나와 있는데 그 꽃은 냄새가 매우 고약하지만 벌레들은 그 냄새를 좋아한대.
Tom: 흠, 이유가 궁금하다.

Listen & Talk 1 B

Clare: _____

Todd: _____

Clare: _____

Todd: _____

Clare: _____

_____

Todd: _____

Clare: 우리가 사자와 친구가 될 수 있을 거라고 생각해, Todd?
Todd: 아니, Clare. 난 그렇게 생각하지 않아.
Clare: 음, 나 두 남자와 사자 사이의 우정에 대한 동영상을 봤어.
Todd: 정말? 그 이야기가 궁금해. 더 얘기해 줄 수 있어?
Clare: 두 남자가 아기 사자를 길러서 야생으로 돌려보냈대. 일 년 후에 그 남자들과 사자가 만났을 때, 그 사자는 그들을 기억했다는 거야.
Todd: 와, 정말 감동적이구나.

Listen & Talk 2 A-1

Dylan: _____

_____

Mina: _____

Dylan: _____

Mina: _____

Dylan: 이 사진 좀 봐, 미나야. 우리 어제 새 강아지를 데리고 왔어. 그 강아지는 2주밖에 안 됐어.
Mina: 오, Dylan, 걔 너무 조그맣다!
Dylan: 맞아. 그 애는 지금 내 손만큼 작지만, 몇 달 뒤에는 훨씬 더 커질 거야.
Mina: 와, 강아지들은 정말 빨리 크네.

Listen & Talk 2 A-2

Kelly: _____

George: _____

Kelly: _____

George: _____

Kelly: _____

Kelly: George, 저기에 있는 빨간 집이 우리 할아버지와 할머니 댁이야.

George: 와, 집 옆에 있는 나무가 굉장히 크네.

Kelly: 사실, 저 나무의 나이는 나랑 같아서 수령이 13년 되었어.

George: 그걸 어떻게 알아, Kelly?

Kelly: 할아버지께서 내가 태어난 해인 2004년에 그 나무를 심으셨거든.

Listen & Talk 2 B

Toby: _____

_____

_____

_____

Toby: 안녕하세요, 저는 Toby입니다. 저는 흰긴수염고래에 대해서 발표를 하려고 해요 그 고래는 세상에서 가장 큰 바다 동물이에요. 얼마나 크냐고요? 음, 길이가 30미터 정도 돼요. 그 말은 그 고래가 농구 경기장보다 길다는 뜻이에요. 또 다른 흥미로운 점은 그 고래의 혀가 코끼리만큼 무겁다는 거예요! 놀랍죠, 그렇지 않나요?

Communication

Emily: _____

Dr. Watson: _____

Emily: _____

Dr. Watson: _____

_____

Emily: _____

Emily: 안녕하세요, Watson 박사님. 박사님의 연구에 대해 이야기해 주시겠어요?

Dr Watson: 전 수백만 년 전에 살았던 동물들을 연구합니다.

Emily: 오, 전 그 동물들이 궁금해요. 흥미로운 동물들이 있었나요?

Dr Watson: 네, 많이 있었죠. 이 동물은 '자이언트 캥거루'입니다. 호주에서 살았어요. 사람 세 명만큼 무거웠고, 잘 뛰지 못했어요.

Emily: 그거 정말 놀랍군요!

※ 다음 우리말과 일치하도록 빈칸에 알맞은 것을 골라 쓰시오.

Date/Time: July 8th / 2:35 p.m.

1 Notes: Today was _____ _____ day _____ Africa.
  A. in   B. first   C. my

2 I _____ lots of _____ _____ elephants.
  A. took   B. of   C. pictures

3 This morning, I _____ an elephant group _____ a small water _____.
  A. by   B. found   C. hole

4 I _____ a baby elephant _____ water _____ her mother.
  A. drinking   B. saw   C. beside

5 Her eyes _____ as _____ _____ stars.
  A. as   B. were   C. bright

6 I _____ _____ a _____, Stella.
  A. her   B. name   C. gave

7 _____ noon, I _____ a group of lions _____ Stella.
  A. saw   B. around   C. approaching

8 The elephants _____ _____ Stella and made a _____ wall.
  A. thick   B. around   C. stood

9 _____ _____ them, Stella was _____.
  A. safe   B. to   C. thanks

Date/Time: July 12th / 7:20 p.m.

10 Notes: _____ sunset, I _____ a strange _____.
  A. heard   B. around   C. sound

11 I _____ the sound and _____ Stella _____ next to her mom.
  A. crying   B. followed   C. found

12 She was _____ _____ and Stella was _____.
  A. dead   B. alone   C. lying

13 _____ is dangerous _____ _____ alone in _____ a wild area.
  A. such   B. it   C. stay   D. to

14 _____ _____, it was _____ to be dark soon.
  A. more   B. what's   C. going

15 Elephants _____ _____ _____ at night.
  A. well   B. can't   C. see

날짜/시간: 7월 8일, 오후 2시 35분

1 기록: 오늘은 내가 아프리카에 온 첫날이었다.

2 나는 코끼리 사진을 많이 찍었다.

3 오늘 아침에 나는 작은 물웅덩이 옆에 있는 흰 코끼리 무리를 발견했다.

4 나는 아기 코끼리 한 마리가 엄마 옆에서 물을 마시고 있는 것을 보았다.

5 그 코끼리의 눈이 별처럼 밝았다.

6 나는 그 코끼리에게 Stella란 이름을 붙여 주었다.

7 정오 즈음에 나는 사자 한 무리가 Stella에게 다가가는 것을 보았다.

8 코끼리들은 Stella 주위에 둘러서서 두꺼운 벽을 만들었다.

9 그 코끼리들 덕분에 Stella는 안전했다.

날짜/시간: 7월 12일, 오후 7시 20분

10 기록: 해질녘에 나는 이상한 소리를 들었다.

11 나는 그 소리를 따라갔고 Stella가 자신의 엄마 옆에서 울고 있는 것을 발견했다.

12 엄마는 죽어서 누워 있었고, Stella는 혼자였다.

13 이러한 야생 지역에서 혼자 있는 것은 위험하다.

14 더욱이 곧 어두워질 것이었다.

15 코끼리들은 밤에 잘 볼 수 없다.

16 So Stella could _____ _____ _____.

    A. attacked   B. be   C. easily

17 I _____ the elephant _____ and _____ help.

    A. for   B. shelter   C. asked   D. called

18 I decided to _____ her _____ the rescue team came.

    A. until   B. by   C. stay

Date/Time: July 12th / 10:40 p.m.

19 Notes: The night was _____ and _____.

    A. quiet   B. dark

20 I _____ my eyes _____ Stella _____ my night camera.

    A. with   B. kept   C. on

21 Stella was _____ _____ _____ her mom.

    A. next   B. to   C. still

22 She was _____ her mom's _____ body _____ her nose.

    A. lifeless   B. with   C. touching

23 It was sad _____ _____ Stella _____ close to her mom.

    A. see   B. staying   C. to

24 I hope Stella _____ _____ _____ the night.

    A. throughout   B. safe   C. stays

Date/Time: July 13th / 6:00 a.m.

25 Notes: A _____ elephant group _____ and Stella _____ them.

    A. new   B. approached   C. appeared

26 At first, I _____ _____ they would not _____ Stella _____ their group.

    A. in   B. let   C. thought   D. that

27 _____ I was _____.

    A. wrong   B. but

28 An elephant, probably the _____ allowed Stella to _____ _____ of the group.

    A. part   B. oldest   C. become   D. female

29 The _____ elephants also _____ to _____ Stella.

    A. seemed   B. other   C. welcome

30 _____, _____ of the _____ elephants _____ Stella.

    A. one   B. fed   C. female   D. unbelievably

31 She _____ _____ Stella as _____ as Stella's mom _____.

    A. did   B. for   C. warmly   D. cared

32 This was _____ an _____!

    A. moment   B. amazing   C. such

---

16 그래서 Stella는 쉽게 공격을 받을 수 있었다.

17 나는 코끼리 보호소에 전화를 해서 도움을 요청했다.

18 나는 구조대가 올 때까지 Stella 곁에 머물기로 결정했다.

날짜/시간: 7월 12일, 오후 10시 40분

19 기록: 밤은 어둡고 조용했다.

20 나는 야간용 카메라를 이용해서 Stella를 계속 지켜보았다.

21 Stella는 여전히 엄마 곁에 있었다.

22 Stella는 코로 엄마의 죽은 몸을 어루만지고 있었다.

23 Stella가 엄마 가까이에 머물고 있는 것을 보는 것은 슬픈 일이었다.

24 나는 Stella가 밤새도록 안전하게 있기를 바란다.

날짜/시간: 7월 13일, 오전 6시

25 기록: 새로운 코끼리 무리가 나타났고, Stella는 그 무리에 다가갔다.

26 처음에 나는 그 코끼리들이 Stella를 자신의 무리로 받아들이지 않을 것이라고 생각했다.

27 그러나 내 생각이 틀렸다.

28 아마도 가장 나이가 많은 암컷인 듯한 코끼리 한 마리가 Stella가 그 무리의 일원이 되도록 허락했다.

29 다른 코끼리들도 Stella를 반기는 것처럼 보였다.

30 믿을 수 없게도, 암컷 코끼리 중의 한 마리가 Stella에게 젖을 먹였다.

31 그 코끼리는 Stella의 엄마만큼 따뜻하게 Stella를 보살폈다.

32 이것은 너무나 놀라운 순간이었다.

※ 다음 우리말과 일치하도록 빈칸에 알맞은 말을 쓰시오.

Date/Time: July 8th / 2:35 p.m.

1 Notes: Today _____ _____ _____ day _____ Africa.

2 I _____ _____ of _____ _____ elephants.

3 This morning, I _____ an elephant group _____ a small _____ _____ .

4 I _____ a baby elephant _____ water _____ her mother.

5 Her eyes _____ _____ _____ _____ stars.

6 I _____ _____ _____ _____ , Stella.

7 Around noon, I _____ a group of lions _____ Stella.

8 The elephants _____ _____ Stella and _____ _____ _____ _____ .

9 _____ _____ _____ , Stella was _____ .

Date/Time: July 12th / 7:20 p.m.

10 Notes: _____ _____ , I _____ a strange sound.

11 I _____ the sound and _____ Stella _____ _____ _____ her mom.

12 She was _____ _____ and Stella was _____ .

13 _____ is dangerous _____ _____ alone _____ _____ _____ _____ .

14 _____ _____ , _____ was going to _____ _____ soon.

15 Elephants can't _____ _____ _____ _____ _____ .

날짜/시간: 7월 8일, 오후 2시 35분

1 기록: 오늘은 내가 아프리카에 온 첫날이었다.

2 나는 코끼리 사진을 많이 찍었다.

3 오늘 아침에 나는 작은 물웅덩이 옆에 있는 한 코끼리 무리를 발견했다.

4 나는 아기 코끼리 한 마리가 엄마 옆에서 물을 마시고 있는 것을 보았다.

5 그 코끼리의 눈이 별처럼 밝았다.

6 나는 그 코끼리에게 Stella란 이름을 붙여 주었다.

7 정오 즈음에 나는 사자 한 무리가 Stella에게 다가가는 것을 보았다.

8 코끼리들은 Stella 주위에 둘러서서 두꺼운 벽을 만들었다.

9 그 코끼리들 덕분에 Stella는 안전했다.

날짜/시간: 7월 12일, 오후 7시 20분

10 기록: 해질녘에 나는 이상한 소리를 들었다.

11 나는 그 소리를 따라갔고 Stella가 자신의 엄마 옆에서 울고 있는 것을 발견했다.

12 엄마는 죽어서 누워 있었고, Stella는 혼자였다.

13 이러한 야생 지역에서 혼자 있는 것은 위험하다.

14 더욱이 곧 어두워질 것이었다.

15 코끼리들은 밤에 잘 볼 수 없다.

16 So Stella could _____ _____ _____.

17 I called _____ and _____ help.

18 I decided _____ by her _____ the rescue team came.

Date/Time: July 12th / 10:40 p.m.

19 Notes: The night _____ and _____.

20 I _____ my eyes _____ Stella _____ my night camera.

21 Stella was _____ her mom.

22 She _____ her mom's lifeless body _____ her nose.

23 _____ was sad _____ Stella _____ _____ her mom.

24 I hope Stella _____ the night.

Date/Time: July 13th / 6:00 a.m.

25 Notes: A new elephant group _____ and Stella _____ them.

26 At first, I _____ _____ they would not _____ Stella _____ their group.

27 But I _____ _____.

28 An elephant, probably _____ _____ allowed Stella _____ _____ _____ the group.

29 _____ _____ also _____ to welcome Stella.

30 _____, one of the female _____ _____ Stella.

31 She _____ Stella _____ _____ Stella's mom _____.

32 This was _____ !

16 그래서 Stella는 쉽게 공격을 받을 수 있었다.

17 나는 코끼리 보호소에 전화를 해서 도움을 요청했다.

18 나는 구조대가 올 때까지 Stella 곁에 머물기로 결정했다.

날짜/시간: 7월 12일, 오후 10시 40분

19 기록: 밤은 어둡고 조용했다.

20 나는 야간용 카메라를 이용해서 Stella를 계속 지켜보았다.

21 Stella는 여전히 엄마 곁에 있었다.

22 Stella는 코로 엄마의 죽은 몸을 어루만지고 있었다.

23 Stella가 엄마 가까이에 머물고 있는 것을 보는 것은 슬픈 일이었다.

24 나는 Stella가 밤새도록 안전하게 있기를 바란다.

날짜/시간: 7월 13일, 오전 6시

25 기록: 새로운 코끼리 무리가 나타났고, Stella는 그 무리에 다가갔다.

26 처음에 나는 그 코끼리들이 Stella를 자신의 무리로 받아들이지 않을 것이라고 생각했다.

27 그러나 내 생각이 틀렸다.

28 아마도 가장 나이가 많은 암컷인 듯한 코끼리 한 마리가 Stella가 그 무리의 일원이 되도록 허락했다.

29 다른 코끼리들도 Stella를 반기는 것처럼 보였다.

30 믿을 수 없게도, 암컷 코끼리 중의 한 마리가 Stella에게 젖을 먹였다.

31 그 코끼리는 Stella의 엄마만큼 따뜻하게 Stella를 보살폈다.

32 이것은 너무나 놀라운 순간이었다.

※ 다음 문장을 우리말로 쓰시오.

Date / Time: July 8th / 2:35 p.m.

1 Notes: Today was my first day in Africa.

➡ _____

2 I took lots of pictures of elephants.

➡ _____

3 This morning, I found an elephant group by a small water hole.

➡ _____

4 I saw a baby elephant drinking water beside her mother.

➡ _____

5 Her eyes were as bright as stars.

➡ _____

6 I gave her a name, Stella.

➡ _____

7 Around noon, I saw a group of lions approaching Stella.

➡ _____

8 The elephants stood around Stella and made a thick wall.

➡ _____

9 Thanks to them, Stella was safe.

➡ _____

Date / Time: July 12th / 7:20 p.m.

10 Notes: Around sunset, I heard a strange sound.

➡ _____

11 I followed the sound and found Stella crying next to her mom.

➡ _____

12 She was lying dead and Stella was alone.

➡ _____

13 It is dangerous to stay alone in such a wild area.

➡ _____

14 What's more, it was going to be dark soon.

➡ _____

15 Elephants can't see well at night.

➡ _____

16 So Stella could easily be attacked.

➡ _____

17 I called the elephant shelter and asked for help.

➡ _____

18 I decided to stay by her until the rescue team came.

➡ _____

Date / Time: July 12th / 10:40 p.m.

19 Notes: The night was dark and quiet.

➡ _____

20 I kept my eyes on Stella with my night camera.

➡ _____

21 Stella was still next to her mom.

➡ _____

22 She was touching her mom's lifeless body with her nose.

➡ _____

23 It was sad to see Stella staying close to her mom.

➡ _____

24 I hope Stella stays safe throughout the night.

➡ _____

Date / Time: July 13th / 6:00 a.m.

25 Notes: A new elephant group appeared and Stella approached them.

➡ _____

26 At first, I thought that they would not let Stella in their group.

➡ _____

27 But I was wrong.

➡ _____

28 An elephant, probably the oldest female allowed Stella to become part of the group.

➡ _____

29 The other elephants also seemed to welcome Stella.

➡ _____

30 Unbelievably, one of the female elephants fed Stella.

➡ _____

31 She cared for Stella as warmly as Stella's mom did.

➡ _____

32 This was such an amazing moment!

➡ _____

※ 다음 괄호 안의 단어들을 우리말에 맞도록 바르게 배열하시오.

Date / Time: July 8th / 2:35 p.m.

1 (Notes: / was / today / first / my / in / Africa. / day)
➡ _____

2 (took / I / of / lots / pictures / elephants. / of)
➡ _____

3 (morning, / this / found / I / elephant / an / by / group / a / water / hole. / small)
➡ _____

4 (saw / I / baby / a / drinking / elephant / beside / water / mother. / her)
➡ _____

5 (eyes / her / as / were / bright / stars. / as)
➡ _____

6 (gave / I / a / her / Stella. / name.)
➡ _____

7 (noon, / around / saw / I / group / a / lions / of / Stella. / approaching)
➡ _____

8 (elephants / the / around / stood / Stella / and / a / made / wall. / thick)
➡ _____

9 (to / thanks / them, / was / safe. / Stella)
➡ _____

Date / Time: July 12th / 7:20 p.m.

10 (Notes: / sunset, / around / heard / I / sound. / strange / a)
➡ _____

11 (followed / I / sound / the / and / Stella / found / next / crying / to / mom. / her)
➡ _____

12 (was / she / dead / lying / and / alone. / was / Stella)
➡ _____

13 (is / it / dangerous / stay / to / alone / such / in / area. / wild / a)
➡ _____

14 (more, / what's / was / it / to / going / be / soon. / dark)
➡ _____

15 (can't / elephants / well / see / night. / at)
➡ _____

날짜/시간: 7월 8일, 오후 2시 35분

1 기록: 오늘은 내가 아프리카에 온 첫날이었다.

2 나는 코끼리 사진을 많이 찍었다.

3 오늘 아침에 나는 작은 물웅덩이 옆에 있는 한 코끼리 무리를 발견했다.

4 나는 아기 코끼리 한 마리가 엄마 옆에서 물을 마시고 있는 것을 보았다.

5 그 코끼리의 눈이 별처럼 밝았다.

6 나는 그 코끼리에게 Stella란 이름을 붙여 주었다.

7 정오 즈음에 나는 사자 한 무리가 Stella에게 다가가는 것을 보았다.

8 코끼리들은 Stella 주위에 둘러서서 두꺼운 벽을 만들었다.

9 그 코끼리들 덕분에 Stella는 안전했다.

날짜/시간: 7월 12일, 오후 7시 20분

10 기록: 해질녘에 나는 이상한 소리를 들었다.

11 나는 그 소리를 따라갔고 Stella가 자신의 엄마 옆에서 울고 있는 것을 발견했다.

12 엄마는 죽어서 누워 있었고, Stella는 혼자였다.

13 이러한 야생 지역에서 혼자 있는 것은 위험하다.

14 더욱이 곧 어두워질 것이었다.

15 코끼리들은 밤에 잘 볼 수 없다.

16 (Stella / so / easily / could / attacked. / be)
➡ _____

17 (called / I / elephant / the / and / shelter / for / help. / asked)
➡ _____

18 (decided / I / stay / to / her / by / the / until / team / came. / rescue)
➡ _____

Date / Time: July 12th / 10:40 p.m.
19 (Notes: / night / the / dark / was / quiet. / and)
➡ _____

20 (kept / I / eyes / my / Stella / on / my / with / camera. / night)
➡ _____

21 (was / Stella / next / still / her / mom. / to)
➡ _____

22 (was / she / her / touching / mom's / lifeless / with / body / nose. / her)
➡ _____

23 (was / it / to / sad / Stella / see / close / staying / to / mom. / her)
➡ _____

24 (hope / I / stays / Stella / safe / the / night. / throughout)
➡ _____

Date / Time: July 13th / 6:00 a.m.
25 (Notes: / new / a / elephant / appeared / group / Stella / and / them. / approached)
➡ _____

26 (first, / at / thought / I / that / would / they / not / Stella / let / their / group. / in)
➡ _____

27 (I / but / wrong. / was)
➡ _____

28 (elephant, / an / the / probably / oldest / the / female / Stella / allowed / to / part / become / the / group. / of)
➡ _____

29 (other / the / elephants / seemed / also / to / Stella. / welcome)
➡ _____

30 (unbelievably, / of / one / female / the / Stella. / fed / elephants)
➡ _____

31 (cared / she / for / as / Stella / warmly / as / mom / did. / Stella's)
➡ _____

32 (was / this / an / such / moment! / amazing)
➡ _____

16 그래서 Stella는 쉽게 공격을 받을 수 있었다.

17 나는 코끼리 보호소에 전화를 해서 도움을 요청했다.

18 나는 구조대가 올 때까지 Stella 곁에 머물기로 결정했다.

날짜/시간: 7월 12일, 오후 10시 40분

19 기록: 밤은 어둡고 조용했다.

20 나는 야간용 카메라를 이용해서 Stella를 계속 지켜보았다.

21 Stella는 여전히 엄마 곁에 있었다.

22 Stella는 코로 엄마의 죽은 몸을 어루만지고 있었다.

23 Stella가 엄마 가까이에 머물고 있는 것을 보는 것은 슬픈 일이었다.

24 나는 Stella가 밤새도록 안전하게 있기를 바란다.

날짜/시간: 7월 13일, 오전 6시

25 기록: 새로운 코끼리 무리가 나타났고, Stella는 그 무리에 다가갔다.

26 처음에 나는 그 코끼리들이 Stella를 자신의 무리로 받아들이지 않을 것이라고 생각했다.

27 그러나 내 생각이 틀렸다.

28 아마도 가장 나이가 많은 암컷인 듯한 코끼리 한 마리가 Stella가 그 무리의 일원이 되도록 허락했다.

29 다른 코끼리들도 Stella를 반기는 것처럼 보였다.

30 믿을 수 없게도, 암컷 코끼리 중의 한 마리가 Stella에게 젖을 먹였다.

31 그 코끼리는 Stella의 엄마만큼 따뜻하게 Stella를 보살폈다.

32 이것은 너무나 놀라운 순간이었다.

※ 다음 우리말을 영어로 쓰시오.

날짜/시간: 7월 8일, 오후 2시 35분

1 기록: 오늘은 내가 아프리카에 온 첫날이었다.

➡ _____

2 나는 코끼리 사진을 많이 찍었다.

➡ _____

3 오늘 아침에 나는 작은 물웅덩이 옆에 있는 한 코끼리 무리를 발견했다.

➡ _____

4 나는 아기 코끼리 한 마리가 엄마 옆에서 물을 마시고 있는 것을 보았다.

➡ _____

5 그 코끼리의 눈이 별처럼 밝았다.

➡ _____

6 나는 그 코끼리에게 Stella란 이름을 붙여 주었다.

➡ _____

7 정오 즈음에 나는 사자 한 무리가 Stella에게 다가가는 것을 보았다.

➡ _____

8 코끼리들은 Stella 주위에 둘러서서 두꺼운 벽을 만들었다.

➡ _____

9 그 코끼리들 덕분에 Stella는 안전했다.

➡ _____

날짜/시간: 7월 12일, 오후 7시 20분

10 기록: 해질녘에 나는 이상한 소리를 들었다.

➡ _____

11 나는 그 소리를 따라갔고 Stella가 자신의 엄마 옆에서 울고 있는 것을 발견했다.

➡ _____

12 엄마는 죽어서 누워 있었고, Stella는 혼자였다.

➡ _____

13 이러한 야생 지역에서 혼자 있는 것은 위험하다.

➡ _____

14 더욱이 곧 어두워질 것이었다.

➡ _____

15 코끼리들은 밤에 잘 볼 수 없다.

➡ _____

16 그래서 Stella는 쉽게 공격을 받을 수 있었다.

➡ _____

17 나는 코끼리 보호소에 전화를 해서 도움을 요청했다.

➡ _____

18 나는 구조대가 올 때까지 Stella 곁에 머물기로 결정했다.

➡ _____

날짜/시간: 7월 12일, 오후 10시 40분

19 기록: 밤은 어둡고 조용했다.

➡ _____

20 나는 야간용 카메라를 이용해서 Stella를 계속 지켜보았다.

➡ _____

21 Stella는 여전히 엄마 곁에 있었다.

➡ _____

22 Stella는 코로 엄마의 죽은 몸을 어루만지고 있었다.

➡ _____

23 Stella가 엄마 가까이에 머물고 있는 것을 보는 것은 슬픈 일이었다.

➡ _____

24 나는 Stella가 밤새도록 안전하게 있기를 바란다.

➡ _____

날짜/시간: 7월 13일, 오전 6시

25 기록: 새로운 코끼리 무리가 나타났고, Stella는 그 무리에 다가갔다.

➡ _____

26 처음에 나는 그 코끼리들이 Stella를 자신의 무리로 받아들이지 않을 것이라고 생각했다.

➡ _____

27 그러나 내 생각이 틀렸다.

➡ _____

28 아마도 가장 나이가 많은 암컷인 듯한 코끼리 한 마리가 Stella가 그 무리의 일원이 되도록 허락했다.

➡ _____

29 다른 코끼리들도 Stella를 반기는 것처럼 보였다.

➡ _____

30 믿을 수 없게도, 암컷 코끼리 중의 한 마리가 Stella에게 젖을 먹였다.

➡ _____

31 그 코끼리는 Stella의 엄마만큼 따뜻하게 Stella를 보살폈다.

➡ _____

32 이것은 너무나 놀라운 순간이었다.

➡ _____

※ 다음 우리말과 일치하도록 빈칸에 알맞은 말을 쓰시오.

Read and Think

1. Some lions _____ _____ _____ Stella.

2. The elephant group made a _____ wall _____ _____ her.

3. Stella _____ _____ _____ _____ her dead mother.

4. I _____ her _____ _____.

5. The _____ _____ elephant of a new group _____ Stella _____ _____ _____ _____ them.

1. 사자 몇 마리가 Stella를 공격하려고 했다.
2. 코끼리 무리는 Stella를 보호하기 위해 두꺼운 벽을 만들었다.
3. Stella는 그녀의 죽은 엄마 옆에서 울고 있었다.
4. 나는 밤새 그녀를 지켜보았다.
5. 새로운 무리의 가장 나이 많은 암컷 코끼리는 Stella를 그들의 일원이 되도록 허락했다.

Think & Write C

1. _____ _____

2. Date: _____ _____, 2019

3. Write about _____ _____ _____:

4. Today, I _____ a plant. It _____ _____ a pitcher plant.

5. It is _____ green and red. It _____ _____ a pitcher.

6. _____ for _____ _____, it is _____ 15cm long. It is _____ _____ _____ my hand.

7. _____ is interesting _____ the plant _____ _____ and eats them.

1. 식물 일기
2. 날짜: 6월 15일, 2019년
3. 네가 본 것을 써 봐:
4. 오늘, 나는 식물 하나를 봤다. 그것은 벌레잡이 식물이라고 불린다.
5. 그것은 밝은 녹색에 붉은색이다. 그것은 항아리처럼 생겼다.
6. 크기에 대해 말하자면, 그것은 대략 15cm이다. 그것은 내 손만큼 길다.
7. 그 식물이 벌레를 끌어들이고 그것들을 먹는 것은 흥미롭다.

Wrap Up 1

1. Minho: Look! _____ that a _____ _____?

2. Sue: _____, no. It's a _____ _____.

3. Minho: Oh, really? I'm _____ _____ the difference _____ them.

4. Sue: _____ _____ the tail _____. A sea dragon has a _____ _____, but a sea horse _____ _____.

5. Minho: Oh, I can _____ _____ _____ now!

1. Minho: 봐! 저거 해마 아니야?
2. Sue: 사실은 아니야. 그건 해룡이야.
3. Minho: 아, 정말? 난 그 둘의 차이점이 궁금해.
4. Sue: 꼬리를 주의해서 봐. 해룡은 꼬리가 곧지만, 해마는 그렇지 않아.
5. Minho: 오, 나 이제 구별할 수 있겠다!

※ 다음 우리말을 영어로 쓰시오.

Read and Think

1. 사자 몇 마리가 Stella를 공격하려고 했다.
   ➡ _____

2. 코끼리 무리는 Stella를 보호하기 위해 두꺼운 벽을 만들었다.
   ➡ _____

3. Stella는 그녀의 죽은 엄마 옆에서 울고 있었다.
   ➡ _____

4. 나는 밤새 그녀를 지켜보았다.
   ➡ _____

5. 새로운 무리의 가장 나이 많은 암컷 코끼리는 Stella를 그들의 일원이 되도록 허락했다.
   ➡ _____

Think & Write C

1. 식물 일기
   ➡ _____

2. 날짜: 6월 15일, 2019년
   ➡ _____

3. 네가 본 것을 써 봐:
   ➡ _____

4. 오늘, 나는 식물 하나를 봤다. 그것은 벌레잡이 식물이라고 불린다.
   ➡ _____

5. 그것은 밝은 녹색에 붉은색이다. 그것은 항아리처럼 생겼다.
   ➡ _____

6. 크기에 대해 말하자면, 그것은 대략 15cm이다. 그것은 내 손만큼 길다.
   ➡ _____

7. 그 식물이 벌레를 끌어들이고 그것들을 먹는 것은 흥미롭다.
   ➡ _____

Wrap Up 1

1. Minho: 봐! 저거 해마 아니야?
   ➡ _____

2. Sue: 사실은 아니야. 그건 해룡이야.
   ➡ _____

3. Minho: 아, 정말? 난 그 둘의 차이점이 궁금해.
   ➡ _____

4. Sue: 꼬리를 주의해서 봐. 해룡은 꼬리가 곧지만, 해마는 그렇지 않아.
   ➡ _____

5. Minho: 오, 나 이제 구별할 수 있겠다!
   ➡ _____

※ 다음 영어를 우리말로 쓰시오.

01 prince _____

02 classical _____

03 melt _____

04 produce _____

05 direction _____

06 exhibit _____

07 feather _____

08 artist _____

09 promise _____

10 brush _____

11 landscape _____

12 novel _____

13 despite _____

14 art work _____

15 teen _____

16 maze _____

17 production _____

18 notice _____

19 wonder _____

20 flat _____

21 seaside _____

22 detail _____

23 tragedy _____

24 prefer _____

25 wing _____

26 modern _____

27 queen _____

28 rock _____

29 real _____

30 novelist _____

31 since _____

32 myth _____

33 tourist _____

34 version _____

35 wax _____

36 canvas _____

37 prefer A to B _____

38 loot at _____

39 glance at _____

40 stay away from _____

41 right away _____

42 take a look _____

43 move on _____

※ 다음 우리말을 영어로 쓰시오.

01 녹다

02 생산하다

03 깃털

04 날개

05 방향

06 왕비, 여왕

07 예술가

08 붓

09 왕자

10 전시하다

11 개구리

12 미로

13 약속하다

14 소설

15 ~에도 불구하고

16 현대의

17 납작한

18 십 대

19 ~을 알아차리다

20 풍경

21 예술 작품

22 (어떤 것의) 변형

23 세부 사항

24 신화

25 생산

26 비극

27 더 좋아하다

28 궁금해하다

29 진짜의, 현실적인

30 화폭, 캔버스

31 관광객

32 밀랍, 왁스

33 록 음악

34 소설가

35 희극

36 ~ 때문에, ~이므로

37 해변, 바닷가

38 ~로 이동하다, 넘어가다

39 A를 B보다 더 좋아하다

40 ~을 힐끗 보다

41 ~을 보다

42 ~을 가까이하지 않다

43 즉시, 바로

※ 다음 영영풀이에 알맞은 단어를 <보기>에서 골라 쓴 후, 우리말 뜻을 쓰시오.

1 _____ : one of the light soft things that cover a bird's body: _____

2 _____ : an area that is close to the sea: _____

3 _____ : to change from a solid to a liquid by applying heat: _____

4 _____ : a very sad event, especially one involving death: _____

5 _____ : the way something or someone moves, faces, or is aimed: _____

6 _____ : to want to know more about something because it interests you: _____

7 _____ : an area of countryside, especially in relation to its appearance: _____

8 _____ : to see or become conscious of something or someone: _____

9 _____ : to put it in a position where other people can see a part of your body: _____

10 _____ : someone who produces art: _____

11 _____ : one of the parts of a bird's or insect's body that it uses for flying: _____

12 _____ : a single piece of some information of fact about something: _____

13 _____ : to show something in a public place for people to enjoy or to give them information: _____

14 _____ : a kind of popular music with a strong beat that is played on instruments that are made louder electronically: _____

15 _____ : a piece of thick cloth used by artists for painting on, usually with oil paints, or the painting itself: _____

16 _____ : an ancient story, especially one invented in order to explain natural or historical events: _____

보기			
canvas	melt	seaside	landscape
wonder	myth	notice	wing
direction	stick	artist	tragedy
feather	rock	detail	exhibit

※ 다음 우리말과 일치하도록 빈칸에 알맞은 말을 쓰시오.

Listen & Talk 1 A-1

W: Brian, is your band _____ _____ _____ at the Teen Music Festival?

M: Yes, we're _____ _____ _____ - _____.

W: _____ _____ _____ _____ are you going to play this year?

M: Rock music. We'll _____ _____ from the _____.

Listen & Talk 1 A-2

W: Can you help me? I don't know _____ _____ _____ _____ _____.

M: _____ _____ _____ _____ were you _____?

W: This _____ _____.

M: _____ you _____ lines, a _____ brush is _____. _____ this one.

W: Okay, thank you.

Listen & Talk 1 B

W: (ringing) Hello, Steve.

M: Hi, Anna. We're _____ at the arts festival tomorrow at 1:30, _____?

W: Right. What kind of _____ _____ _____ _____ _____ _____ _____?

M: I _____ _____ watch the hip-hop dance _____ first.

W: _____ good. It's at 2 p.m. at the gym, _____?

M: Yeah, and how _____ _____ _____ _____ _____, Romeo and Juliet, at 4 p.m.?

W: Oh, _____ _____ at the Main Hall _____ the gym? Sure!

Listen & Talk 2 A-1

M: What _____ you _____, Jina?

W: The novel, Life of Pi. It's _____ _____ of a boy and a tiger.

M: It's a great book. I've _____ the movie _____ _____, _____. I _____ the movie _____ the novel.

W: _____ do you _____ it _____?

M: The _____ are very beautiful. And the tiger _____ so _____.

Listen & Talk 2 A-2

W: _____ you _____ to Jane's new song, *Girl Friend*?

M: Yeah, it's really _____. The guitar _____ is _____.

W: There is also a _____ _____ of the song on the album.

M: I've _____ _____ it, but _____ _____ _____ _____ to the dance version. It _____ her voice _____.

W: 너는 Jane의 새 노래인 '여자 친구'를 들어 봤니?

M: 응, 정말 멋져. 기타 부분이 굉장하지.

W: 앨범에는 그 노래의 댄스 버전도 있어.

M: 나는 그것을 들었는데 댄스 버전보다는 기타 버전이 더 좋아. 그 버전이 그녀의 목소리와 더 잘 어울리거든.

Listen & Talk 2 B

W: I saw an _____ _____ in an art book. _____ _____ this.

M: Wow, it _____ _____ da Vinci's *Mona Lisa*.

W: Actually, it's *Mona Lisa* by Fernando Botero. _____ _____ _____ _____?

M: I _____ da Vinci's _____ Botero's. Da Vinci's *Mona Lisa* has an interesting _____. _____ _____ _____?

W: Well, I _____ Botero's _____ da Vinci's. His *Mona Lisa* is cute, and it _____ _____.

W: 나 미술 책에서 흥미로운 그림을 봤어. 이것 봐.

M: 와, 그것은 다빈치의 '모나리자'처럼 보이는데.

W: 사실 이 그림은 페르난도 보테로의 '모나리자'야. 넌 어느 것이 더 마음에 드니?

M: 나는 보테로의 그림보다 다빈치의 모나리자가 더 좋아. 다빈치의 '모나리자'에는 흥미로운 미소가 있어. 너는 어때?

W: 음, 나는 다빈치의 모나리자보다는 보테로의 모나리자가 더 좋아. 그의 '모나리자'는 귀엽고 현대적으로 보여.

Communication

M: Hi, we _____ _____ a school festival, _____ we want to _____ _____ students' favorite types of performances. _____ I _____ you _____ _____ _____?

W: Sure.

M: _____ _____ _____ _____ do you like best?

W: I like music _____ _____.

M: Okay. Then, which _____ you _____, rock or hip-hop?

W: I _____ _____ _____ _____ _____.

M: Who's your _____ _____?

W: My _____ _____ is TJ.

M: Great. _____ you _____ your answers.

M: 안녕하세요, 저희는 학교 축제를 계획 중이고, 그래서 학생들이 어떤 종류의 공연을 좋아하는지 알고 싶습니다. 몇 가지 질문을 해도 될까요?

W: 물론이죠.

M: 어떤 종류의 공연을 가장 좋아하나요?

W: 저는 음악 공연을 가장 좋아해요.

M: 알겠습니다. 그러면 록과 힙합 중 어떤 것을 더 좋아하나요?

W: 저는 힙합보다 록을 더 좋아해요.

M: 가장 좋아하는 뮤지션은 누구인가요?

W: 제가 가장 좋아하는 뮤지션은 TJ입니다.

M: 좋습니다. 답변해 주셔서 감사합니다.

Wrap Up 1

M: _____ you _____ me? I want _____ _____ a guitar.

W: There are _____ _____ of guitars. _____ _____ _____ _____ do you want _____ _____?

M: I _____ _____ play pop songs.

W: Then you _____ _____ a classical guitar.

M: Okay, I will _____ a _____ _____.

M: 저 좀 도와주시겠어요? 저는 기타를 하나 사고 싶어요.

W: 다양한 종류의 기타가 있어요. 어떤 종류의 음악을 연주하고 싶으신가요?

M: 저는 팝송을 연주하려고 해요.

W: 그럼 클래식 기타를 사셔야 해요.

M: 알겠습니다, 클래식 기타로 살게요.

Step2

※ 다음 우리말에 맞도록 대화를 영어로 쓰시오.

Listen & Talk 1 A-1

W: _____
M: _____
W: _____
M: _____

W: Brian, 너희 밴드는 '십 대 음악 축제'에서 연주할 거야?
M: 응, 우리는 거의 매일 연습하고 있어.
W: 너희는 올해 어떤 종류의 음악을 연주하려고 해?
M: 록 음악. 우리는 90년대 곡들을 연주할 거야.

Listen & Talk 1 A-2

W: _____
M: _____
W: _____
M: _____
W: _____

W: 나 좀 도와줄래? 나는 선을 깔끔하게 그리는 방법을 모르겠어.
M: 어떤 종류의 붓을 사용하고 있었니?
W: 이 둥근 붓이야.
M: 선을 그릴 때는 납작한 붓이 더 나아. 이것을 써 봐.
W: 알았어, 고마워.

Listen & Talk 1 B

W: _____
M: _____
W: _____
M: _____
W: _____
M: _____
W: _____

W: (전화벨 소리) 안녕, Steve.
M: 안녕, Anna. 우리 내일 1시 30분에 예술 축제에서 만나는 거 맞지?
W: 맞아. 먼저 어떤 종류의 공연을 보고 싶어?
M: 난 힙합 댄스 공연을 먼저 보고 싶어.
W: 좋은 생각이야. 체육관에서 오후 2시에 하는 거 맞지?
M: 응, 그리고 오후 4시에 '로미오와 줄리엣' 연극을 보는 건 어때?
W: 아, 체육관 근처 대강당에서 하는 연극 말이지? 좋아!

Listen & Talk 2 A-1

M: _____
W: _____
M: _____
W: _____
M: _____

M: 지나야, 너 무엇을 읽고 있니?
W: '파이 이야기'라는 소설이야. 한 소년과 호랑이에 대한 이야기이지.
M: 훌륭한 책이야. 나는 그것을 영화로도 봤어. 나는 소설보다는 영화가 더 좋아.
W: 왜 영화가 더 좋은데?
M: 장면이 매우 아름다워. 그리고 호랑이가 매우 진짜같이 보이거든.

Listen & Talk 2 A-2

W: _____

M: _____

W: _____

M: _____

_____

Listen & Talk 2 B

W: _____

M: _____

W: _____

M: _____

_____

W: _____

Communication

M: _____

_____

W: _____

M: _____

W: _____

M: _____

W: _____

M: _____

W: _____

M: _____

Wrap Up 1

M: _____

W: _____

M: _____

W: _____

M: _____

W: 너는 Jane의 새 노래인 '여자 친구'를 들어 봤니?
M: 응, 정말 멋져. 기타 부분이 굉장하지.
W: 앨범에는 그 노래의 댄스 버전도 있어.
M: 나는 그것을 들었는데 댄스 버전보다는 기타 버전이 더 좋아. 그 버전이 그녀의 목소리와 더 잘 어울리거든.

W: 나 미술 책에서 흥미로운 그림을 봤어. 이것 봐.
M: 와, 그것은 다빈치의 '모나리자'처럼 보이는데.
W: 사실 이 그림은 페르난도 보테로의 '모나리자'야. 넌 어느 것이 더 마음에 드니?
M: 나는 보테로의 그림보다 다빈치의 모나리자가 더 좋아. 다빈치의 '모나리자'에는 흥미로운 미소가 있어. 너는 어때?
W: 음, 나는 다빈치의 모나리자보다는 보테로의 모나리자가 더 좋아. 그의 '모나리자'는 귀엽고 현대적으로 보여.

M: 안녕하세요, 저희는 학교 축제를 계획 중이고, 그래서 학생들이 어떤 종류의 공연을 좋아하는지 알고 싶습니다. 몇 가지 질문을 해도 될까요?
W: 물론이죠.
M: 어떤 종류의 공연을 가장 좋아하나요?
W: 저는 음악 공연을 가장 좋아해요.
M: 알겠습니다. 그러면 록과 힙합 중 어떤 것을 더 좋아하나요?
W: 저는 힙합보다 록을 더 좋아해요.
M: 가장 좋아하는 뮤지션은 누구인가요?
W: 제가 가장 좋아하는 뮤지션은 TJ입니다.
M: 좋습니다. 답변해 주셔서 감사합니다.

M: 저 좀 도와주시겠어요? 저는 기타를 하나 사고 싶어요.
W: 다양한 종류의 기타가 있어요. 어떤 종류의 음악을 연주하고 싶으신가요?
M: 저는 팝송을 연주하려고 해요.
W: 그럼 클래식 기타를 사셔야 해요.
M: 알겠습니다, 클래식 기타로 살게요.

※ 다음 우리말과 일치하도록 빈칸에 알맞은 것을 골라 쓰시오.

1 _____ _____ the World Art Museum _____ .
A. tour　　　　B. to　　　　C. welcome

2 _____ you go to an art museum, how _____ time do you spend _____ at _____ painting?
A. much　　　B. looking　　C. when　　D. each

3 Many visitors _____ at one painting _____ only a _____ seconds before they move _____ .
A. few　　　　B. on　　　　C. for　　　D. glance

4 But you _____ _____ the important details of paintings _____ it is hard to _____ them right away.
A. since　　　B. notice　　C. miss　　D. might

5 Today, we'll look _____ two paintings _____ and I'll _____ you _____ interesting details.
A. closely　　B. see　　　　C. at　　　D. help

6 _____ _____ this painting _____ .
A. at　　　　B. look　　　C. first

7 The _____ landscape is so _____ and beautiful, _____ ?
A. isn't　　　B. peaceful　　C. seaside　　D. it

8 The _____ of this painting _____ *Landscape* _____ *the Fall of Icarus*.
A. is　　　　B. title　　　C. with

9 So, can you see _____ _____ _____ ?
A. Icarus　　B. where　　C. is

10 Do you see two legs _____ are _____ _____ of the water _____ the ship?
A. out　　　B. near　　　C. sticking　　D. that

11 This is Icarus _____ the _____ _____ in Greece.
A. myth　　　B. famous　　C. in

12 In the myth, Icarus' father made _____ for him with _____ and wax and told him to _____ _____ from the sun.
A. away　　　B. feathers　　C. wings　　D. stay

13 _____ , Icarus _____ _____ .
A. didn't　　B. however　　C. listen

14 He _____ too _____ _____ the sun.
A. close　　　B. flew　　　C. to

15 So, the wax _____ and he _____ _____ the water.
A. into　　　B. melted　　C. fell

1 세계 미술관(the World Art Museum)에 오신 것을 환영합니다.

2 미술관에 갈 때 여러분은 각각의 그림을 보는 데 얼마나 많은 시간을 보내나요?

3 많은 방문객들은 이동하기 전에 하나의 그림을 몇 초간만 힐끗 봅니다.

4 하지만 그림의 중요한 세부 사항들을 즉시 알아채는 것은 어렵기 때문에 여러분들은 그것들을 놓칠 수 있습니다.

5 오늘 우리는 두 개의 그림을 자세히 살펴볼 것이고, 여러분이 흥미로운 세부 사항들을 볼 수 있도록 제가 도와드리겠습니다.

6 먼저 이 그림을 보세요.

7 바닷가 풍경이 매우 평화롭고 아름답죠. 그렇지 않나요?

8 이 그림의 제목은 '추락하는 이카루스가 있는 풍경'입니다.

9 그러면 이카루스가 어디에 있는지 보이나요?

10 배 근처에 물 밖으로 나와 있는 두 다리가 보이죠?

11 이것이 그리스의 유명한 신화에 나오는 이카루스입니다.

12 신화에서 이카루스의 아버지는 그를 위해 깃털과 밀랍으로 날개를 만들어 주었고 그에게 태양을 가까이 하지 말라고 말했습니다.

13 하지만 이카루스는 듣지 않았습니다.

14 그는 태양에 너무 가깝게 날았습니다.

15 그래서 밀랍이 녹았고 그는 물에 빠졌습니다.

16 Now, _____ _____ the _____ painting again.

    A. at   B. entire   C. look

17 _____ the tragedy of Icarus, people are _____ _____ with their _____ activities.

    A. on   B. despite   C. going   D. everyday

18 Does the painting _____ _____ _____?

    A. look   B. still   C. peaceful

19 _____ do you _____ the artist is _____ to tell us?

    A. trying   B. think   C. what

20 Now, let's _____ _____ _____ the next painting.

    A. on   B. move   C. to

21 Do you _____ the artist _____ the _____ canvas?

    A. behind   B. see   C. large

22 He is Diego Velázquez, and he _____ _____ this picture.

    A. painted   B. actually

23 _____ do you _____ _____ _____ painting?

    A. think   B. is   C. he   D. who

24 _____ a quick _____.

    A. look   B. take

25 The young princess _____ _____ be the _____ person _____ she is in the center of the painting.

    A. to   B. main   C. seems   D. because

26 But the _____ of the _____ is *The Maids of Honour*.

    A. painting   B. title

27 Then, is the artist _____ the two women _____ the _____?

    A. beside   B. drawing   C. princess

28 _____ a _____ look.

    A. close   B. take

29 It will _____ _____ _____ about the painting more.

    A. wonder   B. make   C. you

30 _____ to see _____ _____ the artist is looking at.

    A. direction   B. try   C. which

31 Can you _____ the king and the queen _____ the _____ in the _____ of the painting?

    A. background   B. in   C. see   D. mirror

32 _____ do you _____ he _____ painting now?

    A. is   B. think   C. who

---

16 이제, 그림 전체를 다시 보세요.

17 이카루스의 비극에도 불구하고 사람들은 일상의 활동을 계속하고 있습니다.

18 그림이 여전히 평화로워 보이나요?

19 화가가 우리에게 무엇을 말하려 한다고 생각하나요?

20 이제, 다음 그림으로 넘어갑시다.

21 커다란 캔버스 뒤에 있는 화가가 보이나요?

22 그는 Diego Velázquez이고, 그가 실제로 이 그림을 그렸습니다.

23 그가 누구를 그리고 있다고 생각하나요?

24 재빨리 봅시다.

25 어린 공주가 그림의 중앙에 있기 때문에 주인공처럼 보입니다.

26 하지만 그림의 제목은 '시녀들'입니다.

27 그렇다면 화가는 공주 옆에 있는 두 여인을 그리고 있나요?

28 자세히 보세요.

29 그림에 대해 더 궁금해하게 될 겁니다.

30 화가가 바라보고 있는 방향을 보려고 노력해 보세요.

31 그림의 배경에 있는 거울 속 왕과 왕비가 보이나요?

32 이제 여러분은 그가 누구를 그리고 있다고 생각하나요?

※ 다음 우리말과 일치하도록 빈칸에 알맞은 말을 쓰시오.

1 _____ _____ the World Art Museum _____.

2 _____ you _____ _____ an art museum, _____ _____ _____ do you _____ _____ _____ each painting?

3 Many visitors _____ _____ one painting _____ only _____ _____ seconds before they _____ _____.

4 But you _____ _____ the important details of paintings _____ it is hard _____ _____ _____ right away.

5 Today, we'll _____ _____ two paintings _____ and I'll _____ _____ _____ interesting _____.

6 _____ _____ this painting _____.

7 The _____ _____ is so _____ and beautiful, _____ _____?

8 The _____ _____ this painting _____ *Landscape with the Fall of Icarus*.

9 So, can you see _____ _____ _____?

10 Do you see two legs that _____ _____ _____ _____ _____ _____ _____ the ship?

11 This is Icarus _____ _____ _____ _____ _____ in Greece.

12 In the myth, Icarus' father _____ _____ _____ _____ _____ and wax and told him _____ _____ _____ _____ the sun.

13 _____, Icarus _____.

14 He _____ _____ _____ to the sun.

15 So, the wax _____ and he _____ _____ the water.

1 세계 미술관(the World Art Museum)에 오신 것을 환영합니다.

2 미술관에 갈 때 여러분은 각각의 그림을 보는 데 얼마나 많은 시간을 보내나요?

3 많은 방문객들은 이동하기 전에 하나의 그림을 몇 초간만 힐끗 봅니다.

4 하지만 그림의 중요한 세부 사항들을 즉시 알아채는 것은 어렵기 때문에 여러분들은 그것들을 놓칠 수 있습니다.

5 오늘 우리는 두 개의 그림을 자세히 살펴볼 것이고, 여러분이 흥미로운 세부 사항들을 볼 수 있도록 제가 도와드리겠습니다.

6 먼저 이 그림을 보세요.

7 바닷가 풍경이 매우 평화롭고 아름답죠, 그렇지 않나요?

8 이 그림의 제목은 '추락하는 이카루스가 있는 풍경'입니다.

9 그러면 이카루스가 어디에 있는지 보이나요?

10 배 근처에 물 밖으로 나와 있는 두 다리가 보이죠?

11 이것이 그리스의 유명한 신화에 나오는 이카루스입니다.

12 신화에서 이카루스의 아버지는 그를 위해 깃털과 밀랍으로 날개를 만들어 주었고 그에게 태양을 가까이 하지 말라고 말했습니다.

13 하지만 이카루스는 듣지 않았습니다.

14 그는 태양에 너무 가깝게 날았습니다.

15 그래서 밀랍이 녹았고 그는 물에 빠졌습니다.

16 Now, _____ _____ the _____ painting again.

17 _____ the tragedy of Icarus, people are _____ _____ _____ their _____ _____.

18 Does the painting _____ _____ _____?

19 _____ _____ _____ _____ _____ the artist is _____ _____ tell us?

20 Now, let's _____ _____ _____ the next painting.

21 Do you _____ the artist _____ the large canvas?

22 He is Diego Velázquez, and he _____ _____ this picture.

23 _____ _____ _____ _____ _____ _____ painting?

24 _____ a _____ _____.

25 The young princess _____ _____ _____ the main person _____ she is _____ _____ _____ of the painting.

26 But the _____ of the _____ is *The Maids of Honour*.

27 Then, is the artist _____ the two women _____ the princess?

28 _____ a _____ _____.

29 It will _____ _____ _____ about the painting more.

30 _____ _____ see _____ _____ _____ _____ _____ _____ _____ looking at.

31 Can you _____ the king and the queen _____ _____ _____ in the _____ of the painting?

32 _____ _____ _____ _____ _____ _____ _____ _____ painting now?

---

16 이제, 그림 전체를 다시 보세요.

17 이카루스의 비극에도 불구하고 사람들은 일상의 활동을 계속하고 있습니다.

18 그림이 여전히 평화로워 보이나요?

19 화가가 우리에게 무엇을 말하려 한다고 생각하나요?

20 이제, 다음 그림으로 넘어갑시다.

21 커다란 캔버스 뒤에 있는 화가가 보이나요?

22 그는 Diego Velázquez이고, 그가 실제로 이 그림을 그렸습니다.

23 그가 누구를 그리고 있다고 생각하나요?

24 재빨리 봅시다.

25 어린 공주가 그림의 중앙에 있기 때문에 주인공처럼 보입니다.

26 하지만 그림의 제목은 '시녀들'입니다.

27 그렇다면 화가는 공주 옆에 있는 두 여인을 그리고 있나요?

28 자세히 보세요.

29 그림에 대해 더 궁금해하게 될 겁니다.

30 화가가 바라보고 있는 방향을 보려고 노력해 보세요.

31 그림의 배경에 있는 거울 속 왕과 왕비가 보이나요?

32 이제 여러분은 그가 누구를 그리고 있다고 생각하나요?

※ 다음 문장을 우리말로 쓰시오.

1 ▶ Welcome to the World Art Museum tour.

➡ _____

2 ▶ When you go to an art museum, how much time do you spend looking at each painting?

➡ _____

3 ▶ Many visitors glance at one painting for only a few seconds before they move on.

➡ _____

4 ▶ But you might miss the important details of paintings since it is hard to notice them right away.

➡ _____

5 ▶ Today, we'll look at two paintings closely and I'll help you see interesting details.

➡ _____

6 ▶ Look at this painting first.

➡ _____

7 ▶ The seaside landscape is so peaceful and beautiful, isn't it?

➡ _____

8 ▶ The title of this painting is *Landscape with the Fall* of Icarus.

➡ _____

9 ▶ So, can you see where Icarus is?

➡ _____

10 ▶ Do you see two legs that are sticking out of the water near the ship?

➡ _____

11 ▶ This is Icarus in the famous myth in Greece.

➡ _____

12 ▶ In the myth, Icarus' father made wings for him with feathers and wax and told him to stay away from the sun.

➡ _____

_____

13 ▶ However, Icarus didn't listen.

➡ _____

14 ▶ He flew too close to the sun.

➡ _____

15 ▶ So, the wax melted and he fell into the water.

➡ _____

16 Now, look at the entire painting again.

➡ _____

17 Despite the tragedy of Icarus, people are going on with their everyday activities.

➡ _____

18 Does the painting still look peaceful?

➡ _____

19 What do you think the artist is trying to tell us?

➡ _____

20 Now, let's move on to the next painting.

➡ _____

21 Do you see the artist behind the large canvas?

➡ _____

22 He is Diego Velázquez, and he actually painted this picture.

➡ _____

23 Who do you think he is painting?

➡ _____

24 Take a quick look.

➡ _____

25 The young princess seems to be the main person because she is in the center of the painting.

➡ _____

26 But the title of the painting is *The Maids of Honour*.

➡ _____

27 Then, is the artist drawing the two women beside the princess?

➡ _____

28 Take a close look.

➡ _____

29 It will make you wonder about the painting more.

➡ _____

30 Try to see which direction the artist is looking at.

➡ _____

31 Can you see the king and the queen in the mirror in the background of the painting?

➡ _____

32 Who do you think he is painting now?

➡ _____

본문 Test

Step4

※ 다음 괄호 안의 단어들을 우리말에 맞도록 바르게 배열하시오.

1 (to / World / the / Welcome / tour. / Museum / Art)
➡ _____

2 (you / when / to / go / art / an / museum, / much / how / do / time / spend / you / at / looking / painting? / each)
➡ _____

3 (visitors / many / at / glance / painting / one / only / for / few / a / seconds / before / on. / move / they)
➡ _____

4 (you / but / miss / might / important / the / of / paintings / details / it / since / is / to / hard / them / notice / away. / right)
➡ _____

5 (today, / look / we'll / two / at / closely / paintings / and / help / I'll / see / you / details. / interesting)
➡ _____

6 (at / look / first. / painting / this)
➡ _____

7 (seaside / the / is / landscape / peaceful / so / and / isn't / beautiful / it?)
➡ _____

8 (title / the / this / of / painting / is / *with* / *Landscape* / *the* / *Icarus.* / *of* / *Fall*)
➡ _____

9 (so, / you / can / see / Icarus / is? / where)
➡ _____

10 (you / do / see / legs / two / are / that / out / sticking / of / water / the / near / ship? / the)
➡ _____

11 (is / this / Icarus / in / famous / the / Greece. / in / myth)
➡ _____

12 (the / in / myth, / father / Icarus' / wings / made / him / for / feathers / with / wax / and / told / to / him / away / stay / from / sun. / the)
➡ _____

13 (Icarus / however, / listen. / didn't)
➡ _____

14 (flew / he / close / too / sun. / the / to)
➡ _____

15 (so, / wax / the / melted / and / fell / he / into / water. / the)
➡ _____

---

1 세계 미술관(the World Art Museum)에 오신 것을 환영합니다.

2 미술관에 갈 때 여러분은 각각의 그림을 보는 데 얼마나 많은 시간을 보내나요?

3 많은 방문객들은 이동하기 전에 하나의 그림을 몇 초간만 힐끗 봅니다.

4 하지만 그림의 중요한 세부 사항들을 즉시 알아채는 것은 어렵기 때문에 여러분들은 그것들을 놓칠 수 있습니다.

5 오늘 우리는 두 개의 그림을 자세히 살펴볼 것이고, 여러분이 흥미로운 세부 사항들을 볼 수 있도록 제가 도와드리겠습니다.

6 먼저 이 그림을 보세요.

7 바닷가 풍경이 매우 평화롭고 아름답죠, 그렇지 않나요?

8 이 그림의 제목은 '추락하는 이카루스가 있는 풍경'입니다.

9 그러면 이카루스가 어디에 있는지 보이나요?

10 배 근처에 물 밖으로 나와 있는 두 다리가 보이죠?

11 이것이 그리스의 유명한 신화에 나오는 이카루스입니다.

12 신화에서 이카루스의 아버지는 그를 위해 깃털과 밀랍으로 날개를 만들어 주었고 그에게 태양을 가까이 하지 말라고 말했습니다.

13 하지만 이카루스는 듣지 않았습니다.

14 그는 태양에 너무 가깝게 날았습니다.

15 그래서 밀랍이 녹았고 그는 물에 빠졌습니다.

16 (now, / at / look / entire / the / again. / painting)
➡ _____

17 (the / despite / tragedy / Icarus, / of / are / people / going / with / on / everyday / their / activities.)
➡ _____

18 (the / does / still / painting / peaceful? / look)
➡ _____

19 (do / what / think / you / artist / the / trying / is / us? / tell / to)
➡ _____

20 (now, / move / let's / to / on / painting. / next / the)
➡ _____

21 (you / do / see / artist / the / the / behind / canvas? / large)
➡ _____

22 (is / he / Velázquez, / Diego / and / actually / he / this / picture. / painted)
➡ _____

23 (do / who / think / you / painting? / is / he)
➡ _____

24 (a / take / look. / quick)
➡ _____

25 (young / the / seems / princess / be / to / main / the / because / person / is / she / the / in / center / the / painting. / of)
➡ _____

26 (the / but / of / title / painting / the / is / *of* / *Maids* / *Honour.* / *The*)
➡ _____

27 (then, / the / is / drawing / artist / the / women / two / princess? / the / beside)
➡ _____

28 (a / take / look. / close)
➡ _____

29 (will / it / you / make / about / wonder / the / more. / about / painting)
➡ _____

30 (to / try / which / direction / see / the / artist / at. / looking / is)
➡ _____

31 (you / can / the / see / king / the / and / queen / the / in / mirror / the / in / background / painting? / the / of)
➡ _____

32 (do / who / think / you / is / he / now? / painting)
➡ _____

16 이제, 그림 전체를 다시 보세요.

17 이카루스의 비극에도 불구하고 사람들은 일상의 활동을 계속하고 있습니다.

18 그림이 여전히 평화로워 보이나요?

19 화가가 우리에게 무엇을 말하려 한다고 생각하나요?

20 이제, 다음 그림으로 넘어갑시다.

21 커다란 캔버스 뒤에 있는 화가가 보이나요?

22 그는 Diego Velázquez이고, 그가 실제로 이 그림을 그렸습니다.

23 그가 누구를 그리고 있다고 생각하나요?

24 재빨리 봅시다.

25 어린 공주가 그림의 중앙에 있기 때문에 주인공처럼 보입니다.

26 하지만 그림의 제목은 '시녀들'입니다.

27 그렇다면 화가는 공주 옆에 있는 두 여인을 그리고 있나요?

28 자세히 보세요.

29 그림에 대해 더 궁금해하게 될 겁니다.

30 화가가 바라보고 있는 방향을 보려고 노력해 보세요.

31 그림의 배경에 있는 거울 속 왕과 왕비가 보이나요?

32 이제 여러분은 그가 누구를 그리고 있다고 생각하나요?

※ 다음 우리말을 영어로 쓰시오.

1 세계 미술관(the World Art Museum)에 오신 것을 환영합니다.

➡ _____

2 미술관에 갈 때 여러분은 각각의 그림을 보는 데 얼마나 많은 시간을 보내나요?

➡ _____

3 많은 방문객들은 이동하기 전에 하나의 그림을 몇 초간만 힐끗 봅니다.

➡ _____

4 하지만 그림의 중요한 세부 사항들을 즉시 알아채는 것은 어렵기 때문에 여러분들은 그것들을 놓칠 수 있습니다.

➡ _____

5 오늘 우리는 두 개의 그림을 자세히 살펴볼 것이고, 여러분이 흥미로운 세부 사항들을 볼 수 있도록 제가 도와드리겠습니다.

➡ _____

6 먼저 이 그림을 보세요.

➡ _____

7 바닷가 풍경이 매우 평화롭고 아름답죠, 그렇지 않나요?

➡ _____

8 이 그림의 제목은 '추락하는 이카루스가 있는 풍경'입니다.

➡ _____

9 그러면 이카루스가 어디에 있는지 보이나요?

➡ _____

10 배 근처에 물 밖으로 나와 있는 두 다리가 보이죠?

➡ _____

11 이것이 그리스의 유명한 신화에 나오는 이카루스입니다.

➡ _____

12 신화에서 이카루스의 아버지는 그를 위해 깃털과 밀랍으로 날개를 만들어 주었고 그에게 태양을 가까이 하지 말라고 말했습니다.

➡ _____

_____

13 하지만 이카루스는 듣지 않았습니다.

➡ _____

14 그는 태양에 너무 가깝게 날았습니다.

➡ _____

15 그래서 밀랍이 녹았고 그는 물에 빠졌습니다.

➡ _____

16 이제, 그림 전체를 다시 보세요.

➡ _____

17 이카루스의 비극에도 불구하고 사람들은 일상의 활동을 계속하고 있습니다.

➡ _____

18 그림이 여전히 평화로워 보이나요?

➡ _____

19 화가가 우리에게 무엇을 말하려 한다고 생각하나요?

➡ _____

20 이제, 다음 그림으로 넘어갑시다.

➡ _____

21 커다란 캔버스 뒤에 있는 화가가 보이나요?

➡ _____

22 그는 Diego Velázquez이고, 그가 실제로 이 그림을 그렸습니다.

➡ _____

23 그가 누구를 그리고 있다고 생각하나요?

➡ _____

24 재빨리 봅시다.

➡ _____

25 어린 공주가 그림의 중앙에 있기 때문에 주인공처럼 보입니다.

➡ _____

26 하지만 그림의 제목은 '시녀들'입니다.

➡ _____

27 그렇다면 화가는 공주 옆에 있는 두 여인을 그리고 있나요?

➡ _____

28 자세히 보세요.

➡ _____

29 그림에 대해 더 궁금해하게 될 겁니다.

➡ _____

30 화가가 바라보고 있는 방향을 보려고 노력해 보세요.

➡ _____

31 그림의 배경에 있는 거울 속 왕과 왕비가 보이나요?

➡ _____

32 이제 여러분은 그가 누구를 그리고 있다고 생각하나요?

➡ _____

※ 다음 우리말과 일치하도록 빈칸에 알맞은 말을 쓰시오.

Listen & Talk

1. M: What _____ you _____, Sally?

2 W: I'm _____ *The Maze Runner*. It's about boys _____ are put _____ _____ _____.

3 M: It's a great story. I've _____ the movie of it, _____. I _____ the novel _____ the movie.

4 W: _____ do you _____ it _____?

5 M: The novel has _____ _____. But the movie didn't _____ some _____ _____ of the story.

Grammar in Real Life

1. Princess, please _____ me _____.

2. _____ are _____?

3. The princess _____ _____, "If you help me, I'll _____ _____ _____ the palace and _____ my friend."

4. Come here. I'll have people _____ _____ some _____ and _____.

5. No! _____ _____ him _____. I don't like him.

6. Don't _____, Frog. I'll _____ _____ _____ _____ her promise.

Think and Write C

1. Today, I went to the _____ _____ _____.

2. At the exhibition, I saw many _____ _____ _____ _____.

3. _____ them, I liked the piece _____ *Moon Tree*.

4. It _____ _____ _____ French artist, David Myriam.

5. _____, sand _____ _____ in this painting.

6. I like it _____ a tree in the moon _____ _____ _____ _____.

7. Now I know that anything _____ _____ _____ _____ make art.

8. _____ is _____!

---

1. M: Sally, 너는 무엇을 읽고 있니?
2. W: 나는 '미로를 달리는 사람'을 읽고 있어. 미로에 갇힌 소년들에 관한 내용이야.
3. M: 그건 대단한 이야기이지. 나는 그것을 영화로도 봤어. 나는 영화보다는 소설이 더 좋아.
4. W: 왜 소설이 더 좋은데?
5. M: 소설에는 다양한 이야기가 담겨 있어. 하지만 영화에서는 이야기의 중요한 몇 부분이 나오지 않았어.

1. 공주님, 저를 들어가게 해 주세요.
2. 그대는 누군가?
3. 공주님은 제게 "네가 날 도와준다면, 나는 너를 궁전에 들어오게 하고 내 친구가 되게 해 주겠어."라고 약속하셨어요.
4. 이쪽으로 오게. 내가 사람들을 시켜 자네에게 과자와 차를 가져다 주게 하겠네.
5. 안 돼요! 그를 들어오게 하지 마세요. 저는 그를 좋아하지 않아요.
6. 걱정 말게, 개구리. 나는 공주가 그녀의 약속을 지키게 하겠네.

1. 오늘 나는 놀라운 미술 전시회에 갔다.
2. 전시회에서, 나는 많은 흥미로운 예술 작품들을 보았다.
3. 그 중에서, 나는 Moon Tree라고 불리는 작품이 좋았다.
4. 그것은 프랑스 예술가 David Myriam에 의해 만들어졌다.
5. 흥미롭게도, 모래가 이 미술품에 사용되었다.
6. 달 속에 있는 나무 한그루가 내 마음을 고요하게 만들기 때문에 나는 그것이 좋다.
7. 이제 나는 어떠한 것이든 미술을 만들기 위해 사용될 수 있다는 사실을 안다.
8. 무엇이든 가능하다!

※ 다음 우리말을 영어로 쓰시오.

Listen & Talk

1. M: Sally, 너는 무엇을 읽고 있니?
➡ _____

2. W: 나는 '미로를 달리는 사람'을 읽고 있어. 미로에 갇힌 소년들에 관한 내용이야.
➡ _____

3. M: 그건 대단한 이야기이지. 나는 그것을 영화로도 봤어. 나는 영화보다는 소설이 더 좋아.
➡ _____

4. W: 왜 소설이 더 좋은데?
➡ _____

5. M: 소설에는 다양한 이야기가 담겨 있어. 하지만 영화에서는 이야기의 중요한 몇 부분이 나오지 않았어.
➡ _____

Grammar in Real Life

1. 공주님, 저를 들어가게 해 주세요.
➡ _____

2. 그대는 누군가?
➡ _____

3. 공주님은 제게 "네가 날 도와준다면, 나는 너를 궁전에 들어오게 하고 내 친구가 되게 해 주겠어."라고 약속하셨어요.
➡ _____

4. 이쪽으로 오게. 내가 사람들을 시켜 자네에게 과자와 차를 가져다 주게 하겠네.
➡ _____

5. 안 돼요! 그를 들어오게 하지 마세요. 저는 그를 좋아하지 않아요.
➡ _____

6. 걱정 말게, 개구리. 나는 공주가 그녀의 약속을 지키게 하겠네.
➡ _____

Think and Write C

1. 오늘 나는 놀라운 미술 전시회에 갔다.
➡ _____

2. 전시회에서, 나는 많은 흥미로운 예술 작품들을 보았다.
➡ _____

3. 그 중에서, 나는 Moon Tree라고 불리는 작품이 좋았다.
➡ _____

4. 그것은 프랑스 예술가 David Myriam에 의해 만들어졌다.
➡ _____

5. 흥미롭게도, 모래가 이 미술품에 사용되었다.
➡ _____

6. 달 속에 있는 나무 한그루가 내 마음을 고요하게 만들기 때문에 나는 그것이 좋다.
➡ _____

7. 이제 나는 어떠한 것이든 미술을 만들기 위해 사용될 수 있다는 사실을 안다.
➡ _____

8. 무엇이든 가능하다!
➡ _____

※ 다음 영어를 우리말로 쓰시오.

01 balance _____

02 counter _____

03 mixture _____

04 sugar-free _____

05 deliver _____

06 thought _____

07 effect _____

08 guidebook _____

09 handwritten _____

10 fry _____

11 bakery _____

12 presence _____

13 hundred _____

14 suggest _____

15 importance _____

16 dependence _____

17 post _____

18 local _____

19 machine _____

20 experience _____

21 moment _____

22 nearby _____

23 trendy _____

24 opinion _____

25 downtown _____

26 creative _____

27 debate _____

28 price _____

29 remain _____

30 scared _____

31 elderly _____

32 donate _____

33 technology _____

34 wisely _____

35 throw away _____

36 can't wait to _____

37 rely on _____

38 even though _____

39 get attention _____

40 pay for _____

41 fall asleep _____

42 keep -ing _____

43 be busy -ing _____

※ 다음 우리말을 영어로 쓰시오.

01 계산대, 판매대

02 (과학) 기술

03 제안하다

04 토론, 논의

05 기계

06 기부하다

07 시내의

08 효과

09 무가당의

10 경험

11 튀기다

12 존재

13 가격

14 손으로 쓴

15 균형을 잡다

16 백, 100

17 중요함

18 생각

19 지역의; 현지인

20 창의적인

21 전달하다, 배달하다

22 근처에

23 최신 유행의

24 의견

25 (웹사이트에 정보, 사진을) 올리다

26 혼합물, 혼합

27 동의하다

28 남아 있다, 남다

29 의존, 의지

30 현명하게

31 순간

32 무서워하는, 겁먹은

33 (여행자 등의) 숙소, 여관

34 나이가 지긋한

35 계속해서 ~하다

36 대금을 지불하다

37 ~하느라 바쁘다

38 ~을 버리다

39 ~에 의존하다

40 비록 ~할지라도

41 잠들다

42 주목을 받다

43 길을 잃다

※ 다음 영영풀이에 알맞은 단어를 <보기>에서 골라 쓴 후, 우리말 뜻을 쓰시오.

1 _____ : to cook something in hot oil: _____

2 _____ : a book of directions and information for travelers: _____

3 _____ : relating to the particular area you live in: _____

4 _____ : a place where bread and cakes are made or sold: _____

5 _____ : to continue to exist or be left after others have gone: _____

6 _____ : a particular point in time: _____

7 _____ : to be in a steady position without falling to one side: _____

8 _____ : knowledge or skill that you gain from doing a job or activity:
_____

9 _____ : to put a message or computer document on the Internet:
_____

10 _____ : in a way that show experience, knowledge, and good judgment:
_____

11 _____ : relating to or located in the center of a town or city: _____

12 _____ : a private house where people can pay to stay and have meals:
_____

13 _____ : to give money, food, clothes, etc. to someone or something, especially a
charity: _____

14 _____ : new machines, equipment, and ways of doing things that are based on
modern scientific knowledge: _____

15 _____ : to tell someone your ideas about what they should do, where they should
go, etc.: _____

16 _____ : the state of needing the help and support of somebody/something in
order to survive or be successful: _____

보기			
suggest	fry	wisely	experience
post	technology	guesthouse	donate
local	remain	balance	moment
downtown	dependence	guidebook	bakery

※ 다음 우리말과 일치하도록 빈칸에 알맞은 말을 쓰시오.

Listen & Talk 1 A-1

Jane: Look, Dad. This is Mom's _____ _____.

Dad: Oh, you're _____ her a _____ _____?

Jane: Yeah, I've made a family _____ _____ for Mom and _____ it on this stick. What do you _____ about the _____?

Dad: I think it's really _____. She'll love it.

Jane: 보세요, 아빠. 이거 엄마의 생신 선물이에요.

Dad: 오, 너는 엄마에게 막대 기억 장치 (메모리 스틱)를 준다는 거지?

Jane: 네, 엄마를 위한 가족 동영상을 만들어서, 그것을 이 막대 기억 장치에 저장했어요. 이 선물에 대해 어떻게 생각하세요?

Dad: 정말 감동적인 것 같구나. 엄마가 그걸 정말 좋아할 거 같아.

Listen & Talk 1 A-2

Mike: Jenny, _____ _____ _____ _____ _____ the new online comic *Scary Night*?

Jenny: I didn't like it. I _____ it had too many _____ _____.

Mike: Really? I thought they _____ the story more _____.

Jenny: Not me. I _____ _____ because I was too _____.

Mike: Jenny, 너는 새로운 온라인 만화 '무서운 밤'에 대해 어떻게 생각하니?

Jenny: 난 그거 별로였어. 거기에 음향 효과가 너무 많다고 생각했어.

Mike: 정말? 나는 그것이 이야기를 더욱 흥미진진하게 만들어 준다고 생각했는데.

Jenny: 난 아니야. 난 너무 무서워서 집중할 수가 없었거든.

Listen & Talk 1 B

Tony: Hey, Julie! _____ you _____ about the *Quiz & Rice* game?

Julie: Yeah, isn't it the one that _____ rice when you get a _____ _____?

Tony: Yeah, _____ do you _____ _____ the game?

Julie: I think it's a _____ game. You can _____ _____ and _____ _____ hungry people. _____ you _____ it yet?

Tony: No, but I'm _____ _____ _____ it _____ this weekend.

Tony: 저기, Julie! 너 '퀴즈와 쌀'이라는 게임에 대해 들어봤어?

Julie: 응, 정답을 맞히면 쌀을 기부하는 게임 아니야?

Tony: 맞아, 넌 그 게임에 대해 어떻게 생각하니?

Julie: 난 그것이 창의적인 게임이라고 생각해. 재미있게 놀면서 배고픈 사람들을 도울 수 있잖아. 너 그거 이미 해 봤어?

Tony: 아니, 하지만 이번 주말에 해 보려고 해.

Listen & Talk 2 A-1

Jack: Sally, did you watch *Super Voice's* Top 10 finalists yesterday?

Sally: Yeah. They all sang much _____ _____ _____.

Jack: Yeah, they did. I think this _____ _____ helps them _____ _____ to their dreams.

Sally: I'm _____ _____ _____. I can't _____ _____ _____ their _____ _____.

Jack: Sally, 너 어제 '슈퍼 보이스'의 상위 10위 결정전을 봤니?

Sally: 응. 그들은 모두 전보다 훨씬 더 노래를 잘 불렀어.

Jack: 맞아, 그랬어. 나는 이 노래 경연 대회가 그들이 자신의 꿈에 더 가까워지도록 도와준다고 생각해.

Sally: 나도 그 말에 동의해. 그들의 다음 공연을 보는 것이 너무 기다려진다.

Listen & Talk 2 A-2

Steve: Hey, Lisa. I've got over a hundred _____ on my SNS posts.

Lisa: Oh, I wouldn't feel _____ _____ _____ my posts with so many people.

Steve: Really? I think it's great _____ a lot of people see my _____.

Lisa: I'm _____ _____ _____ _____ _____. I only want to _____ my posts with my _____ _____.

Listen & Talk 2 B

Emma: Excuse me. Can you _____ me _____ with this machine?

Tom: Sure. First, _____ the Hot Dog button and _____ your hot dog and drink.

Emma: Okay. _____ do I _____ _____ _____ _____?

Tom: Touch the Done button at the _____ and _____ for them.

Emma: Wow, it's so _____. This machine is _____ _____ _____ ordering at the _____.

Tom: I'm _____ _____ on that. It really _____ a lot of _____ _____ there's a long _____.

Communication

Sujin: Now, we will start the three-minute _____. Today's _____ _____ is fast fashion. _____ do you _____ about it? Please, begin, James.

James: I think fast fashion is good. We can wear _____ clothes _____ _____ _____ _____.

Wendy: I'm not _____ you _____ _____. It makes us _____ too much money and _____ _____ clothes too often.

Sujin: It looks like the two of you have different _____ on the first topic. Now, let's _____ _____ to the second topic.

Wrap Up 1

Alex: I've just _____ _____ _____ _____ _____ for Leon, Mom. _____ _____ _____ _____ _____ _____ _____?

Mom: Oh, the title "LOST CAT" in big letters at the top is easy to see.

Alex: Yeah, I did it to _____ _____. _____ _____ these photos _____ the title?

Mom: Hmm... the _____ on the _____ doesn't show Leon's face well.

Alex: Okay, I'll _____ the photo.

Mom: Oh, I _____ we can _____ Leon.

Steve: 저기, Lisa. 나 내 SNS 게시물들에 100개가 넘는 댓글을 받았어.

Lisa: 아, 나는 내 게시물들을 너무 많은 사람들과 공유하는 게 편하지 않을 거야.

Steve: 정말? 나는 많은 사람들이 내 게시물들을 보는 게 정말 좋다고 생각해.

Lisa: 나는 그 점에 있어서 너랑 생각이 달라. 나는 그냥 가까운 친구들하고만 내 게시물들을 공유하고 싶어.

Emma: 실례합니다. 제가 이 기계로 주문하는 것을 좀 도와주실 수 있나요?

Tom: 물론이죠. 먼저 '핫도그' 버튼을 누르시고, 드시고 싶은 핫도그와 음료를 고르세요.

Emma: 알겠습니다. 주문한 것에 대한 지불을 어떻게 하나요?

Tom: 맨 아래에 있는 '완료' 버튼을 누르시고 그것들에 대해 지불하세요.

Emma: 와, 정말 간단하네요. 이 기계가 계산대에서 주문하는 것보다 훨씬 더 빨라요.

Tom: 저도 그렇게 생각해요. 줄이 길 때, 그것은 정말 많은 시간을 절약해 줘요.

Sujin: 자, 3분 토론을 시작하겠습니다. 오늘의 첫 번째 주제는 '패스트 패션'입니다. 여러분들은 그것에 대해 어떻게 생각하십니까? 시작해 주세요, James.

James: 저는 '패스트 패션'이 좋다고 생각합니다. 우리는 보다 저렴한 가격으로 최신 유행의 옷들을 입을 수 있습니다.

Wendy: 저는 그 의견에 동의하지 않습니다. 그것은 우리가 너무 많은 돈을 쓰고 너무 자주 옷을 버리게 합니다.

Sujin: 첫 번째 주제에 대해서는 두 사람이 다른 의견을 갖고 있는 것 같습니다. 이제 두 번째 주제로 넘어가 보도록 하겠습니다.

Alex: 엄마, Leon을 위한 인터넷 게시물 만드는 걸 막 끝냈어요. 이것에 대해 어떻게 생각하세요?

Mom: 오, 맨 위에 큰 글자로 된 제목 "LOST CAT"이 잘 보이는구나.

Alex: 네, 주목을 끌기 위해 그렇게 했어요. 제목 밑에 있는 이 사진들은 어때요?

Mom: 흠… 오른쪽에 있는 사진에서 Leon의 얼굴이 잘 보이지 않아.

Alex: 알겠어요, 그 사진을 바꿀게요.

Mom: 오, 우리가 Leon을 찾을 수 있으면 좋겠구나.

※ 다음 우리말에 맞도록 대화를 영어로 쓰시오.

Listen & Talk 1 A-1

Jane: _____

Dad: _____

Jane: _____

_____

Dad: _____

Jane: 보세요, 아빠. 이거 엄마의 생신 선물이에요.
Dad: 오, 너는 엄마에게 막대 기억 장치(메모리 스틱)를 준다는 거지?
Jane: 네, 엄마를 위한 가족 동영상을 만들어서, 그것을 이 막대 기억 장치에 저장했어요. 이 선물에 대해 어떻게 생각하세요?
Dad: 정말 감동적인 것 같구나. 엄마가 그걸 정말 좋아할 거 같아.

Listen & Talk 1 A-2

Mike: _____

Jenny: _____

Mike: _____

Jenny: _____

Mike: Jenny, 너는 새로운 온라인 만화 '무서운 밤'에 대해 어떻게 생각하니?
Jenny: 난 그거 별로였어. 거기에 음향 효과가 너무 많다고 생각했어.
Mike: 정말? 나는 그것이 이야기를 더욱 흥미진진하게 만들어 준다고 생각했는데.
Jenny: 난 아니야. 난 너무 무서워서 집중할 수가 없었거든.

Listen & Talk 1 B

Tony: _____

Julie: _____

Tony: _____

Julie: _____

_____

Tony: _____

Tony: 저기, Julie! 너 '퀴즈와 쌀'이라는 게임에 대해 들어봤니?
Julie: 응, 정답을 맞히면 쌀을 기부하는 게임 아니야?
Tony: 맞아, 넌 그 게임에 대해 어떻게 생각하니?
Julie: 난 그것이 창의적인 게임이라고 생각해. 재미있게 놀면서 배고픈 사람들을 도울 수 있잖아. 너 그거 이미 해 봤니?
Tony: 아니, 하지만 이번 주말에 해 보려고 해.

Listen & Talk 2 A-1

Jack: _____

Sally: _____

Jack: _____

Sally: _____

Jack: Sally, 너 어제 '슈퍼 보이스'의 상위 10위 결정전을 봤니?
Sally: 응. 그들은 모두 전보다 훨씬 더 노래를 잘 불렀어.
Jack: 맞아, 그랬어. 나는 이 노래 경연 대회가 그들이 자신의 꿈에 더 가까워지도록 도와준다고 생각해.
Sally: 나도 그 말에 동의해. 그들의 다음 공연을 보는 것이 너무 기다려진다.

Listen & Talk 2 A-2

Steve: _____

Lisa: _____

Steve: _____

Lisa: _____

Listen & Talk 2 B

Emma: _____

Tom: _____

Emma: _____

Tom: _____

Emma: _____

Tom: _____

Communication

Sujin: _____
_____

James: _____

Wendy: _____
_____

Sujin: _____
_____

Wrap Up 1

Alex: _____
_____

Mom: _____

Alex: _____

Mom: _____

Alex: _____

Mom: _____

Steve: 저기, Lisa. 나 내 SNS 게시물들에 100개가 넘는 댓글을 받았어.

Lisa: 아, 나는 내 게시물들을 너무 많은 사람들과 공유하는 게 편하지 않을 거야.

Steve: 정말? 나는 많은 사람들이 내 게시물들을 보는 게 정말 좋다고 생각해.

Lisa: 나는 그 점에 있어서 너랑 생각이 달라. 나는 그냥 가까운 친구들하고만 내 게시물들을 공유하고 싶어.

Emma: 실례합니다. 제가 이 기계로 주문하는 것을 좀 도와주실 수 있나요?

Tom: 물론이죠. 먼저 '핫도그' 버튼을 누르시고, 드시고 싶은 핫도그와 음료를 고르세요.

Emma: 알겠습니다. 주문한 것에 대한 지불을 어떻게 하나요?

Tom: 맨 아래에 있는 '완료' 버튼을 누르시고 그것들에 대해 지불하세요.

Emma: 와, 정말 간단하네요. 이 기계가 계산대에서 주문하는 것보다 훨씬 더 빨라요.

Tom: 저도 그렇게 생각해요. 줄이 길 때, 그것은 정말 많은 시간을 절약해 줘요.

Sujin: 자, 3분 토론을 시작하겠습니다. 오늘의 첫 번째 주제는 '패스트 패션'입니다. 여러분들은 그것에 대해 어떻게 생각하십니까? 시작해 주세요, James.

James: 저는 '패스트 패션'이 좋다고 생각합니다. 우리는 보다 저렴한 가격으로 최신 유행의 옷들을 입을 수 있습니다.

Wendy: 저는 그 의견에 동의하지 않습니다. 그것은 우리가 너무 많은 돈을 쓰고 너무 자주 옷을 버리게 합니다.

Sujin: 첫 번째 주제에 대해서는 두 사람이 다른 의견을 갖고 있는 것 같습니다. 이제 두 번째 주제로 넘어가 보도록 하겠습니다.

Alex: 엄마, Leon을 위한 인터넷 게시물 만드는 걸 막 끝냈어요. 이것에 대해 어떻게 생각하세요?

Mom: 오, 맨 위에 큰 글자로 된 제목 "LOST CAT"이 잘 보이는구나.

Alex: 네, 주목을 끌기 위해 그렇게 했어요. 제목 밑에 있는 이 사진들은 어때요?

Mom: 흠… 오른쪽에 있는 사진에서 Leon의 얼굴이 잘 보이지 않아.

Alex: 알겠어요, 그 사진을 바꿀게요.

Mom: 오, 우리가 Leon을 찾을 수 있으면 좋겠구나.

※ 다음 우리말과 일치하도록 빈칸에 알맞은 것을 골라 쓰시오.

1 Last summer, my father _____ a _____ event: a family trip _____ smartphones!

A. surprising   B. without   C. suggested

2 He said, "I hate _____ see you _____ together and only _____ _____ your smartphones."

A. looking   B. to   C. at   D. sitting

3 My sister and I _____ the need for smartphones, but he _____ _____ that we could not _____ enjoy the trip with them.

A. saying   B. kept   C. explained   D. fully

4 So we _____ a technology-free _____ _____ a new city, Barcelona, Spain.

A. trip   B. to   C. started

5 Our _____ day was _____.

A. terrible   B. first

6 On the _____ to our guesthouse _____ Plaza Reial, we got _____ in _____ Barcelona.

A. lost   B. way   C. downtown   D. around

7 Dad was _____ _____ at the map and _____ for directions with a _____ Spanish words he got _____ a tour guidebook.

A. few   B. looking   C. asking   D. busy

8 _____ _____ our guesthouse was _____ next to the Plaza, it took us about two hours to _____ there.

A. get   B. though   C. right   D. even

9 We were _____ _____ _____ we could not go _____ for dinner.

A. out   B. tired   C. that   D. so

10 I went to bed but couldn't _____ _____ because I was _____ about what would _____ the next day.

A. asleep   B. happen   C. worried   D. fall

11 After _____ _____ Gaudi's Park Guell, we decided to _____ seafood _____ rice for lunch.

A. looking   B. fried   C. have   D. around

12 _____, we didn't know _____ restaurant to go _____.

A. which   B. to   C. however

13 We needed help, so Mom went _____ to an _____ lady and _____ to ask for _____ to a popular seafood restaurant.

A. directions   B. elderly   C. up   D. tried

---

1 지난여름, 아빠가 깜짝 놀랄 만한 이벤트로 스마트폰 없는 가족 여행을 제안하셨다!

2 아빠는 "나는 우리 가족이 함께 앉아서 각자의 스마트폰만 보고 있는 걸 보는 게 참 싫구나."라고 말씀하셨다.

3 여동생과 내가 스마트폰이 필요하다고 설명했지만, 아빠는 스마트폰이 있으면 여행을 충분히 즐길 수 없을 거라고 계속해서 말씀하셨다.

4 그래서 우리는 새로운 도시인 스페인의 바르셀로나로 '첨단 과학 기술 없는 여행'을 시작했다.

5 우리의 첫째 날은 엉망이었다.

6 레이알 광장 주변에 있는 여행자 숙소로 가는 길에 우리는 바르셀로나 시내에서 길을 잃었다.

7 아빠는 지도를 보며 여행안내 책자에서 배운 스페인어 몇 마디로 길을 묻느라 분주하셨다.

8 우리의 숙소가 광장 바로 옆에 있었음에도 불구하고, 우리가 그곳에 도착하는 데는 거의 두 시간이 걸렸다.

9 우리는 너무 피곤해서 저녁을 먹으러 나갈 수가 없었다.

10 나는 잠자리에 들었지만 내일 무슨 일이 일어날지 걱정이 되어서 잠들 수가 없었다.

11 가우디가 지은 구엘 공원을 둘러본 후, 우리는 점심으로 해산물 볶음밥을 먹기로 했다.

12 그러나 우리는 어떤 식당으로 가야 할지 몰랐다.

13 우리는 도움이 필요해서, 엄마가 한 노부인에게 가서 인기 있는 해산물 식당으로 가는 길을 물어보려고 애쓰셨다.

14 Luckily, she _____ to _____ Mom's few Spanish _____.

    A. understand   B. words   C. seemed

15 She _____ us to a small _____ restaurant _____.

    A. local   B. took   C. nearby

16 The seafood _____ _____ was _____.

    A. rice   B. amazing   C. fried

17 I really wanted to _____ pictures of the food and _____ them on my _____.

    A. post   B. take   C. blog

18 But _____ my phone, I just _____ to _____ the _____.

    A. enjoy   B. without   C. moment   D. decided

19 During the _____ days, we _____ more and more _____ the locals.

    A. on   B. remaining   C. relied

20 We were _____ to meet and talk with _____ people _____ the _____, in the bakeries, and in the parks.

    A. various   B. able   C. streets   D. on

21 They were always _____ _____ to show us different _____ of Barcelona with a smile.

    A. sides   B. enough   C. kind

22 Also, our family _____ a lot _____ each _____.

    A. other   B. with   C. talked

23 We spent _____ of our time _____ _____ the Spanish train, on the bus, and at the restaurants.

    A. together   B. much   C. on

24 Our technology-free _____ was a new and _____ _____.

    A. different   B. trip   C. experience

25 Before the trip, I was so _____ _____ my smartphone _____ I couldn't do anything _____ it.

    A. without   B. dependent   C. that   D. on

26 But now I see _____ I can enjoy the _____ _____ it.

    A. without   B. that   C. moment

27 _____ the experience, I have _____ the _____ of a _____ use of the smartphone.

    A. importance   B. balanced   C. learned   D. from

28 _____, next time, _____ I _____ without a smartphone?

    A. travel   B. would   C. so

29 _____ not. But I will _____ to use it more _____.

    A. wisely   B. probably   C. try

---

14 운이 좋게도 그녀는 몇 마디 안 되는 엄마의 스페인어를 이해하는 듯했다.

15 그녀는 우리를 근처에 있는 작은 현지 식당으로 데려다 주었다.

16 그 해산물 볶음밥은 놀랍도록 맛있었다.

17 나는 음식 사진을 찍어 그것을 내 블로그에 올리고 싶은 마음이 정말 간절했다.

18 그러나 스마트폰이 없었기 때문에 나는 그냥 그 순간을 즐기기로 했다.

19 (여행의) 남아 있는 날들 동안, 우리는 점점 더 현지 사람들에게 의존하게 되었다.

20 우리는 거리에서, 빵집에서, 공원에서 다양한 사람들을 만나 이야기할 수 있었다.

21 그들은 항상 웃으면서 너무나 친절히도 바르셀로나의 다양한 면을 우리에게 보여 주었다.

22 또한 우리 가족은 서로 많은 대화를 나누었다.

23 우리는 스페인의 기차에서, 버스에서, 그리고 식당에서 많은 시간을 함께 보냈다.

24 우리의 '첨단 과학 기술 없는' 여행은 새롭고 색다른 경험이었다.

25 여행 전에 나는 내 스마트폰에 너무 의존해서 그것 없이는 아무것도 할 수 없었다.

26 하지만 지금은 내가 스마트폰 없이도 그 순간을 즐길 수 있음을 알고 있다.

27 그 경험을 통해, 나는 스마트폰을 균형 있게 사용하는 것이 중요함을 배우게 되었다.

28 그러면, 다음번에 나는 스마트폰 없이 여행을 하게 될까?

29 아마도 그렇지는 않을 것이다. 하지만 나는 그것을 좀 더 현명하게 사용하기 위해 노력할 것이다.

※ 다음 우리말과 일치하도록 빈칸에 알맞은 말을 쓰시오.

1 Last summer, my father _____ a _____ event: a _____ _____ _____ smartphones!

2 He said, "I _____ _____ _____ you _____ _____ and only _____ _____ your smartphones."

3 My sister and I _____ the need for smartphones, but he _____ _____ _____ we could _____ _____ _____ the trip with them.

4 So we _____ a technology-free _____ _____ a new city, Barcelona, Spain.

5 Our _____ _____ was _____.

6 _____ _____ _____ _____ _____ our guesthouse _____ Plaza Reial, we _____ _____ _____ _____ Barcelona.

7 Dad _____ _____ _____ at the map and _____ _____ directions _____ _____ Spanish words he got _____ a tour guidebook.

8 _____ _____ our guesthouse was _____ _____ _____ the Plaza, _____ _____ us about two hours _____ _____ there.

9 We _____ _____ _____ _____ _____ we _____ _____ _____ _____ for dinner.

10 I _____ _____ _____ but couldn't _____ _____ because I was _____ about _____ _____ _____ the next day.

11 _____ _____ _____ Gaudi's Park Guell, we decided _____ _____ seafood _____ rice for lunch.

12 However, we didn't know _____ _____ _____ _____ _____.

13 We needed help, so Mom _____ _____ _____ an elderly lady and _____ _____ _____ _____ _____ _____ _____ to a popular seafood restaurant.

---

1 지난여름, 아빠가 깜짝 놀랄 만한 이벤트로 스마트폰 없는 가족 여행을 제안하셨다!

2 아빠는 "나는 우리 가족이 함께 앉아서 각자의 스마트폰만 보고 있는 걸 보는 게 참 싫구나."라고 말씀하셨다.

3 여동생과 내가 스마트폰이 필요하다고 설명했지만, 아빠는 스마트폰이 있으면 여행을 충분히 즐길 수 없을 거라고 계속해서 말씀하셨다.

4 그래서 우리는 새로운 도시인 스페인의 바르셀로나로 '첨단 과학 기술 없는 여행'을 시작했다.

5 우리의 첫째 날은 엉망이었다.

6 레이알 광장 주변에 있는 여행자 숙소로 가는 길에 우리는 바르셀로나 시내에서 길을 잃었다.

7 아빠는 지도를 보며 여행안내 책자에서 배운 스페인어 몇 마디로 길을 묻느라 분주하셨다.

8 우리의 숙소가 광장 바로 옆에 있었음에도 불구하고, 우리가 그곳에 도착하는 데는 거의 두 시간이 걸렸다.

9 우리는 너무 피곤해서 저녁을 먹으러 나갈 수가 없었다.

10 나는 잠자리에 들었지만 내일 무슨 일이 일어날지 걱정이 되어서 잠들 수가 없었다.

11 가우디가 지은 구엘 공원을 둘러본 후, 우리는 점심으로 해산물 볶음밥을 먹기로 했다.

12 그러나 우리는 어떤 식당으로 가야 할지 몰랐다.

13 우리는 도움이 필요해서, 엄마가 한 노부인에게 가서 인기 있는 해산물 식당으로 가는 길을 물어보려고 애쓰셨다.

14 Luckily, she _____ _____ _____ Mom's few Spanish _____.

15 She _____ _____ to a small local restaurant _____.

16 The seafood _____ _____ was _____.

17 I really wanted to _____ _____ _____ the food and _____ _____ on my blog.

18 But _____ my phone, I just _____ _____ _____ the moment.

19 _____ the _____ days, we _____ more and more _____ the locals.

20 We _____ _____ _____ _____ and _____ _____ various people on the streets, in the bakeries, and in the parks.

21 They were always _____ _____ _____ _____ us different sides of Barcelona _____ _____ _____.

22 Also, our family _____ a lot _____ _____ _____.

23 We spent _____ _____ _____ _____ _____ on the Spanish train, on the bus, and at the restaurants.

24 Our technology-free trip was a _____ _____ _____ _____.

25 Before the trip, I was _____ _____ _____ my smartphone _____ I _____ do anything _____ it.

26 But now I see _____ I can enjoy the moment _____ _____.

27 _____ the experience, I _____ _____ the _____ of a _____ _____ of the smartphone.

28 So, next time, _____ _____ _____ without a smartphone?

29 Probably not. But I will _____ _____ _____ more _____.

14 운이 좋게도 그녀는 몇 마디 안 되는 엄마의 스페인어를 이해하는 듯했다.

15 그녀는 우리를 근처에 있는 작은 현지 식당으로 데려다 주었다.

16 그 해산물 볶음밥은 놀랍도록 맛있었다.

17 나는 음식 사진을 찍어 그것을 내 블로그에 올리고 싶은 마음이 정말 간절했다.

18 그러나 스마트폰이 없었기 때문에 나는 그냥 그 순간을 즐기기로 했다.

19 (여행의) 남아 있는 날들 동안, 우리는 점점 더 현지 사람들에게 의존하게 되었다.

20 우리는 거리에서, 빵집에서, 공원에서 다양한 사람들을 만나 이야기할 수 있었다.

21 그들은 항상 웃으면서 너무나 친절히도 바르셀로나의 다양한 면을 우리에게 보여 주었다.

22 또한 우리 가족은 서로 많은 대화를 나누었다.

23 우리는 스페인의 기차에서, 버스에서, 그리고 식당에서 많은 시간을 함께 보냈다.

24 우리의 '첨단 과학 기술 없는' 여행은 새롭고 색다른 경험이었다.

25 여행 전에 나는 내 스마트폰에 너무 의존해서 그것 없이는 아무것도 할 수 없었다.

26 하지만 지금은 내가 스마트폰 없이도 그 순간을 즐길 수 있음을 알고 있다.

27 그 경험을 통해, 나는 스마트폰을 균형 있게 사용하는 것이 중요함을 배우게 되었다.

28 그러면, 다음번에 나는 스마트폰 없이 여행을 하게 될까?

29 아마도 그렇지는 않을 것이다. 하지만 나는 그것을 좀 더 현명하게 사용하기 위해 노력할 것이다.

※ 다음 문장을 우리말로 쓰시오.

1 Last summer, my father suggested a surprising event: a family trip without smartphones!

➡ _____

2 He said, "I hate to see you sitting together and only looking at your smartphones."

➡ _____

3 My sister and I explained the need for smartphones, but he kept saying that we could not fully enjoy the trip with them.

➡ _____
_____

4 So we started a technology-free trip to a new city, Barcelona, Spain.

➡ _____

5 Our first day was terrible.

➡ _____

6 On the way to our guesthouse around Plaza Reial, we got lost in downtown Barcelona.

➡ _____

7 Dad was busy looking at the map and asking for directions with a few Spanish words he got from a tour guidebook.

➡ _____

8 Even though our guesthouse was right next to the Plaza, it took us about two hours to get there.

➡ _____

9 We were so tired that we could not go out for dinner.

➡ _____

10 I went to bed but couldn't fall asleep because I was worried about what would happen the next day.

➡ _____

11 After looking around Gaudi's Park Guell, we decided to have seafood fried rice for lunch.

➡ _____

12 However, we didn't know which restaurant to go to.

➡ _____

13 We needed help, so Mom went up to an elderly lady and tried to ask for directions to a popular seafood restaurant.

➡ _____

14 Luckily, she seemed to understand Mom's few Spanish words.

➡ _____

15 She took us to a small local restaurant nearby.

➡ _____

16 The seafood fried rice was amazing.

➡ _____

17 I really wanted to take pictures of the food and post them on my blog.

➡ _____

18 But without my phone, I just decided to enjoy the moment.

➡ _____

19 During the remaining days, we relied more and more on the locals.

➡ _____

20 We were able to meet and talk with various people on the streets, in the bakeries, and in the parks.

➡ _____

21 They were always kind enough to show us different sides of Barcelona with a smile.

➡ _____

22 Also, our family talked a lot with each other.

➡ _____

23 We spent much of our time together on the Spanish train, on the bus, and at the restaurants.

➡ _____

24 Our technology-free trip was a new and different experience.

➡ _____

25 Before the trip, I was so dependent on my smartphone that I couldn't do anything without it.

➡ _____

26 But now I see that I can enjoy the moment without it.

➡ _____

27 From the experience, I have learned the importance of a balanced use of the smartphone.

➡ _____

28 So, next time, would I travel without a smartphone?

➡ _____

29 Probably not. But I will try to use it more wisely.

➡ _____

※ 다음 괄호 안의 단어들을 우리말에 맞도록 바르게 배열하시오.

1 (summer, / last / father / my / suggested / surprising / a / event: / family / a / trip / smartphones! / without)
➡ _____

2 (said, / he / hate / "I / see / to / sitting / you / and / together / only / at / looking / smarphones." / your)
➡ _____

3 (sister / my / I / and / the / explained / need / smartphones, / for / but / he / saying / kept / that / could / we / not / enjoy / fully / trip / them. / with / the)
➡ _____

4 (we / so / a / started / technology-free / to / trip / new / a / city, / Spain. / Barcelona,)
➡ _____

5 (first / our / day / terrible. / was)
➡ _____

6 (the / on / way / our / to / around / guesthouse / Reial, / Plaza / got / we / lost / in / Barcelona. / downtown)
➡ _____

7 (was / Dad / looking / busy / at / map / the / and / for / asking / with / directions / a / few / words / Spanish / got / he / from / guidebook. / tour / a)
➡ _____

8 (though / even / guesthouse / our / was / next / right / the / to / Plaza, / took / it / us / two / about / hours / there. / to / get)
➡ _____

9 (were / we / tired / so / that / could / we / go / not / dinner. / for / out)
➡ _____

10 (went / I / bed / to / couldn't / but / asleep / fall / because / was / I / worried / about / would / what / happen / day. / the / next)
➡ _____

11 (looking / after / Gaudi's / around / Guell, / Park / decided / we / have / to / seafood / fried / for / lunch. / rice)
➡ _____

12 (we / however, / know / didn't / which / to / resturant / to. / go)
➡ _____

13 (needed / we / help, / Mom / so / went / to / up / an / lady / elderly / and / to / tired / ask / to / directions / for / popular / a / restaurant. / seafood)
➡ _____

1 지난여름, 아빠가 깜짝 놀랄 만한 이벤트로 스마트폰 없는 가족 여행을 제안하셨다!

2 아빠는 "나는 우리 가족이 함께 앉아서 각자의 스마트폰만 보고 있는 걸 보는 게 참 싫구나."라고 말씀하셨다.

3 여동생과 내가 스마트폰이 필요하다고 설명했지만, 아빠는 스마트폰이 있으면 여행을 충분히 즐길 수 없을 거라고 계속해서 말씀하셨다.

4 그래서 우리는 새로운 도시인 스페인의 바르셀로나로 '첨단 과학 기술 없는 여행'을 시작했다.

5 우리의 첫째 날은 엉망이었다.

6 레이알 광장 주변에 있는 여행자 숙소로 가는 길에 우리는 바르셀로나 시내에서 길을 잃었다.

7 아빠는 지도를 보며 여행안내 책자에서 배운 스페인어 몇 마디로 길을 묻느라 분주하셨다.

8 우리의 숙소가 광장 바로 옆에 있었음에도 불구하고, 우리가 그곳에 도착하는 데는 거의 두 시간이 걸렸다.

9 우리는 너무 피곤해서 저녁을 먹으러 나갈 수가 없었다.

10 나는 잠자리에 들었지만 내일 무슨 일이 일어날지 걱정이 되어서 잠들 수가 없었다.

11 가우디가 지은 구엘 공원을 둘러본 후, 우리는 점심으로 해산물 볶음밥을 먹기로 했다.

12 그러나 우리는 어떤 식당으로 가야 할지 몰랐다.

13 우리는 도움이 필요해서, 엄마가 한 노부인에게 가서 인기 있는 해산물 식당으로 가는 길을 물어보려고 애쓰셨다.

14 (she / luckily, / to / seemed / understand / Mom's / Spanish / few / words.)
➡ _____

15 (took / she / to / us / a / local / small / nearby. / restaurant)
➡ _____

16 (seafood / the / rice / fried / amazing. / was)
➡ _____

17 (really / I / to / wanted / pictures / take / the / of / food / and / them / post / on / blog. / my)
➡ _____

18 (without / but / phone, / my / just / I / to / decided / enjoy / moment. / the)
➡ _____

19 (the / during / days, / remaining / relied / we / and / more / on / more / locals. / the)
➡ _____

20 (were / we / to / able / meet / and / with / talk / people / various / on / streets, / the / in / bakeries, / the / and / parks. / the / in)
➡ _____

21 (were / they / kind / always / enough / show / to / us / sides / different / of / with / Barcelona / smile. / a)
➡ _____

22 (our / also, / family / a / talked / lot / with / other. / each)
➡ _____

23 (spent / we / of / much / our / together / time / the / Spanish / on / train, / the / on / bus, / and / the / restaurants. / at)
➡ _____

24 (technology-free / our / trip / was / new / a / and / experience. / different)
➡ _____

25 (the / before / trip, / I / so / was / dependent / my / on / that / smartphone / I / do / couldn't / anything / it. / without)
➡ _____

26 (now / but / see / I / that / can / I / enjoy / moment / the / it. / without)
➡ _____

27 (the / from / experience, / have / I / learned / importance / the / of / balanced / a / use / of / smartphone. / the)
➡ _____

28 (next / so, / time, / I / would / without / travel / smartphone? / a)
➡ _____

29 (not. / probably // but / will / I / to / try / it / use / wisely. / more)
➡ _____

14 운이 좋게도 그녀는 몇 마디 안 되는 엄마의 스페인어를 이해하는 듯했다.

15 그녀는 우리를 근처에 있는 작은 현지 식당으로 데려다 주었다.

16 그 해산물 볶음밥은 놀랍도록 맛있었다.

17 나는 음식 사진을 찍어 그것을 내 블로그에 올리고 싶은 마음이 정말 간절했다.

18 그러나 스마트폰이 없었기 때문에 나는 그냥 그 순간을 즐기기로 했다.

19 (여행의) 남아 있는 날들 동안, 우리는 점점 더 현지 사람들에게 의존하게 되었다.

20 우리는 거리에서, 빵집에서, 공원에서 다양한 사람들을 만나 이야기할 수 있었다.

21 그들은 항상 웃으면서 너무나 친절히도 바르셀로나의 다양한 면을 우리에게 보여 주었다.

22 또한 우리 가족은 서로 많은 대화를 나누었다.

23 우리는 스페인의 기차에서, 버스에서, 그리고 식당에서 많은 시간을 함께 보냈다.

24 우리의 '첨단 과학 기술 없는' 여행은 새롭고 색다른 경험이었다.

25 여행 전에 나는 내 스마트폰에 너무 의존해서 그것 없이는 아무것도 할 수 없었다.

26 하지만 지금은 내가 스마트폰 없이도 그 순간을 즐길 수 있음을 알고 있다.

27 그 경험을 통해, 나는 스마트폰을 균형 있게 사용하는 것이 중요함을 배우게 되었다.

28 그러면, 다음번에 나는 스마트폰 없이 여행을 하게 될까?

29 아마도 그렇지는 않을 것이다. 하지만 나는 그것을 좀 더 현명하게 사용하기 위해 노력할 것이다.

※ 다음 우리말을 영어로 쓰시오.

1 지난여름, 아빠가 깜짝 놀랄 만한 이벤트로 스마트폰 없는 가족 여행을 제안하셨다!

➡ _____

2 아빠는 "나는 우리 가족이 함께 앉아서 각자의 스마트폰만 보고 있는 걸 보는 게 참 싫구나."라고 말씀하셨다.

➡ _____

3 여동생과 내가 스마트폰이 필요하다고 설명했지만, 아빠는 스마트폰이 있으면 여행을 충분히 즐길 수 없을 거라고 계속해서 말씀하셨다.

➡ _____

_____

4 그래서 우리는 새로운 도시인 스페인의 바르셀로나로 '첨단 과학 기술 없는 여행'을 시작했다.

➡ _____

5 우리의 첫째 날은 엉망이었다.

➡ _____

6 레이알 광장 주변에 있는 여행자 숙소로 가는 길에 우리는 바르셀로나 시내에서 길을 잃었다.

➡ _____

7 아빠는 지도를 보며 여행안내 책자에서 배운 스페인어 몇 마디로 길을 묻느라 분주하셨다.

➡ _____

8 우리의 숙소가 광장 바로 옆에 있었음에도 불구하고, 우리가 그곳에 도착하는 데는 거의 두 시간이 걸렸다.

➡ _____

9 우리는 너무 피곤해서 저녁을 먹으러 나갈 수가 없었다.

➡ _____

10 나는 잠자리에 들었지만 내일 무슨 일이 일어날지 걱정이 되어서 잠들 수가 없었다.

➡ _____

_____

11 가우디가 지은 구엘 공원을 둘러본 후, 우리는 점심으로 해산물 볶음밥을 먹기로 했다.

➡ _____

12 그러나 우리는 어떤 식당으로 가야 할지 몰랐다.

➡ _____

13 우리는 도움이 필요해서, 엄마가 한 노부인에게 가서 인기 있는 해산물 식당으로 가는 길을 물어보려고 애쓰셨다.

➡ _____

_____

14 운이 좋게도 그녀는 몇 마디 안 되는 엄마의 스페인어를 이해하는 듯했다.

➡ _____

15 그녀는 우리를 근처에 있는 작은 현지 식당으로 데려다 주었다.

➡ _____

16 그 해산물 볶음밥은 놀랍도록 맛있었다.

➡ _____

17 나는 음식 사진을 찍어 그것을 내 블로그에 올리고 싶은 마음이 정말 간절했다.

➡ _____

18 그러나 스마트폰이 없었기 때문에 나는 그냥 그 순간을 즐기기로 했다.

➡ _____

19 (여행의) 남아 있는 날들 동안, 우리는 점점 더 현지 사람들에게 의존하게 되었다.

➡ _____

20 우리는 거리에서, 빵집에서, 공원에서 다양한 사람들을 만나 이야기할 수 있었다.

➡ _____

21 그들은 항상 웃으면서 너무나 친절히도 바르셀로나의 다양한 면을 우리에게 보여 주었다.

➡ _____

22 또한 우리 가족은 서로 많은 대화를 나누었다.

➡ _____

23 우리는 스페인의 기차에서, 버스에서, 그리고 식당에서 많은 시간을 함께 보냈다.

➡ _____

24 우리의 '첨단 과학 기술 없는' 여행은 새롭고 색다른 경험이었다.

➡ _____

25 여행 전에 나는 내 스마트폰에 너무 의존해서 그것 없이는 아무것도 할 수 없었다.

➡ _____

26 하지만 지금은 내가 스마트폰 없이도 그 순간을 즐길 수 있음을 알고 있다.

➡ _____

27 그 경험을 통해, 나는 스마트폰을 균형 있게 사용하는 것이 중요함을 배우게 되었다.

➡ _____

28 그러면, 다음번에 나는 스마트폰 없이 여행을 하게 될까?

➡ _____

29 아마도 그렇지는 않을 것이다. 하지만 나는 그것을 좀 더 현명하게 사용하기 위해 노력할 것이다.

➡ _____

※ 다음 우리말과 일치하도록 빈칸에 알맞은 말을 쓰시오.

Read and Think

1. _____ _____ to Barcelona

2. Last summer, I had a _____ and _____ _____: a family trip _____ smartphones.

3. _____

4. _____ the first day, we got lost _____ _____ _____ _____ the guesthouse.

5. I couldn't _____ _____ _____ the food and _____ them _____ my blog.

6. _____

7. I _____ the places and the people _____ me.

8. I talked _____ _____ with my family _____ _____ _____ and everywhere.

9. Changes _____ the Trip

10. My _____ on _____ a smartphone

11. Before: I _____ _____ _____ without it.

12. Now: I understand the _____ of a _____ _____ of it.

1. 바르셀로나로의 첨단 과학 기술 없는 여행
2. 지난여름, 나는 새롭고 색다른 경험으로 '스마트폰 없는 가족 여행'을 갔다.
3. 힘들었던 점
4. 첫째 날, 우리는 숙소로 가는 도중에 길을 잃었다.
5. 나는 음식 사진을 찍어 블로그에 올릴 수 없었다.
6. 좋았던 점
7. 나는 내 주위에 있는 장소들과 사람들을 즐겼다.
8. 나는 가족들과 언제 어디서든 많은 대화를 나누었다.
9. 여행 후 달라진 점
10. 스마트폰 사용에 대한 나의 생각
11. 이전: 나는 그것 없이는 아무것도 할 수 없었다.
12. 지금: 나는 그것을 균형 있게 사용하는 것이 중요함을 이해한다.

Grammar in Real Life B

1. _____ one apple under _____ water and _____ it _____ small _____.

2. Cook the _____ apple pieces _____ brown sugar on _____ _____.

3. _____ salt, milk, and a beaten egg _____ _____ the egg _____.

4. _____ the bread _____ and _____ the cooked apple _____ on it.

5. Put the _____ _____ in the egg mixture and _____ _____ _____ quickly. Then _____ it for 3 _____.

6. _____ a dish with the bread rolls and the _____ _____ _____.

1. 사과 한 개를 흐르는 물에 씻어 작은 조각으로 자르세요.
2. 잘라진 사과 조각들을 노란 설탕과 함께 약한 불에서 조리세요.
3. 계란 혼합물을 만들기 위해 소금, 우유, 그리고 휘저은 계란을 더하세요.
4. 식빵을 얇게 밀어서 펴고 그 위에 조린 사과 소를 올리세요.
5. 돌돌 말은 빵을 계란 혼합물에 넣었다가 빠르게 꺼내세요. 그러고 나서 그것을 3분간 구우세요.
6. 돌돌 말은 빵과 남아 있는 사과 소로 접시를 장식하세요.

※ 다음 우리말을 영어로 쓰시오.

Read and Think

1. 바르셀로나로의 첨단 과학 기술 없는 여행
   ➡ _____

2. 지난여름, 나는 새롭고 색다른 경험으로 '스마트폰 없는 가족 여행'을 갔다.
   ➡ _____

3. 힘들었던 점
   ➡ _____

4. 첫째 날, 우리는 숙소로 가는 도중에 길을 잃었다.
   ➡ _____

5. 나는 음식 사진을 찍어 블로그에 올릴 수 없었다.
   ➡ _____

6. 좋았던 점
   ➡ _____

7. 나는 내 주위에 있는 장소들과 사람들을 즐겼다.
   ➡ _____

8. 나는 가족들과 언제 어디서든 많은 대화를 나누었다.
   ➡ _____

9. 여행 후 달라진 점
   ➡ _____

10. 스마트폰 사용에 대한 나의 생각
    ➡ _____

11. 이전: 나는 그것 없이는 아무것도 할 수 없었다.
    ➡ _____

12. 지금: 나는 그것을 균형 있게 사용하는 것이 중요함을 이해한다.
    ➡ _____

Grammar in Real Life B

1. 사과 한 개를 흐르는 물에 씻어 작은 조각으로 자르세요.
   ➡ _____

2. 잘라진 사과 조각들을 노란 설탕과 함께 약한 불에서 조리세요.
   ➡ _____

3. 계란 혼합물을 만들기 위해 소금, 우유, 그리고 휘저은 계란을 더하세요.
   ➡ _____

4. 식빵을 얇게 밀어서 펴고 그 위에 조린 사과 소를 올리세요.
   ➡ _____

5. 돌돌 말은 빵을 계란 혼합물에 넣었다가 빠르게 꺼내세요. 그러고 나서 그것을 3분간 구우세요.
   ➡ _____

6. 돌돌 말은 빵과 남아 있는 사과 소로 접시를 장식하세요.
   ➡ _____

※ 다음 영어를 우리말로 쓰시오.

01 beard _____

02 cart _____

03 grandchild _____

04 wife _____

05 ground _____

06 stone _____

07 trouble _____

08 destroy _____

09 glad _____

10 hand _____

11 arrive _____

12 bear _____

13 warn _____

14 log _____

15 magic _____

16 cow _____

17 delight _____

18 nothing _____

19 reward _____

20 free _____

21 decide _____

22 season _____

23 dwarf _____

24 explain _____

25 field _____

26 tooth _____

27 unless _____

28 go by _____

29 look forward to _____

30 get rid of _____

31 throw away _____

32 be proud of _____

33 change into _____

34 far from _____

35 try to _____

36 give birth _____

37 go away _____

38 keep ~ from -ing _____

39 on one's way to _____

40 worry about _____

41 keep -ing _____

※ 다음 우리말을 영어로 쓰시오.

01 도착하다

02 계절

03 기쁨

04 빼내다, 풀어 주다

05 땅, 지면

06 결심하다, 결정하다

07 경고하다

08 설명하다

09 ~하지 않는 한

10 들판

11 수염

12 아내, 부인

13 기쁜

14 건네주다

15 통나무

16 마술의

17 파괴하다, 없애다

18 이, 치아

19 손주

20 아무것도 ~아닌 것

21 수레, 우마차

22 돌

23 (새끼를) 낳다

24 소, 암소

25 보상, 보답

26 난쟁이

27 문제

28 ~에서 멀리

29 ~을 자랑스러워하다

30 ~가 …하지 못하게 하다

31 ~하려고 노력하다

32 ~을 없애다

33 떠나가다

34 ~으로 바꾸다

35 계속 ~하다

36 ~을 기대하다, ~을 고대하다

37 ~로 가는 길에

38 흐르다, 지나가다

39 ~을 버리다

40 ~에 대해 걱정하다

41 새끼를 낳다, 출산하다

※ 다음 영영풀이에 알맞은 단어를 <보기>에서 골라 쓴 후, 우리말 뜻을 쓰시오.

1 _____ : a small piece of rock of any shape: _____

2 _____ : to pass or give something to somebody: _____

3 _____ : to give birth to a child: _____

4 _____ : a child of your son or daughter: _____

5 _____ : hair that grows on the chin and cheeks of a man's face: _____

6 _____ : the woman that somebody is married to: _____

7 _____ : to get to a place, especially at the end of a journey: _____

8 _____ : to damage something so badly that it no longer exists, works, etc.: _____

9 _____ : a thick piece of wood that is cut from or has fallen from a tree: _____

10 _____ : a large animal that is raised by people for milk or meat usually on a farm: _____

11 _____ : any of the four main periods of the year: spring, summer, fall, and winter: _____

12 _____ : an area of land in the country, especially one where crops are grown or animals feed on grass: _____

13 _____ : a vehicle with two or four wheels that is pulled by a horse and used for carrying loads: _____

14 _____ : a thing that you are given because you have done something good, worked hard, etc.: _____

15 _____ : to tell somebody about something, especially something dangerous or unpleasant that is likely to happen, so that they can avoid it: _____

16 _____ : to remove something that is unpleasant or not wanted from somebody/ something: _____

보기			
arrive	stone	bear	log
warn	free	reward	grandchild
beard	hand	wife	destroy
field	season	cow	cart

※ 다음 우리말과 일치하도록 빈칸에 알맞은 것을 골라 쓰시오.

1 _____ day, Maibon was _____ _____ the road on his horse and cart _____ he saw an old man.

　A. when　　　　B. down　　　　C. one　　　　D. driving

2 The old man _____ very _____. Maibon began to _____ _____ growing old.

　A. sick　　　　B. about　　　　C. looked　　　　D. worry

3 _____ that day, he _____ a dwarf, Doli, in the _____.

　A. field　　　　B. saw　　　　C. later

4 He was trying to _____ his leg _____ from _____ a log.

　A. out　　　　B. get　　　　C. under

5 Maibon _____ the log _____ and _____ the dwarf.

　A. away　　　　B. pulled　　　　C. freed

6 "You'll _____ your _____. What do you _____?"

　A. reward　　　　B. have　　　　C. want

7 "I've _____ that you have magic stones _____ can _____ a man _____. I want one."

　A. keep　　　　B. that　　　　C. heard　　　　D. young

8 "Oh, you _____ have it all _____. Those stones don't make you young again. They only _____ you _____ getting older."

　A. wrong　　　　B. from　　　　C. humans　　　　D. keep

9 "Just as good!" Doli _____ to _____ the problem _____ the stones, but Maibon didn't _____.

　A. explain　　　　B. with　　　　C. listen　　　　D. tried

10 So Doli _____ him a magic stone and _____ _____.

　A. away　　　　B. handed　　　　C. went

11 After _____ _____ days, Maibon saw that his beard didn't _____ at _____.

　A. few　　　　B. grow　　　　C. all　　　　D. a

12 He _____ happy, but his wife, Modrona, _____ _____.

　A. got　　　　B. became　　　　C. upset

13 The eggs don't _____ _____ chickens!" "Oh, the season's _____, that's all."

　A. into　　　　B. slow　　　　C. change

14 But she was not happy. "The cow doesn't give _____!" Maibon, then, told her about the stone, and she _____ very angry and told him to _____ it _____.

　A. away　　　　B. birth　　　　C. throw　　　　D. got

15 He didn't want to, but he _____ _____ his wife and _____ the stone _____ the window.

　A. to　　　　B. out　　　　C. listened　　　　D. threw

16 However, the next morning, he _____ the stone _____ the window!

　A. sitting　　　　B. found　　　　C. by

1 어느 날, Maibon이 한 노인을 보았을 때, 그는 마차를 타고 길을 내려가고 있던 중이었다.

2 그 노인은 매우 아파 보였다. Maibon은 늙어 가는 것이 걱정되기 시작했다.

3 그날 오후, 그는 들판에서 Doli라는 난쟁이를 보았다.

4 그는 통나무 아래에 깔린 그의 다리를 빼내려고 하고 있었다.

5 Maibon은 통나무를 잡아당겨서 난쟁이를 풀어주었다.

6 "너는 보상을 받게 될 거야. 원하는게 뭐니?"

7 "나는 네가 사람의 젊음을 유지해 주는 마법의 돌들을 가지고 있다고 들었어. 나는 그것을 원해."

8 "오, 너희 인간들은 잘못 알고 있어. 그 돌들은 너희들이 다시 젊어지게 해 주지 않아. 단지 더 늙지 않게 막아 줄 뿐이라고."

9 "그것대로 좋아!" Doli는 그 돌에 관한 문제를 설명하려고 했지만, Maibon은 듣지 않았다.

10 그래서 Doli는 그에게 마법의 돌을 건네고는 가버렸다.

11 며칠이 지나서, Maibon은 그의 수염이 전혀 자라지 않았음을 알았다.

12 그는 행복해졌지만, 그의 아내 Modrona는 화가 났다.

13 "달걀이 닭이 되지 않아요!" "아, 시기가 더딘 거예요. 그 뿐이에요."

14 하지만 그녀는 탐탁해하지 않았다. "소가 새끼를 낳지 않아요!" 그때 Maibon은 그 돌에 대해 그녀에게 이야기를 했고 그녀는 매우 화를 내며 그에게 그것을 버리라고 말했다.

15 그는 원하지 않았지만, 아내의 말을 듣고 창밖으로 돌을 던졌다.

16 그러나 다음날 아침 그는 창가에 그 돌이 있는 것을 발견했다!

17 Maibon was _____ _____ the animals, but he was glad _____ he was _____ young.

    A. about   B. that   C. worried   D. still

18 Now Maibon's baby was _____ _____. No _____ was _____ in his mouth.

    A. seen   B. trouble   C. having   D. tooth

19 His wife told him to _____ _____ the stone and this time, Maibon _____ the stone _____ the ground.

    A. put   B. away   C. under   D. throw

20 But, the next day, the stone came _____! Time _____ and nothing _____ or changed.

    A. by   B. back   C. grew   D. went

21 Maibon began to _____. "There's nothing to _____ to, _____ to show for my work."

    A. forward   B. nothing   C. worry   D. look

22 Maibon tried to _____ the stone, but it _____ coming _____.

    A. destroy   B. back   C. kept

23 Maibon decided to _____ _____ the stone _____ _____ his house.

    A. far   B. throw   C. from   D. away

24 _____ his _____ to the field, he saw the dwarf. Maibon _____ with him.

    A. got   B. on   C. angry   D. way

25 "Why _____ you _____ me _____ the stone?"

    A. warn   B. didn't   C. about

26 "I _____ to, but you _____ _____."

    A. listen   B. tried   C. wouldn't

27 Doli _____ that Maibon couldn't get _____ _____ the stone _____ he really wanted to.

    A. rid   B. explained   C. unless   D. of

28 "I want no _____ of it. _____ may happen, _____ it _____!"

    A. let   B. more   C. whatever   D. happen

29 Doli told him to _____ the stone _____ the ground and go _____ home.

    A. onto   B. back   D. throw

30 Maibon did _____ Doli said. When he _____ home, Modrona told him the good news — the eggs _____ into chickens and the cow _____ her baby.

    A. changed   B. as   C. bore   D. arrived

31 And Maibon laughed _____ _____ when he saw the first _____ in his baby's _____.

    A. delight   B. tooth   C. with   D. mouth

32 Maibon, Modrona and _____ children and grandchildren _____ many _____.

    A. for   B. years   C. lived   D. their

33 Maibon was _____ _____ his white hair and long _____.

    A. of   B. proud   C. beard

---

17 Maibon은 동물들이 걱정되긴 했지만, 자신이 여전히 젊어서 기뻤다.

18 이제 Maibon의 아기에게 문제가 생겼다. 아기의 입에서 이가 보이지 않았다.

19 그의 아내는 그에게 그 돌을 버리라고 말했고 Maibon은 이번엔 그 돌을 땅속에 묻었다.

20 그런데 그 다음날 그 돌은 다시 돌아왔다! 시간이 흘렀고 어떤 것도 자라거나 변하지 않았다.

21 Maibon은 걱정이 되기 시작했다. "기대할 것도 내 일의 결과를 보여 줄 것도 아무것도 없어."

22 Maibon은 그 돌을 없애려고 노력했지만 돌은 계속 되돌아왔다.

23 Maibon은 그 돌을 그의 집에서 멀리 떨어진 곳에 버리기로 결심했다.

24 그는 들판으로 가는 길에 난쟁이를 보았다. Maibon은 그에게 화를 냈다.

25 "너는 왜 내게 그 돌에 대해 경고하지 않았어?"

26 "나는 하려고 했지만, 너는 들으려 하지 않았어."

27 Doli는 Maibon이 진심으로 원하지 않는 한 그 돌을 없앨 수 없다고 설명했다.

28 "나는 그것을 더 이상 원하지 않아. 무슨 일이 있어도 일어나게 해!"

29 Doli는 그에게 그 돌을 땅에 던지고 집으로 돌아가라고 말했다.

30 Maibon은 Doli가 말한 대로 했다. 그가 집에 도착했을 때, Modrona는 그에게 달걀이 닭이 되고 소가 새끼를 낳았다는 좋은 소식을 말해 주었다.

31 그리고 Maibon은 아기의 입에 첫 이가 난 것을 보고 기뻐서 웃었다.

32 Maibon과 Modrona, 그리고 그들의 자녀들과 손주들은 오랫동안 살았다.

33 Maibon은 그의 흰 머리와 긴 수염을 자랑스러워했다.

※ 다음 우리말과 일치하도록 빈칸에 알맞은 말을 쓰시오.

1 One day, Maibon was _____ _____ the road _____
_____ _____ and cart _____ he saw an old man.

2 The old man _____ very _____. Maibon began _____
_____ _____ _____ _____.

3 _____ _____ _____, he saw a _____, Doli, in the field.

4 He was _____ _____ _____ his leg _____ _____
under a log.

5 Maibon _____ the log _____ and _____ the dwarf.

6 "You'll have your _____. What _____ you _____?"

7 "I've _____ that you have magic stones _____ can _____
a man _____. I want one."

8 "Oh, you humans have _____ _____ _____. Those stones
don't make you _____ _____. They only _____ you
_____ _____ _____."

9 "Just as good!" Doli _____ _____ _____ the problem
with the stones, but Maibon _____ _____.

10 So Doli _____ _____ a magic stone and went away.

11 After _____ _____ _____, Maibon saw that his beard
didn't _____ _____ _____.

12 He _____ happy, but his wife, Modrona, _____ _____.

13 The eggs don't _____ _____ _____ _____!" "Oh, the season's
_____, that's all."

14 But she was not happy. "The cow doesn't _____ _____!"
Maibon, then, told her about the stone, and she _____ very
_____ and told him _____ _____ _____ _____.

15 He didn't want to, but he _____ _____ his wife and
_____ the stone _____ the window.

16 _____, the next morning, he _____ the stone _____
_____ the window!

1 어느 날, Maibon이 한 노인을 보았을 때, 그는 마차를 타고 길을 내려가고 있던 중이었다.

2 그 노인은 매우 아파 보였다. Maibon은 늙어 가는 것이 걱정되기 시작했다.

3 그날 오후, 그는 들판에서 Doli라는 난쟁이를 보았다.

4 그는 통나무 아래에 깔린 그의 다리를 빼내려고 하고 있었다.

5 Maibon은 통나무를 잡아당겨서 난쟁이를 풀어주었다.

6 "너는 보상을 받게 될 거야. 원하는게 뭐니?"

7 "나는 네가 사람의 젊음을 유지해 주는 마법의 돌들을 가지고 있다고 들었어. 나는 그것을 원해."

8 "오, 너희 인간들은 잘못 알고 있어. 그 돌들은 너희들이 다시 젊어지게 해 주지 않아. 단지 더 늙지 않게 막아 줄 뿐이라고."

9 "그것대로 좋아!" Doli는 그 돌에 관한 문제를 설명하려고 했지만, Maibon은 듣지 않았다.

10 그래서 Doli는 그에게 마법의 돌을 건네고는 가버렸다.

11 며칠이 지나서, Maibon은 그의 수염이 전혀 자라지 않았음을 알았다.

12 그는 행복해졌지만, 그의 아내 Modrona는 화가 났다.

13 "달걀이 닭이 되지 않아요!" "아, 시기가 더딘 거예요. 그 뿐이에요."

14 하지만 그녀는 탐탁해하지 않았다. "소가 새끼를 낳지 않아요!" 그때 Maibon은 그 돌에 대해 그녀에게 이야기를 했고 그녀는 매우 화를 내며 그에게 그것을 버리라고 말했다.

15 그는 원하지 않았지만, 아내의 말을 듣고 창밖으로 돌을 던졌다.

16 그러나 다음날 아침 그는 창가에 그 돌이 있는 것을 발견했다!

17 Maibon was _____ _____ the animals, but he was _____ _____ he was _____ _____.

18 Now Maibon's baby was _____ _____. _____ _____ was _____ in his mouth.

19 His wife told him _____ _____ _____ the stone and this time, Maibon _____ the stone _____ _____ _____.

20 But, the next day, the stone _____ _____! Time _____ _____ and _____ _____ or _____.

21 Maibon began _____ _____. "There's _____ _____ _____, nothing to show for my work."

22 Maibon _____ _____ _____ the stone, but it _____ _____ _____.

23 Maibon _____ _____ _____ the stone _____ his house.

24 _____ _____ _____ _____ the field, he saw the dwarf. Maibon _____ _____ with him.

25 "Why _____ _____ _____ me about the stone?"

26 "I _____ _____, but you wouldn't _____."

27 Doli _____ that Maibon couldn't _____ _____ _____ the stone _____ he really _____ _____.

28 "I want _____ _____ _____ it. _____ may happen, _____ it _____!"

29 Doli told him _____ _____ the stone _____ the ground and _____ _____ _____.

30 Maibon _____ as Doli _____. When he _____ home, Modrona told him the good news — the eggs _____ chickens and the cow _____ her baby.

31 And Maibon _____ _____ _____ when he saw the first tooth in _____ _____ _____.

32 Maibon, Modrona and their children and grandchildren _____ _____ _____ _____.

33 Maibon _____ _____ _____ his white hair and long beard.

17 Maibon은 동물들이 걱정되긴 했지만, 자신이 여전히 젊어서 기뻤다.

18 이제 Maibon의 아기에게 문제가 생겼다. 아기의 입에서 이가 보이지 않았다.

19 그의 아내는 그에게 그 돌을 버리라고 말했고 Maibon은 이번엔 그 돌을 땅속에 묻었다.

20 그런데 그 다음날 그 돌은 다시 돌아왔다! 시간이 흘렀고 어떤 것도 자라거나 변하지 않았다.

21 Maibon은 걱정이 되기 시작했다. "기대할 것도 내 일의 결과를 보여 줄 것도 아무것도 없어."

22 Maibon은 그 돌을 없애려고 노력했지만 돌은 계속 되돌아왔다.

23 Maibon은 그 돌을 그의 집에서 멀리 떨어진 곳에 버리기로 결심했다.

24 그는 들판으로 가는 길에 난쟁이를 보았다. Maibon은 그에게 화를 냈다.

25 "너는 왜 내게 그 돌에 대해 경고하지 않았어?"

26 "나는 하려고 했지만, 너는 들으려 하지 않았어."

27 Doli는 Maibon이 진심으로 원하지 않는 한 그 돌을 없앨 수 없다고 설명했다.

28 "나는 그것을 더 이상 원하지 않아. 무슨 일이 있어도 일어나게 해!"

29 Doli는 그에게 그 돌을 땅에 던지고 집으로 돌아가라고 말했다.

30 Maibon은 Doli가 말한 대로 했다. 그가 집에 도착했을 때, Modrona는 그에게 달걀이 닭이 되고 소가 새끼를 낳았다는 좋은 소식을 말해 주었다.

31 그리고 Maibon은 아기의 입에 첫 이가 난 것을 보고 기뻐서 웃었다.

32 Maibon과 Modrona, 그리고 그들의 자녀들과 손주들은 오랫동안 살았다.

33 Maibon은 그의 흰 머리와 긴 수염을 자랑스러워했다.

※ 다음 문장을 우리말로 쓰시오.

1   One day, Maibon was driving down the road on his horse and cart when he saw an old man.

➡ _____

2   The old man looked very sick. Maibon began to worry about growing old.

➡ _____

3   Later that day, he saw a dwarf, Doli, in the field.

➡ _____

4   He was trying to get his leg out from under a log.

➡ _____

5   Maibon pulled the log away and freed the dwarf.

➡ _____

6   "You'll have your reward. What do you want?"

➡ _____

7   "I've heard that you have magic stones that can keep a man young. I want one."

➡ _____

8   "Oh, you humans have it all wrong. Those stones don't make you young again. They only keep you from getting older."

➡ _____

➡ _____

9   "Just as good!" Doli tried to explain the problem with the stones, but Maibon didn't listen.

➡ _____

10   So Doli handed him a magic stone and went away.

➡ _____

11   After a few days, Maibon saw that his beard didn't grow at all.

➡ _____

12   He became happy, but his wife, Modrona, got upset.

➡ _____

13   "The eggs don't change into chickens!" "Oh, the season's slow, that's all."

➡ _____

14   But she was not happy. "The cow doesn't give birth!" Maibon, then, told her about the stone, and she got very angry and told him to throw it away.

➡ _____

➡ _____

15   He didn't want to, but he listened to his wife and threw the stone out the window.

➡ _____

16   However, the next morning, he found the stone sitting by the window!

➡ _____

17 Maibon was worried about the animals, but he was glad that he was still young.

➡ _____

18 Now Maibon's baby was having trouble. No tooth was seen in his mouth.

➡ _____

19 His wife told him to throw away the stone and this time, Maibon put the stone under the ground.

➡ _____

20 But, the next day, the stone came back! Time went by and nothing grew or changed.

➡ _____

21 Maibon began to worry. "There's nothing to look forward to, nothing to show for my work."

➡ _____

22 Maibon tried to destroy the stone, but it kept coming back.

➡ _____

23 Maibon decided to throw away the stone far from his house.

➡ _____

24 On his way to the field, he saw the dwarf. Maibon got angry with him.

➡ _____

25 "Why didn't you warn me about the stone?"

➡ _____

26 "I tried to, but you wouldn't listen."

➡ _____

27 Doli explained that Maibon couldn't get rid of the stone unless he really wanted to.

➡ _____

28 "I want no more of it. Whatever may happen, let it happen!"

➡ _____

29 Doli told him to throw the stone onto the ground and go back home.

➡ _____

30 Maibon did as Doli said. When he arrived home, Modrona told him the good news
— the eggs changed into chickens and the cow bore her baby.

➡ _____

_____

31 And Maibon laughed with delight when he saw the first tooth in his baby's mouth.

➡ _____

32 Maibon, Modrona and their children and grandchildren lived for many years.

➡ _____

33 Maibon was proud of his white hair and long beard.

➡ _____

※ 다음 괄호 안의 단어들을 우리말에 맞도록 바르게 배열하시오.

1 (day, / one / was / Maibon / driving / the / down / load / his / on / horse / and / when / cart / saw / he / old / an / man.)
➡ _____

2 (old / the / man / very / looked / sick. // Maibon / to / began / worry / growing / old. / about)
➡ _____

3 (that / later / day, / saw / he / dwarf, / a / Doli, / field. / the / in)
➡ _____

4 (was / he / trying / get / to / leg / his / from / out / log. / a / under)
➡ _____

5 (pulled / Maibon / log / the / and / away / the / freed / dwarf.)
➡ _____

6 (have / "you'll / reward. / your // do / what / want?" / you)
➡ _____

7 ("I've / that / heard / have / you / stones / magic / can / that / keep / a / young. / man // one." / want / I)
➡ _____

8 ("oh, / humans / you / it / have / wrong. / all // stones / those / make / don't / you / again. / young // only / they / keep / from / you / older." / getting)
➡ _____

9 (as / good!" / "just // tried / Doli / explain / to / problem / the / with / stones, / the / but / didn't / Maibon / listen.)
➡ _____

10 (Doli / so / him / handed / magic / a / stone / away. / and / went)
➡ _____

11 (a / after / days. / few / saw / Maibon / that / beard / his / grow / didn't / all. / at)
➡ _____

12 (became / he / happy, / but / wife, / his / got / Modrona, / upset.)
➡ _____

13 ("the / don't / eggs / chickens!" / into / change // "oh, / season's / the / slow, / all." / that's)
➡ _____

14 (she / but / not / happy. / was // "the / doesn't / cow / birth!" / give // then, / Maibon / her / told / the / about / stone, / and / got / she / angry / very / and / him / told / throw / to / away. / it)
➡ _____

15 (didn't / he / to, / want / but / listened / he / his / to / wife / and / the / threw / stone / the / out / window.)
➡ _____

16 (however, / the / morning, / next / found / he / stone / the / by / sitting / window! / the)
➡ _____

1 어느 날, Maibon이 한 노인을 보았을 때, 그는 마차를 타고 길을 내려가고 있던 중이었다.

2 그 노인은 매우 아파 보였다. Maibon은 늙어 가는 것이 걱정되기 시작했다.

3 그날 오후, 그는 들판에서 Doli라는 난쟁이를 보았다.

4 그는 통나무 아래에 깔린 그의 다리를 빼내려고 하고 있었다.

5 Maibon은 통나무를 잡아당겨서 난쟁이를 풀어주었다.

6 "너는 보상을 받게 될 거야. 원하는게 뭐니?"

7 "나는 네가 사람의 젊음을 유지해 주는 마법의 돌들을 가지고 있다고 들었어. 나는 그것을 원해."

8 "오, 너희 인간들은 잘못 알고 있어. 그 돌들은 너희들이 다시 젊어지게 해 주지 않아. 단지 더 늙지 않게 막아 줄 뿐이라고."

9 "그것대로 좋아!" Doli는 그 돌에 관한 문제를 설명하려고 했지만, Maibon은 듣지 않았다.

10 그래서 Doli는 그에게 마법의 돌을 건네고는 가버렸다.

11 며칠이 지나서, Maibon은 그의 수염이 전혀 자라지 않았음을 알았다.

12 그는 행복해졌지만, 그의 아내 Modrona는 화가 났다.

13 "달걀이 닭이 되지 않아요!" "아, 시기가 더딘 거예요. 그 뿐이에요."

14 하지만 그녀는 탐탁해하지 않았다. "소가 새끼를 낳지 않아요!" 그때 Maibon은 그 돌에 대해 그녀에게 이야기를 했고 그녀는 매우 화를 내며 그에게 그것을 버리라고 말했다.

15 그는 원하지 않았지만, 아내의 말을 듣고 창밖으로 돌을 던졌다.

16 그러나 다음날 아침 그는 창가에 그 돌이 있는 것을 발견했다!

17 (was / Maibon / worried / the / about / animals, / but / was / he / glad / that / was / he / young. / still)

➡ _____

18 (Maibon's / now / was / baby / trouble. / having // tooth / no / seen / was / mouth. / his / in)

➡ _____

19 (wife / his / him / told / throw / to / the / away / stone / and / time, / this / Maibon / the / put / under / stone / ground. / the)

➡ _____

20 (but, / next / the / day, / stone / the / back! / came // went / time / and / by / grew / nothing / changed. / or)

➡ _____

21 (began / Maibon / worry. / to // "there's / to / nothing / look / to, / forward / to / nothing / show / for / work." / my)

➡ _____

22 (tired / Maibon / destory / to / stone, / the / it / but / back. / coming / kept)

➡ _____

23 (decided / Maibon / throw / to / away / stone / the / from / far / house. / his)

➡ _____

24 (his / on / to / way / field, / the / saw / he / dwarf. / the // got / Maibon / him. / with / angry)

➡ _____

25 ("why / you / didn't / me / warm / about / stone?" / the)

➡ _____

26 ("I / to, / tried / you / but / listen." / wouldn't)

➡ _____

27 (Doli / that / explained / Maibon / get / couldn't / rid / the / of / unless / stone / he / to. / wanted / really)

➡ _____

28 ("I / no / want / of / more / it. // may / whatever / happen, / let / happen!" / it)

➡ _____

29 (told / Doli / him / throw / to / stone / the / onto / ground / the / and / back / home. / go)

➡ _____

30 (did / Maibon / Doli / as / said. // he / when / home, / arrived / Modrona / him / told / good / the / news / – / eggs / the / into / changed / chickens / the / and / bore / cow / baby. / her)

➡ _____

31 (Maibon / and / with / laughed / delight / with / when / saw / he / first / the / tooth / his / in / mouth. / baby's)

➡ _____

32 (Modrona / Maibon, / and / children / their / and / lived / grnadchildren / for / years. / many)

➡ _____

33 (was / Maibon / proud / of / white / his / hair / beard. / long / and)

➡ _____

17 Maibon은 동물들이 걱정되긴 했지만, 자신이 여전히 젊어서 기뻤다.

18 이제 Maibon의 아기에게 문제가 생겼다. 아기의 입에서 이가 보이지 않았다.

19 그의 아내는 그에게 그 돌을 버리라고 말했고 Maibon은 이번엔 그 돌을 땅속에 묻었다.

20 그런데 그 다음날 그 돌은 다시 돌아왔다! 시간이 흘렀고 어떤 것도 자라거나 변하지 않았다.

21 Maibon은 걱정이 되기 시작했다. "기대할 것도 내 일의 결과를 보여 줄 것도 아무것도 없어."

22 Maibon은 그 돌을 없애려고 노력했지만 돌은 계속 되돌아왔다.

23 Maibon은 그 돌을 그의 집에서 멀리 떨어진 곳에 버리기로 결심했다.

24 그는 들판으로 가는 길에 난쟁이를 보았다. Maibon은 그에게 화를 냈다.

25 "너는 왜 내게 그 돌에 대해 경고하지 않았어?"

26 "나는 하려고 했지만, 너는 들으려 하지 않았어."

27 Doli는 Maibon이 진심으로 원하지 않는 한 그 돌을 없앨 수 없다고 설명했다.

28 "나는 그것을 더 이상 원하지 않아. 무슨 일이 있어도 일어나게 해!"

29 Doli는 그에게 그 돌을 땅에 던지고 집으로 돌아가라고 말했다.

30 Maibon은 Doli가 말한 대로 했다. 그가 집에 도착했을 때, Modrona는 그에게 달걀이 닭이 되고 소가 새끼를 낳았다는 좋은 소식을 말해 주었다.

31 그리고 Maibon은 아기의 입에 첫 이가 난 것을 보고 기뻐서 웃었다.

32 Maibon과 Modrona, 그리고 그들의 자녀들과 손주들은 오랫동안 살았다.

33 Maibon은 그의 흰 머리와 긴 수염을 자랑스러워했다.

※ 다음 우리말을 영어로 쓰시오.

1 어느 날, Maibon이 한 노인을 보았을 때, 그는 마차를 타고 길을 내려가고 있던 중이었다.
➡ _____

2 그 노인은 매우 아파 보였다. Maibon은 늙어 가는 것이 걱정되기 시작했다.
➡ _____

3 그날 오후, 그는 들판에서 Doli라는 난쟁이를 보았다.
➡ _____

4 그는 통나무 아래에 깔린 그의 다리를 빼내려고 하고 있었다.
➡ _____

5 Maibon은 통나무를 잡아당겨서 난쟁이를 풀어 주었다.
➡ _____

6 "너는 보상을 받게 될 거야. 원하는 게 뭐니?"
➡ _____

7 "나는 네가 사람의 젊음을 유지해 주는 마법의 돌들을 가지고 있다고 들었어. 나는 그것을 원해."
➡ _____

8 오, 너희 인간들은 잘못 알고 있어. 그 돌들은 너희들이 다시 젊어지게 해 주지 않아. 단지 더 늙지 않게 막아 줄 뿐이라고."
➡ _____

9 "그것대로 좋아!" Doli는 그 돌에 관한 문제를 설명하려고 했지만, Maibon은 듣지 않았다.
➡ _____

10 그래서 Doli는 그에게 마법의 돌을 건네고는 가버렸다.
➡ _____

11 며칠이 지나서, Maibon은 그의 수염이 전혀 자라지 않았음을 알았다.
➡ _____

12 그는 행복해졌지만, 그의 아내 Modrona는 화가 났다.
➡ _____

13 "달걀이 닭이 되지 않아요!" "아, 시기가 더딘 거예요. 그 뿐이에요."
➡ _____

14 하지만 그녀는 탐탁해하지 않았다. "소가 새끼를 낳지 않아요!" 그때 Maibon은 그 돌에 대해 그녀에게 이야기를 했고 그녀는 매우 화를 내며 그에게 그것을 버리라고 말했다.
➡ _____
_____

15 그는 원하지 않지만, 아내의 말을 듣고 창밖으로 돌을 던졌다.
➡ _____

16 그러나 다음날 아침 그는 창가에 그 돌이 있는 것을 발견했다!
➡ _____

17 Maibon은 동물들이 걱정되긴 했지만, 자신이 여전히 젊어서 기뻤다.

➡ _____

18 이제 Maibon의 아기에게 문제가 생겼다. 아기의 입에서 이가 보이지 않았다.

➡ _____

19 그의 아내는 그에게 그 돌을 버리라고 말했고 Maibon은 이번엔 그 돌을 땅속에 묻었다.

➡ _____

20 그런데 그 다음날 그 돌은 다시 돌아왔다! 시간이 흘렀고 어떤 것도 자라거나 변하지 않았다.

➡ _____

21 Maibon은 걱정이 되기 시작했다. "기대할 것도 내 일의 결과를 보여 줄 것도 아무것도 없어."

➡ _____

22 Maibon은 그 돌을 없애려고 노력했지만 돌은 계속 되돌아왔다.

➡ _____

23 Maibon은 그 돌을 그의 집에서 멀리 떨어진 곳에 버리기로 결심했다.

➡ _____

24 그는 들판으로 가는 길에 난쟁이를 보았다. Maibon은 그에게 화를 냈다.

➡ _____

25 "너는 왜 내게 그 돌에 대해 경고하지 않았어?"

➡ _____

26 "나는 하려고 했지만, 너는 들으려 하지 않았어."

➡ _____

27 Doli는 Maibon이 진심으로 원하지 않는 한 그 돌을 없앨 수 없다고 설명했다.

➡ _____

28 "나는 그것을 더 이상 원하지 않아. 무슨 일이 있어도 일어나게 해!"

➡ _____

29 Doli는 그에게 그 돌을 땅에 던지고 집으로 돌아가라고 말했다.

➡ _____

30 Maibon은 Doli가 말한 대로 했다. 그가 집에 도착했을 때, Modrona는 그에게 달걀이 닭이 되고 소가 새끼를 낳았다는 좋은 소식을 말해 주었다.

➡ _____

➡ _____

31 그리고 Maibon은 아기의 입에 첫 이가 난 것을 보고 기뻐서 웃었다.

➡ _____

32 Maibon과 Modrona, 그리고 그들의 자녀들과 손주들은 오랫동안 살았다.

➡ _____

33 Maibon은 그의 흰 머리와 긴 수염을 자랑스러워했다.

➡ _____

MEMO

MEMO

영어 기출 문제집

적중100 plus
2학기 전과정

2학기

정답 및 해설

비상 | 김진완

중 2

적중100

영어 기출 문제집

적중100

2학기

정답 및 해설

비상 | 김진완

중 2

Explore Your Feelings!

시험대비 실력평가
p.08

01 (h)ate　　02 ⑤　　03 (1) alone　(2) lines
　(3) limit　(4) since　　04 ⑤
05 (1) I can't stand the cold very well.
　(2) They talked about the matter.
　(3) Give me some advice, please.
　(4) was upset because she used my stuff without asking me first.　　06 ④

01 주어진 관계는 반의어 관계를 나타낸다. hate: 싫어하다
02 ⑤번 문장에서 line은 '대사'를 뜻한다. rude: 무례한
03 alone: 혼자, line: 대사, limit: 제한, since: ~ 이후로
04 '누군가가 특정한 상황에서 해야 하는 것에 대한 의견 또는 제안'을 가리키는 말은 advice(조언)이다.
05 stand: 참다, matter: 문제, advice: 조언, stuff: 물건
06 주어진 문장에서 stand는 '참다, 견디다'를 의미하며 이와 같은 의미로 쓰인 것은 ④번이다. 나머지는 모두 '서다, 서 있다'를 의미한다. arrogant: 거만한

서술형 시험대비
p.09

01 toothache
02 (1) lunch break(= lunch time)　(2) advice　(3) hurt
03 (1) on purpose　(2) gain weight　(3) focus on
　(4) In the end
04 (1) He sometimes puts people down.
　(2) She always points out my mistakes.
　(3) Set an alarm before you go to bed.
05 (1) Thank you for pointing out some mistakes in my report.
　(2) Here are your scripts, so practice your lines.
　(3) The reason I called was to ask about the plans for Saturday.
　(4) It is important to take measures to avoid the risk of fire.

01 치아의 아픔을 가리키는 말은 toothache(치통)이다.
02 lunch break: 점심시간, advice: 조언, hurt: 다치게 하다
03 on purpose: 고의로, gain weight: 체중이 늘다, focus on: ~에 집중하다, in the end: 결국

04 put down: 깎아내리다, point out: 지적하다, set an alarm: 자명종을 맞추다
05 point out: 지적하다, script: 대본, reason: 이유, take measures: 조치를 취하다

교과서 Conversation

핵심 Check
p.10~11

1 (1) nervous, What's the matter(= problem)
　(2) Why do you look so sad
　(3) wrong / What should I do
2 (1) I think you should
　(2) advise
　(3) Why don't you

교과서 대화문 익히기

Check(√) True or False
p.12

1 T　2 F　3 T　4 F

교과서 확인학습
p.14~15

Listen & Talk 1-A-1
don't look, matter / wore, got / what to do

Listen & Talk 1-A-2
look down, What's the matter / haircut, funny / Take off / used to

Listen & Talk 1-B
tired / I didn't have breakfast this morning / too bad, lunch break / snack bar / make, suggestion / post

Listen & Talk 2 A-1
how to do, advice / solve / solve, focus on / ones / got

Listen & Talk 2 A-2
late for, wake up / set an alarm / turn it off / far from, That way

Listen & Talk 2 B
stop playing computer games. What should I do / set, limit, shuts down / I think you should / out of, into / advice

Communication
on the air / matter / sharing, with, stuff / feelings, make some rules / I'll try that

01 (D) → (A) → (C) → (B)   02 ③   03 ②, ④

04 ②

01 (D) 자신의 고민을 이야기함 → (A) 자명종을 맞춰 두는지 질
문 → (C) 대답 → (B) 조언

02 이어지는 문장에서 매점이 있어야 하는 이유를 설명하고 있으므
로 (C)가 적절하다.

03 ⓐ는 상대방의 의견에 동의하는 표현이다.

01 ⑤   02 ①

03 her sister's favorite T-shirt

04 suggestion

05 They can post it on the suggestion board.

06 ①, ③   07 (C) → (B) → (A) → (D)

08 I think you should focus on the ones you got
wrong.   09 ⑤   10 ⓐ → playing

11 how about using a special program?   12 ④

13 She couldn't wake up in the morning.

14 Because she will have to get out of bed to turn it
off.

01 (A)는 상대방의 기분이 언짢아 보일 때 무슨 일이 있는지 묻는
표현이다. ⑤번은 직업을 묻는 표현이다.

02 언니의 티셔츠에 포도 주스를 쏟아 어찌할 바를 모르고 있는 여자
의 심정으로 worried(걱정스러운)가 적절하다.

04 '다른 누군가가 그것에 관해 생각하도록 당신이 언급한 의견 또
는 계획'을 가리키는 말은 suggestion(제안)이다.

05 Jane과 Tom은 제안 게시판에 그것을 게시할 수 있다.

06 (A)는 안타까움 또는 유감을 나타내는 표현으로 이와 바꾸어 쓸
수 있는 표현은 ①, ③번이다.

07 (C) 무슨 일이 있는지 질문 → (B) 기분이 좋지 않은 이유 설명
→ (A) 모자를 벗고 보여줄 것을 요청 → (D) 반응

09 ⑤번을 제외한 (a)와 나머지 모두는 조언해 줄 것을 요청하는 표
현이다.

10 stop+to부정사: ~하기 위해 멈추다, stop+~ing: ~하던 것을
멈추다

11 why don't you ~?는 '~하는 게 어때?'라고 제안하는 표현으
로 'how about ~?'과 바꾸어 쓸 수 있다.

13 Emily는 아침에 일어날 수 없어서 수업에 늦었다.

14 Tom이 자명종을 침대에서 멀리 놓으라고 조언한 이유는 그녀가
그것을 끄기 위해 일어날 수밖에 없기 때문이다.

01 (방송에) 연결되었습니다.

02 Because her little sister uses Amy's stuff without
asking her first.

03 tell her my feelings and make some rules with
her

04 She doesn't know how to do better in math.

05 Sujin should focus on the math problems she got
wrong.

06 (A) He can't stop playing computer games
(B) set a time limit, (C) his room, (D) the living room

01 be on the air: 전파를 타다

03 만약 내가 너라면 나는 그녀에게 내 기분에 대해 이야기하고 그
녀와 함께 몇 가지 규칙을 정할 거야.

04 Sujin은 수학을 더 잘하는 법을 모른다.

05 Sujin은 그녀가 틀린 수학 문제에 집중해야 한다.

교과서
Grammar

1 (1) has studied   (2) has, arrived   (3) have done

2 (1) which(또는 that) you made

  (2) which(또는 that) he bought

  (3) who(m)(또는 that) Helen came with

01 (1) have you left → did you leave

  (2) teach → teaches

  (3) did → have done

  (4) whom → which[that]

02 (1) Have you found the pen that[which] you lost?

  (2) Did she take the class which[that] James
taught?

  (3) I want to meet the boy whom[who/that] you
speak highly of.

  (4) Molly likes the movie which[that] Tom Cruise
starred in.

03 (1) I haven't finished my lunch yet.

  (2) She has been to the church two times.

  (3) I gave her all the money that I had.

  (4) Where is the report which we handed in?

01 (1) 의미상 그 장소를 언제 떠났는지를 묻고 있으므로 과거시제를 쓰는 것이 옳다. (2) Mr. Pang이 주어이므로 단수 동사를 쓴다. (3) 지금까지 오랫동안 이 일을 해 왔다는 것이므로 현재완료 시제를 쓴다. (4) 사물이 선행사이므로 which[that]를 쓰는 것이 옳다.

02 관계대명사 which, who(m)를 대신하여 that을 써도 무방하며, 목적격 관계대명사이므로 생략해도 좋다.

03 (2) '~에 가 보았다'라는 경험은 have been to로 표현한다.

01 ④   02 ⑤   03 ③
04 like the dress which you want to buy
05 ⑤   06 ②   07 ③
08 whom you invited   09 ②   10 ④
11 Tell me about the people who(m) you met in the hospital.   12 ③   13 ②   14 ④
15 The letter that you sent to me has not arrived yet.
16 ④   17 ⑤   18 ③
19 Have you ever been to India before?   20 ③
21 I have lost my cap.
22 The I-pad which[that] I got from my father was my birthday present.
23 that the children play with

01 ④ Have you ~?로 물을 때에는 Yes, I have. 혹은 No, I haven't.로 답한다.

02 'Jamie가 쓴 책'이므로 which Jamie wrote이 the book을 수식하도록 문장을 만든다.

03 현재완료가 쓰이고 있으므로 과거를 나타내는 어구는 빈칸에 쓰일 수 없다.

04 which를 대신하여 that을 써도 무방하다.

05 '~에 가 본 적이 있다'는 표현은 have been to를 쓴다. have gone to는 '~에 가고 없다'는 의미이다.

06 ② 과거를 나타내는 a few minutes ago는 현재완료 시제와 함께 쓸 수 없다.

07 현재완료 시제와 함께 쓰일 때 기간을 이끌 수 있는 전치사는 for이다. since는 특정 시점을 이끈다.

08 whom을 대신하여 who나 that을 써도 무방하다.

09 첫 번째 빈칸은 유명인을 만나본 적이 있느냐는 경험을 묻는 말이므로 현재완료 시제를 쓰는 것이 옳으며, 두 번째 빈칸에는 현재 그가 휴가를 즐기는 중이라는 말로 미루어 보아 '이탈리아에 가고 없다'는 표현이 들어가는 것이 옳다.

10 두 시간 전에 그 주제에 관하여 대화하기 시작하여 여전히 대화하고 있다는 것이므로 두 시간 동안 그 주제에 관하여 대화하고 있다는 것을 현재완료 시제로 나타낼 수 있다.

11 who(m)를 대신하여 that을 써도 무방하다.

12 모두 현재완료의 '완료' 용법이지만, ③번은 '계속'으로 쓰였다.

13 목적격 관계대명사나 '주격 관계대명사+be동사'를 생략할 수 있다.

14 사람과 동물이 함께 있는 선행사는 관계대명사 that으로 받는다.

15 '네가 나에게 보낸 그 편지'라고 하였으므로 관계대명사절 that you sent to me가 The letter를 수식하도록 문장을 쓴다.

16 (A) 특정 시점을 나타내고 있으므로 since, (B) 과거를 나타내는 last week은 현재완료와 함께 쓰일 수 없으며, (C) 지금까지 벽을 두 번 칠했다는 의미이므로 현재완료를 쓰는 것이 옳다.

17 ①~④는 주격 관계대명사로 쓰였으나 ⑤번은 목적격 관계대명사로 쓰인 that이다.

18 3년 전에 쓴 책이므로 과거시제를 쓰고 선행사가 사물이므로 which 혹은 that을 쓰는 것이 적절하다.

19 경험을 묻는 말이므로 현재완료 시제를 쓰는 것이 적절하다.

20 ③ 현재완료 시제는 명백한 과거를 나타내는 어구와 함께 쓰일 수 없다. 따라서 had로 쓰는 것이 옳다.

21 모자를 잃어버려 현재까지 그 상황이 이어지고 있으므로 현재완료 시제를 써서 한 문장으로 표현할 수 있다.

22 해석: 아버지로부터 받은 그 아이패드는 내 생일 선물이었다.

23 해석: 그 아이들이 가지고 노는 장난감은 더러워 보인다.

01 It has been sunny since yesterday.
02 which you are drinking
03 since / for / ago / since
04 The missing boy whom people were looking for came home last night.
05 have you lived / ago, have lived, for
06 (1) What is the name of the man whom[who] you want to meet?
　(2) This is the car which my friend hopes to buy someday.
　(3) Where is the red sweater which I put in my drawer?
07 Have you seen an elephant before?
　No, I haven't.
08 (1) Did you throw a party for her yesterday?
　(2) I have been to Boston many times.
　(3) The sandwich which[that] he made for us is very delicious.
09 Kevin has lost his umbrella.
10 (1) isn't much information which you can get
　(2) gave Tim the pants which he always liked
　(3) he the man whom you respect very much

11 This is the desk which[that] my father made.

12 (1) The tennis game he played yesterday was great.

(2) Do you know the boy talking with your sister?

(3) The subject Jane is interested in is history and Korean.

13 that[which] she doesn't like

14 have lost

15 which you attended

01 현재완료 시제를 이용하여 어제 이후로 계속 맑다는 문장을 쓸 수 있다.

02 which 대신에 that을 써도 좋다. 또, drinking 대신에 having을 써도 좋다.

03 특정 시점 앞에는 전치사나 접속사 since, 기간 앞에는 전치사 for를 쓰며, ago는 과거동사와 함께 어울리는 부사이다.

04 '사람들이 찾던 그 실종 소년'이므로 The missing boy whom people were looking for라고 쓰는 것이 옳다.

05 이 집에서 얼마나 오랫동안 살았는지를 묻는 말이다. 현재완료의 '계속' 용법을 이용하여 문장을 완성할 수 있다. 기간을 이끄는 전치사는 for이다.

06 (1) 네가 만나기를 원하는 그 남자의 이름이 뭐야? (2) 이것이 내 친구가 언젠가 사기를 원하는 차야. (3) 내가 옷장에 넣어둔 빨간색 스웨터는 어디에 있어?

07 경험을 묻는 말을 현재완료 시제를 사용하여 쓸 수 있다.

08 (1) 과거를 나타내는 yesterday는 현재완료 시제와 함께 쓸 수 없다. (2) '~에 가고 없다'는 의미의 have gone to는 3인칭 주어에만 쓸 수 있다. (3) 선행사가 사물이므로 관계대명사는 which[that]를 쓰는 것이 옳다.

09 Kevin이 우산을 잃어버린 상황이 과거부터 현재까지 이어지므로 현재완료 시제를 써서 한 문장으로 표현할 수 있다.

10 which를 대신하여 that을 써도 무방하며, whom을 대신하여 who나 that을 써도 좋다. (1) 네가 얻을 수 있는 많은 정보가 없어. (2) 나는 Tim이 항상 좋아하는 바지를 그에게 줬다. (3) 그가 네가 아주 존경하는 그 남자니?

11 '우리 아빠가 만드신 책상'이므로 관계사절이 the desk를 수식하도록 문장을 만든다.

12 목적격 관계대명사와 '주격 관계대명사+be동사'를 생략할 수 있다.

13 '그녀가 좋아하지 않는 음식'이므로 that[which] she doesn't like라고 쓰는 것이 옳다.

14 신발을 잃어버렸다는 결과를 나타내는 것이므로 현재완료 시제를 이용한다.

15 which를 대신하여 that을 써도 좋다. attend a party: 파티에 참석하다, 파티에 가다

Reading

확인문제　　　　　　　　　　　　　p.28

1 T　2 F　3 T　4 F　5 T

확인문제　　　　　　　　　　　　　p.29

1 T　2 F　3 T　4 F　5 T　6 T

교과서 확인학습 A　　　　　　　p.30~31

01 years old, these days, going up and down

02 looks down

03 feelings, find out why'

04 What a day, yelled at, after

05 because, forgot, lines

06 that Bella made

07 could, in front of

08 did not mean to hurt

09 have been, since

10 what, saying

11 would never put

12 that, not going to be friends　13 too far, see

14 forgive, say a word　　　　　15 even look at

16 has never been

17 ate alone during　　　　　　18 best friend

19 that we don't know about

20 stand, any longer　　　　　　21 go, tell, about

22 to be hurt　　23 let it go　　24 work it out

25 that, are talking　　　　　　26 talked to her

27 avoid, on purpose

28 a way to say　29 any more problems

30 part of growing up

31 Just like, face, solve them, wiser

교과서 확인학습 B　　　　　　　p.32~33

1 Bella is 15 years old this year and these days her feelings are going up and down.

2 Today, she looks down.

3 Let's listen to Bella's feelings and find out why.

4 What a day! I can't believe Jenny yelled at Bella after the school play.

5 Well, that's because Bella forgot her lines on stage.

6 Jenny pointed out the mistake that Bella made.

7 How could she do that in front of everyone?

8 But I'm sure Jenny did not mean to hurt Bella.

9 They have been best friends since elementary school. Remember?

10 That's what I'm saying.

11 A true friend would never put Bella down like that.

12 I'm worried that they are not going to be friends anymore.

13 Come on, Fear. Don't go too far. We'll see.

14 I can't forgive Jenny. She didn't say a word to Bella.

15 Jenny didn't even look at her.

16 Jenny has never been this cold before.

17 Bella ate alone during lunch today. Poor Bella!

18 Jenny is Bella's best friend.

19 I'm sure there is a reason that we don't know about.

20 I can't stand this any longer.

21 Bella should just go and tell her about her feelings.

22 I don't want Bella to be hurt again.

23 She should let it go.

24 They are good friends. They will work it out.

25 Whew! I'm so happy that they are talking again.

26 Yeah, Bella went to Jenny and talked to her first.

27 Jenny didn't avoid Bella on purpose.

28 Yeah, Jenny didn't know a way to say sorry.

29 I hope Bella doesn't have any more problems like this.

30 Me, too. But problems are part of growing up.

31 Just like this time, Bella will face the problems, solve them, and become wiser in the end.

 시험대비 실력평가   p.34~37

01 down   02 ①, ②   03 **실수를 지적하는 것**

04 ③   05 ④

06 That's because Bella forgot her lines on stage.

07 ③   08 ③   09 ④   10 forgive

11 ⑤   12 part of growing up   13 ①

14 Bella and Jenny are talking again   15 ④

16 She feels up and down.

17 Fear is worried that Bella and Jenny are not going to be friends anymore.   18 ②   19 ③

20 ⑤   21 she ate alone during lunch today

22 Anger wants Bella to go and tell Jenny about her

feelings.   23 ②   24 ④   25 ②

26 wiser   27 have not talked

01 오늘 있었던 일로 미루어 보아 Bella의 기분이 안 좋아 보인다고 하는 것이 옳다. down: 우울한

02 사물을 선행사로 취하는 목적격 관계대명사 which 혹은 that이 들어갈 수 있다.

03 Jenny가 Bella의 실수를 지적한 것을 의미한다.

04 현재완료에서 since는 특정 시점을 이끌고, for는 기간을 이끈다. 따라서 ③번에는 for가 들어간다.

05 Bella가 무대에서 왜 대사를 잊어버렸는지는 글을 읽고 알 수 없다.

06 Jenny가 Bella에게 소리를 지른 이유는 Bella가 무대에서 그녀의 대사를 잊어버렸기 때문이라고 하였다.

07 밑줄 친 (A)는 현재완료의 '경험'을 나타내는 말이다. 따라서 ③번이 옳다.

08 ⓒ는 Jenny를, 나머지는 모두 Bella를 가리키는 말이다.

09 Fear가 말하는 let it go는 '상황을 내버려 두다'라는 의미로 Bella가 Jenny를 가게 해야만 한다는 것이 아니다.

10 누군가에게 화를 내거나 비난하는 것을 멈추는 것은 '용서하다(forgive)'이다.

11 on purpose: 일부러, 고의로 ① be satisfied with: ~에 만족하다 ② give up: 포기하다 ③ take part in: ~에 참가하다 ④ come up with: (생각을) 떠올리다 ⑤ turn on: ~을 켜다

12 전치사 of의 목적어로 동명사구를 쓰는 것에 유의한다.

13 in the end는 '결국, 마침내'라는 의미이다. 따라서 ①번이 옳다.

14 Joy가 행복한 이유는 'Bella와 Jenny가 다시 이야기하게 되어서'라고 하였다.

15 (A) listen은 자동사이므로 전치사 to와 함께 쓰일 때 목적어를 받음 (B) Jenny가 Bella에게 소리를 지른 이유를 설명하고 있으므로 that's because, (C) 초등학교 때부터 현재까지 가장 친한 친구라는 의미이므로 현재완료.

16 그녀의 기분은 좋다가 안 좋다가 한다고 하였다.

17 Fear는 Bella와 Jenny가 더 이상 친구로 지내지 않을까 봐 걱정된다고 하였다.

18 ⓐ는 '(연극, 영화의) 대사'라는 의미로 쓰인 line이다. 모두 line을 풀이한 말이며 ① (표면에 그려진) 선, 줄 ② 대사 ③ 주름살 ④ 윤곽선 ⑤ 줄, 열을 의미한다.

19 ③ Joy는 Jenny가 Bella에게 상처를 주려고 했던 것은 아니라고 확신한다. intend to: ~을 의도하다

20 밑줄 친 (A)는 불완전한 문장을 이끄는 관계대명사이다. ⑤는 접속사로 완전한 문장을 이끌고 있다.

21 Sadness가 Bella를 가엾어 하는 이유는 Bella가 오늘 점심시

간에 혼자 밥을 먹어서이다.

22 Anger는 Bella가 Jenny에게 가서 자신의 감정을 말하기를 원한다.

23 ② Fear는 Bella가 다시 상처받는 것을 원치 않는다고 하였다.

24 이번처럼 Bella는 문제를 피하는 것이 아니라 직면하게 될 것이다. avoid → face

25 Joy의 첫 번째 말로 미루어 보아 두 사람은 서로 이야기를 하지 않고 있다가 다시 이야기하게 되었으므로 ②번이 가장 적절하다.

26 문제를 해결하면서 Bella는 결국 더 현명해질 것이라 하였다.

27 이틀 동안 서로 대화를 하지 않았다는 의미로 현재완료 시제를 써서 나타낼 수 있다.

서술형 시험대비   p.38~39

01 why she looks down today

02 Bella made the mistake.
Jenny pointed out the mistake.

03 They have been best friends since elementary school.

04 She forgot her lines on stage.

05 She yelled at Bella.

06 Jenny didn't say a word to Bella and she didn't even look at her.

07 I have forgiven my best friend before.

08 It's because she ate alone during lunch today.

09 She went to Jenny and talked to her first

10 that we face

11 she didn't know a way to say sorry

12 I want to tell you a problem that I have.

13 have had   14 I don't know what to do.

15 my terrible math grades

---

01 Bella의 감정에 귀 기울여 보고 기분이 안 좋은 이유를 알아보자는 의미이다.

02 the mistake를 선행사로 하여 만든 문장이므로 다른 하나의 문장은 Bella made the mistake.로 쓸 수 있다.

03 초등학교 때부터 가장 친한 친구였다는 의미이므로 현재완료 시제를 써서 표현할 수 있다.

04 Bella가 저지른 실수는 무대에서 대사를 잊어버린 것이다.

05 Jenny는 Bella에게 학교 연극이 끝난 후 소리를 질렀다고 하였다.

06 Jenny는 Bella에게 한마디도 말을 안 했고 심지어 Bella를 쳐다보지도 않았다고 하였다.

07 현재완료의 '경험'을 나타내는 말로 위 글의 표현을 이용하여 영어로 쓸 수 있다.

08 Sadness가 "가엾은 Bella"라고 말한 것은 그녀가 오늘 점심시

간에 혼자 밥을 먹었기 때문이다.

09 Bella가 Jenny에게 먼저 말을 걸어서 화해를 하게 되었다.

10 관계대명사 that을 대신하여 which를 써도 무방하다. 해석: Joy에 따르면 우리가 직면하는 문제들은 우리가 더 현명해 지도록 돕는다.

11 Jenny는 사과하는 방법을 몰랐기 때문에 Bella를 피한 것이라고 하였다.

12 'I have a problem that I want to tell you.'라고 써도 좋다. that을 대신하여 which를 써도 무방하다.

13 since를 쓰며 현재의 문제를 이야기하고 있으므로 현재완료 시제를 쓰는 것이 가장 적절하다.

14 what to do: 무엇을 해야 할지

15 형편없는 수학 점수를 의미한다.

영역별 핵심문제   p.41~45

01 ②   02 ④

03 (1) You should focus on the problem at hand.
(2) We can face a problem again.
(3) Children grow up so fast these days.

04 elementary   05 ②   06 ②

07 ②   08 ③

09 (A) share my room with her, (B) advice, (C) tell my little sister my feelings and make some rules with her

10 (C) → (D) → (B) → (A)

11 ②   12 ②

13 Because he got a haircut but it's too short.

14 She thought it looked fine.   15 ①

16 ⑤   17 ②, ③

18 whom I care about most   19 ②, ⑤   20 ③

21 ⑤   22 she has gone to   23 ③

24 I will read the book which I borrowed from the library.   25 ③   26 ④

27 She forgot her lines on stage.   28 ⑤

29 ③

30 Bella and Jenny finally made up with each other.

31 ④

---

01 '당신에게 해롭게 하거나 화나게 하거나 또는 불안하게 하는 무언가를 한 사람에게 화내는 감정을 그만두다'를 나타내는 말은 forgive(용서하다)이다.

02 on purpose는 '고의로'를 의미한다.

03 at hand: 가까이에 (있는), face a problem: 문제에 직면하다, grow up: 성장하다

04 주어진 관계는 반의어 관계를 나타낸다. advanced: 상급의, 고등의, elementary: 초급의, 초보의

05 주어진 문장에서 lines는 '대사'를 나타내며 이와 같은 의미로

쓰인 것은 ②번이다. 나머지는 모두 '선'을 뜻한다.

06 mean은 동사로 '의미하다', 형용사로 '비열한, 인색한', means 는 명사로 '수단, 방법'을 뜻한다.

07 (A) late: 늦은, lately: 최근에, (B) turn on: ~을 켜다 turn off: ~을 끄다, (C) close to: ~에 가까이, far from: ~에서 멀리

09 나는 오늘도 화가 났었다. 왜냐하면 내 여동생이 내게 먼저 물어보지도 않고 내 물건을 사용했기 때문이다. 나는 그녀와 더 이상 방을 같이 쓰고 싶지 않았다. 이 문제를 해결하기 위해, 나는 Solomon에게 전화를 해서 내게 조언을 해 줄 것을 요청하였다. 그는 내게 내 기분을 그녀에게 이야기하고 나의 여동생과 몇 가지 규칙을 정해볼 것을 조언하였다. 이것은 내게 훌륭한 조언이었으며 그것을 해 보기로 결정했다.

10 (C) 무슨 일이 있는지 질문 → (D) 기분이 좋지 않은 이유 설명 → (B) 반응 및 질문 → (A) 대답

11 이어서 특별한 프로그램의 기능을 설명하고 있으므로 (B)가 알맞다.

12 ② 위 대화를 통해 왜 Eric이 컴퓨터 게임을 멈출 수 없는지는 알 수 없다.

13 David는 머리를 잘랐는데 너무 짧아 침울하다.

14 Sora는 David의 머리가 괜찮아 보인다고 생각했다.

15 목적격 관계대명사가 생략된 문장이다. 선행사인 The watch 뒤에 위치하는 것이 옳다.

16 Mr. Kim taught the students English에서 온 문장이므로 ⑤번은 옳지 않다.

17 사물을 선행사로 취하는 목적격 관계대명사이므로 that이나 which를 쓰는 것이 옳다.

18 about whom I care most라고 써도 무방하다.

19 주어진 문장은 Jason이 여행에서 집으로 돌아왔다는 것으로 Jason이 과거에 여행을 떠났다가 현재 돌아와 집에 있다는 것을 말하는 문장이다.

20 우산을 잃어버렸지만 지금은 그것을 가지고 있다는 것이므로 '우산을 잃어버리고 있다'라는 두 번째 문장과 의미가 같지 않다.

21 주어진 문장의 현재완료는 '경험'을 나타낸다. ①, ④ 완료 ②, ③ 계속을 나타내는 현재완료이다.

22 Sally가 집에 가서 없다는 의미이므로 has gone to를 쓴다.

23 ③ yesterday는 과거를 나타내는 어구이므로 현재완료 시제와 함께 쓸 수 없다.

24 목적격 관계대명사 which를 대신하여 that을 쓰거나 생략해도 무방하다.

25 밑줄 친 (A)는 관계대명사 that으로 불완전한 문장을 이끈다. 따라서 ③번이 답이다.

26 Bella와 Jenny가 더 이상 친구가 되지 않을 것이라는 생각을 하지 말라는 의미이다.

27 Bella는 무대에서 그녀의 대사를 잊어버렸다고 하였다.

28 학교 연극의 이름이 무엇인지는 알 수 없다.

29 on purpose, intentionally: 고의로

30 두 사람은 마침내 화해하였다. make up with: 화해하다

31 Bella가 이러한 문제들에 직면하게 되지 않기를 바라는 것은 Fear의 희망이지, Bella가 원치 않는 것이 아니다.

단원별 예상문제 p.46~49

01 ④　　　02 ⑤
03 Because he didn't have breakfast this morning.
04 They should wait for two more hours.
05 They can have a quick breakfast or snacks.
06 I think you should tell her your feelings.　07 ⑤
08 ③　　　09 ②, ④
10 (B) → (D) → (C) → (A)　　　11 ④
12 (1) Where is the man? You cheered for him.
　(2) The car is very expensive. Tony Stark drives
　　the car in the movie.
13 ⑤　　14 ③　　15 ⑤
16 I have lost my cell phone.
17 have seen, for　　18 ③
19 I'm sure there is a reason.
　We don't know about the reason.
20 ③　　　21 Fear wants her not to be hurt again.
22 ⑤
23 Fear hopes that Bella doesn't have any more
　problems like this.　　24 ③　　25 ①, ④
26 I have had this problem since last year.

01 나머지는 모두 조언을 요청하는 표현이지만 ④번은 도움을 제안하는 표현이다.

02 ⑤번을 제외한 (A)와 나머지는 모두 조언을 하는 표현이다.

03 Mike는 오늘 아침에 아침을 먹지 않아 피곤해 보인다.

04 Jane과 Mike는 점심시간까지 두 시간 이상 기다려야 한다.

05 Jane과 Mike는 학교에 매점이 있다면 간단한 아침이나 간식을 먹을 수 있다.

07 Amy가 그녀의 여동생과 어떻게 화해할지는 알 수 없다.

08 Kevin은 엄마의 새 안경을 깨뜨려 걱정하고 있다.

09 빈칸 (A)는 유감이나 동정을 나타내는 표현이 적절하므로 ②, ④번이 적절하다.

10 (B) Daisy에게 지각함을 알림 → (D) 사과 및 지각한 이유 설명 → (C) 조언 → (A) 반응

11 주어진 문장은 현재완료의 '완료'를 나타내고 있다. ④번은 경험을 나타내는 현재완료이다.

12 (1) 네가 응원했던 그 남자는 어디에 있니? (2) 그 영화에서 Tony Stark가 운전하는 차는 아주 비싸다.

13 사람과 사물을 모두 선행사로 취할 수 있는 관계대명사는 that이다.

14 ③ 관계대명사로 이어진 문장이므로 it을 쓰지 않아야 한다.

15 목적격 관계대명사 혹은 '주격 관계대명사+be동사'를 생략할 수 있다.

16 휴대전화기를 잃어버린 상황이 현재까지 지속되고 있으므로 현재완료 시제를 써서 한 문장으로 표현할 수 있다.

17 '우리는 두 시간 동안 그 영화를 보고 있다'라고 쓸 수 있다.

18 (A) Jenny가 Bella를 쳐다보지도 않았다는 의미가 적절하므로 at, (B) 명사를 이끌고 있으므로 전치사 during, (C) 타동사는 대명사 목적어를 부사 앞에 위치시키므로 work it out이 옳다.

19 a reason이 선행사임에 유의하여 문장을 둘로 나눈다.

20 Bella가 혼자 점심을 먹었다고 하였으므로 ③번은 옳지 않다.

21 Fear는 Bella가 다시 상처받지 않기를 원한다고 하였다.

22 밑줄 친 (A)는 앞의 명사를 수식하는 형용사로 쓰인 to부정사이다. 따라서 ⑤번이 답이다.

23 Fear는 Bella에게 이번과 같은 문제가 더 이상 없기를 바란다고 하였다.

24 Jenny가 Bella를 의도적으로 피한 것이 아니라고 하였으므로 ③번은 글의 내용과 일치하지 않는다.

25 선행사가 사물이므로 that이나 which를 써서 관계사절을 만든다.

26 작년 이래로 계속 이 문제를 가지고 있다는 것이므로 현재완료 시제로 표현할 수 있다.

서술형 실전문제
p.50~51

01 What should I do?

02 The computer shuts down at the set time.

03 She advises him to move it out of his room and into the living room.

04 (1) Have you ever been to Busan?
  (2) She has gone to Busan.

05 The box which she is lifting is not that heavy.
  The restaurant which Paul runs is crowded with people.
  The children whom I take care of are very noisy.

06 How long have you known each other?

07 The girl whom Tom is looking at is Danny's friend.

08 which[that] Jimmy is wearing

09 A: has, played   B: when, has played, for

10 Jenny yelled at Bella after the school play.

11 A true friend would never put Bella down like that.

12 Jenny pointed out my mistake in front of everyone

13 ©–@–ⓑ

14 whom I have known since elementary school

---

02 Eric이 특별한 프로그램을 사용하여 시간 제한을 설정하면 정해진 시간에 컴퓨터가 종료된다.

03 Ms. Morris는 Eric에게 컴퓨터를 그의 방에서 거실로 옮길 것을 조언하였다.

04 (1) 현재완료 시제를 이용하여 경험을 묻는 말을 쓸 수 있고, (2) '~에 가고 없다'는 결과 역시 현재완료 시제로 표현할 수 있다.

05 which를 대신하여 that을 쓸 수 있으며 whom 대신 who나 that을 써도 좋다. 모두 목적격 관계대명사이므로 생략해도 무방하다.

06 대답으로 미루어 보아 서로를 얼마나 오랫동안 알아왔는지를 묻는 말이 들어가는 것이 옳다.

07 'Tom이 바라보고 있는 그 소녀'이므로 관계사절 whom Tom is looking at이 명사 the girl을 수식하도록 문장을 쓸 수 있다.

08 wear a helmet: 헬멧을 쓰다

09 남동생이 얼마나 오랫동안 골프를 쳐 왔는지를 묻는 말에, 일곱 살 때 골프를 배워 지금까지 5년 동안 골프를 쳐 오고 있다는 대답을 하고 있다.

10 Jenny가 Bella에게 소리를 지른 것을 가리키는 말이다.

11 never는 빈도부사로 일반동사 앞, 조동사 뒤에 위치하는 것에 유의한다. put A down: A를 깎아내리다

12 Jenny는 모든 사람 앞에서 Bella의 실수를 지적하였다. in front of: ~ 앞에서

13 Bella가 자신의 대사를 잊어버리자 이를 지적하며 Jenny가 Bella에게 소리를 질렀고 Bella는 그것 때문에 슬펐다는 것이 사건의 순서이다.

14 whom을 대신하여 who 또는 that을 써도 무방하다.

창의사고력 서술형 문제
p.52

|모범답안|

01 (A) I didn't have breakfast
  (B) two more hours
  (C) our school should have a snack bar
  (D) the suggestion board

02 (1) I have argued with my best friend several times.
  (2) My friends have visited my house once.
  (3) I have never had a snow fight with my friend.
  (4) I have known Sumin since 2015.
  (5) I have been to a concert with my friends before.

03 (1) has lived in New York
  (2) has been to Spain
  (3) has raised Cooper since
  (4) and John have known each other since

9

01 나는 늦게 일어나 버스를 거의 놓칠 번했다. 다행히, 학교에 지각하지 않았다. 하지만 나는 너무 피곤하고 배고팠다. 왜냐하면 아침을 먹지 않았기 때문이다. 심지어, 나는 점심시간을 위해 두 시간 이상을 기다려야 했다. 나는 우리학교가 배고픈 학생들을 위해 매점이 있어야 한다고 생각했다. 내가 이것에 대해 Jane과 이야기 했을 때 그녀는 내 생각에 동의했다. 나는 곧 내 생각을 제안 게시판에 게시할 계획을 세웠다.

단원별 모의고사
p.53~56

01 (1) suggestion (2) repeat (3) forgive 02 ⑤
03 (1) stay up late (2) up and down (3) wake up
   (4) work out
04 (1) explain (2) yell (3) worry (4) pack (5) fight
05 ②   06 ④   07 ③   08 ①
09 (A) breakfast, (B) hungry, (C) have a snack barin
   our school
10 Because she stayed up late again last night.
11 She should pack her bag the night before.
12 (1) I can't stand working with him any more.
   (2) Minho has to memorize his lines in English.
   (3) I was embarrassed when he pointed out my
       mistakes.   13 ③   14 ⑤
15 ④
16 I have just eaten the cake that you bought for me.
17 I have not found my gold necklace yet.   18 ④
19 No, she didn't. She pointed out my mistake in
   front of everyone   20 ④   21 stand
22 ③   23 they are good friends

---

01 suggestion: 제안, repeat: 반복하다, forgive: 용서하다

02 since는 전치사로 '~부터, ~ 이래로', 접속사로 '~한 이래로, ~ 이기 때문에'를 의미한다.

03 stay up late: 늦게까지 자지 않고 있다, up and down: 좋다 가 나쁘다가 하는, wake up: 잠에서 깨다, work out: 해결하다

04 explain: 설명하다, yell: 소리치다, worry: 걱정하다, pack: (짐을) 싸다, fight like cat and dog: 싸우다, 격렬하게 서로 으르렁거리다

05 위 대화에서 @down은 '우울한'을 의미하며 이와 같은 의미로 쓰인 것은 ②번이다.

06 David는 새로운 그의 머리 스타일 때문에 기분이 좋지 않다.

07 이어서 Amy가 그녀의 여동생과 방을 같이 쓰기 싫은 이유를 설명하고 있으므로 (C)가 적절하다.

08 Amy와 Solomon은 직접 마주하여 이야기를 하는 것이 아니라 통화하고 있다.

09 몇몇 학생들이 아침을 먹지 않아 배고픔을 느낀다. 우리 학교에

매점이 있어야 한다.

10 Daisy는 지난밤에 또 늦게까지 자지 않고 깨어 있었기 때문에 지각하였다.

11 Daisy는 아침에 시간을 절약하기 위해 전날 밤에 가방을 싸야 한다.

13 현재완료에서 'since+시점', 'for+기간'으로 쓰이는 것에 유의하자.

14 관계대명사가 전치사의 목적어로 쓰인 경우에 유의하자. talk about: ~에 대하여 말하다

15 어제 이후로 아무것도 먹지 않았다는 의미이므로 have eaten을 쓰는 것이 옳다.

16 '네가 나에게 사 주었던 그 케이크'이므로 the cake that you bought for me라고 쓰는 것이 옳다.

17 현재완료 시제를 이용하여 나는 아직 내 금목걸이를 찾지 못했다는 의미로 쓸 수 있다.

18 연극이 끝난 후에 Jenny가 Bella에게 소리를 질렀다고 하였다.

19 Jenny는 모든 사람들 앞에서 Bella의 실수를 지적하였다.

20 우울해 보이는 것은 Jenny가 아니라 Bella이다.

21 어려운 상황을 받아들이거나 잘 다룰 수 있는 것은 'stand(참다, 견디다)'이다.

22 Bella가 자신의 감정을 Jenny에게 말해야 한다고 Anger가 말했을 뿐, 실제로 Bella가 Jenny에게 먼저 말을 걸지는 않았다.

23 Joy는 Bella와 Jenny가 좋은 친구이므로 잘 해낼 것이라고 생각한다.

Doors to the Wild

03 care for: ~을 돌보다, keep one's eyes on ~: ~에서 눈을 떼지 못하다, take a picture of ~의 사진을 찍다
04 probably: 아마도, seem: ~처럼 보이다, feed: 먹이를 주다, female: 암컷의, allow: 허락하다
05 careless: 부주의한, curious: 호기심이 많은, allow: 허락하다
06 shelter: 보호소, restless: 가만히 있지 않는, adventurous: 모험심이 강한

시험대비 실력평가   p.60

01 thin   02 ②   03 ④
04 (1) trunk   (2) whale   (3) Female
05 (1) Elephants rarely attack humans.
   (2) The rescue team arrived on time.
   (3) These rings symbolize our friendship
06 ④   07 ①

01 주어진 관계는 반의어 관계를 나타낸다. giant: 거대한, tiny: 작은, thick: 두꺼운, thin: 얇은
02 '볼 수 없는'을 뜻하는 말은 blind(눈이 먼)이다.
03 appear: 나타나다
04 trunk: (코끼리의) 코, whale: 고래, female: 암컷; 암컷의
05 rarely: 좀처럼 ~하지 않는, attack: 공격하다, rescue: 구조, symbolize: 상징하다
06 주어진 문장에서 bat은 '박쥐'를 뜻하며 이와 같은 의미로 쓰인 것은 ④번이다. 나머지는 모두 '방망이'를 뜻한다.
07 sense: (명) 감각, (동) 감지하다 approach: 다가가다

서술형 시험대비   p.61

01 careless   02 ①
03 (1) care for   (2) her eyes   (3) take a picture
04 (1) seem   (2) allow   (3) Female   (4) feed
   (5) probably
05 (1) The careless driver didn't see the light turn red.
   (2) Children are curious about everything around them.
   (3) My parents won't allow me to play computer games.
06 (1) I visited a local animal shelter last weekend.
   (2) He was restless at that time.
   (3) We need to be more adventurous and stronger.

01 주어진 관계는 반의어 관계를 나타낸다. careful: 주의 깊은, careless: 부주의한
02 '사람이나 동물에게 먹을 것을 주다'를 뜻하는 말은 feed(먹이다)이다.

교과서 Conversation

핵심 Check   p.62~63

1 (1) curious about / Let's read
  (2) blind / wonder
  (3) communicate / I'm curious about the way / find out
2 (1) big / as big as   (2) color / as red as a rose
  (3) as well as dogs / to know about them more

교과서 대화문 익히기

Check(√) True or False   p.64

1 T   2 F   3 T   4 F

교과서 확인학습   p.66~67

Listen & Talk 1 A-1
topic / I'm curious about weather change, doing

Listen and Talk 1 A-2
huge / bigger / curious about, says, insects / why

Listen and Talk 1 B
be friends / think so / friendship / curious about / raised, back, wild, a year later / touching

Listen and Talk 2 A-1
puppy / so small / as small as, much bigger / grow

Listen and Talk 2 A-2
over there / really big / as old as me / planted, was, born

Listen and Talk 2 B
give a presentation, the biggest, longer than, as heavy as, isn't it

Communication
millions of / curious, any / many, as heavy as / amazing

01 ④   02 weather change
03 (A) biggest   (B) longer   04 ④

03 (A) the+최상급: 가장 ~한, (B) 비교급+than: …보다 ~한
04 Toby의 설명에 따르면 흰긴수염고래는 농구 경기장보다 더 길다.

01 I'm curious about weather change.   02 ⑤
03 (1) biggest   (2) about 30m   (3) a basketball court
     (4) Its tongue is as heavy as an elephant.
04 insect   05 ④   06 ②   07 ②
08 ②   09 1년 후에 사자가 자기를 키워준 두 남자를
기억한 것   10 ⑤

02 Judy가 날씨 변화에 관심이 있다는 설명은 대화의 내용과 일치하지 않는다.
04 '6개의 다리와 3부분으로 나누어지는 몸을 가진 작은 생명체'를 나타내는 말은 insect(곤충)이다
05 대화를 통해 왜 벌레들이 커다란 꽃의 향기를 좋아하는지는 알 수 없다.
06 (A)는 'as+원급+as' 구문으로 원급인 small, (B)는 비교급을 수식할 수 있는 much, (C)는 동사를 수식하는 부사가 적절하므로 quickly가 적절하다.
07 Dylan은 Mina에게 사진을 보여주고 있다.
08 (A) between A and B: A와 B 사이에, (B) raised와 병렬 구조이므로 sent, (C) touching: 감동적인
10 나무는 Kelly의 할머니 할아버지만큼 오래되었다는 설명은 대화의 내용과 일치하지 않는다.

01 It is about 30 meters long.
02 A blue whale is longer than a basketball court.
03 It is as heavy as an elephant.
04 (A) bigger   (B) picture   (C) insects
     (D) they love the smell
05 It was about friendship between two men and a lion.
06 She remembered the two men who had raised her.
07 (D) → (B) → (A) → (C)

01 흰긴수염고래는 약 30미터 정도이다.
02 흰긴수염고래가 농구 경기장보다 더 길다.
03 흰긴수염고래의 혀는 코끼리만큼 무겁다.

04 Jane은 사진에서, 사람보다 큰 꽃을 발견하였다. 흥미롭게도, 이 꽃은 냄새가 고약하지만 벌레들은 그 냄새를 좋아한다. Tom은 왜 벌레들이 그 냄새를 좋아하는지 궁금해 하였다.
05 Clare가 본 비디오는 두 남자와 사자 사이의 우정에 대한 것이다.
06 사자는 그녀를 길렀던 두 남자를 기억했다.
07 (D) 주제 선택 여부 질문 → (B) 대답 및 질문 → (A) 궁금한 것 표현하기 → (C) 반응

1 (1) It, to exercise   (2) It, to go   (3) It, not to use
2 (1) not as[so] poor as   (2) twice as expensive as
     (3) as well as

01 (1) to being → to be
     (2) simply → simple
     (3) drive → to drive
     (4) three time → three times
02 (1) as fun as   (2) not as[so] long as
     (3) twice as warm as   (4) as sweet as
03 (1) It is important to help people in need.
     (2) It is beneficial to help each other.
     (3) He is not as foolish as you are.
     (4) The movie is not as boring as Amazing Amy.

01 (1), (3) 진주어를 to부정사로 쓰는 것이 옳다. (2) be동사의 보어가 비어 있으므로 as ~ as 사이 에는 형용사를 써야 한다. (2) 배수사 as+원급+as: ~보다 몇 배 …한
02 (1), (4) '~만큼 …한'이란 의미의 동등비교는 'as+형용사 또는 부사의 원급+as'로 나타낼 수 있 다. (2) 두 대상이 서로 같지 않음을 나타낼 때에는 동등비교의 부정 표현을 이용한다. (3) 배수사 +as+원급+as: ~보다 몇 배 …한
03 (1), (2) '어려움에 처한 사람들을 돕는 것', '서로 돕는 것'이 주어이므로 이를 진주어로 만들어 문장을 쓸 수 있다. (3), (4) 동등비교의 부정인 'not as+원급+as'를 이용하여 두 대상간의 차이를 나타낼 수 있다.

01 ⑤   02 ③   03 ⑤

04 It is difficult to solve the puzzle in an hour.

05 ④   06 ②   07 ⑤

08 It is dangerous to go outside alone late at night.

09 ④   10 ④   11 ③

12 Alex gets up as early as I (do).   13 ③

14 ④   15 ⑤   16 ④

17 ④   18 are not as[so] tall as   19 ③

20 It is natural that you worry about her.   21 ④

22 ③   23 ④

24 It is safe to drink this water.

01 문맥상 as ~ as 사이에는 형용사의 원급이 들어간다. '형용사+ly'는 부사로 쓰이지만 '명사+ly'는 형용사로 쓰이는 것에 유의한다.

02 모두 가주어로 쓰인 It이지만 ③번은 인칭대명사 It으로 '그것'이라고 해석된다.

03 fast는 형용사와 부사의 형태가 같다. 따라서 '빠르게 달리다'는 것은 run fast로 표현한다.

04 '그 퍼즐을 푸는 것'이 주어이므로 이를 to solve the puzzle로 진주어의 문장을 만들 수 있다.

05 진주어는 to부정사가 가능하며, 두 번째 문장의 의미는 '잘 먹는 것은 잘 자는 것만큼 중요하다'는 것이다. be동사의 보어가 필요하므로 as와 as 사이에 형용사를 써서 문장을 완성할 수 있다.

06 위 문장을 영어로 쓰면 'It is a good exercise to ride a bike.'이다.

07 ⑤ 원급 비교 as ~ as 사이에 문맥상 형용사의 원급이 온다.

08 '밤늦게 밖에 혼자 나가는 것'이 주어이므로 이를 진주어로 하여 문장을 쓰며, to부정사를 진주어로 쓴다.

09 Jason의 몸무게는 70kg이며 Paul의 몸무게는 64kg이므로 Jason은 Paul보다 무겁다고 말하는 것이 옳다.

10 빈칸에는 명사절 접속사 that이 오는 것이 옳다.

11 It is true that John lied to me.라고 쓰는 것이 옳다.

12 Alex와 나는 똑같이 오전 6시에 일어난다. 따라서 'Alex는 나만큼 일찍 일어난다.'라는 말을 할 수 있다.

13 to부정사의 부정형은 not to V 형태이다.

14 Zach이 Clara보다 더 긴장하고 있다는 것은 Clara는 Zach만큼 긴장하고 있지 않다는 의미이다.

15 모두 to부정사의 부사적 용법 중 '목적'으로 쓰여 '~하기 위'

16 문장을 이끌고 있으므로 첫 번째 빈칸에는 진주어 역할을 하는 명사절 접속사 that이 들어가는 것이 옳으며, TV를 보는 것은 시간의 양이므로 much를 쓰는 것이 옳다.

17 진주어로 to부정사를 쓸 수 있다. obey: 따르다, 준수하다

18 남동생의 키는 170cm이므로 '너는 나의 남동생만큼 키가 크지 않다'고 말할 수 있다.

19 '너의 시계는 나의 시계보다 더 비싸다'는 것은 '나의 시계는 너의 시계만큼 비싸지 않다'는 것이므로 My watch is not as expensive as yours.라고 쓰는 것이 옳다.

20 '네가 그녀를 걱정하는 것'은 문장으로 써야 하므로 가주어 it에 진주어절 명사절 that을 써서 문장을 만드는 것이 적절하다.

21 Kelly가 Julia보다 일을 더 열심히 한다는 것은 Julia가 Kelly만큼 열심히 일하지 않는다는 것과 같다.

22 ⓐ 진주어는 to부정사를 쓴다. 따라서 to see the man make a speech, ⓑ 노래를 잘 부르는 것이므로 sing을 수식하는 부사가 들어가는 것이 옳다. 따라서 as well as, ⓒ 진주어이므로 to부정사로 만들어 to find를 쓴다.

23 David가 Gloria보다 더 많은 친구를 가지고 있으므로 Gloria는 David만큼 친구를 많이 가지고 있지 않다고 표현 하는 것이 옳다.

24 진주어로 to부정사를 써서 문장을 만든다.

01 have two times as many balloons as Jinsu has

02 It is possible to walk to the top of this mountain.

03 as much money as

04 is safe to wear a helmet

05 is not as[so] old as

06 It is hard to see something without my glasses. I am as blind as a bat without my glasses.

07 (1) It is important that we try to save energy.

  (2) It is impossible to get there in time.

  (3) It was difficult to hear her singing.

  (4) It is foolish to want to be rich without working hard.

  (5) It is unsafe to play with matches.

08 is as light as

09 (1) is not as[so] tall as   (2) are not as[so] big as

  (3) are as big as   (4) is as heavy as

  (5) is as tall as   (6) is not as[so] heavy as

10 It is necessary to protect the animals on Earth.

11 as cold as

12 easy to answer his questions

13 (1) wrong to feed animals

  (2) exciting to take a zoo tour

  (3) dangerous to enter a cage

  (4) unsafe to take pets to the zoo

14 is twice as long as / is as long as mine

15 A: Is it fun to fly a kite?

  B: is as fun as playing a computer game

01 나는 진수보다 풍선을 두 배 더 많이 가지고 있다는 말로 쓸 수 있다. two times 대신 twice를 써도 좋다.

02 가주어 it을 쓰고 진주어로 to walk를 쓴다.

03 네가 나보다 돈을 더 많이 가지고 있다는 것은 '나는 너만큼 돈을 많이 가지고 있지 않다'는 의미와 같다.

04 가주어 it을 이용하여 같은 의미의 문장을 만드는 것이다.

05 Jackson씨의 나이는 Jackson 여사의 나이만큼 들지 않았다는 문장을 쓸 수 있다.

06 가주어 it과 원급 비교 구문을 이용한다.

07 가주어 it을 이용하여 문장을 만드는 문제이다. 주어가 to부정사 구이거나 명사절 접속사 that절인 경우 긴 주어를 뒤로 보내고 가주어 it을 사용하여 주어 자리를 채울 수 있다.

08 상자가 깃털만큼 가볍다는 이야기이다. 따라서 원급비교 as ~ as를 이용하여 문장을 완성할 수 있다.

09 (1) Mike의 키는 John보다 크지 않다. (2) John의 발 크기는 Mike의 발 크기만큼 크지 않다. (3) Betty의 발 크기는 John의 발 크기만큼 크다. (4) John은 Mike만큼 무겁다. (5) Mike는 Betty만큼 키가 크다. (6) Betty는 Mike와 John만큼 무겁지 않다.

10 '지구에 사는 동물들을 보호하는 것'을 주어로 만들어 문장을 쓸 수 있다.

11 피자가 얼음처럼 차가웠기 때문에 데워야만 했다고 말하는 것이 자연스럽다.

12 대답으로 미루어 보아 '그의 질문에 대답하는 것이 쉬웠는지'를 묻고 있음을 알 수 있다.

13 가주어로 it이 나와 있으므로 진주어로 to부정사를 쓴다. (4) unsafe를 대신하여 not safe를 써도 좋다.

14 나의 밧줄은 50cm이고 너의 밧줄은 1미터이므로, 너의 밧줄은 나의 밧줄보다 두 배만큼 더 길다고 할 수 있다. 수지의 밧줄은 나의 밧줄과 같다고 하였으므로 나의 밧줄만큼 길다고 할 수 있다.

15 연을 날리는 것과 컴퓨터 게임을 하는 것이 동등하게 재미있다고 말하고 있으므로 동등 비교 표현인 as ~ as를 활용하여 답을 쓸 수 있다.

Reading

확인문제	p.80

1 T 2 F 3 T 4 F

확인문제	p.81

1 F 2 F 3 T 4 F 5 T 6 T 7 F

교과서 확인학습 A p.82~83

01 was my first, in
02 took, pictures of   03 found, by
04 saw, drinking, beside   05 were, bright
06 gave her   07 saw, approaching
08 stood around, a thick   09 them, safe
10 Around, heard 11 followed, found, crying
12 lying dead, alone   13 It, to stay, in
14 What's more, it   15 see well
16 easily be attacked
17 the elephant shelter, asked for 18 to stay, until
19 was dark, quiet   20 kept, on
21 still next to   22 was touching, with
23 It, to see, staying   24 stays safe
25 appeared, approached   26 that, let, in
27 wrong   28 the oldest female, to become
29 The other elephants   30 elephants fed
31 as warmly as, did
32 such an amazing

교과서 확인학습 B p.84~85

1 Notes: Today was my first day in Africa.
2 I took lots of pictures of elephants.
3 This morning, I found an elephant group by a small water hole.
4 I saw a baby elephant drinking water beside her mother.
5 Her eyes were as bright as stars.
6 I gave her a name, Stella.
7 Around noon, I saw a group of lions approaching Stella.
8 The elephants stood around Stella and made a thick wall.
9 Thanks to them, Stella was safe.
10 Notes: Around sunset, I heard a strange sound.
11 I followed the sound and found Stella crying next to her mom.
12 She was lying dead and Stella was alone.
13 It is dangerous to stay alone in such a wild area.
14 What's more, it was going to be dark soon.
15 Elephants can't see well at night.
16 So Stella could easily be attacked.
17 I called the elephant shelter and asked for help.
18 I decided to stay by her until the rescue team came.
19 Notes: The night was dark and quiet.

20 I kept my eyes on Stella with my night camera.

21 Stella was still next to her mom.

22 She was touching her mom's lifeless body with her nose.

23 It was sad to see Stella staying close to her mom.

24 I hope Stella stays safe throughout the night.

25 Notes: A new elephant group appeared and Stella approached them.

26 At first, I thought that they would not let Stella in their group.

27 But I was wrong.

28 An elephant, probably the oldest female allowed Stella to become part of the group.

29 The other elephants also seemed to welcome Stella.

30 Unbelievably, one of the female elephants fed Stella.

31 She cared for Stella as warmly as Stella's mom did.

32 This was such an amazing moment!

시험대비 실력평가
p.86~89

01 ⑤   02 ②   03 The writer found an elephant group by a small water hole. 04 to stay
05 ③   06 ④   07 shelter   08 ④
09 Seeing Stella staying close to her mom 10 ④
11 (C)–(B)–(D)–(A)   12 ③   13 ②
14 ⑤   15 ⑤   16 The writer wrote it in Africa.   17 ③   18 was dangerous to stay alone in such a wild area   19 ⑤
20 It's because elephants can't see well at night.
21 ③   22 ④   23 It is interesting to see a pitcher plant eat insects. 24 warmly   25 ④
26 ③

01 아기 코끼리가 마시고 있는 것은 엄마의 젖이 아니라 물이라고 하였다.

02 글쓴이가 기록을 한 날은 7월 8일이다.

03 글쓴이는 7월 8일 아침에 작은 물웅덩이 옆에 있는 한 코끼리 무리를 발견하였다.

04 진주어로 쓰일 수 있는 것은 to부정사이다.

05 '더욱이', '게다가'라는 의미의 연결어가 들어가는 것이 적절하다. 따라서 ③번은 적절하지 않다.

06 코끼리들은 밤에 잘 볼 수 없다고 하였다.

07 '나쁜 날씨, 위험, 또는 공격으로부터 보호를 제공하기 위해 만들어진 건물'은 '보호소'이다.

08 빈칸 (A)에는 전치사 on이 들어간다. ① turn off: ~을 끄다 ② look forward to: ~을 기대하다 ③ be full of: ~으로 가득 차 있다 ④ put on: ~을 입다, 쓰다 ⑤ pick up: ~을 태우러 가다

09 Stella가 그녀의 엄마 가까이에 머물고 있는 것을 보는 것이 슬픈 일이었다고 하였다.

10 글의 내용으로 보아 Stella의 엄마가 죽었음을 알 수 있다

11 (C) 글쓴이는 Stella가 무리에게 거절당할 것이라고 예상 - (B) 그러나 가장 나이 많은 코끼리가 Stella를 받아 줌 - (D) 나머지 코끼리도 Stella를 환영 - (A) 심지어 Stella에게 젖을 먹이는 코끼리도 있음

12 'such+a(n)+형용사+명사'의 어순이 옳다.

13 Stella는 새로운 코끼리 무리에 다가갔다고 하였다. 따라서 ②번이 글의 내용과 일치한다.

14 much는 셀 수 없는 명사를 수식한다.

16 글쓴이는 이 글을 아프리카에서 썼다.

17 Stella라고 이름을 지어준 것은 아기 코끼리였다.

18 가주어 it을 활용하여 같은 의미의 문장을 쓸 수 있다.

19 (B)는 비인칭 주어로 날씨, 날짜, 거리, 명암 등을 나타낼 때 쓰이는 주어이다. ⑤번은 가주어 It이다.

20 Stella가 밤에 공격을 받기 쉬운 이유는 코끼리들이 밤에 잘 볼 수 없기 때문이다.

21 글쓴이가 전화를 건 곳은 코끼리 보호소였다.

22 벌레잡이 식물이 글쓴이의 손만큼 길다고 하였다.

23 it을 가주어로 하고 진주어로 to부정사를 쓴다.

24 동사를 수식하는 부사가 들어가는 것이 적절하다.

25 stay는 보어로 형용사를 취하는 2형식 동사이다. 따라서 safe라고 쓰는 것이 옳다.

26 글쓴이는 코끼리들이 Stella를 자신의 무리로 받아들이지 않을 것이라고 생각했다. 따라서 Unlike가 아닌 Like라고 쓰는 것이 옳다.

서술형 시험대비
p.90~91

01 Her eyes were as bright as stars.

02 They stood around Stella and made a thick wall.

03 see a group of lions

04 It was scaring to see a group of lions approaching Stella.

05 I decided to stay by her

06 He found Stella crying next to her mom.

07 Stella가 야생 지역에 혼자 남아 있고, 코끼리들은 밤에 잘 볼 수 없어서 공격받기 쉽기 때문에

08 I am as blind as elephants at night.

09 She cared for Stella as warmly as her mother did.

01 그녀의 눈이 밝았고 별같이 밝았다고 하였으므로 '그녀의 눈은 별처럼 밝았다'는 표현을 할 수 있다.

02 코끼리들은 Stella 주위에 둘러서서 두꺼운 벽을 만들어 Stella를 보호하였다.

03 정오 즈음이라고 답하는 것으로 보아 언제 한 무리의 사자를 보았는지 묻는 말이 들어가는 것이 옳다.

04 it을 가주어로 하고 to부정사를 진주어로 쓴다.

05 '나는 그녀 곁에 머물기로 결정했다'는 의미이다.

06 이상한 소리를 따라간 글쓴이는 Stella가 자신의 엄마 옆에서 울고 있는 것을 발견했다.

07 야생 지역에 혼자 남은 Stella는 코끼리의 특성상 밤에 잘 볼 수 없기 때문에 공격을 당하기 쉬우므로 글쓴이는 코끼리 보호소에 전화를 걸어 도움을 요청한 것이다.

08 blind: 앞이 안 보이는

09 그녀는 Stella를 Stella의 엄마만큼 따뜻하게 돌보았다는 문장으로 쓸 수 있다.

10 가주어 It을 활용하여 같은 의미의 문장을 쓸 수 있다.

11 새로운 코끼리 무리를 가리키는 대명사이다.

12 Stella는 코로 엄마의 죽은 몸을 어루만지고 있었다고 하였다.

13 Stella 앞에 새로운 코끼리 무리가 나타났다고 하였다.

14 글쓴이는 처음에 코끼리 무리가 Stella를 받아주지 않을 것이라고 생각하였다.

15 벌레잡이 풀은 글쓴이의 손만큼 길다고 하였고, 벌레잡이 풀의 길이는 대략 15cm라고 하였다.

16 식물은 항아리 같이 생겼다고 하였다.

영역별 핵심문제 p.93~97

01 ①   02 ③

03 (1) rescue (2) tail (3) strength   04 ②

05 (1) Do you know the girl next to the little boy?

(2) Millions of people around the world use the Internet.

(3) She loves to take a picture of her daughter.

06 (A) give (B) tell (C) keep

07 ⓑ → bigger   08 ①

09 (B) → (D) → (C) → (E) → (A)

01 '입안에서 이리저리 움직이는, 맛을 보거나 삼키거나 말을 하는 데 사용되는 부드러운 부분'을 지칭하는 말은 tongue(혀)이다.

02 thick: 두꺼운

03 rescue: 구조, tail: 꼬리, strength: 힘

04 주어진 문장에서 approach는 '다가가다'를 의미하며 이와 같은 의미로 쓰인 것은 ②번이다. 나머지는 모두 '접근, 접근법'을 뜻한다.

05 next to: ~ 옆에, millions of: 수백만의, take a picture of ~: ~의 사진을 찍다

06 give a presentation 발표하다, tell the difference: 차이를 구별하다, keep one's eyes on: ~에서 눈을 떼지 않다

08 Jane과 Tom이 정원에서 커다란 꽃을 보고 있다는 설명은 대화의 내용과 일치하지 않는다.

09 (B) 질문에 대한 대답 → (D) 비디오 소개 → (C) 궁금함을 표현 → (E) 비디오 내용 설명 → (A) 반응

11 빈칸 (A)에 비교급을 강조하는 표현이 들어갈 수 있다. very는 비교급을 강조할 수 없다.

13 위 대화를 통해 Dylan이 강아지를 돌보기 위해 무엇을 해야 하는지는 알 수 없다.

14 진주어로 쓰일 수 있는 것은 to부정사나 명사절 접속사 that이다. that의 경우 주어와 동사가 있는 문장을 이끌어야 한다.

15 진주어이므로 to부정사를 쓰는 것이 옳다.

16 ③ to부정사구 주어는 단수 취급한다. 따라서 is라고 쓰는 것이 옳다.

17 '물 없이 사는 것'이 주어이므로 to live without water를 진주어로 하여 문장을 만든다.

18 표에서 오렌지를 좋아하는 여성들이 15명이고, 남성들이 8명이라고 하였으므로 여성은 남성보다 오렌지를 더 좋아한다고 답했음을 알 수 있다.

19 '그녀가 노래 부르는 것을 듣는 것'이 주어이므로 'to hear her singing[sing]'을 주어로 하여 문장을 만들 수 있다.

20 모두 가주어로 쓰인 It이지만 ⑤번은 인칭대명사 It이다.

21 James의 개와 나의 개는 둘 다 세 살이다. 따라서 James의 개는 나의 개만큼 나이가 들었다고 말할 수 있다

22 진주어로 to부정사가 적절하다

23 (A) 지각동사+목적어+동사원형 혹은 Ving (B) be동사의 보어가 필요하므로 형용사 (C) 지칭하는 대상이 the elephants로 복수 명사이므로 them

24 글쓴이는 아기 코끼리에게 Stella라는 이름을 지어주었다.

25 몇 마리의 사자가 Stella에게 다가가고 있었는지는 알 수 없다.

26 코끼리들이 아기 코끼리 주위를 둘러서서 두꺼운 벽을 만든 이유는 사자로부터 아기 코끼리를 보호해 주기를 원해서이다.

27 새로운 코끼리 무리가 Stella를 받아주지 않을 것이라고 생각했던 것이 틀렸고, Stella는 무리의 일원이 되었다는 흐름이 자연스럽다.

28 (A) Stella는 엄마 옆에 있었다는 의미이므로 beside (B) approach는 타동사로 전치사 없이 목적어를 받아주므로 approached (C) 일반동사를 받아주는 동사이므로 did를 쓰는 것이 옳다. besides: 게다가

29 B의 말로 미루어 보아 암컷 코끼리 중 한 마리가 Stella에게 젖을 준 것을 말하는 것이다.

30 Stella는 코로 엄마의 죽은 몸을 어루만지고 있었다.

단원별 예상문제 p.98~101

01 (1) humorous (2) careless (3) wild
  (4) blind (5) sheet

02 (1) Wild animals can be dangerous.
  (2) We need to have a sense of humor.
  (3) Don't feed the animals in the zoo.

03 ③   04 해룡은 꼬리가 곧지만 해마는 그렇지 않다.

05 ③   06 ⑤

07 (A) that (B) as (C) planted   08 ⑤

09 They're talking about the science project topic.

10 He is wondering about weather change.

11 ③   12 ③

13 It was possible to see the object at night.

14 ③   15 ②

16 This room is about two times as large as that one.

17 It was wonderful to see fish swim in the water.

18 It is dangerous to stay alone in such a wild area.

19 ④   20 ③   21 ⑤   22 ②, ④

23 The writer heard a strange sound.

24 It is interesting that the plant attracts insects and eats them.

25 ④

---

01 careless: 부주의한, humorous: 재미있는, sheet: (종이) 한 장, blind: 눈 먼, wild: 야생의

02 wild: 야생의, sense: 감각, feed: 먹이를 주다

03 밑줄 친 (A)는 '구별하다'라는 의미로 쓰였으며 이와 같은 뜻으로 쓰인 것은 ③번이다. 나머지는 모두 '말하다'를 의미한다.

---

05 주어진 문장은 궁금증을 표현하고 있고 Dr. Watson의 연구에 대한 소개에 대한 반응으로 자연스러우므로 (C)가 적절하다.

06 자이언트 캥거루는 사람 세 명만큼 무거웠으므로 자이언트 캥거루가 세 명보다 더 무거웠다는 설명은 대화의 내용과 일치하지 않는다.

07 (A) 지시형용사 that이 알맞다. (B) 'as+원급+as' 구문이므로 as가 적절하다. (C) plant는 '심다'를 나타내는 동사로 과거시제로 나타내야 하므로 planted가 적절하다.

08 위 대화를 통해 Kelly의 할아버지가 2004년에 무슨 나무를 심었는지는 알 수 없다.

09 Judy와 Ryan은 과학 프로젝트 주제에 대해 이야기하고 있다.

10 Ryan은 날씨 변화에 대해 궁금해하고 있다.

11 주어진 문장의 밑줄 친 부분은 가주어 It이다. ① 인칭대명사 ② 비인칭 주어 ③ 가주어 ④ 비인칭 주어 ⑤ 인칭대명사

12 가주어로 쓰일 수 있는 것은 It이다.

13 '밤에 그 사물을 보는 것'이 주어이므로 to see the object at night을 진주어로 하여 문장을 만든다.

14 Jill이 나보다 많은 사람들을 알고 있다는 것은 결국 나는 Jill만큼 많은 사람들을 알지 못한다는 의미가 된다.

15 진주어가 쓰일 자리이므로 to부정사를 쓰는 것이 옳다.

16 '배수사+as+원급+as: ~보다 …배 더 ~한 / as를 추가한다.

17 swim을 대신하여 swimming을 써도 좋다.

18 '이러한 야생 지역에서 혼자 있는 것'이 주어이므로 진주어로 to stay alone in such a wild area를 쓸 수 있다.

19 (A) 죽은 엄마 옆에서 Stella가 울고 있는 소리를 들었으므로 strange (B) 글쓴이가 사건을 목격한 시점은 해질녘으로 곧 어두워진다고 말하며 코끼리가 밤에 잘 볼 수 없음을 걱정하는 말이 들어가는 것이 자연스러우므로 dark (C) Stella의 엄마가 죽어 있었다고 하였으므로 lifeless가 옳다.

20 (D)는 가주어로 사용된 It이다. 모두 가주어 It이지만 ③번은 '그것'이라고 해석되는 인칭대명사 It이다.

21 오후 10시 40분에도 Stella는 엄마 곁에 남아 있었으므로 ⑤번은 글의 내용과 일치하지 않는다.

22 Stella는 홀로 남아 있었고 구조팀이 도착

23 해질녘에 글쓴이는 이상한 소리를 들었다고 하였다.

24 '그 식물이 곤충을 끌어들이고 그것들을 먹는 것'이 주어이므로 진주어 that절을 활용하여 문장을 만든다.

25 식물이 곤충을 끌어들이는 방법은 알 수 없다.

서술형 실전문제 p.102~103

01 ⓐ old ⓑ was born

02 It is thirteen years old.

03 He planted the tree when Kelly was born.

04 It is important to be kind to your classmates.

05 A yellow pencil is as cheap as a green pencil.

06 possible to live without electricity

07 goes to bed as early as

08 as well as

09 as white as

10 My eyes are not as[so] bright as her eyes.

11 A group of lions approached Stella.

12 ⑤번 → safe

13 She cared for Stella as warmly as Stella's mom did.

14 Stella become part of the group

15 would let Stella in

01 'as+원급+as' 구문이므로 원급인 old가 적절하다. be born: 태어나다

02 빨간 집 옆에 있는 나무는 수령이 13년 되었다.

03 Kelly의 할아버지는 Kelly가 태어났을 때 나무를 심었다.

04 '학급 친구들에게 친절하게 대하는 것'이 주어이므로 to be kind to your classmates를 진주어로 하여 문장을 만든다.

05 두 색깔의 연필이 가격이 같으므로 '노란색 연필은 초록색 연필만큼 싸다.'는 문장을 쓸 수 있다.

06 대답으로 미루어 보아 전기 없이 사는 것이 가능한지 묻는 말이 들어가는 것이 적절하다.

07 두 사람은 같은 시간에 잠든다. 따라서 'Brian은 June만큼 일찍 잠자리에 든다.'는 문장을 완성할 수 있다.

08 대화의 내용상 '그들만큼 축구를 잘하지 못했다'는 말이 들어가는 것이 적절하다.

09 Helen의 얼굴은 종이만큼 하얗다는 문장을 완성할 수 있다.

10 'as hers'라고 써도 무방하다.

11 Stella에게 다가간 것은 한 무리의 사자들이다.

12 Stella 주변을 둘러서서 보호해 준 코끼리들 덕분에 Stella는 안전했다고 말하는 것이 적절하다.

13 as ~ as 사이에는 형용사나 부사의 원급이 쓰일 수 있다. 앞 문장에서 She cared for Stella라는 완전한 문장이 쓰였고 '따뜻하게 보살피다'라는 의미이므로 부사 warmly를 써서 문장을 쓰는 것에 유의한다.

14 '사역동사(let)+목적어+동사원형' 형태에 유의하여 답을 쓴다.

15 글쓴이는 새로운 코끼리 무리가 Stella를 새로운 일원으로 받아주는 것이 불가능하다고 생각했다.

창의사고력 서술형 문제　　　　　　　　　p.104

|모범답안|

01 (A) lions   (B) friendship   (C) raised her

02 (1) It is interesting to see elephants protect a baby elephant.

(2) It is amazing to read that the female elephant took good care of Stella.

(3) It was really touching to see the new elephants accept Stella as a group member.

03 moss ball, dark green, like, about 4cm, as big as, it floats up when it gets enough sunlight

단원별 모의고사　　　　　　　　　p.105~108

01 (D) → (A) → (C) → (B)

02 He studies animals that lived millions of years ago.

03 It lived in Australia.

04 It was as heavy as three men.

05 ③　　　　　06 ⑤

07 She is curious about the huge flower in the picture.

08 It smells very bad.

09 (1) tell the difference   (2) become part of
(3) give a presentation   (4) next to
(5) Thanks to

10 that tree is as old as me 11 ②

12 (C) → (B) → (D) → (E) → (A)　　　　　13 ④

14 as long as, twice as long as

15 ⑤　　　　　16 ⑤

17 It is important to listen to what he says. It's because his opinion is as important as yours.

18 ③　　　　19 ③　　　　20 ④　　　　21 ②

22 the elephant shelter / alone / to stay alone / dark

23 ⑤

24 He saw a baby elephant with her mother.

25 We will be there as soon as possible.

01 (D) 자신의 새 강아지 소개 → (A) 반응 → (C) 작은 강아지 설명 → (B) 강아지가 빨리 자란다는 사실 설명

02 Dr. Watson은 수백만 년 전에 살았던 동물들을 연구한다.

03 자이언트 캥거루는 호주에서 살았었다.

04 자이언트 캥거루는 3명의 사람만큼 무거웠다.

05 주어진 문장은 궁금증을 표현하고 있으므로 이어서 구체적인 설명을 요구하는 (C)가 적절하다.

06 Todd가 두 남자와 사자 사이에 우정에 대한 이야기에 감동 받았다는 설명이 위 대화의 내용과 일치한다.

07 Jane은 사진에 있는 커다란 꽃에 대해 궁금해하고 있다.

08 커다란 꽃의 냄새는 매우 나쁘다.

09 become part of: ~의 일원이 되다, give a presentation: 발표하다, thanks to: ~ 덕분에, next to: ~ 옆에, tell the difference: 차이를 구별하다

11 위 대화에서 Kelly와 George는 빨간 집 옆에 있는 나무에 대해 이야기하고 있다.

12 (C) 연구 소개 요청 → (B) 연구 소개 → (D) 궁금증 표현 및 연구에 대한 질문 → (E) 질문에 대한 대답 및 연구 결과 설명 → (A) 놀라움 표현

13 주어진 문장의 밑줄 친 부분은 진주어로 쓰인 to부정사이다. ① 부사적 용법 중 목적 ② 형용사적 용법 ③ 부사적 용법 중 목적 ④ 진주어 ⑤ 부사적 용법 중 목적

14 세 사람의 공부 시간을 보면, Smith는 Clara만큼 오랜 시간 공부하지 않고, Clara는 Zach보다 두 시간 더 공부한다고 말할 수 있다.

15 'so ~ as'로 쓰는 경우는 부정일 때이며 긍정의 경우는 'as ~ as'로 쓴다.

16 가주어가 될 수 있는 것은 It이며, 진주어는 to부정사가 적절하다. 'as soon as possible'은 'as soon as you can'과 같다.

17 yours를 대신하여 your opinion이라고 써도 좋다.

18 코끼리들이 Stella 주위에 둘러서서 두꺼운 벽을 만든 이유는 사자들로부터 Stella를 보호하기 위한 것이다.

19 '그들 덕분에'라는 의미가 적절하다. ①, ④ ~에도 불구하고 ② ~ 대신에 ③ ~ 덕분에 ⑤ ~을 제외하고

20 구조팀이 올 때까지 그녀 곁에 머물기로 하였다고 말하는 것이 가장 자연스럽다.

21 밑줄 친 (a)는 가주어로 쓰인 It이다. ①, ③, ⑤ 인칭대명사 ② 가주어 ④ 비인칭 주어

22 코끼리 보호소에 전화한 글쓴이는 아기 코끼리가 혼자 있다고 말하자 야생에서 혼자 있는 것은 위험하다고 답하고, 곧 어두워져서 코끼리가 걱정된다고 말하는 것이 글의 내용과 일치한다.

23 Stella의 엄마가 왜 죽었는지는 위 글을 읽고 알 수 없다.

24 글쓴이는 아기 코끼리가 그녀의 엄마와 함께 있는 모습을 보았다.

25 as soon as we can이라고 써도 좋다

Art around Us

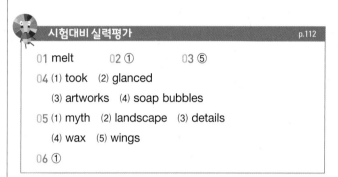

시험대비 실력평가 p.112

01 melt 02 ① 03 ⑤
04 (1) took (2) glanced
  (3) artworks (4) soap bubbles
05 (1) myth (2) landscape (3) details
  (4) wax (5) wings
06 ①

01 주어진 단어의 관계는 반의어 관계이다. melt: 녹다, freeze: 얼다

02 특히 자연적이거나 역사적인 사건을 설명하기 위해 만들어진 고대의 이야기를 가리키는 말은 myth(신화)이다.

03 despite: ~에도 불구하고

04 (1) take a look at: ~을 보다 (2) glance at: ~을 힐끗 보다 (3) artwork: 미술 작품 (4) soap bubble: 비눗방울

06 주어진 문장에서 notice는 '알아차리다'라는 의미를 나타내며 이와 같은 의미로 쓰인 것은 ①번이다. 나머지는 모두 '통지, 공고'라는 의미로 쓰였다.

서술형 시험대비 p.113

01 princess
02 (1) melts (2) exhibition (3) feathers
03 (1) landscape (2) notice (3) stick
  (4) promise (5) seaside
04 (1) I wonder why he invited me to his party.
  (2) Production of new cars will start next month.
  (3) Nobody noticed me at first.
05 melt
06 (1) Stay away from windows during a storm.
  (2) May I take a look at your movie ticket?
  (3) I called the police right away.

01 prince: 왕자, princess: 공주

02 melt: 녹다, exhibition: 전시회, feather: 깃털

03 notice: 알아차리다, landscape: 풍경, stick: 내밀다, promise: 약속하다, seaside: 해안가

05 열을 가함으로써 고체에서 액체로 변하는 것을 가리키는 말은 melt(녹다)이다.

06 (1) stay away from: ~을 가까이 하지 않다 (2) take a look at: ~을 보다 (3) right away: 즉시, 바로

Can, help / various kinds, What kind of music / want to / should get

교과서
Conversation

01 ①, ④   02 What kind of brush were you using?
03 (A) *Life of Pi* (B) the movie   04 ④

01 (A)는 도움을 요청하는 표현이다.
04 ④ Minsu는 소설보다 영화를 더 선호한다.

1 (1) What kind of concert
  (2) movie do you want to see   (3) type
2 (1) Which do you prefer
  (2) taking photos, drawing pictures
  (3) I prefer dogs to cats

01 ⑤   02 (A) Jane's new song (= *Girl Friend*)
(B) a dance version   (C) the guitar version
03 ④   04 ⑤   05 (A) Jack (B) Mina
(C) It has an interesting smile. (D) His Mona Lisa is cute, and it looks modern. 06 ③   07 which do you prefer 08 She likes rock better.   09 (C) → (B) → (D) → (A)

03 ④ Tony는 Jane의 목소리가 기타 버전에 잘 어울린다고 생각한다.
04 ⑤ Steve가 '로미오와 줄리엣' 연극 볼 것을 왜 제안하는지 는 알 수 없다.
08 Emily는 록을 더 좋아한다.
09 (C) 어떠한 종류의 음악을 연주하고 싶은지 질문→ (B) 대답 → (D) 기타 추천 → (A) 구매

교과서 대화문 익히기

1 T 2 F 3 T 4 T

교과서 확인학습

Listen & Talk 1 A-1
going to play / almost every day / What kind of music / play songs

Listen & Talk 1 A-2
how to paint clean lines / What kind of brush / flat, better, Try

Listen & Talk 1 B
meeting, right / do you want to watch first / want to / Sounds, right / watching the play / the one

Listen & Talk 2 A-1
a story / of it, prefer, to / like, better / scenes, real

Listen & Talk 2 A-2
Have, listened / cool, part / dance version / I prefer the guitar version / matches

Listen & Talk 2 B
interesting painting / looks like / Which do you prefer / prefer, to / How about you / prefer, to / modern

Communication
so, find out, May, ask / What kind of performance / do, prefer / prefer rock to hip–hop / favorite musician / Thank, for

01 (A) ⓑ (B) ⓒ (C) ⓐ
02 They have listened to *Girl Friend*.
03 Because he thinks that the guitar version matches Jane's voice better.
04 I prefer the movie to the novel.
05 It's about a boy and a tiger.
06 It's because he thinks that the scenes are very beautiful and the tiger looks so real.

02 Tony와 Sue가 Jane의 앨범에서 들은 노래는 *Girl Friend* 이다.
03 Tony는 기타 버전이 Jane의 목소리와 더 잘 어울린다고 생각하기 때문이다.

04 prefer A to B: A를 B보다 선호하다

05 *Life of Pi* 는 소년과 호랑이에 관한 이야기이다.

06 민수가 소설보다 영화를 더 선호한 이유는 장면이 매우 아름답고 호랑이가 매우 진짜처럼 보이기 때문이다.

Grammar
교과서

p.124~125

핵심 Check

1 (1) me watch   (2) him use   (3) my dad come
2 (1) who she is   (2) why you study   (3) where you went

시험대비 기본평가

p.126

01 (1) to read → read
   (2) was the weather → the weather was
   (3) buying → buy
   (4) were you → you were
02 (1) Oliver wanted to ask if[whether] she was satisfied with his service.
   (2) Can you tell me where we are going?
   (3) I'd like to know what you do during your free time.
   (4) I wonder how often you water the plant.
03 (1) The boss made him stay in the office.
   (2) Did you let your friend borrow your bicycle?
   (3) We had him wear a straw hat.
   (4) Please let me see the answer.

01 (1), (3) 사역동사의 목적격 보어는 동사원형 형태이다. (2), (4) 의문사가 이끄는 문장이 명사 역할을 할 때 '의문사+주어+동사'의 어순임에 유의하자.

02 의문사가 없는 경우는 if나 whether를 사용하여 간접의문문을 만들

03 사역동사 make, have, let은 목적격 보어로 동사원형 형태를 사용한다. 이때 목적어와 목적격 보어의 관계는 주어와 서술어의 관계가 성립하여 '목적어가 ~ 하도록 시키다'라고 해석한다.

시험대비 실력평가

p.127~129

01 ⑤   02 ③   03 ④   04 ⑤
05 come   06 will   07 ③   08 ③
09 Who do you suppose broke the window?
10 ②   11 ③

---

12 Why do you think she made you do it again?
13 I made him repair my watch.
14 ④   15 ④   16 ③   17 ③
18 ④   19 ⑤   20 ③   21 ④
22 what you do when you are free
23 ③   24 ②
25 I want to know if[whether] she liked the present.

01 want는 목적격 보어로 to부정사를 취하는 동사이다.

02 '목적어가 ~하도록 시키다'라는 의미로 쓰이는 동사는 사역동사이다.

03 간접의문문의 의문사를 문두에 배치하는 동사는 추측동사로 think, imagine, guess, suppose, believe 등이 이에 속한다.

04 모두 목적격 보어로 동사원형 형태를 취할 수 있는 동사이지만, allow는 목적격 보어로 to부정사를 취하는 동사이다.

05 make는 사역동사이므로 목적격 보어로 동사원형 형태를 취한다.

06 주어진 문장을 영어로 옮기면 'I wonder when you will arrive here.'이다.

07 ⓑ when they will call me ⓒ let me wear라고 쓰는 것이 옳다.

08 간접의문문을 만드는 문제이다. 간접의문문의 어순은 '의문사+주어+동사'이다.

09 suppose가 있는 문장에서 간접의문문의 주어를 문두에 배치하는 것에 유의한다.

10 '누가 한글을 만들었는지'라는 의미이므로 who made Hanguel이라고 쓰는 것이 옳다.

11 사역동사의 목적격 보어는 동사원형의 형태를 취하며, '너의 부모님이 집에 없는 동안 너를 누가 돌볼 것인지를 말해 달라'는 것이므로 간접의문문을 이용하여 who will take care of you라고 쓰는 것이 옳다.

12 think가 있는 문장이므로 간접의문문의 의문사를 문두에 배치해야 한다.

13 '그가 내 시계를 고치게 했다'는 것은 사역동사를 이용하여 나타낼 수 있다.

14 주어진 말을 영어로 쓰면 What time do you think it is?이다.

15 allow는 목적격 보어로 to부정사를 취하는 동사이다. help는 목적격 보어로 to부정사나 동사원형 형태를 취한다.

16 간접의문문의 어순은 '의문사+주어+동사'임에 유의한다.

17 사역동사로 쓰인 make이므로 목적격 보어로 동사원형 형태를 쓴다.

18 3형식, 4형식, 5형식으로 모두 쓰이면서 목적격 보어로 동사원형 형태까지 취할 수 있는 것은 동사 make이다.

19 Who do you guess built the building?이라고 쓰는 것이 옳다.

20 대답으로 미루어 보아 몇 학년인지를 묻는 말이 들어가는 것이 가장 적절하다. 간접의문문의 어순인 '의문사+주어+동사'에 유의한다.

21 목적격 보어로 동사원형 형태를 취하는 동사는 사역동사이다.

22 답변으로 보아 여가 시간에 무엇을 하는지를 묻는 말이 들어가는 것이 적절하다.

23 think가 있는 문장이므로 Who do you think you are? 라고 쓰는 것이 옳다.

24 엄마가 내게 무언가를 하라고 말하는 것이므로 ②번이 내용상 가장 적절하다.

25 의문사가 없는 문장의 간접의문문은 if 혹은 whether를 써서 만든다.

p.130~131

서술형 시험대비

01 Mom made me and my sister clean the house.

02 Who do you think stole the money?

03 Can you tell me when they let you go home?

04 (1) me drive his car
   (2) him bring her
   (3) me look at

05 Brad made me accept the job.

06 (1) I don't know where he lives.
   (2) How old do you guess he is?
   (3) Can you tell me why you were absent from school?
   (4) I want to know when you met him for the first time.
   (5) When do you think the concert starts?
   (6) Why do you imagine the baby is crying?
   (7) Do you know if(또는 whether) Charley was sleeping at that time?

07 I helped my cousin (to) do his homework.

08 (1) play   (2) published   (3) take
   (4) work   (5) will report

09 the oranges are / how many oranges he wants to buy

10 The woman lets the man drink water.

11 The suit makes me look fancy.

12 A: How do you think the movie was?
   B: It made me feel sleepy.

13 Do you know who drove the car yesterday?

14 (1) Can you tell me when she wrote this book?
   (2) You can lead a horse to water, but you can't make him drink.
   (3) I wonder if(또는 whether) he is full or not.

01 make는 '목적어에게 ~하도록 시키다'라는 의미의 사역동사이다. 따라서 목적격 보어로 동사원형 형태를 써서 문장을 만든다.

02 think가 있는 문장에서는 간접의문문의 의문사를 문두로 배치한

다. 이 문장에서 who는 의문사이자 주어 역할을 동시에 하고 있음에 유의한다.

03 tell의 직접목적어로 간접의문문을 쓰며, '그들이 너를 집에 가게 했다'고 하였으므로 사역동사를 이용하여 문장을 만들 수 있다.

04 위 문장에서 let, make, have는 모두 사역동사로 쓰이고 있으므로 목적격 보어로 동사원형 형태를 쓰는 것에 유의한다.

05 force+목적어+to부정사: 목적어가 ~하도록 강요하다

06 의문사가 이끄는 문장이 절 내에서 주어, 목적어, 보어 역할을 할 때 이를 간접의문문이라고 한다. 간접의문문의 어순은 '의문사+주어+동사'의 어순이며 think, believe, suppose, imagine, guess와 같은 동사가 있을 때에는 의문사를 문두로 배치한다.

07 help는 목적격 보어로 to부정사나 동사원형 형태를 취한다.

08 (1), (3), (4) 사역농사의 목적격 보어는 동사원형의 형태를 취한다. (2) 작년에 이 책을 누가 출간했는지를 궁금해 하는 내용이므로 과거 시제를 쓴다. (5) 내일 무엇을 보고할 것이라고 생각하느냐는 문장이다. 내용에 맞게 미래 시제를 써서 나타낸다.

09 Andy는 오렌지 가격이 얼마인지 알고 싶어한다. 그래서 Paul은 Andy에게 얼마나 많은 오렌지를 사길 원하는지 묻는다.

10 사역동사 let은 목적격 보어로 동사원형 형태를 취한다.

11 정장이 나를 멋지게 보이도록 하는 것이므로 주어는 the suit, 목적어는 me로 하여 사역동사를 써서 문장을 완성할 수 있다.

12 Do you think?와 How was the movie?를 하나의 문장으로 만들어 How do you think the movie was?를 만들 수 있다.

13 who가 의문사와 주어 역할을 동시에 하고 있으므로 who drove the car의 어순으로 쓸 수 있다.

14 의문사가 있는 간접의문문은 '의문사+주어+동사'의 어순을 쓰고 의문사가 없는 경우 if나 whether를 써서 간접의문문을 나타낼 수 있다. 사역 동사는 목적격 보어로 동사원형 형태를 취한다.

Reading

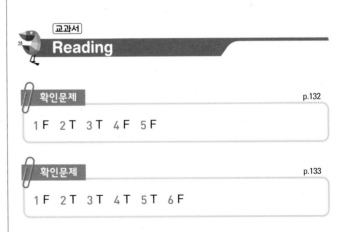

확인문제   p.132

1 F 2 T 3 T 4 F 5 F

확인문제   p.133

1 F 2 T 3 T 4 T 5 T 6 F

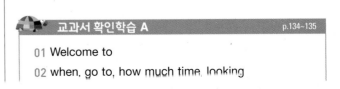

교과서 확인학습 A   p.134~135

01 Welcome to

02 when, go to, how much time, looking

03 glance at, for, a few, on

04 might miss, since, to notice them

05 look at, closely, help you see   06 at, first

07 seaside landscape, peaceful, isn't it

08 title, is   09 where Icarus is

10 are sticking out of the water

11 in the famous myth

12 made wings for him, to stay away from

13 However, listen   14 flew too close

15 melted, fell into   16 at, entire

17 Despite, going on with

18 still look peaceful

19 What do you think   20 move on to

21 see, behind   22 actually painted

23 Who do you think he is   24 Take

25 seems to be, because   26 title, painting

27 drawing, beside   28 Take

29 make you wonder

30 which direction the artist is

31 see, in the mirror, background

32 Who do you think he is

1 Welcome to the World Art Museum tour.

2 When you go to an art museum, how much time do you spend looking at each painting?

3 Many visitors glance at one painting for only a few seconds before they move on.

4 But you might miss the important details of paintings since it is hard to notice them right away.

5 Today, we'll look at two paintings closely and I'll help you see interesting details.

6 Look at this painting first.

7 The seaside landscape is so peaceful and beautiful, isn't it?

8 The title of this painting is *Landscape with the Fall of Icarus*.

9 So, can you see where Icarus is?

10 Do you see two legs that are sticking out of the water near the ship?

11 This is Icarus in the famous myth in Greece.

12 In the myth, Icarus' father made wings for him with feathers and wax and told him to stay away from the sun.

13 However, Icarus didn't listen.

14 He flew too close to the sun.

15 So, the wax melted and he fell into the water.

16 Now, look at the entire painting again.

17 Despite the tragedy of Icarus, people are going on with their everyday activities.

18 Does the painting still look peaceful?

19 What do you think the artist is trying to tell us?

20 Now, let's move on to the next painting.

21 Do you see the artist behind the large canvas?

22 He is Diego Velázquez, and he actually painted this picture.

23 Who do you think he is painting?

24 Take a quick look.

25 The young princess seems to be the main person because she is in the center of the painting.

26 But the title of the painting is *The Maids of Honour*.

27 Then, is the artist drawing the two women beside the princess?

28 Take a close look.

29 It will make you wonder about the painting more.

30 Try to see which direction the artist is looking at.

31 Can you see the king and the queen in the mirror in the background of the painting?

32 Who do you think he is painting now?

01 ①   02 notice   03 ③

04 We will look at two paintings closely.

05 Can you see where Icarus is?

06 ①   07 ②

08 It is *Landscape with the Fall of Icarus*.

09 ③   10 ④   11 wonder   12 ③

13 The young princess seems to be the main person because she is in the center of the painting.

14 We can find him behind the large canvas.

15 ⑤   16 ②

17 It takes them only a few seconds to see one painting.

18 ③   19 ③   20 ⑤   21 ②

22 ⑤

23 He told Icarus to stay away from the sun.

24 ③   25 ④   26 ④

27 The young princess is in the middle of the painting.

28 ②

23

01 문장에서 since는 이유를 나타내는 접속사로 쓰였다. 따라서 ① 번이 옳다.

02 '무언가를 혹은 어떤 사람을 인식하게 되다'는 '알아차리다 (notice)'이다.

03 (B)는 진주어로 쓰인 to부정사이다. ① 명사적 용법 중 목적어 ② 부사적 용법 중 감정의 원인 ③ 명사적 용법 중 진주어 ④ 형용사적 용법 ⑤ 명사적 용법 중 보어

04 두 개의 그림을 자세히 살펴볼 것이라고 하였다.

05 간접의문문을 만드는 문제이다. '의문사+주어+동사'의 어순에 유의하여 문장을 만든다.

06 이카루스의 비극에도 불구하고 사람들은 일상의 활동을 계속하고 있다는 의미가 가장 자연스럽다. 따라서 despite와 같은 의미인 in spite of를 쓰는 것이 옳다.

07 이카루스의 아버지는 날개를 만들어 주며 태양에 가까이 가지 말라고 말했지만 이카루스는 그의 말을 듣지 않았다는 순서가 자연스러우며 ②번 이하의 문장은 주어진 문장의 결과 이다.

08 그림의 제목은 '추락하는 이카루스가 있는 풍경'이라고 하였다.

09 그림에서 이카루스는 물에 빠져서 두 다리만 보이는 상황이다. 따라서 ③번은 그림에서 찾아볼 수 없다.

10 이카루스의 날개는 그의 아버지가 만들어 준 것이다.

11 사역동사의 목적격 보어 자리이다. 따라서 동사원형 형태를 쓰는 것이 옳다.

12 (B)는 진행형을 만드는 현재분사이다. 모두 동명사이지만 ③번은 현재분사이다.

13 seem to부정사: ~인 것 같다

14 두 번째 그림의 화가는 커다란 캔버스 뒤에 있다고 하였다.

15 그림이 얼마나 큰지는 글을 읽고 알 수 없다.

16 (A) 시간은 셀 수 없으므로 how much (B) the important details of paintings를 가리키므로 복수 대명사 them (C) help는 목적격 보어로 to부정사나 동사원 형 형태를 취한다.

17 많은 방문객들은 이동하기 전에 하나의 그림을 몇 초간만 힐 끗 본다고 하였다. It takes+사람+시간+to V: 사람이 … 하는 데 ~만큼의 시간이 걸리다

18 두 개의 그림을 자세히 살펴보며 흥미로운 세부 사항들을 볼 수 있게 도와준다고 하였으므로 ③번이 가장 적절하다.

19 아버지가 태양에 가까이 가지 말라고 이야기했지만 이카루스는 그의 말을 듣지 않고 태양에 가깝게 날았다는 내용이므로 However가 옳다.

20 이카루스가 어디에 보이는지 물음 - (C) 그림 속에서 이카루스가 어디에 있는지 설명하며 이카루스는 그리스 신화에 나오는 인물임을 언급함 - (B) 그리스 신화에 나오는 이카루스의 이야기 - (A) 아버지의 말을 듣지 않은 이카루스는 물에 빠짐

21 의문사가 이끄는 문장이 절 내에서 명사 역할을 하는 간접의문문의 어순은 '의문사+주어+동사'의 어순이다.

22 이카루스는 아버지의 말을 듣지 않고 태양 가까이로 날았다가 밀랍이 녹아 물에 빠졌다고 하였다.

23 이카루스의 아버지는 그에게 태양에 가까이 가지 말라고 이야기 하였다.

24 make는 목적격 보어로 동사원형을 취하는 사역동사이며 feel은 형용사를 보어로 취하는 감각동사이다.

25 ④ David Myriam이 그의 작품에서 사용한 것은 모래라고 하였다.

26 추측동사 believe, think, guess, imagine, suppose가 있는 문장에서는 간접의문문의 의문사를 문두로 배치한다. know는 이러한 동사에 해당하지 않는다.

27 그림의 중앙에 있는 사람은 공주라고 하였다.

28 커다란 캔버스 뒤에 있는 화가가 Diego Velázquez이므로 그가 그림에 등장하지 않는다는 것은 글의 내용과 일치하지 않는다.

서술형 시험대비
p.142~143

01 how much time you spend looking at each painting

02 the important details of paintings

03 I'll help you (to) see interesting details.

04 What do you think the artist is trying to tell us?

05 tragedy

06 He made wings for him.

07 melt

08 where Icarus is, are sticking out of the water

09 actually

10 Diego Velázquez painted the picture.

11 **그림을 자세히 보는 것**

12 They are the king and the queen.

13 I wonder who actually painted this picture.

14 what the artist used

15 Because a tree in the moon makes the writer feel calm.

01 간접의문문을 완성하는 문제이다. '의문사+주어+동사' 어순에 유의하여 답을 쓴다.

02 그림의 중요한 세부 사항들을 가리키는 말이다.

03 help는 목적격 보어로 to부정사나 동사원형을 모두 쓸 수 있는 준사역동사이다.

04 문장의 동사가 think인 경우 간접의문문의 의문사를 문두에 배치하는 것에 유의하여 답을 쓴다.

05 화가가 그림을 통해 말하려는 것은 우리는 타인의 비극을 알 수 없다는 것이다.

06 이카루스의 아버지는 그를 위하여 날개를 만들어 주었다고 하였다.

07 무엇이 밀랍을 녹게 만들었느냐는 질문을 쓰는 것이 옳다. 사역 동사의 목적격 보어 자리이므로 동사원형 형태를 쓰는 것에 유의한다.

08 두 사람의 대화로 미루어 보아 A는 이카루스가 어디에 있는지 묻고 있으며 B가 알려주는 중임을 알 수 있다.

09 동사를 수식하므로 부사로 고쳐야 한다.

10 그림을 그린 사람은 Diego Velázquez라고 하였다.

11 It은 앞 문장 전체인 'Take a close look.'을 가리킨다.

12 그림의 배경에 있는 거울 속 사람들은 왕과 왕비라고 하였다.

13 간접의문문을 이용하여 문장을 만들 수 있다. 여기에서 who는 의문사와 주어 역할을 동시에 하는 것에 유의한다.

14 답변으로 미루어 보아 작가가 그림에 무엇을 사용했는지 묻는 말이 들어가는 것이 옳다.

15 글쓴이가 그 그림을 좋아하는 이유는 달에 있는 나무가 차분한 기분을 느끼게 해 주어서라고 하였다.

🎨 **영역별 핵심문제**   p.145~169

01 tragedy   02 ⑤   03 ④

04 (1) tourists   (2) stick   (3) novelist

05 (1) I prefer the novel to the poem.

    (2) My family will take a trip to the seaside.

    (3) The war was a tragedy for the whole world.

06 ②   07 ①   08 ⑤   09 ③

10 What kind of performance do you want to watch first?

11 ⑤   12 ③   13 ③   14 ⑤

15 She doesn't know how to paint clean lines.

16 She will use a flat brush. 17 ③   18 ⑤

19 ④   20 Where do you think she is now?

21 ②   22 ③   23 ⑤

24 help, do   25 ①

26 The monster made the children scream.

27 (1) I didn't hear what you said.

    (2) I'd like to know if you are friends with Jina.

28 ①, ②   29 ③

30 They were made of feathers and wax. 31 ⑤

32 if the painting still looks peaceful

33 tragedy   34 (A) looking   (B) a few   (C) closely

35 We might miss the important details of a painting.

36 ③

---

01 주어진 단어의 관계는 반의어 관계이다. comedy: 희극, tragedy: 비극

02 특히 죽음과 관련된 매우 슬픈 사건을 가리키는 말은 tragedy(비극)이다.

03 flat: 평평한

06 주어진 문장은 '내밀다'라는 뜻을 나타내며 이와 같은 의미로 쓰인 것은 ②번이다. ①, ④ ~을 붙이다, ③, ⑤ 막대기

07 direct: ~으로 향하다, (길을) 안내하다[알려주다], direct flight: 직행 항공편

08 주어진 문장은 소설을 더 좋아하는 이유로 적절하므로 (E)가 알맞다.

09 ③ Jean이 Sally와 함께 영화 *The Maze Runner*를 보았다는 설명은 대화의 내용과 일치하지 않는다.

13 주어진 문장은 영화를 선호한다는 것으로 다음에 이유를 질문하는 문장에 자연스럽게 이어지므로 (C)가 적절하다.

14 대화를 통해 민수가 언제 영화를 봤는지 알 수 없다.

15 Sora는 선을 깔끔하게 그리는 방법을 모른다.

16 Sora는 선을 그릴 때 납작한 붓을 사용할 것이다.

17 파티에 초대한 주체가 who이므로 who invited you의 어순이 옳다.

18 조건절과 명사절을 동시에 이끌 수 있는 접속사는 if이다.

19 let은 사역동사로 목적격 보어로 동사원형 형태를 취한다. 따라서 use라고 쓰는 것이 옳다.

20 Do you think?와 Where is she now?를 하나로 만든 문장이다.

21 주어진 문장을 영어로 쓰면 I wonder who made you send me this flower.이다.

22 Who kicked the ball?에서 Who는 의문사이자 주어 역할을 동시에 하고 있으므로 ③번이 가장 적절하다.

23 tell은 목적격 보어로 to부정사를 취하는 동사이다.

24 help는 목적격 보어로 to부정사나 동사원형 형태를 모두 쓸 수 있는 동사이다.

25 ⓐ who you are talking with ⓑ have them go to school ⓓ what Jason does ⓔ if(또는 whether) you have brothers or sisters라고 쓰는 것이 옳다.

26 '아이들이 비명을 지르게 하는 것'이므로 사역동사를 이용하여 문장을 만들 수 있다. 사역동사의 목적격 보어는 동사원형 형태임에 유의한다.

27 (2)번은 if를 대신하여 whether를 써도 좋다.

28 의문사가 없는 의문문에는 whether나 if를 써서 간접의문문을 만든다.

29 모두 이카루스를 지칭하는 말이지만 ③번은 이카루스의 아버지를 가리키고 있다.

30 이카루스의 날개는 깃털과 밀랍으로 이루어졌다고 하였다. be made of: ~으로 이루어지다

31 밀랍과 깃털로 이루어진 날개를 달고 태양 가까이 날아간 것 때문에 이카루스는 물에 빠지게 되었다. 따라서 ⑤번은 옳지 않다.

32 의문사가 없는 문장의 간접의문문은 if나 whether를 써서 만든다.

33 '특히 죽음과 관련된 아주 슬픈 사건'은 '비극(tragedy)'이라고 한다.

34 (A) spend+시간+Ving: V하는 데에 시간을 쓰다 (B) 셀 수 있는 seconds를 수식하므로 a few (C) '자세히'라는 의미의 부사가 적절하므로 closely

35 하나의 그림을 몇 초간만 힐끗 보는 것의 문제는 그림의 중요한 세부 사항들을 놓칠 수 있다는 것이다.

36 ⓐ는 가주어로 쓰인 it이다. ① 비인칭 주어 ② 비인칭 주어 ③ 가주어 ④ 인칭대명사 ⑤ 인칭대명사

01 (D) than→ to   02 ⑤

03 What kind of performance do you like best?

04 Which musician do you like best?

05 ④   06 performance

07 (A) 2:00 p.m.   (B) gym   (C) Play   (D) Main Hall

08 ④   09 ⑤

10 (C) → (B) → (E) → (D) → (A)   11 ③

12 ④   13 what you wore   14 ⑤

15 ③   16 ②

17 My parents let me sleep late on weekends.

18 ④   19 ③   20 ②   21 ①

22 what happened to Icarus

23 I wonder if you saw many interesting pieces of art.

24 ④

01 prefer A to B: A보다 B를 선호하다

02 Tony가 Girl Friend 의 댄스 버전에 대해 어떻게 생각하는지는 알 수 없다.

08 주어진 문장은 상대방의 의견을 물어보는 표현이므로 (D)가 적절하다.

09 왜 보테로의 '모나리자'가 현대적으로 보이는지는 알 수 없다.

10 (C) Jina가 무엇을 읽고 있는지 질문 → (B) 대답 → (E) 자신은 영화도 보았다며 소설보다 영화를 더 선호함을 말함 → (D) 이유 질문 → (A) 이유 대답

11 '누가 너에게 그 비밀을 말해 줬는지'이므로 who가 간접의문문의 주어 역할을 하는 것이 옳다.

12 사역동사의 목적어와 목적격보어가 능동 관계일 경우 목적격보어로 동사원형 형태를 쓴다. drop by: ~에 들르다

13 간접의문문의 어순은 '의문사+주어+동사'이다. 과거시제를 사용하고 있으므로 what you wore라고 쓰는 것에 유의한다.

14 목적격보어로 동사원형 형태를 취할 수 있는 것은 사역동사와 help이다.

15 사역동사 let의 목적격 보어로 동사원형 형태를 쓰는 것이 옳다.

16 What kind of fruit do you like most?를 간접의문문으로 만든 것이므로 '의문사+주어+동사' 어순에 맞는 것을 답으로 고른다.

17 let은 목적격보어로 동사원형 형태를 취하는 사역동사이다.

18 화가가 그리려고 했던 대상이 그림의 중앙에 있는 공주처럼 보이지만 그림의 제목이 '시녀들'이라면 화가가 그리려던 대상이 공주 옆에 있는 두 여인일지 묻는 말로 이어지는 것이 가장 자연스럽다.

19 그림의 제목이 '시녀들'이라고 말하며 '그렇다면 화가는 공주 옆에 있는 두 여자를 그리고 있나요?'라고 하였으므로 시녀들은 두 명임을 알 수 있다.

20 그림에서 왕자는 등장하지 않는다.

21 태양으로 가까이 간 결과 밀랍이 녹아서 물에 빠졌다는 것이다. 따라서 결과를 이끄는 연결어가 나오는 것이 옳다.

22 간접의문문을 이용하여 답을 쓸 수 있다. 이때 what은 의문사와 주어 역할을 동시에 하는 것에 유의한다.

23 if를 대신하여 whether를 써도 무방하다.

01 They will go to the arts festival.

02 They will watch it at the gym.

03 It is at 4. p.m. at the Main Hall.

04 (1) Tell me where Maria lives.

   (2) I wonder if you are married.

   (3) May I ask if he is alone?

   (4) Can you tell me who drove your car?

05 Nothing will make me change my mind.

06 who opened the door

07 to know how many books you read last year

08 (A) melted   (B) fell into

09 What do you think the artist is trying to tell us?

10 near the ship, sticking out of the water

11 He couldn't make his son stay away from the sun.

12 flew, close, wax, melted

13 (D)-(A)-(C)-(B)

14 ⓐ on   ⓑ in

01 Anna와 Steve는 예술 축제에 갈 것이다.

02 Anna와 Steve는 체육관에서 힙합 댄스 공연을 볼 것이다.

03 로미오와 줄리엣은 4시에 Main Hall에서 공연한다.

04 (2), (3)번은 if를 대신하여 whether를 써도 무방하다.

05 make를 사역동사로 사용하고, 마음을 바꾸는 주체가 '나'이므로 이를 목적어로 사용하여 문장을 완성한다.

06 의문사가 주어 역할을 겸하고 있는 간접의문문이다. 이때 동사가 바로 이어져 나올 수 있다.

07 작년에 얼마나 많은 책을 읽었는지 알고 싶다는 문장을 완성 할 수 있다.

08 태양에 의해 밀랍이 녹아 물에 빠졌다고 하는 것이 적절하다.

09 think가 있는 문장에서는 간접의문문의 의문사를 문두로 보낸다.

10 이카루스는 배 가까이에 있으며 그의 두 다리가 물 밖으로 나와 있다고 하였다.

11 아들이 태양에서 멀리 떨어지도록 시키지 못했다는 것이므로 사역동사의 목적어로 his son, 목적격보어로 동사원형 형태를 써서 문장을 만들 수 있다.

12 이카루스는 태양에 너무 가깝게 날아서 날개의 밀랍이 녹았다.

13 주어진 글의 질문에 이어 (D)에서 Velázquez라고 답하고 누구를 그리려고 했는지 질문하고 (A)에서 공주가 주인공인 것처럼 보인다고 답하며 (C)에서 But으로 상반되는 제목을 소개하여 그림을

더 자세히 보라고 말하며 (B)에서 궁금하게 만들 것이라고 언급한 뒤. 화가가 보고 있는 방향 을 보라고 한 후 누구라고 생각하는지 묻는 것이 자연스럽다.

14 move on to: ~으로 옮기다, in the background of: ~ 의 배경에

01 오늘 나는 미술책에서 재미있는 그림을 보았다. 그것은 다빈치의 '모나리자'처럼 보이는데 사실은 페르난도 보테로의 '모나리자'였다. 둘 중에, Jack은 보테로의 그림보다 페르난도 '모나지라'를 더욱 좋아하였다. 왜냐하면 다빈치의 '모나리자'에 있는 흥미로운 미소 때문이었다. 그와 반대로, 나는 보테로의 '모나리자'가 훨씬 더욱 좋았다. 왜냐하면 그의 모나리자는 귀엽고 현대적으로 보였기 때문이었다.

01 brush: 붓; ~을 닦다

05 기타를 추천하고 구매하는 상황이므로 손님과 점원의 관계가 적절하다.

06 (A) a few: 몇몇의, few: 거의 없는, (B) 이어지는 대답에서 가장 좋아하는 공연의 종류를 설명하고 있으므로 most, (C) 둘 중에 어느 것을 더 좋아하느냐고 묻고 있으므로 or(또는)가 적절하다.

07 위 대화에서 왜 Emily가 TJ를 가장 좋아하는지 알 수 없다.

08 '어느 것을 더 좋아하니?'라는 의미의 선호를 물어보는 질문이 적절하므로 'which'가 적절하다.

10 almost = nearly: 거의

12 ninety: 90, nineties: 90년대

13 라푼젤의 엄마는 라푼젤이 탑 안에 머물게 했다는 의미이다. make는 목적격보어로 동사원형 형태를 쓰는 사역동사이다.

14 '네가 기분이 더 좋아지도록 만들다'이므로 사역동사 make 를 활용하여 문장을 만들 수 있다. 기분이 좋아지는 주체는 you이므로 이를 목적어로 사용한다.

15 what made Tom upset이라고 쓰는 것이 옳다. 간접의문문에서 의문사가 주어 역할을 동시에 하는 경우에 유의한다.

16 간접의문문의 어순은 '의문사+주어+동사'임에 유의한다.

17 의문사가 주어인 경우이므로 who turned off the lights라고 쓰는 것이 옳다.

18 빈칸 (A)에는 전치사 from이 들어간다. ① listen to: ~을 듣다 ② take care of: ~을 돌보다 ③ suffer from: ~으로 고통받다 ④ turn off: ~을 끄다 ⑤ be satisfied with: ~에 만족하

19 They were going on with their everyday activities.'라고 써도 무방하다.

20 이카루스의 다리는 물 밖으로 나와 있다.

21 대답으로 미루어 보아 이카루스의 날개가 녹은 이유를 묻는 말이 들어가는 것이 옳다. 간접의문문을 이용하여 답을 쓸 수 있다.

22 화가가 누구를 그리고 있는지를 추측하는 내용이 이어지고 있으므로 ②번이 적절하다.

23 간접의문문이므로 '의문사+주어+동사' 어순으로 써야 한다. 따라서 which direction the artist is looking at이라고 쓰는 것이 옳다.

24 '그림을 그리기 위해서 미술가들에 의해 사용되는 두꺼운 헝겊 조각'은 '화폭, 캔버스(canvas)'이다.

25 '시녀들'의 작가는 그림의 배경에 있는 거울 속에 왕과 왕비를 그렸다고 하였다.

Lesson
8

Changes Ahead

시험대비 실력평가 p.164

01 disagree 02 ② 03 ⑤

04 (1) donate (2) local (3) hand-free

05 (1) We should know the importance of the environment.

   (2) I try to balance work and play.

   (3) My younger[little] brother works in downtown Seattle.

06 ②

01 주어진 관계는 반의어 관계를 나타낸다. agree: 동의하다, disagree: 반대하다

02 '누군가에게 그들이 해야 하는 것, 그들이 가야 하는 곳 등에 대해 당신의 생각을 말하다'를 가리키는 말은 suggest(제안하다)이다.

03 mixture: 혼합물

04 donate: 기부하다, local: 지역의, 현지의, hand-free: 손을 쓸 필요

05 importance: 중요성, balance: 균형을 잡다, downtown: 시내의

06 주어진 문장에서 'post'는 '게시하다'를 의미하며 이와 같은 의미로 쓰인 것은 ②번이다. ①: 직책, ③: 우편, ④: 우편물, ⑤: (우편물을) 발송하다

서술형 시험대비 p.171

01 unimportant

02 (1) throw away (2) rely on

   (3) get attention (4) Even though (5) fall asleep

03 (1) Spend your time wisely.

   (2) We will post these pictures on the Internet.

   (3) The job needs some creative imagination.

04 bakery

05 (1) Some scientists say sugar-free drinks are bad for your teeth.

   (2) The little girl felt shy in the boy's presence.

   (3) My classmates threw a surprise party for me.

   (4) What do you think about my new dress?

   (5) The trip was one of the most exciting moments in my life.

01 주어진 관계는 반의어 관계를 나타낸다. important: 중요한, unimportant: 중요하지 않은

02 get attention: 주목을 받다, throw away: 버리다, rely on: ~에 의존하다, fall asleep: 잠들다, even though: 비록 ~할지라도

03 wisely: 현명하게, post: 올리다, 게시하다, creative: 창의적인

04 '빵과 케이크를 만들거나 파는 곳'을 가리키는 말은 bakery(빵집)이다.

05 sugar-free: 무가당의, presence: 존재, throw a party: 파티를 열다, What do you think about ~?: ~에 대해 어떻게 생각하니? moment: 순간

교과서
Conversation

핵심 Check p.166~167

1 (1) What do you think about / fresh vegetables, greener

   (2) do you feel about / I think it's good, for free

   (3) What's / in need, healthy

2 (1) online, offline / with, on / I don't think so

   (2) theater / not with you, effects

교과서 대화문 익히기

Check(√) True or False p.168

1 F 2 T 3 F 4 F

교과서 확인학습 p.170~171

Listen & Talk 1 A-1

memory stick / saved, think, present / touching

Listen & Talk 1 A-2

what do you think about / sound effects / interesting / scared

Listen & Talk 1 B

heard / donates / what / creative, have fun, help out / try, out

Listen & Talk 2 A-1

better than before / get closer / with you on that, wait to watch

시험대비 기본평가
p.172

01 ⓔ → try it out 　　02 ⑤ 　　03 ②

04 He thinks that this singing contest helps the singers get closer to their dreams.

01 이어동사의 목적어가 인칭대명사일 때 대명사는 동사와 부사 사이에 위치한다.

03 I can't wait to ~: ~하기를 기대하다

04 Jack은 이 노래 경연 대회가 가수들이 그들의 꿈에 좀 더 가까워지도록 도와준다고 생각한다.

시험대비 실력평가
p.173~174

01 What do you think about the present?

02 (A) a family video clip 　(B) the present 　03 ⑤

04 ④ 　　05 ⑤ 　　06 (C)→ (B) → (A) → (D)

07 ⑤ 　　08 ②, ⑤

09 (A) Choose your hog dog and drink.
　　(B) Pay for your order.

10 ③ 　　11 ④

03 아빠가 Jane의 가족 동영상을 보았다는 설명은 대화에서 알 수 없다.

04 주어진 문장은 의견을 묻는 질문에 대한 대답이므로 (D)가 적절하다.

05 위 대화를 통해 Tony가 얼마나 많은 쌀을 배고픈 사람들에게 기부할지는 알 수 없다.

06 (C) 의견 질문 → (B) 좋아하지 않음과 이유 설명 → (A) 반대되는 의견 주장 → (D) 자신의 의견 설명

07 very는 비교급을 강조할 수 없다.

08 ⓐ는 도움을 요청하는 표현으로 ②, ⑤와 바꾸어 쓸 수 있다.

10 (A) finish는 목적어로 동명사를 취하므로 making, (B) 주어

가 the title "LOST CAT" in big letters로 단수이므로 is, (C) get attention: 주의를 끌다. attentive: 주의 깊은

11 Alex는 제목 밑에 있는 사진들을 모두 버꾸는 것이 아니라 오른쪽에 있는 사진을 바꿀 것이다.

서술형 시험대비
p.175

01 She is talking about her mom's birthday gift with him.

02 She will give her mom a memory stick for a birthday gift.

03 She saved a family video clip on it.

04 (A) too many sound effects
　　(B) scared
　　(C) the sound effects

05 what do you think about the game?

06 (A) right 　(B) donate
　　(C) help out hungry people

01 Jane과 그녀의 아빠는 엄마의 생일 선물에 대해 이야기하고 있다.

02 Jane은 생일 선물로 엄마에게 막대 기억 장치(메모리 스틱)를 줄 것이다.

03 Jane이 준비한 막대 기억 장치에는 Jane이 만든 가족 동영상이 있다.

04 오늘 나는 Mike와 새 온라인 만화 '무서운 밤'에 대해 이야기했다. 사실 나는 너무 많은 음향 효과 때문에 그것이 마음에 들지 않았다. 나는 너무 무서워서 이야기에 집중할 수 없었다. 반면에 Mike는 내게 음향 효과가 이야기를 더 흥미진진하게 만들었다고 말했다.

06 정답을 맞혀 쌀을 기부하자. 당신은 재미있게 놀면서 배고픈 사람들을 도와줄 수 있다.

교과서

Grammar

핵심 Check
p.176~177

1 (1) so young that, can't work / too young to work
　(2) so tired that, couldn't / too tired to

2 (1) singing 　(2) written 　(3) writing

01 (1) so big → too big　(2) can't → couldn't

　　(3) excited → exciting　(4) thrown → throwing

02 (1) to take　(2) burning　(3) to attract

　　(4) named　(5) talking

03 (1) Olivia felt so cold that she couldn't fall asleep.

　　(2) The house is warm enough to live in.

　　(3) I looked at the falling leaves.

　　(4) A spectator is someone watching a game or a

　　　play.

01 (1) to부정사가 이어지고 있으므로 'too ~ to V' 구문을 쓰는
것이 적절하다. (2) 주절이 과거시제 이므로 종속절의 시제를 일
치시켜 couldn't라고 써야 한다. (3) bowling game이 흥분을
유발 하는 것이므로 exciting을 써야 한다. (4) 소년은 공을 던
지는 주체이므로 현재분사로 수식하는 것이 적절하다.

02 (1) 'too+부사+to V'로 '너무 ~해서 …할 수 없다'는 의미이다.
(2) 무언가가 '타고 있는' 것이므로 현재분사로 수식한다. (3)
'형용사+enough+to V'는 '~하기에 충분히 …한'이라는 의미
이다. (4) '~라고 이름 지어진'이라는 의미이므로 과거분사로 수
식한다. (5) 로봇이 말하는 주체가 되므로 현재분사로 수식한다.

03 (1) 'so+형용사+that+주어+can't+동사원형'은 '너무 ~해서
…할 수 없다'라는 의미이다. (2) '살기에 충분히 따뜻해'라고 하
였으므로 warm enough to live in'이라고 쓰는 것이 적절하
다. (3) '떨어지는 낙엽'이므로 falling leaves라고 쓴다. (4)
someone이 지켜보는 주체가 되므로 현재분사가 someone을
수식하도록 문장을 만든다.

01 ④　　　　02 ③　　　　03 ②

04 is too hot for me to drink　　　　　05 ⑤

06 ③　　　　07 ⑤

08 (1) This wallet was too big to put in my pocket.

　　(2) This wallet was so big that I couldn't put it in
　　　my pocket.

09 ④　　　　10 ④　　　　11 ⑤

12 We like to walk on fallen leaves.

13 ④　　　　14 ②, ⑤　　　15 so, can't

16 dancing boy　　　　17 ⑤　　　　18 ③

19 He hit the flying ball.

20 sleeping, so cute that I can't

21 ④　　　　22 ③

23 surprising news made me excited

24 too fast, to catch

01 'too ~ to V'는 '너무 ~해서 V할 수 없다'라는 의미로, 'to+
동사원형'을 쓴다.

02 '책을 읽는' 소녀이므로 현재분사로, '깨진 유리창'이므로 과거분
사로 각각 수식하는 것이 적절하다.

03 'too+형용사+to V'로 '너무 ~해서 …할 수 없다'는 의미로
'so+형용사+that+주어+can't+동사원형'과 같다.

04 우유가 너무 뜨거워서 마실 수 없다는 의미이므로 'too+형용사
+to V'를 사용하여 같은 의미의 문장을 만들 수 있다.

05 '너무 ~해서 …할 수 없다'은 'too ~ to V'로 나타낼 수 있다.

06 주어진 문장의 밑줄 친 부분은 '~하는 것'이라고 해석되는 동명
사 다. ③번은 '당황스러운 순간'이라는 의미로 embarrass를
유발하는 순간 을 의미한다. embarrass: 당황스럽게 만들다

07 too high to climb 혹은 so high that we couldn't climb이라
고 쓰는 것이 적절하다.

08 'too ~ to V'는 'so ~ that 주어 can't'와 같으며 '너무 ~해서 …
할 수 없는'이라고 해석된다.

09 '너무 ~해서 …할 수 없는'은 'too ~ to V'와 'so ~ that 주어
can't'로 표현할 수 있다.

10 '사진이 찍히도록 하는 것'이므로 had our picture taken 이라
고 쓰는 것이 적절하다.

11 영화가 감동을 유발하는 것이므로 moving이라고 쓰는 것이 적
절하다.

12 낙엽은 떨어진 잎을 말하는 것이므로 'fallen leaves'라고 쓸 수
있다.

13 너무 멀리 있어서 듣지 못했다는 의미이므로 'too far away to
hear' 혹은 'so far away that I couldn't hear'라고 쓰는 것
이 적절하다.

14 목적격 보어로 과거분사를 취할 수 없는 동사는 want와 appear
이다.

15 주어진 문장을 지시에 맞게 영어로 쓰면 He is so lazy that he
can't do the job.이다.

16 '춤추는 소년'이므로 현재분사 dancing이 소년을 수식하도록
문장을 완성한다.

17 '너무 ~해서 …할 수 없는'은 'too ~ to V'나 'so ~ that 주어
can't'로 표현할 수 있다. he couldn't say hello라고 쓰는 것
이 적절하다.

18 이어지는 문장으로 보아 첫 번째 빈칸에는 너무 늦어서 회의 에 참
석할 수 없었다는 것이 들어가야 하고, 두 번째 빈칸에는 차를 살
만큼 부자지만 차를 사지 않았다는 말이 들어가는 것이 적절하다.

19 '날아오는 공'이므로 현재분사로 ball을 수식하도록 문장을 만든다.

20 '잠자는 고양이'이므로 현재분사 sleeping으로 cat을 수식하
도록 해야 하고, '너무 ~해서 …할 수 없다'는 'so ~ that 주어
can't 동사원형'이다.

21 '구워진 생선'이란 의미로 baked fish를 쓰는 것이 적절하다.

22 영화에 지루함을 느낀 것이므로 'bored'라고 쓰는 것이 적절하다.

23 '놀라운 뉴스'이므로 surprise를 현재분사형으로 만들어 news 를 수식하게 만들고, 내가 흥분을 느끼는 것이므로 과거분사 excited로 me를 설명하는 목적격 보어를 만들어준다.

24 'too ~ to V'는 'so ~ that 주어 can't'와 같으며 to부정사의 의미상의 주어는 'for+목적격'으로 나타낸다.

p.182~183

서술형 시험대비

01 (1) The table was too heavy to move.
  (2) The table was so heavy that nobody could move it.

02 Show me the broken chair.

03 Her family was so poor that they couldn't buy the house.

04 too young to stay / so young that he can't stay

05 (1) playing (2) exciting (3) repaired
  (4) amazing (5) hit

06 (1) 해석: Jane은 얇게 썰어진 치즈를 좋아한다.
  (2) 해석: Jane은 치즈를 얇게 써는 것을 좋아한다.
  (3) 어법상 차이: sliced는 '썰어진 (치즈)'라는 의미의 과거분사로 cheese를 수식하고, slicing은 '(치즈를) 써 는 것'이라는 의미로 동명사로 쓰였다

07 The room is so small that you can't invite all the friends to your party.

08 hidden

09 The news is so good that it can't be true.

10 Santa Claus checks his phone so often that he can't focus on his work.

11 annoyed / remaining

12 (1) I was too tired to open my eyes.
  (2) I was so tired that I couldn't open my eyes.

13 (1) Daisy was so nervous that she couldn't speak in front of many people.
  (2) Christopher is tall enough to be a model.
  (3) Jamie is so scared that he can't be alone at home.
  (4) Amelia was so rich that she could throw a big party for her friend.

14 It sounds like an exciting game.

15 (1) He has too much work to sleep.
  (2) He has so much work that he can't sleep.

01 'too ~ to V'는 'so ~ that 주어 can't'와 같으며 '너무 ~ 해서 …할 수 없다'라고 해석된다. 주절의 시제에 맞추어 couldn't 를 쓰는 것에 주의한다.

02 '부서진 의자'라고 하였으므로 과거분사로 chair를 수식하도록 문장을 만든다.

03 '너무 ~해서 …할 수 없다'는 'so ~ that 주어 can't 동사원 형'으

로 표현할 수 있다.

05 (1) 배드민턴을 치고 있는 소녀는 나의 여동생이다. (2) 나는 너에게 해 줄 흥미진진한 이야기가 있어. (3) 우리는 그 차가 Potter와 Parker에 의해 수리되게 하였다. (4) Jina는 놀라운 농구 선수이다. (5) 너는 그 건물이 덤프 트럭에 부딪친 것을 보 았니?

06 like는 동명사를 목적어로 취할 수 있는 동사이며, 위 문장 에서 치즈는 slice의 주체가 될 수 없으므로 slicing이 현재 분사라고 볼 수 없다.

07 방이 너무 작아서 모든 친구들을 초대할 수 없다는 말이다. 'so ~ that 주어 can't 동사원형'으로 표현할 수 있다.

08 '숨겨진 보물'이므로 과거분사 hidden으로 treasure를 수식하는 것이 적절하다.

09 'too ~ to V'는 'so ~ that 주어 can't'와 같으며 '너무 ~ 해서 … 할 수 없는'이라는 의미이다.

10 '너무 ~해서 …할 수 없다'는 'so ~ that 주어 can't'이다.

11 내가 성가심을 느끼는 것이므로 첫 번째 빈칸에는 과거분사를 쓰 는 것이 옳고, '남아 있는 날들 동안'이라는 의미이므로 두 번째 빈칸에는 현재분사를 쓰는 것이 적절하다.

12 '너무 ~해서 …할 수 없는'은 'too ~ to V'와 'so ~ that 주어 can't'로 표현할 수 있다.

13 'too ~ to V'는 'so ~ that 주어 can't 동사원형'과 같고, '~ enough to V'는 'so ~ that 주어 can 동사원형'과 같다.

14 게임이 신나는 감정을 유발하는 것이므로 현재분사 exciting으 로 game을 수식하도록 문장을 만든다.

15 주어진 문장은 '그는 많은 일을 가지고 있기 때문에 잠을 잘 수 없 다'는 의미이다. 따라서 'too ~ to V'와 'so ~ that 주어 can't 동 사원형'을 사용하여 문장을 만들 수 있다

교과서
Reading

확인문제   p.184

1 T 2 T 3 F 4 F

확인문제   p.185

1 T 2 F 3 F 4 F 5 T

01 suggested, surprising, without

02 to see, sitting, looking at

03 explained, kept saying that   04 started, to

05 terrible   06 On the way to, got lost

07 was busy looking, asking, with, from

08 Even though, right next to, it, to get

09 were so tired that

10 fall alseep, worried, what would happen

11 After, to have, fried

12 which restaurant to go to

13 went up to, tired to ask

14 to understand, words   15 took us, nearby

16 fried rice, amazing

17 take pictures of, them

18 without, to enjoy

19 remaining, relied, on

20 were able to meet

21 kind enough to show   22 talked, with

23 much of our time together

24 new and different

25 so dependent on, that

26 that, without it

27 From, have learned, balanced use

28 would I travel   29 try to use it

1 Last summer, my father suggested a surprising event: a family trip without smartphones!

2 He said, "I hate to see you sitting together and only looking at your smartphones."

3 My sister and I explained the need for smartphones, but he kept saying that we could not fully enjoy the trip with them.

4 So we started a technology-free trip to a new city, Barcelona, Spain.

5 Our first day was terrible.

6 On the way to our guesthouse around Plaza Reial, we got lost in downtown Barcelona.

7 Dad was busy looking at the map and asking for directions with a few Spanish words he got from a tour guidebook.

8 Even though our guesthouse was right next to the Plaza, it took us about two hours to get there.

9 We were so tired that we could not go out for dinner.

10 I went to bed but couldn't fall asleep because I was worried about what would happen the next day.

11 After looking around Gaudi's Park Guell, we decided to have seafood fried rice for lunch.

12 However, we didn't know which restaurant to go to.

13 We needed help, so Mom went up to an elderly lady and tried to ask for directions to a popular seafood restaurant.

14 Luckily, she seemed to understand Mom's few Spanish words.

15 She took us to a small local restaurant nearby.

16 The seafood fried rice was amazing.

17 I really wanted to take pictures of the food and post them on my blog.

18 But without my phone, I just decided to enjoy the moment.

19 During the remaining days, we relied more and more on the locals.

20 We were able to meet and talk with various people on the streets, in the bakeries, and in the parks.

21 They were always kind enough to show us different sides of Barcelona with a smile.

22 Also, our family talked a lot with each other.

23 We spent much of our time together on the Spanish train, on the bus, and at the restaurants.

24 Our technology-free trip was a new and different experience.

25 Before the trip, I was so dependent on my smartphone that I couldn't do anything without it.

26 But now I see that I can enjoy the moment without it.

27 From the experience, I have learned the importance of a balanced use of the smartphone.

28 So, next time, would I travel without a smartphone?

29 Probably not. But I will try to use it more wisely.

01 ②   02 saying

03 They went to Barcelona, Spain.   04 ⑤

05 ④   06 ⑤   07 It was terrible.

08 ③   09 ③   10 ⑤

11 balance

12 The writer learned the importance of a balanced

use of the smartphone.　　13 ③　　14 ④

15 (to) our guesthouse

16 He suggested a family trip without smartphones.

17 ③　　18 ③　　19 ⑤

20 He wanted to take pictures of the food and post
them on his blog.

21 ⑤　　22 our technology-free trip

23 ④　　24 ③　　25 ⑤

26 He will try to use his smartphone more wisely.

---

01 글쓴이와 여동생이 스마트폰의 필요성을 설명했지만 아버지는 계속해서 주장을 굽히지 않으셨다는 의미이다. 따라서 대조의 문장을 이끄는 접속사 but이 가장 적절하다.

02 keep+Ving: 계속해서 V하다

03 그들은 가족 여행으로 스페인의 바르셀로나로 갔다.

04 글쓴이의 아버지는 글쓴이와 동생이 함께 앉아 있는 것을 보기 싫어한 것이 아니라 함께 앉아 스마트폰만 쳐다보고 있는 것을 보기 싫다고 하셨다.

05 '광장 바로 옆에'라는 의미이다.

06 레이알 광장이 얼마나 큰지는 위 글을 읽고 알 수 없다.

07 글쓴이는 여행 첫 날은 엉망이었다고 하였다.

08 점심으로 해산물 볶음밥을 먹기로 했지만 어느 식당으로가야 할지 몰랐다는 의미이다. 따라서 However가 가장 적절하다.

09 엄마가 한 노부인에게 길을 물었는데 다행히도 그녀가 엄마의 말을 알아들어 식당으로 안내했다는 순서가 자연스럽다.

10 스마트폰이 없어서 사진을 찍지 못했다고 하였으므로 Frank는 글을 잘못 이해하였다.

11 한 쪽으로 넘어지지 않고 꾸준한 위치를 유지하는 것은 '균형을 잡다(balance)'이다.

12 글쓴이는 여행을 통해 스마트폰을 균형 있게 사용하는 것의 중요성을 배웠다고 하였다.

13 글쓴이의 가족은 '첨단 과학 기술이 없는' 여행을 하였다.

14 (A) 의미상 sitting과 연결되므로 looking, (B) '길을 잃었다'는 수동이므로 'got lost', (C) It takes 시간 to V: V하는 데 ~만큼의 시간이 걸리다

15 글쓴이 가족의 여행자 숙소를 가리킨다.

16 아빠는 스마트폰이 없는 가족 여행을 제안하였다.

17 길을 잃었고, 너무 피곤해서 저녁도 먹을 수 없었지만 다음날이 걱정되어 잠을 잘 수도 없었다고 하였으므로 ③번이 가장 적절하다. anxious: 걱정스러운 embarrassed: 당황한

18 너무 피곤해서 저녁을 먹을 수 없었다고 하였다. 따라서 ③번은 글을 읽고 답할 수 없다.

19 점심으로 해산물 볶음밥을 먹기로 함 - (C) 그러나 어느 식당으로 가야 할지 몰라 한 노부인에게 물어 봄 - (B) 다행히 노부인이 엄마의 말을 이해하고 식당으로 데려다 줌 - (A) 해산물 볶음밥이 맛있었음

---

20 글쓴이는 스마트폰으로 음식 사진을 찍어 블로그에 올리고 싶었다고 하였다.

21 노부인은 글쓴이의 가족을 식당으로 직접 데려다 주었다.

22 글쓴이가 경험한 것은 '첨단 과학 기술 없는 여행'이다.

23 바르셀로나의 다양한 면을 보여준 것은 현지 주민들이었다.

24 각각 ① dependent, ② different, ④ new, ⑤ more의 반의어이다. sensibly는 '분별력 있게, 현명하게'라는 의미로 wisely와 유의어이다.

25 글쓴이는 스마트폰 없이 여행을 하게 되지는 않을 것 같다고 하였다.

26 여행 후에 글쓴이는 스마트폰을 좀 더 현명하게 사용하기 위해 노력할 것이라고 하였다.

서술형 시험대비　　p.194~195

01 It is a trip without smartphones.

02 He explained the need for smartphones with his sister.

03 We were too tired to go out for dinner.

04 He got them from a tour guidebook.

05 enjoy the trip, without smartphones

06 It was right next to the Plaza.

07 It's because they didn't know which restaurant to go to.

08 enough to take　　09 pictures of the food

10 ⑤번 → without　　11 balanced

12 met and talked, talked a lot

13 No, it wasn't, was a new and different experience

14 travel without a smartphone

15 They depended on the locals.

---

01 '첨단 과학 기술 없는 여행'이란 스마트폰을 사용하지 않는 여행이다.

02 아빠의 제안을 들은 글쓴이는 여동생과 함께 스마트폰이 필요하다고 설명했다.

03 'so ~ that 주어 can't 동사원형'은 'too ~ to V'와 같다.

04 아빠는 여행안내 책자에서 스페인어를 배웠다고 하였다.

05 여행을 완전히 즐기기 위해서, 우리는 스마트폰 없이 여행해야 해.

06 가족의 숙소는 광장 바로 옆에 있었다.

07 도움이 필요했던 이유는 어떤 식당으로 가야 할지 몰라서이다.

08 식구들을 근처에 있는 작은 현지 식당으로 데려다 줄 만큼 친절했다는 의미이다.

09 음식의 사진을 가리키는 말이다.

10 음식 사진을 찍어 블로그에 올리고 싶었지만 스마트폰이 없었기 때문에 그 순간을 즐기기로 한 것이 자연스럽다.

11 '균형 잡힌 사용'이라는 의미이므로 과거분사로 use를 수식하는 것이 적절하다.

12 가족들은 바르셀로나에서 다양한 사람들을 만나 이야기했을 뿐

만 아니라 서로 많은 대화를 나누었다. not only A but also B: A뿐만 아니라 B도

13 '첨단 기술 없는 여행'은 글쓴이에게 새롭고 색다른 경험이었다고 하였다.

14 아마도 나는 스마트폰 없이 여행을 하지 않을 것이지만, 나는 그것을 좀 더 현명하게 사용하기 위해 노력할 것이다.

15 남아 있는 날들 동안 글쓴이의 가족은 현지 사람들에게 의존하였다.

영역별 핵심문제 p.197~201

01 present   02 fry   03 ③
04 (1) wait to   (2) keep going   (3) pay for   05 ④
06 (1) importance   (2) side   (3) thought   (4) effect
07 ⑤   08 ①
09 He thought they made the story more interesting.
10 She was too scared.
11 ⑤   12 ②   13 ③   14 ⑤
15 ③   16 ④   17 ③
18 My room is so dirty that I can't invite my friends.
19 ④   20 ⑤   21 ③   22 ⑤
23 ④   24 I was too upset to hear the news.
25 ③   26 ③   27 ④
28 he hated to see the writer and his sister sitting together and only looking at their smartphones
29 ④   30 ⑤번 → post   31 ④
32 ⑤

01 주어진 관계는 반의어 관계를 나타낸다. present: 출석한, absent: 결석한

02 '뜨거운 기름으로 무언가를 요리하다'를 가리키는 말은 fry(튀기다)이다.

03 suggest: 제안하다, beneficial: 유익한

04 can't wait to: ~하기를 기대하다, keep -ing: 계속해서 ~하다, pay for: 지불하다

05 experience: (동) 경험하다, (명) 경험

06 importance: 중요성, thought: 생각, side: 측면, effect: 영향, 효과, scared: 무서워하는, 겁먹은

07 주어진 문장과 나머지는 모두 '계산대'를 뜻하지만 ⑤번은 '반대의'를 의미한다.

08 terrified: 무서운, 겁에 질린, terrific: 멋진, brilliant: 똑똑한, pleased: 기쁜

09 Mike는 Scary Night의 음향 효과가 이야기를 더 흥미진진하게 만들어 주었다고 생각했다.

10 Jenny는 Scary Night을 보면서 너무 무서웠다.

11 ⑤번을 제외하고 (A)와 나머지는 상대방의 의견에 이의를 나타낸다.

12 Lisa는 게시물 공유에 관해 Steve와 다른 의견을 갖고 있다.

13 Wendy가 James의 의견에 반대되는 주장을 설명하고 있으므로 주어진 문장은 (C)가 적절하다.

14 대화를 통해 Wendy가 무엇을 자주 버렸는지는 알 수 없다.

15 have는 목적어와 목적격 보어의 관계가 수동인 경우 목적격 보어로 과거분사를 사용하는 사역동사이다. 신발에 광이 나게 한다는 의미이므로 과거분사를 쓰는 것이 적절하다.

16 2형식 동사의 보어가 필요하므로 빈칸에는 형용사가 들어가야 한다.

17 첫 번째 빈칸에는 I를 설명하는 보어가 필요하므로 형용사를 쓰는 것이 옳으며, 두 번째 빈칸에는 '할인된 가격'이라는 의미이므로 과거분사로 수식하는 것이 적절하다.

18 '너무 ~해서 …할 수 없다'는 'so ~ that 주어 can't 동사원형'이다.

19 kind enough to take care of ~라고 쓰는 것이 적절하다.

20 만족을 느끼는 것이므로 satisfied라고 쓰는 것이 적절하다.

21 주어진 문장의 밑줄 친 부분은 동명사이다. 따라서 '~하는 중인'이라는 의미의 현재분사로 쓰인 ③번이 답이다.

22 '~ enough to V' 혹은 'so ~ that 주어 can 동사원형'을 써서 문장을 완성할 수 있다.

23 ①, ②, ③ '~을 사용하는'이라는 의미의 현재분사, ⑤ 동명사, ④번에는 과거분사 used가 쓰여 '중고차'라는 의미를 만든다.

24 '너무 ~해서 …할 수 없는'은 'too ~ to V'로 표현한다.

25 숙소가 광장 바로 옆에 있었지만 가는 데 약 2시간이 걸렸다는 의미이다. 따라서 내용상 반대되는 문장을 이끄는 접속사 Although가 적절하다.

26 '스마트폰이 있으면 여행을 충분히 즐길 수 없다'고 말하는 것이 자연스럽다. 따라서 with them이라고 쓰는 것이 적절하다.

27 (B)와 ④의 take는 '(~ 만큼의 시간이) 걸리다'라는 의미로 쓰였다. ① ~로 안내하다, 데려가다 ② 가져가다 ③ 선택하다, 사다 ⑤ (~을) 타다

28 아빠가 스마트폰 없는 여행을 제안한 이유는 필자와 그의 여동생이 함께 앉아 각자의 스마트폰만 보고 있는 걸 보는 것이 싫어서이다.

29 지도를 보느라 바빴던 것은 글쓴이의 아버지이다.

30 사진을 찍어 블로그에 올리기를 원한 것이므로 to take와 병렬 연결되어 (to) post라고 쓰는 것이 적절하다. posted라고 쓸 경우 '사진을 찍기를 원했고 블로그에 올렸다'라는 의미가 된다.

31 공원 근처에 있는 현지 식당이다. 따라서 ④번은 not far from 이라고 쓰는 것이 적절하다.

32 해산물 식당이 얼마나 인기 있는지는 위 글을 읽고 알 수 없다.

단원별 예상문제 p.202~205

01 (A) the new online comic *Scary Night*
    (B) many sound effects
02 ③   03 I can donate rice.
04 She thinks it's a creative game.
05 He will try it out this weekend.   06 ③

34 정답 및 해설

07 I'm looking forward to watching their next performances.

08 They are debating the fast fashion.

09 Because he thinks that we can wear trendy clothes at a cheaper price.

10 She thinks that it makes us spend too much money and throw away clothes too often.

11 ④　　　**12** ①

13 The walking robot is my favorite toy.

14 ②　　　**15** ⑤

16 so busy that she couldn't

17 writing, written

18 (C) → (B) → (A)　　　**19** ③

20 They met and talked with various people on the streets, in the bakeries, and in the parks.

21 ③　　　**22** ③　　　**23** ②　　　**24** ④

25 ⑤

02 Mike와 Jenny의 Scary Night에 대한 의견이 같다는 설명은 대화의 내용과 일치하지 않는다.

03 당신은 '퀴즈와 쌀' 게임에서 정답을 맞히면 쌀을 기부할 수 있다.

04 Julie는 '퀴즈와 쌀' 게임이 창의적인 게임이라고 생각한다.

05 Tony는 '퀴즈와 쌀' 게임을 이번 주말에 해보려고 한다.

06 ⑤번을 제외한 나머지는 모두 상대방의 의견과 같음을 표현하고 있다.

07 can't wait to = look forward to ~ing: ~하기를 기대 하다, 고대하다

08 학생들은 패스트 패션에 대해 토론하고 있다.

09 James는 우리가 보다 저렴한 가격으로 최신 유행의 옷들을 입을 수 있기 때문에 패스트 패션이 좋다고 생각한다.

10 Wendy는 패스트 패션이 우리가 너무 많은 돈을 쓰고 너무 자주 옷을 버리게 한다고 생각한다.

11 첫 번째 빈칸에는 'too ~ to V', 두 번째 빈칸에는 'enough to V', 마지막 빈칸에는 '놀라움을 주는 선물'이라 는 의미이므로 현재분사를 쓰는 것이 적절하다.

12 'too ~ to V'와 'so ~ that 주어 can't'는 '너무 ~해서 …할 수 없다'는 의미이다. 절을 이끄는 that이 쓰이고 있으므로 too가 아닌 so를 쓰는 것이 적절하다.

13 '걷고 있는 로봇'이라고 하였으므로 walk를 현재분사형으로 만들어 robot을 수식하게 만든다.

14 ⓐ와 ⓒ는 '~하는'이라고 해석되거나 '~한 감정을 유발하는'이 라고 해석되는 현재분사이고, ⓑ와 ⓓ는 '~하는 것'이라고 해석 되는 동명사이다.

15 나무는 심어지는 것이므로 planted in the garden이라고 쓰는 것이 적절하다.

16 'too ~ to V'는 'so ~ that 주어 can't 동사원형'과 같다.

17 '~을 쓰고 있는 소년'이라는 의미이므로 현재분사로 the boy를 수식하고, '한국어로 쓰여진'이라는 의미이므로 과거 분사로 a letter를 수식하는 것이 적절하다.

18 현지인들에 의존함 - (C) 다양한 현지인들을 만나고 대화함 - (B) 그들은 친절했음 - (A) 또한 가족들과 많은 대화를 나눔

19 글쓴이는 스마트폰 없이 순간을 즐길 수 있다는 사실을 안다고 하였다.

20 그들은 다양한 현지인들을 길거리에서, 빵집에서, 공원에서 만 나 이야기할 수 있었다고 하였다.

21 가족들이 현지인들을 만난 곳은 길거리, 빵집, 공원이었다. 식당 에서는 가족들 간에 함께 시간을 보냈다.

22 '3분 동안'이라는 의미이므로 전치사 for가 적절하다.

23 잘라진 사과 조각을 의미하므로 과거분사로 수식하는 것이 적절 하다.

24 식빵 위에 올릴 사과 소는 약한 불에서 조린 것을 올리는 것이므 로 혜준이 글의 내용을 잘못 이해하였다.

25 잘라진 사과 조각들을 약한 불에서 얼마나 조리하는지는 위 글 에 나와 있지 않다.

🦉 서술형 실전문제

p.206~207

01 I'm not with you on that.

02 He thinks (that) it's great.

03 She wants to share them with her close friends.

04 (C) → (B) → (D) → (A)

05 encouraging, encouraged

06 (1) cheering　(2) sliced

07 (1) She is tall enough to reach the top shelf.

　(2) She is so tall that she can reach the top shelf.

08 the dog was so hungry that he couldn't bark at a stranger

09 He asked for directions with a few Spanish words he got from a tour guidebook.

10 Because he was worried about what would happen the next day.

11 They got lost in downtown Barcelona.

12 He was too sleepy to focus during class.

13 He felt moved.

14 I was so moved that I couldn't say anything.

02 Steve는 많은 사람들과 게시물들을 공유하는 것에 대해 좋다고 생각한다.

03 Lisa는 친한 친구들과 게시물들을 공유하고 싶어 한다.

04 (C) 엄마의 생일 선물 보여 줌 → (B) 질문 → (D) 대답 및 선물 설명 → (A) 반응

05 '격려하는 말'이라는 의미이므로 현재분사로 words를 수식하고, 이 말에 내가 용기와 격려를 느낀 것이므로 과거분사를 써서 문장 을 완성할 수 있다.

06 (1) 능동의 의미이므로 현재분사 (2) 수동의 의미이므로 과거 분사

07 '~할 만큼 …한'은 '~ enough to V' 혹은 'so ~ that 주어 can 동사원형'을 써서 표현할 수 있다.

08 '너무 배가 고파서 낯선 사람을 보고 짖을 수 없었다'는 말이 들어가는 것이 타당하다.

09 아빠는 여행 안내 책자에서 배운 스페인어 몇 마디로 길을 물었다고 하였다.

10 글쓴이가 잠들 수 없었던 이유는 내일 무슨 일이 일어날지 걱정되어서라고 하였다.

11 그들이 길을 잃은 곳은 바르셀로나 시내라고 하였다.

12 너무 졸려서 수업에 집중할 수 없었다고 하였다. 'so ~ that 주어 couldn't 동사원형'이 쓰이고 있으므로 'too ~ to부정사'로 나타낼 수 있다.

13 Jesse는 감동하였다.

14 'too ~ to부정사'는 'so ~ that 주어 can't 동사원형'과 같다.

창의사고력 서술형 문제　　　　　　　　p.208

|모범답안|

01 (A) find　(B) big letters　(C) two photos
　(D) it didn't show Leon's face well

02 (1) The man was too shocked to say anything.
　(2) The book was too difficult to be read easily.
　(3) The dog was too hungry to bark at a stranger.
　(4) She was too frightened to phone us.

02 'so ~ that 주어 can't 동사원형'은 'too ~ to V'과 같다. 이때 주절의 시제가 과거인 경우 couldn't를 쓰는 것에 유의한다.

단원별 모의고사　　　　　　　　　　p.209~212

01 ⑤　　　02 (1) Even though　(2) get, attention
03 (1) guidebook　(2) handwritten　(3) guesthouse
　(4) elderly　(5) local
04 (1) I was busy cleaning my room.
　(2) I couldn't fall asleep after drinking a cup of coffee.
　(3) Young people rely on technology too much.
05 She should touch the Done button at the bottom.
06 He thinks (that) it really saves a lot of time when there's a long line.
07 debate　　08 ⓒ → throw
09 ③　　　10 ⑤　　　11 ⑤
12 I think shopping online is better than shopping at the stores.
13 She will be disappointed with the shocking news.
14 ①, ⑤　　15 ④　　16 ④　　17 ⑤
18 They spent their time together on the Spainish train, on the bus, and at the restaurants.
19 They were always kind enough to show them different sides of Barcelona with a smile.
20 ③　　　　21 so late that I couldn't　22 ⑤
23 ②

---

01 thought: (명) 생각, (동) think의 과거, 과거분사

02 even though: 비록 ~ 할지라도, get one's attention: ~의 관심을 얻다

03 elderly: 나이가 지긋한, handwritten: 손으로 쓴, guidebook: (여행) 안내서, local: 지역의, 현지의, guesthouse: 숙소, 여관 organic: 유기농의

04 be busy -ing: ~하느라 바쁘다, fall asleep: 잠들다, rely on: 의존하다

05 Emma는 주문한 것을 결제하기 전에 맨 아래에 있는 '완료' 버튼을 눌러야 한다.

06 Tom은 줄이 길 때, 기계가 정말 많은 시간을 절약해 준다고 생각한다.

07 '다른 의견들을 표현하는 논쟁 또는 토론'을 나타내는 말은 debate(토론, 토의)이다.

08 ⓒ는 spend와 병렬 구조로 throw가 적절하다.

09 Wendy는 James와 패스트 패션에 대해 다른 의견을 갖고 있다. pros and cons: 장단점

10 주어진 문장은 상대방의 의견에 동의를 나타내고 있으므로 (E)가 적절하다.

13 실망을 느끼는 것이므로 과거분사를, 충격을 유발하는 소식이므로 현재분사를 써서 문장을 만든다.

14 수프가 너무 뜨거워서 먹을 수 없다는 의미이다.

15 주절이 과거 동사이므로 종속절 역시 과거 동사를 쓰는 것이 적절하다. 따라서 couldn't라고 써야 한다.

16 각각 ① moment ② post ③ elderly ④ guidebook ⑤ bakery를 풀이한 말이다.

17 구엘 공원에서 식당까지 얼마나 멀었는지는 알 수 없다.

18 그들은 스페인의 기차에서, 버스에서, 그리고 식당에서 많은 시간을 함께 보냈다고 하였다.

19 현지 사람들은 항상 웃으면서 너무나 친절히도 바르셀로나의 다양한 면을 보여주었다고 하였다.

20 너무 들떠서 잠을 제대로 자지 못할 정도였지만 생일의 시작이 좋지 않았다는 연결이 자연스럽다. 따라서 However가 적절하다.

21 너무 늦게 일어나서 생일상을 받을 수 없었다고 하였다. 'too ~ to부정사'는 'so ~ that 주어 can't 동사원형'과 같다.

22 깜짝 파티를 예상치 못한 일이라고 말했으므로 ⑤번은 그의 내용과 일치하지 않는다.

23 (B) 여행 전에는 스마트폰에 의존적이었음 - (A) 그러나 여행 후에는 스마트폰을 균형 있게 사용하는 것이 중요함을 배움 - (C) 다음번 여행에 스마트폰 없이 여행을 하게 되지는 않겠지만 현명하게 사용하려고 노력일 것임

The Stone

Reading

확인문제 p.216

1 F 2 T 3 T 4 T

확인문제 p.217

1 F 2 F 3 T

교과서 확인학습 A p.218~219

01 driving down, when
02 looked, sick, to worry about 03 Later that day
04 to get, out from
05 pulled, away, freed 06 reward
07 that, young
08 it all wrong, young again, keep from
09 to explain, listen 10 handed him
11 a few, grow at all
12 become, got upset
13 change into, slow
14 give birth, got, angry, to throw it away
15 listen to, threw, out 16 found, sitting
17 worried about, glad that
18 having trouble, seen
19 to throw away, put, under
20 came back, went by, grew, changed
21 to worry, nothing to look forward to
22 to destroy, coming back
23 to throw away, far from
24 On, to, got angry
25 didn't you warn 26 listen
27 explained, get rid of, unless
28 no more of, Whatever, let, happen
29 to throw, onto
30 did, said, arrived, changed into, bore
31 laughed with delight
32 lived for 33 was proud of

교과서 확인학습 B p.220~221

1 One day, Maibon was driving down the road on his horse and cart when he saw an old man.

2 The old man looked very sick. Maibon began to worry about growing old.

3 Later that day, he saw a dwarf, Doli, in the field.

4 He was trying to get his leg out from under a log.

5 Maibon pulled the log away and freed the dwarf.

6 "You'll have your reward. What do you want?"

7 "I've heard that you have magic stones that can keep a man young. I want one."

8 "Oh, you humans have it all wrong. Those stones don't make you young again. They only keep you from getting older."

9 "Just as good!" Doli tried to explain the problem with the stones, but Maibon didn't listen.

10 So Doli handed him a magic stone and went away.

11 After a few days, Maibon saw that his beard didn't grow at all.

12 He became happy, but his wife, Modrona, got upset.

13 "The eggs don't change into chickens!" "Oh, the season's slow, that's all."

14 But she was not happy. "The cow doesn't give birth!" Maibon, then, told her about the stone, and she got very angry and told him to throw it away.

15 He didn't want to, but he listened to his wife and threw the stone out the window.

16 However, the next morning, he found the stone sitting by the window!

17 Maibon was worried about the animals, but he was glad that he was still young.

18 Now Maibon's baby was having trouble. No tooth was seen in his mouth.

19 His wife told him to throw away the stone and this time, Maibon put the stone under the ground.

20 But, the next day, the stone came back! Time went by and nothing grew or changed.

21 Maibon began to worry. "There's nothing to look forward to, nothing to show for my work."

22 Maibon tried to destroy the stone, but it kept coming back.

23 Maibon decided to throw away the stone far from his house.

24 On his way to the field, he saw the dwarf. Maibon got angry with him.

25 "Why didn't you warn me about the stone?"

26 "I tried to, but you wouldn't listen."

27 Doli explained that Maibon couldn't get rid of the stone unless he really wanted to.

28 "I want no more of it. Whatever may happen, let it happen!"

29 Doli told him to throw the stone onto the ground and go back home.

30 Maibon did as Doli said. When he arrived home, Modrona told him the good news — the eggs changed into chickens and the cow bore her baby.

31 And Maibon laughed with delight when he saw the first tooth in his baby's mouth.

32 Maibon, Modrona and their children and grandchildren lived for many years.

33 Maibon was proud of his white hair and long beard.

---

04 tell은 to부정사를 목적격 보어로 취하는 동사이며, to부정사의 부정은 not to V으로 표기한다. plan은 to부정사를 목적어로 취하는 동사이다.

05 (1) 목적어가 my car이므로 이를 주어로 하고, 과거시제이므로 동사는 was repaired를 써서 수동태를 만들 수 있다. (2) 수동태의 행위 주체를 능동태의 주어로 하여 능동태를 만들 수 있다.

06 (D) 난쟁이 Doli가 통나무 아래에 깔린 다리를 빼내려 함 - (A) Maibon은 통나무를 잡아당겨 난쟁이를 풀어 주자 이에 난쟁이는 보상으로 무엇을 원하는지 물음 - (C) 젊음을 유지해 주는 마법의 돌을 요구함 - (E) 다시 젊어지게 해 주는 것이 아니라 늙지 않게 해 주는 돌이라 말함 - (B) 그것대로 좋다고 말함

07 그 노인은 아파 보였다고 하였다.

08 Maibon은 늙어가는 것이 걱정되었다.

09 난쟁이의 이름은 Doli이다.

10 magic stones 중 하나를 의미하는 말이다.

11 Modrona는 Maibon의 아내이다.

12 앞선 문장의 to부정사 이하를 생략한 문장이다. 따라서 to throw it away를 써서 나타낼 수 있다.

13 그는 창가에 돌이 있는 것을 발견했다.

서술형 실전문제 p.222~223

01 (1) bore (2) beard (3) field (4) logs

02 (1) goes by (2) went away (3) Throw away
    (4) worry about (4) change into

03 (1) I try to get rid of my bad habits.
    (2) My teacher keeps us from using cell phones in school.
    (3) My aunt gave birth to a cute baby.

04 (1) They told us not to use the computer.
    (2) I plan to visit my uncle this weekend.

05 (1) My car was repaired by David yesterday.
    (2) A car hit the man on the street.

06 (D)–(A)–(C)–(E)–(B)

07 He looked very sick.

08 He worried about growing old.

09 It is Doli.

10 사람의 젊음을 유지해 주는 마법의 돌

11 She is Maibon's wife

12 He didn't want to throw it away

13 He found the stone sitting by the window.

단원별 예상문제 p.224~228

01 ⑤   02 ①

03 (1) warn (2) hand (3) reward (4) trouble (5) glad

04 ①

05 (1) I don't need this chair. Let's throw it away.
    (2) My hometown is not far from Seoul.
    (3) I'm looking forward to visiting Hong Kong.
    (4) On my way to school, I met a foreigner.
    (5) As years go by, the work becomes more difficult.

06 ④

07 Paul met a woman who knew Ann's best friend.

08 ③   09 ④   10 ⑤

11 She kept talking about her life.

12 (1) to drink (2) to say

13 (1) handed me two flowers (2) bought us pizza

14 ③   15 ⑤   16 He went away.

17 He was driving down the road on his horse and cart.

18 ④

19 No, it can only keep people from getting older

20 He tried to explain the problem with the stones.

21 ②   22 ③   23 coming back

24 ③, ⑤   25 No tooth was seen in his mouth.

26 Because time went by and nothing grew or changed.

27 It's because he was still young.

28 No, he tried to, but he failed to destroy it.

---

01 bear: 아이를 낳다, beard: 수염, filed: 들판, log: 통나무

02 throw away: 버리다, change into: ~으로 바꾸다, worry about: ~에 대해 걱정하다, go by: 흐르다, 지나가다, go away: 떠나가다

03 get rid of ~을 없애다, keep ~ from -ing ~가 -하지 못 하게 하다, give birth (아기를[새끼를]) 낳다

29 ⑤　　　　30 ②　　　　31 ④

32 He told Maibon to throw the stone onto the ground and go back home.

33 Because he didn't really want to.

34 Because he saw the first tooth in his baby's mouth.

35 He was proud of his white hair and long beard.

01 free: 풀어 주다

02 bear: (동) 참다, 아이를 낳다, (명) 곰

03 reward: 보상, 보답, trouble: 문제, 골칫거리, warn: 경고하다, glad: 기쁜, hand: 건네주다, chore: 집안일

04 남자 얼굴의 턱과 뺨에 자라는 털을 가리키는 말은 beard(수염)이다.

05 throw away: 버리다, look forward to: ~을 기대하다, on one's way to: ~로 가는 길에, go by: 흐르다, 지나 가다

06 목적격 보어로 쓰일 수 있는 것은 부사가 아닌 형용사이다.

07 주격 관계대명사 who를 대신하여 that을 써도 좋다.

08 목적격 보어로 원형부정사를 취하는 동사는 help와 사역동사 make, let, have이다. tell은 목적격 보어로 to부정사를 받는 동사이다.

09 모두 명사로 쓰인 to부정사이지만 ④번은 형용사로 쓰인 to부정사이다.

10 주어진 문장의 that은 완전한 절을 이끄는 명사절 접속사이다. ⑤번은 관계대명사로 불완전한 절을 이끈다.

11 keep Ving: 계속 V하다

12 형용사적 용법의 to부정사이다.

13 hand와 buy는 모두 4형식 동사로, '사람+사물' 어순으로 간접목적어와 직접목적어를 취한다.

14 통나무 아래에 깔린 다리를 빼내는 것을 돕기 위해 통나무를 잡아당겨서 난쟁이를 풀어 준 것이다.

15 Doli가 들판으로 간 이유는 알 수 없다.

16 마법의 돌을 보상으로 준 Doli는 돌을 건넨 후 가버렸다.

17 Maibon이 한 노인을 보았을 때 그는 마차를 타고 길을 내려가고 있던 중이었다.

18 보상을 주고자 한 것은 난쟁이였다. 난쟁이가 Maibon에게 보상을 주겠다고 하였다.

19 사람들을 젊어지게 해 주는 것이 아니라 더 늙지 않게 막아 주는 돌이다.

20 Doli는 돌에 관한 문제를 설명하려고 애썼다.

21 아내의 말대로 창 밖으로 돌을 버렸지만 다음날 아침 돌이 창가에 있었다고 하였으므로 '그러나'가 가장 적절하다.

22 go by: 흐르다, 지나가다, by: ~ 옆에

23 돌이 계속해서 되돌아왔다는 의미이다. keep Ving는 '계속 해서 V하다'는 뜻으로 쓰인다.

24 아기에게 문제가 생기자 Maibon은 돌을 버렸고, 두 번째로 돌을 버리려고 했을 때에는 땅 속에 돌을 묻었다고 하였다.

25 아기의 입에서 이가 보이지 않는 문제가 생겼다.

26 시간이 지나도 아무것도 자라거나 변하지 않았기 때문이다.

27 자신이 여전히 젊었으므로 기뻤다고 하였다.

28 Maibon은 돌을 없애려고 노력했지만 돌이 계속해서 되돌아와 결국 실패하였다.

29 decide는 to부정사를 목적어로 취하는 동사이며, 사역동사 let은 목적격 보어로 동사원형을 취한다.

30 ②번은 난쟁이를 가리키는 대명사이다.

31 난쟁이에게 화가 났지만, 난쟁이의 조언을 받아들인 후 그는 기뻐하였다. relieved: 안도한

32 Doli는 Maibon에게 돌을 땅에 던지고 집으로 돌아가라고 말했다.

33 진정으로 돌을 없애길 원하지 않기 때문에 돌을 없앨 수 없었음을 알 수 있다.

34 아기의 입에 첫 이가 난 것을 보고 기뻐서 웃었다고 하였다.

35 그의 흰 머리와 긴 수염을 자랑스러워했다고 하였다.

교과서 파헤치기

Lesson 5

단어 TEST Step 1   p.02

01 피하다	02 제안	03 속상한, 마음이 상한
04 걱정하다; 걱정	05 접촉, 닿음	06 조언
07 싸우다	08 이발, 머리 깎기	09 홀로, 혼자
10 물건	11 다치게 하다, 아프게 하다	
12 어질러진, 더러운	13 현명한	14 공유하다, 나누다
15 점심시간	16 반복하다	17 문제
18 소리치다, 소리 지르다		19 ~부터, ~ 이후
20 의도하다, 작정하다		21 싫어하다
22 참다, 견디다	23 한계, 제한	24 설명하다
25 조언하다, 충고하다		26 아직
27 싸다, 꾸리다	28 어려운	29 용서하다
30 초보의, 초급의	31 두려움, 공포	32 이유, 까닭
33 풀다, 해결하다	34 (연극, 영화의) 대사	
35 ~에 집중하다	36 잠에서 깨다	
37 늦게까지 자지 않고 있다		38 체중이 늘다
39 고의로, 일부러	40 (기계가) 멈추다, 정지하다	
41 해결하다	42 결국, 마침내	43 지적하다

단어 TEST Step 2   p.03

01 mirror	02 elementary	03 share
04 difficult	05 repeat	06 yell
07 contact	08 advise	09 matter
10 pack	11 fight	12 lunch break
13 haircut	14 stuff	15 hurt
16 stand	17 avoid	18 limit
19 yet	20 toothache	21 suggestion
22 alone	23 worry	24 messy
25 upset	26 reason	27 hate
28 line	29 advice	30 forgive
31 explain	32 fear	33 wise
34 solve	35 in the end	36 focus on
37 shut down	38 gain weight	39 up and down
40 stay up late	41 on purpose	42 set an alarm
43 wake up		

단어 TEST Step 3   p.04

1 messy, 어질러진, 더러운   2 hate, 싫어하다

3 toothache, 치통   4 contact, 접촉

5 haircut, 이발, 머리 깎기   6 line, 대사   7 repeat, 반복하다

8 share, 공유하다   9 suggestion, 제안   10 fear, 두려움,

11 avoid, 피하다   12 elementary, 초급의

13 hurt, 다치게 하다   14 yell, 소리 지르다

15 advice, 조언   16 forgive, 용서하다

대화문 TEST Step 1   p.05~06

Listen & Talk 1-A-1

look, happy, matter / wore, sister's favorite, got / Did, tell / not yet, what to do

Listen & Talk 1-A-2

look down, What's the matter / got a haircut, funny / Take off, let me see, looks fine / not used to

Listen & Talk 1-B

look tired, the matter / I didn't have breakfast this morning / too bad, until lunch break / snack bar, could have / think so, too, How, make, suggestion / can post, suggestion

Listen & Talk 2 A-1

how to do better, give me some advice / solve a lot of / solve, should focus on, ones, got wrong

Listen & Talk 2 A-2

was late for class, wake up / set an alarm / turn it off / think you should, far from, That way, get out of bed

Review 1

stop playing computer games, What should I do / why don't you use, set, limit, shuts down / a good idea / I think you should move, out of, into / I think, should, for the advice

Communication

on the air / What's the matter / sharing, with, stuff without asking, What should, do / tell her your feelings, make some rules / I'll try that, Thanks for

대화문 TEST Step 2   p.07~08

Listen & Talk 1-A-1

M: You don't look so happy today. What's the matter?

W: I wore my sister's favorite T-shirt. But I got grape juice on it.

M: Oh, no. Did you tell your sister?

W: No, not yet. I don't know what to do .

Listen & Talk 1-A-2

Sora: David, you look down today. What's the matter?

David: I got a haircut but it's too short. I look funny.

Sora: Take off your hat and let me see. (*pause*) Oh, it looks fine.

David: Really? I guess I'm just not used to it yet.

Listen & Talk 1-B

Jane: You look tired. What's the matter?

Mike: I didn't have breakfast this morning. I'm so hungry.

Jane: Oh, that's too bad. We still have two more hours until lunch break.

Mike: Our school should have a snack bar. Then, we could have a quick breakfast or snacks.

Jane: I think so, too. How can we make that suggestion?

Mike: We can post it on the suggestion board.

Listen & Talk 2 A-1

Sujin: I don't know how to do better in math. Can you give me some advice?

Jake: How do you study for tests?

Sujin: I just solve a lot of problems.

Jake: Well, don't solve everything. I think you should focus on the ones you got wrong.

Listen & Talk 2 A-2

Emily: I was late for class again. I just can't wake up in the morning.

Tom: Do you set an alarm?

Emily: Yeah, but I turn it off and go back to sleep.

Tom: I think you should put it far from your bed. That way, you'll have to get out of bed.

Review 1

Eric: Ms. Morris, I just can't stop playing computer games. What should I do?

Ms. Morris: Well, why don't you use a special program? When you set a time limit, the computer shuts down at that time.

Eric: Oh, that's a good idea.

Ms. Morris: And I think you should move the computer out of your room and into the living room.

Eric: I think I should. Thank you for the advice, Ms. Morris.

Communication

Solomon: Hello, you're on the air.

Amy: Hi, Solomon. I'm Amy.

Solomon: Hi, Amy. What's the matter?

Amy: I hate sharing my room with my little sister. She uses my stuff without asking me first. What should I do?

Solomon: Hmm.... I think you should tell her your feelings. And you should also make some rules with your sister.

Amy: Oh, I'll try that. Thanks for the advice.

본문 TEST Step 1 · p.09~10

01 old, these, going, down
02 looks down
03 Let's, feelings, find
04 What, yelled at, after
05 because, forgot, lines
06 out, that, made
07 could, in front
08 sure, mean, hurt
09 have been, since
10 what, saying
11 never put, down
12 that, going, be
13 Don't, far, see
14 forgive, say, word
15 even look at
16 has never been
17 alone during
18 best friend
19 reason, know about
20 stand, any longer
21 go, tell, about
22 want, to, hurt
23 let, go
24 work, out
25 so, that, talking
26 went, talked, her
27 avoid, on purpose
28 didn't, way, say
29 doesn't, any more
30 too, part, up
31 like, face, wiser, end

본문 TEST Step 2 · p.11~12

01 years old, these days, going up and down
02 looks down
03 Let's listen to, feelings, find out why
04 What a day, yelled at, after
05 because, forgot, lines on stage
06 pointed out, that Bella made
07 could, in front of
08 sure, did not mean to hurt
09 have been, since elementary school
10 what, saying
11 would never put, down
12 that, not going to be friends anymore
13 Don't go too far, see
14 can't forgive, didn't say a word
15 didn't even look at
16 has never been
17 ate alone during
18 Bella's best friend
19 reason that we don't know about
20 can't stand, any longer
21 go, tell, about
22 want, to be hurt
23 should let it go
24 work it out

25 that, are talking

26 went to, talked to her

27 didn't avoid, on purpose

28 a way to say sorry

29 any more problems like

30 Me, too, part of growing up

31 Just like, face, solve them, wiser, end

1 Bella는 올해 15세이고 요즘 그 애의 기분은 좋다가 안 좋다가 한다.

2 오늘 그 애는 우울해 보인다.

3 Bella의 감정에 귀 기울여 보고 그 이유를 알아보자.

4 정말 끔찍한 하루야! 학교 연극이 끝난 후 Jenny가 Bella에게 소리를 지르다니 믿을 수가 없어.

5 글쎄, 그건 Bella가 무대에서 그녀의 대사를 잊어버렸기 때문이잖아.

6 Jenny는 Bella가 저지른 실수를 지적했잖아.

7 어떻게 모든 사람 앞에서 그렇게 할 수가 있니?

8 하지만 난 Jenny가 Bella에게 상처를 주려고 했던 건 아니었다고 확신해.

9 그들은 초등학교 때부터 가장 친한 친구였잖아. 기억하지?

10 내 말이 바로 그거야.

11 진정한 친구라면 절대로 그런 식으로 Bella를 깎아내리지 않을 거야.

12 나는 그들이 더 이상 친구로 지내지 않을까봐 걱정돼.

13 자, Fear. 너무 극단적으로 생각하지 마. 곧 알게 되겠지.

14 난 Jenny를 용서할 수 없어. 그 애는 Bella에게 한마디도 말을 안 했어.

15 Jenny는 심지어 Bella를 쳐다보지도 않았어.

16 Jenny가 전에 이렇게 차가웠던 적이 없었어.

17 Bella는 오늘 점심시간에 혼자 밥을 먹었잖아. 가엾은 Bella!

18 Jenny는 Bella의 가장 친한 친구야.

19 나는 우리가 모르는 어떤 이유가 있다고 확신해.

20 나는 더 이상 이 상황을 못 참아.

21 Bella는 일단 가서 Jenny에게 자신의 감정을 말해야 해.

22 나는 Bella가 또다시 상처받는 걸 원하지 않아.

23 그 애는 그냥 내버려 두어야 해.

24 그 애들은 좋은 친구야. 그 애들이 잘 해낼 거야.

25 휘! 나는 그 애들이 다시 이야기하게 되어 무척 기뻐.

26 그래, Bella가 Jenny에게 가서 그 애에게 먼저 말을 걸었지.

27 Jenny는 일부러 Bella를 피한 게 아니었어.

28 맞아, Jenny는 사과하는 방법을 몰랐던 거야.

29 나는 Bella에게 이번과 같은 문제가 더 이상 없기를 바라.

30 나도 그래. 하지만 문제들은 성장의 일부야.

31 이번과 꼭 마찬가지로 Bella는 문제들에 직면하게 될 거고, 그것들을 해결할 거고, 그리고 결국 더 현명해질 거야.

1 Bella is 15 years old this year and these days her feelings are going up and down.

2 Today, she looks down.

3 Let's listen to Bella's feelings and find out why.

4 What a day! I can't believe Jenny yelled at Bella after the school play.

5 Well, that's because Bella forgot her lines on stage.

6 Jenny pointed out the mistake that Bella made.

7 How could she do that in front of everyone?

8 But I'm sure Jenny did not mean to hurt Bella.

9 They have been best friends since elementary school. Remember?

10 That's what I'm saying.

11 A true friend would never put Bella down like that.

12 I'm worried that they are not going to be friends anymore.

13 Come on, Fear. Don't go too far. We'll see.

14 I can't forgive Jenny. She didn't say a word to Bella.

15 Jenny didn't even look at her.

16 Jenny has never been this cold before.

17 Bella ate alone during lunch today. Poor Bella!

18 Jenny is Bella's best friend.

19 I'm sure there is a reason that we don't know about.

20 I can't stand this any longer.

21 Bella should just go and tell her about her feelings.

22 I don't want Bella to be hurt again.

23 She should let it go.

24 They are good friends. They will work it out.

25 Whew! I'm so happy that they are talking again.

26 Yeah, Bella went to Jenny and talked to her first.

27 Jenny didn't avoid Bella on purpose.

28 Yeah, Jenny didn't know a way to say sorry.

29 I hope Bella doesn't have any more problems like this.

30 Me, too. But problems are part of growing up.

31 Just like this time, Bella will face the problems, solve them, and become wiser in the end.

Wrap up 1

1. late again

2. stayed up late, last night

3. should try to, earlier

4. should also pack, save time

5. try your advice

Read & Think

1. upset when, pointed out, in front of others

2. mean to hurt

3. Thanks for coming up

Think & Write

1. Worry Doll

2. want to tell, have

3. worried about, math grades

4. have had, since last year

5. do better

6. try to study, can't focus on

7. what to do

8. have not had, because of

9. take, away

구석구석지문 TEST Step 2 p.20

Wrap up 1

1. Mr. Jones: Daisy, you're late again.

2. Daisy: I'm really sorry, Mr. Jones. I stayed up late again last night.

3. Mr. Jones: Well, I think you should try to go to bed earlier.

4. You should also pack your bag the night before, so you can save time in the morning.

5. Daisy: Okay, Mr. Jones. I'll try your advice.

Read & Think

1. Bella: Jenny, I was upset when you pointed out my mistake in front of others.

2. But I'm sure you didn't mean to hurt my feelings.

3. Jenny: I'm so sorry, Bella. Thanks for coming up to me first.

Think & Write

1. Dear Worry Doll,

2. I want to tell you a problem that I have.

3. I'm worried about my terrible math grades.

4. I have had this problem since last year.

5. I want to do better in math.

6. But when I try to study math, I just can't focus on it.

7. I don't know what to do.

8. I have not had a good night's sleep because of this worry.

9. Can you take my worries away?

단어 TEST Step 1   p.21

01 눈 먼, 맹인인   02 죽은   03 ~처럼 보이다

04 끌다, ~을 끌어당기다   05 부주의한

06 ~ 동안, ~ 내내   07 궁금한, 호기심이 많은

08 감각   09 위험한   10 거대한

11 두꺼운   12 나타나다   13 생강

14 먹이를 주다   15 공격하다   16 보호소

17 구조   18 거대한   19 가만히 못 있는

20 혀   21 우정   22 (코끼리의) 코

23 힘   24 꼬리

25 재미있는, 유머러스한   26 곤충, 벌레

27 허락하다   28 믿을 수 없을 정도로

29 고래   30 죽은, 생명이 없는 31 다가가다, 다가오다

32 아마   33 암컷의   34 모험심이 강한

35 ~ 덕분에   36 ~에서 눈을 떼지 않다

37 태어나다   38 ~을 돌보다   39 차이를 구별하다

40 수백만의   41 ~의 일원이 되다 42 발표하다

43 ~ 옆에

단어 TEST Step 2   p.22

01 giant[huge]   02 appear   03 rescue

04 curious   05 dead   06 adventurous

07 allow   08 dolphin   09 friendship

10 snake   11 dangerous   12 approach

13 ginger   14 lifeless   15 attack

16 hole   17 careless   18 sense

19 humorous   20 throughout   21 female

22 tongue   23 sheet   24 insect

25 language   26 restless   27 unbelievably

28 strength   29 blind   30 feed

31 shelter   32 attract   33 thick

34 trunk   35 thanks to   36 next to

37 care for   38 become part of

39 millions of   40 give a presentation

41 be born   42 keep one's eyes on

43 tell the difference

단어 TEST Step 3   p.23

1 dead, 죽은   2 trunk, (코끼리의) 코

3 blind, 눈 먼, 맹인인   4 curious, 호기심이 많은

5 feed, 먹이를 주다   6 adventurous, 모험심이 강한

7 approach, 다가가다   8 friendship, 우정   9 insect, 곤충

10 whale, 고래   11 rescue, 구조하다   12 shelter, 보호소

13 tongue, 혀   14 allow, 허락하다   15 careless, 부주의한

16 tail, 꼬리

대화문 TEST Step 1   p.24~25

Listen & Talk 1 A-1

choose, topic / How about / I'm curious about weather change, thinking about doing / interesting topic

Listen and Talk 1 A-2

Look at, huge / bigger than / curious about, says, smells, bad, insects / wonder why

Listen and Talk 1 B

be friends / don't think so / watched, friendship between, and / curious about / raised, sent, back, wild, a year later / touching

Listen and Talk 2 A-1

Look at, puppy, two weeks / so small / as small as, much bigger, few months / grow

Listen and Talk 2 A-2

over there, grandparents' / by, really big / as old as me / How, know / planted, was, born

Listen and Talk 2 B

going, give a presentation, the biggest, How big, longer than, Another interesting thing, as heavy as, isn't it

Communication

tell us / millions of years ago / curious about, any / many, giant, as heavy as, couldn't jump / amazing

대화문 TEST Step 2   p.26~27

Listen & Talk 1 A-1

Ryan: Judy, did you choose a topic for your science project?

Judy: Not yet. How about you, Ryan?

Ryan: I'm curious about weather change. So I'm thinking about doing the project on that.

Judy: That's an interesting topic!

Listen and Talk 1 A-2

Jane: Look at this picture of a huge flower.

Tom: Wow, it is bigger than a person.

Jane: Yeah. I'm really curious about this flower. It also says here that the flower smells very bad, but insects love the smell.

Tom: Hmm, I wonder why.

Listen and Talk 1 B

Clare: Do you think we can be friends with lions, Todd?

Todd: No, Clare. I don't think so.

Clare: Well, I watched a video clip about friendship between two men and a lion.

Todd: Really? I'm curious about the story. Can you tell me more?

Clare: The two men raised a baby lion and sent her back into the wild. When the men and the lion met a year later, she remembered them.

Todd: Wow, that's so touching.

Listen and Talk 2 A-1

Dylan: Look at this picture, Mina. We got a new puppy yesterday. He's only two weeks old.

Mina: Oh, Dylan, he's so small!

Dylan: Yeah. He's as small as my hand now, but he'll get much bigger in a few months.

Mina: Wow, puppies grow very quickly.

Listen and Talk 2 A-2

Kelly: George, that red house over there is my grandparents' house.

George: Wow, the tree by the house is really big.

Kelly: Actually, that tree is as old as me, thirteen years old.

George: How do you know that, Kelly?

Kelly: My grandfather planted the tree in 2004 when I was born.

Listen and Talk 2 B

Toby: Hi, I'm Toby. I'm going to give a presentation about the blue whale. It's the biggest sea animal in the world. How big is it? Well, it's about 30m long. That means it's longer than a basketball court. Another interesting thing is that its tongue is as heavy as an elephant! Surprising, isn't it?

Communication

Emily: Hello, Dr. Watson. Can you tell us about your study?

Dr. Watson: I study animals that lived millions of years ago.

Emily: Oh, I'm curious about those animals. Were there any interesting ones?

Dr. Watson: Yes, there were many. This is the giant kangaroo. It lived in Australia. It was as heavy as three men and it couldn't jump well.

Emily: That's amazing!

본문 TEST Step 1   p.28~29

01 my first, in   02 took, pictures of
03 found, by, hole
04 saw, drinking, beside
05 were, bright as
06 gave her, name
07 Around, saw, approaching
08 stood around, thick
09 Thanks to, safe
10 Around, heard, sound
11 followed, found, crying
12 lying dead, alone
13 It, to stay, such
14 What's more, going   15 can't see well
16 easily be attacked
17 called, shelter, asked for   18 stay by, until
19 dark, quiet   20 kept, on, with
21 still next to   22 touching, lifeless, with
23 to see, staying
24 stays safe throughout
25 new, appeared, approached
26 thought that, let, in
27 But, wrong   28 oldest female, become part
29 other seemed, welcome
30 Unbelievably, one, female, fed
31 cared for, warmly, did
32 such, amazing moment

본문 TEST Step 2   p.30~31

01 was my first, in
02 took lots, pictures of
03 found, by, water hole
04 saw, drinking, beside
05 were as bright as
06 gave her a name
07 saw, approaching
08 stood around, made a thick wall
09 Thanks to them, safe
10 Around sunset, heard
11 followed, found, crying next to
12 lying dead, alone
13 It, to stay, in such a wild area
14 What's more, it, be dark
15 see well at night
16 easily be attacked
17 the elephant shelter, asked for 18 to stay, until

19 was dark, quiet   20 kept, on, with

21 still next to   22 was touching, with

23 It, to see, staying close to

24 stays safe throughout

25 appeared, approached

26 thought that, let, in

27 was wrong

28 the oldest female, to become part of

29 The other elephants, seemed

30 Unbelievably, elephants fed

31 cared for, as warmly as, did

32 such an amazing moment

27 그러나 내 생각이 틀렸다.

28 아마도 가장 나이가 많은 암컷인 듯한 코끼리 한 마리가 Stella 가 그 무리의 일원이 되도록 허락했다.

29 다른 코끼리들도 Stella를 반기는 것처럼 보였다.

30 믿을 수 없게도, 암컷 코끼리 중의 한 마리가 Stella에게 젖을 먹였다.

31 그 코끼리는 Stella의 엄마만큼 따뜻하게 Stella를 보살폈다.

32 이것은 너무나 놀라운 순간이었다.

본문 TEST Step 3   p.32~33

1 기록: 오늘은 내가 아프리카에 온 첫날이었다.

2 나는 코끼리 사진을 많이 찍었다.

3 오늘 아침에 나는 작은 물웅덩이 옆에 있는 한 코끼리 무리를 발견했다.

4 나는 아기 코끼리 한 마리가 엄마 옆에서 물을 마시고 있는 것을 보았다.

5 그 코끼리의 눈이 별처럼 밝았다.

6 나는 그 코끼리에게 Stella란 이름을 붙여 주었다.

7 정오 즈음에 나는 사자 한 무리가 Stella에게 다가가는 것을 보았다.

8 코끼리들은 Stella 주위에 둘러서서 두꺼운 벽을 만들었다.

9 그 코끼리들 덕분에 Stella는 안전했다.

10 기록: 해질녘에 나는 이상한 소리를 들었다.

11 나는 그 소리를 따라갔고 Stella가 자신의 엄마 옆에서 울고 있는 것을 발견했다.

12 엄마는 죽어서 누워 있었고, Stella는 혼자였다.

13 이러한 야생 지역에서 혼자 있는 것은 위험하다.

14 더욱이 곧 어두워질 것이었다.

15 코끼리들은 밤에 잘 볼 수 없다.

16 그래서 Stella는 쉽게 공격을 받을 수 있었다.

17 나는 코끼리 보호소에 전화를 해서 도움을 요청했다.

18 나는 구조대가 올 때까지 Stella 곁에 머물기로 결정했다.

19 기록: 밤은 어둡고 조용했다.

20 나는 야간용 카메라를 이용해서 Stella를 계속 지켜보았다.

21 Stella는 여전히 엄마 곁에 있었다.

22 Stella는 코로 엄마의 죽은 몸을 어루만지고 있었다.

23 Stella가 엄마 가까이에 머물고 있는 것을 보는 것은 슬픈 일이었다.

24 나는 Stella가 밤새도록 안전하게 있기를 바란다.

25 기록: 새로운 코끼리 무리가 나타났고, Stella는 그 무리에 다가갔다.

26 처음에 나는 그 코끼리들이 Stella를 자신의 무리로 받아들이지 않을 것이라고 생각했다.

본문 TEST Step 4~Step 5   p.34~37

1 Notes: Today was my first day in Africa.

2 I took lots of pictures of elephants.

3 This morning, I found an elephant group by a small water hole.

4 I saw a baby elephant drinking water beside her mother.

5 Her eyes were as bright as stars.

6 I gave her a name, Stella.

7 Around noon, I saw a group of lions approaching Stella.

8 The elephants stood around Stella and made a thick wall.

9 Thanks to them, Stella was safe.

10 Notes: Around sunset, I heard a strange sound.

11 I followed the sound and found Stella crying next to her mom.

12 She was lying dead and Stella was alone.

13 It is dangerous to stay alone in such a wild area.

14 What's more, it was going to be dark soon.

15 Elephants can't see well at night.

16 So Stella could easily be attacked.

17 I called the elephant shelter and asked for help.

18 I decided to stay by her until the rescue team came.

19 Notes: The night was dark and quiet.

20 I kept my eyes on Stella with my night camera.

21 Stella was still next to her mom.

22 She was touching her mom's lifeless body with her nose.

23 It was sad to see Stella staying close to her mom.

24 I hope Stella stays safe throughout the night.

25 Notes: A new elephant group appeared and Stella approached them.

26 At first, I thought that they would not let Stella in their group.

27 But I was wrong.

28 An elephant, probably the oldest female allowed Stella to become part of the group.

29 The other elephants also seemed to welcome Stella.

30 Unbelievably, one of the female elephants fed Stella.

31 She cared for Stella as warmly as Stella's mom did.

32 This was such an amazing moment!

구석구석지문 TEST Step 1   p.38

Read and Think

1. tried to attack
2. thick, to protect
3. was crying next to
4. watched, all night
5. oldest female, allowed, to become part of

Think & Write C

1. Plant Diary
2. June 15th
3. what you saw
4. saw, is called
5. bright, looks like
6. As, its size , about, as long as
7. It, that, attracts insects

Wrap Up 1

1. Isn't, sea horse
2. Actually, sea dragon
3. curious about , between
4. Look at, carefully, straight one, does not
5. tell the difference

구석구석지문 TEST Step 2   p.39

Read and Think

1. Some lions tried to attack Stella.
2. The elephant group made a thick wall to protect her.
3. Stella was crying next to her dead mother.
4. I watched her all night.
5. The oldest female elephant of a new group allowed Stella to become part of them.

Think & Write C

1. Plant Diary
2. Date: June 15th , 2019
3. Write about what you saw :

4. Today, I saw a plant. It is called a pitcher plant.

5. It is bright green and red. It looks like a pitcher.

6. As for its size, it is about 15cm long. It is as long as my hand.

7. It is interesting that the plant attracts insects and eats them.

Wrap Up 1

1. Minho: Look! Isn't that a sea horse?

2. Sue: Actually, no. It's a sea dragon.

3. Minho: Oh, really? I'm curious about the difference between them.

4. Sue: Look at the tail carefully. A sea dragon has a straight one, but a sea horse does not.

5. Minho: Oh, I can tell the difference now!

15 canvas, 화폭, 캔버스　16 myth, 신화

단어 TEST Step 1　　　　　　p.40

01 왕자	02 클래식의	03 녹다
04 생산하다	05 방향	06 전시하다
07 깃털	08 예술가, 미술가	09 약속하다
10 붓	11 풍경	12 소설
13 ~에도 불구하고	14 예술 작품	15 십 대
16 미로	17 생산	18 ~을 알아차리다
19 궁금해하다	20 납작한	21 해변, 바닷가
22 세부 사항	23 비극	24 더 좋아하다
25 날개	26 현대의	27 왕비, 여왕
28 록 음악	29 진짜의, 현실적인	30 소설가
31 ~ 때문에, ~이므로		32 신화
33 관광객	34 (어떤 것의) 변형	35 밀랍, 왁스
36 화폭, 캔버스	37 A를 B보다 더 좋아하다	
38 ~을 보다	39 ~을 힐끗 보다	
40 ~을 가까이하지 않다		41 즉시, 바로
42 ~을 보다	43 ~로 이동하다, 넘어가다	

단어 TEST Step 2　　　　　　p.41

01 melt	02 produce	03 feather
04 wing	05 direction	06 queen
07 artist	08 brush	09 prince
10 exhibit	11 frog	12 maze
13 promise	14 novel	15 despite
16 modern	17 flat	18 teen
19 notice	20 landscape	21 art work
22 version	23 detail	24 myth
25 production	26 tragedy	27 prefer
28 wonder	29 real	30 canvas
31 tourist	32 wax	33 rock
34 novelist	35 comedy	36 since
37 seaside	38 move on	39 prefer A to B
40 glance at	41 take a look[look at]	
42 stay away from		43 right away

단어 TEST Step 3　　　　　　p.42

1 feather, 깃털　2 seaside, 해변, 바닷가　3 melt, 녹다

4 tragedy, 비극　5 direction, 방향　6 wonder, 궁금해하다

7 landscape, 풍경　8 notice, 알아차리다　9 stick, 내밀다

10 artist, 예술가　11 wing, 날개　12 detail, 세부 사항

13 exhibit, 전시하다　14 rock, 록 음악

대화문 TEST Step 1　　　　　　p.43~44

Listen & Talk 1 A-1

going to play / practicing almost every day / What kind of music / play songs, nineties

Listen & Talk 1 A-2

how to paint clean lines / What kind of brush, using / round brush / When, paint, flat, better, Try

Listen & Talk 1 B

meeting, right / performance do you want to watch first / want to, performance / Sounds, right / about watching the play / the one, near

Listen & Talk 2 A-1

are, reading / a story / seen, of it, too, prefer, to / Why, like, better / scenes, looks, real

Listen & Talk 2 A-2

Have, listened / cool, part, great / dance version / listened to, I prefer the guitar version, matches, better

Listen & Talk 2 B

interesting painting, Look at / looks like / Which do you prefer / prefer, to / smile, How about you / prefer, to / looks modern

Communication

are planning, so, fine out, May, ask, a few questions / What kind of performance / performances best / do, prefer / prefer rock to hip-hop / favorite musician / favorite musicia / Thank, for

Wrap Up 1

Can, help, to buy / various kinds, What kind of music, to play / want to / should get / take, classical guitar

대화문 TEST Step 2　　　　　　p.45~46

Listen & Talk 1 A-1

W: Brian, is your band going to play at the Teen Music Festival?

M: Yes, we're practicing almost every day.

W: What kind of music are you going to play this year?

M: Rock music. We'll play songs from the nineties.

Listen & Talk 1 A-2

W: Can you help me? I don't know how to paint clean lines.

M: What kind of brush were you using?

W: This round brush.

M: When you paint lines, a flat brush is better. Try this one.

W: Okay, thank you.

W: (*ringing*) Hello, Steve.

M: Hi, Anna. We're meeting at the arts festival tomorrow at 1:30, right?

W: Right. What kind of performance do you want to watch first?

M: I want to watch the hip-hop dance performance first.

W: Sounds good. It's at 2 p.m. at the gym, right?

M: Yeah, and how about watching the play, Romeo and Juliet, at 4 p.m.?

W: Oh, the one at the Main Hall near the gym? Sure!

M: What are you reading, Jina?

W: The novel, Life of Pi. It's a story of a boy and a tiger.

M: It's a great book. I've seen the movie of it, too. I prefer the movie to the novel.

W: Why do you like it better?

M: The scenes are very beautiful. And the tiger looks so real.

W: Have you listened to Jane's new song, Girl Friend?

M: Yeah, it's really cool. The guitar part is great.

W: There is also a dance version of the song on the album.

M: I've listened to it, but I prefer the guitar version to the dance version. It matches her voice better.

W: I saw an interesting painting in an art book. Look at this.

M: Wow, it looks like da Vinci's Mona Lisa.

W: Actually, it's Mona Lisa by Fernando Botero. Which do you prefer?

M: I prefer da Vinci's to Botero's. Da Vinci's Mona Lisa has an interesting smile. How about you?

W: Well, I prefer Botero's to da Vinci's. His Mona Lisa is cute, and it looks modern.

M: Hi, we are planning a school festival, so we want to find out students' favorite types of performances. May I ask you a few questions?

W: Sure.

M: What kind of performance do you like best?

W: I like music performances best.

M: Okay. Then, which do you prefer, rock or hip-hop?

W: I prefer rock to hip-hop.

M: Who's your favorite musician?

W: My favorite musician is TJ.

M: Great. Thank you for your answers.

M: Can you help me? I want to buy a guitar.

W: There are various kinds of guitars. What kind of music do you want to play?

M: I want to play pop songs.

W: Then you should get a classical guitar.

M: Okay, I will take a classical guitar.

01 Welcome to, tour

02 when, much, looking, each

03 glance, for, few, on

04 might miss, since, notice

05 at, closely, help, see   06 Look at, first

07 seaside, peaceful, isn't it   08 title, is, with

09 where Icarus is

10 that, sticking out, near

11 in, famous myth

12 wings, feathers, stay away

13 However, didn't listen   14 flew, close to

15 melted, fell into   16 look at, entire

17 Despite, going on, everyday

18 still look peaceful

19 What, think, trying   20 move on to

21 see, behind, large

22 actually painted

23 Who, think he is   24 Take, look

25 seems to, main, because   26 title, painting

27 drawing, beside, princess   28 Take, close

29 make you wonder

30 Try, which direction

31 see, in, mirror, background   32 Who, think, is

01 Welcome to, tour

02 when, go to, how much time, spend looking at

03 glance at, for, a few, move on

04 might miss, since, to notice them

05 look at, closely, help you see, details

06 Look at, first

07 seaside landscape, peaceful, isn't it

08 title of, is　　09 where Icarus is

10 are sticking out of the water near

11 in the famous myth

12 made wings for him with feathers, to stay away from

13 However, didn't listen　　14 flew too close

15 melted, fell into　　16 look at, entire

17 Despite, going on with, everyday activities

18 still look peaceful

19 What do you think, trying to　　20 move on to

21 see, behind　　22 actually painted

23 Who do you think he is

24 Take, quick look

25 seems to be, because, in the center

26 title, painting

27 drawing, beside

28 Take, close look

29 make you wonder

30 Try to, which direction the artist is

31 see, in the mirror, background

32 Who do you think he is

16 이제, 그림 전체를 다시 보세요.

17 이카루스의 비극에도 불구하고 사람들은 일상의 활동을 계속하고 있습니다.

18 그림이 여전히 평화로워 보이나요?

19 화가가 우리에게 무엇을 말하려 한다고 생각하나요?

20 이제, 다음 그림으로 넘어갑시다.

21 커다란 캔버스 뒤에 있는 화가가 보이나요?

22 그는 Diego Vel②zquez이고, 그가 실제로 이 그림을 그렸습니다.

23 그가 누구를 그리고 있다고 생각하나요?

24 재빨리 봅시다.

25 어린 공주가 그림의 중앙에 있기 때문에 주인공처럼 보입니다.

26 하지만 그림의 제목은 '시녀들'입니다.

27 그렇다면 화가는 공주 옆에 있는 두 여인을 그리고 있나요?

28 자세히 보세요.

29 그림에 대해 더 궁금해하게 될 겁니다.

30 화가가 바라보고 있는 방향을 보려고 노력해 보세요.

31 그림의 배경에 있는 거울 속 왕과 왕비가 보이나요?

32 이제 여러분은 그가 누구를 그리고 있다고 생각하나요?

1 세계 미술관(the World Art Museum)에 오신 것을 환영합니다.

2 미술관에 갈 때 여러분은 각각의 그림을 보는 데 얼마나 많은 시간을 보내나요?

3 많은 방문객들은 이동하기 전에 하나의 그림을 몇 초간만 힐끗 봅니다.

4 하지만 그림의 중요한 세부 사항들을 즉시 알아채는 것은 어렵기 때문에 여러분들은 그것들을 놓칠 수 있습니다.

5 오늘 우리는 두 개의 그림을 자세히 살펴볼 것이고, 여러분이 흥미로운 세부 사항들을 볼 수 있도록 제가 도와드리겠습니다.

6 먼저 이 그림을 보세요.

7 바닷가 풍경이 매우 평화롭고 아름답죠, 그렇지 않나요?

8 이 그림의 제목은 '추락하는 이카루스가 있는 풍경'입니다.

9 그러면 이카루스가 어디에 있는지 보이나요?

10 배 근처에 물 밖으로 나와 있는 두 다리가 보이죠?

11 이것이 그리스의 유명한 신화에 나오는 이카루스입니다.

12 신화에서 이카루스의 아버지는 그를 위해 깃털과 밀랍으로 날개를 만들어 주었고 그에게 태양을 가까이 하지 말라고 말했습니다.

13 하지만 이카루스는 듣지 않았습니다.

14 그는 태양에 너무 가깝게 날았습니다.

15 그래서 밀랍이 녹았고 그는 물에 빠졌습니다.

1 Welcome to the World Art Museum tour.

2 When you go to an art museum, how much time do you spend looking at each painting?

3 Many visitors glance at one painting for only a few seconds before they move on.

4 But you might miss the important details of paintings since it is hard to notice them right away.

5 Today, we'll look at two paintings closely and I'll help you see interesting details.

6 Look at this painting first.

7 The seaside landscape is so peaceful and beautiful, isn't it?

8 The title of this painting is *Landscape with the Fall of Icarus*.

9 So, can you see where Icarus is?

10 Do you see two legs that are sticking out of the water near the ship?

11 This is Icarus in the famous myth in Greece.

12 In the myth, Icarus' father made wings for him with feathers and wax and told him to stay away from the sun.

13 However, Icarus didn't listen.

14 He flew too close to the sun.

15 So, the wax melted and he fell into the water.

16 Now, look at the entire painting again.

17 Despite the tragedy of Icarus, people are going on with their everyday activities.

18 Does the painting still look peaceful?

19 What do you think the artist is trying to tell us?

20 Now, let's move on to the next painting.

21 Do you see the artist behind the large canvas?

22 He is Diego Velázquez, and he actually painted this picture.

23 Who do you think he is painting?

24 Take a quick look.

25 The young princess seems to be the main person because she is in the center of the painting.

26 But the title of the painting is *The Maids of Honour*.

27 Then, is the artist drawing the two women beside the princess?

28 Take a close look.

29 It will make you wonder about the painting more.

30 Try to see which direction the artist is looking at.

31 Can you see the king and the queen in the mirror in the background of the painting?

32 Who do you think he is painting now?

구석구석지문 TEST Step 1   p.57

Listen & Talk

1. are, reading
2. reading, who, in a maze
3. seen, too, prefer, to
4. Why, like, better
5. various stories, show, important parts

Grammar in Real Life

1. let, in
2. Who, you
3. promised me, let you enter, be
4. serve you, cookies, tea
5. Never let, in
6. worry, make the princess keep

Think and Write C

1. Amazing Art exhibition
2. interesting pieces of art
3. Among, called
4. was made by
5. Interestingly, was used
6. because, makes me feel calm
7. can be used to
8. Anything, possible

구석구석지문 TEST Step 2   p.58

Listen & Talk

1. M: What are you reading, Sally?

2. W: I'm reading *The Maze Runner*. It's about boys who are put in a maze.

3. M: It's a great story. I've seen the movie of it, too. I prefer the novel to the movie.

4. W: Why do you like it better?

5. M: The novel has various stories. But the movie didn't show some important parts of the story.

Grammar in Real Life

1. Princess, please let me in.

2. Who are you?

3. The princess promised me, "If you help me, I'll let you enter the palace and be my friend."

4. Come here. I'll have people serve you some cookies and tea.

5. No! Never let him in. I don't like him.

6. Don't worry, Frog. I'll make the princess keep her promise.

Think and Write C

1. Today, I went to the Amazing Art exhibition.

2. At the exhibition, I saw many interesting pieces of art.

3. Among them, I liked the piece called Moon Tree.

4. It was made by French artist, David Myriam.

5. Interestingly, sand was used in this painting.

6. I like it because a tree in the moon makes me feel calm.

7. Now I know that anything can be used to make art.

8. Anything is possible!

단어 TEST Step 1   p.59

01 균형을 잡다   02 계산대, 판매대   03 혼합물, 혼합

04 무가당의   05 전달하다, 배달하다

06 생각   07 효과   08 (여행) 안내서

09 손으로 쓴   10 튀기다   11 빵집, 제과점

12 존재   13 백, 100   14 제안하다

15 중요함   16 의존, 의지

17 (웹 사이트에 정보, 사진을) 올리다

18 지역의, 현지의; 주민, 현지인   19 기계

20 경험   21 순간   22 근처에

23 최신 유행의   24 의견   25 시내의

26 창의적인   27 토론, 논의   28 가격

29 남아 있다, 남다   30 무서워하는, 겁먹은

31 나이가 지긋한   32 기부하다   33 (과학) 기술

34 현명하게   35 ~을 버리다   36 ~하기를 기대하다

37 ~에 의존하다   38 비록 ~할지라도   39 주목을 받다

40 대금을 지불하다   41 잠들다   42 계속해서 ~하다

43 ~하느라 바쁘다

단어 TEST Step 2   p.60

01 counter   02 technology   03 suggest

04 debate   05 machine   06 donate

07 downtown   08 effect   09 sugar-free

10 experience   11 fry   12 presence

13 price   14 handwritten   15 balance

16 hundred   17 importance   18 thought

19 local   20 creative   21 deliver

22 nearby   23 trendy   24 opinion

25 post   26 mixture   27 agree

28 remain   29 dependence   30 wisely

31 moment   32 scared   33 guesthouse

34 elderly   35 keep -ing   36 pay for

37 be busy -ing   38 throw away   39 rely on

40 even though   41 fall asleep   42 get attention

43 get lost

단어 TEST Step 3   p.61

1 fry, 튀기다   2 guidebook, (여행) 안내서

3 local, 지역의, 현지의   4 bakery, 빵집, 제과점

5 remain, 남아 있다, 남다   6 moment, 순간

7 balance, 균형을 잡다   8 experience, 경험

9 post, (웹사이트에 정보, 사진을) 올리다

10 wisely, 현명하게   11 downtown, 시내의, 도심지의

12 guesthouse, (여행자 등의) 숙소, 여관

13 donate, 기부하다   14 technology, (과학) 기술

15 suggest, 제안하다   16 dependence, 의지, 의존

대화문 TEST Step 1   p.62~63

Listen & Talk 1 A-1

birthday gift / giving, memory stick / video clip, saved, think, present / touching

Listen & Talk 1 A-2

what do you think about / thought, sound effects / made, interesting / couldn't focus, scared

Listen & Talk 1 B

Have, heard / donates, right answer / what, think about / creative, have fun, help out, Have, played / going to try, out

Listen & Talk 2 A-1

better than before / singing contest, get closer / with you on that, wait to watch, next performances

Listen & Talk 2 A-2

comments / comfortable to share / that, posts / not with you on that, share, close friends

Listen & Talk 2 B

help, order / press, choose / How, pay for my order / bottom, pay / simple, much faster than, counter / with you, saves, time, when, line

Communication

debate, first topic What, think / trendy, at a cheaper price / with, on that, spend, throw away / opinions, move on

Wrap Up 1

finished making the posting, What do you think about it / get attention, How about, below / one, right / change / hope, find

대화문 TEST Step 2   p.64~65

Listen & Talk 1 A-1

Jane: Look, Dad. This is Mom's birthday gift.

Dad: Oh, you're giving her a memory stick?

Jane: Yeah, I've made a family video clip for Mom and saved it on this stick. What do you think about the present?

Dad: I think it's really touching. She'll love it.

Mike: Jenny, what do you think about the new online comic Scary Night?

Jenny: I didn't like it. I thought it had too many sound effects.

Mike: Really? I thought they made the story more interesting.

Jenny: Not me. I couldn't focus because I was too scared.

Tony: Hey, Julie! Have you heard about the Quiz & Rice game?

Julie: Yeah, isn't it the one that donates rice when you get a right answer?

Tony: Yeah, what do you think about the game?

Julie: I think it's a creative game. You can have fun and help out hungry people. Have you played it yet?

Tony: No, but I'm going to try it out this weekend.

Jack: Sally, did you watch Super Voice's Top 10 finalists yesterday?

Sally: Yeah. They all sang much better than before.

Jack: Yeah, they did. I think this singing contest helps them get closer to their dreams.

Sally: I'm with you on that. I can't wait to watch their next performances.

Steve: Hey, Lisa. I've got over a hundred comments on my SNS posts.

Lisa: Oh, I wouldn't feel comfortable to share my posts with so many people.

Steve: Really? I think it's great that a lot of people see my posts.

Lisa: I'm not with you on that. I only want to share my posts with my close friends.

Emma: Excuse me. Can you help me order with this machine?

Tom: Sure. First, press the Hot Dog button and choose your hot dog and drink.

Emma: Okay. How do I pay for my order?

Tom: Touch the Done button at the bottom and pay for them.

Emma: Wow, it's so simple. This machine is much faster than ordering at the counter.

Tom: I'm with you on that. It really saves a lot of time when there's a long line.

Sujin: Now, we will start the three-minute debate. Today's first topic is fast fashion. What do you think about it? Please, begin, James.

James: I think fast fashion is good. We can wear trendy clothes at a cheaper price.

Wendy: I'm not with you on that. It makes us spend too much money and throw away clothes too often.

Sujin: It looks like the two of you have different opinions on the first topic. Now, let's move on to the second topic.

Alex: I've just finished making the posting for Leon, Mom. What do you think about it?

Mom: Oh, the title "LOST CAT" in big letters at the top is easy to see.

Alex: Yeah, I did it to get attention. How about these photos below the title?

Mom: Hmm... the one on the right doesn't show Leon's face well.

Alex: Okay, I'll change the photo.

Mom: Oh, I hope we can find Leon.

01 suggested, surprising, without

02 to, sitting, looking at

03 explained, kept saying, fully   04 started, trip to

05 first, terrible   06 way, around, lost, downtown

07 busy looking, asking, few, from

08 Even though, right, get

09 so tired that, out

10 fall alseep, worried, happen

11 looking around, have, fried

12 However, which, to

13 up, elderly, tired, directions

14 seemed, understand, words

15 took, local, nearby

16 fried rice, amazing

17 take, post, blog

18 without, decided, enjoy, moment

19 remaining, relied, on

20 able, various, on, streets

21 kind enough, sides

22 talked, with, other

23 much, together on

24 trip, different experience
25 dependent on, that, without
26 that, moment without
27 From, learned, importance, balanced
28 So, would, travel
29 Probalby, try, wisely

01 suggested, surprising, family trip without
02 hate to see, sitting together, looking at
03 explained, kept saying that, not fully enjoy
04 started, trip to
05 first day, terrible
06 On the way to, around, got lost in downtown
07 was busy looking, asking for, with a few, from
08 Even though, right next to, it took, to get
09 were so tired that, could not go out
10 went to bed, fall alseep,worried, what would happen
11 After looking around, to have, fried
12 which restaurant to go to
13 went up to, tired to ask for directions
14 seemed to understand, words   15 took us, nearby
16 fried rice, amazing
17 take pictures of, post them
18 without, decided to enjoy
19 During, remaining, relied, on
20 were able to meet, talk with
21 kind enough to show, with a smile
22 talked, with each other
23 much of our time together
24 new and different experience
25 so dependent on, that, couldn't, without
26 that, without it
27 From, have learned, importance, balanced use
28 would I travel   29 try to use it, wisely

1 지난여름, 아빠가 깜짝 놀랄 만한 이벤트로 스마트폰 없는 가족 여행을 제안하셨다!
2 아빠는 "나는 우리 가족이 함께 앉아서 각자의 스마트폰만 보고 있는 걸 보는 게 참 싫구나."라고 말씀하셨다.
3 여동생과 내가 스마트폰이 필요하다고 설명했지만, 아빠는 스마트폰이 있으면 여행을 충분히 즐길 수 없을 거라고 계속해서 말씀하셨다.

4 그래서 우리는 새로운 도시인 스페인의 바르셀로나로 '첨단 과학 기술 없는 여행'을 시작했다.
5 우리의 첫째 날은 엉망이었다.
6 레이알 광장 주변에 있는 여행자 숙소로 가는 길에 우리는 바르셀로나 시내에서 길을 잃었다.
7 아빠는 지도를 보며 여행안내 책자에서 배운 스페인어 몇 마디로 길을 묻느라 분주하셨다.
8 우리의 숙소가 광장 바로 옆에 있었음에도 불구하고, 우리가 그곳에 도착하는 데는 거의 두 시간이 걸렸다.
9 우리는 너무 피곤해서 저녁을 먹으러 나갈 수가 없었다.
10 나는 잠자리에 들었지만 내일 무슨 일이 일어날지 걱정이 되어서 잠들 수가 없었다.
11 가우디가 지은 구엘 공원을 둘러본 후, 우리는 점심으로 해산물 볶음밥을 먹기로 했다.
12 그러나 우리는 어떤 식당으로 가야 할지 몰랐다.
13 우리는 도움이 필요해서, 엄마가 한 노부인에게 가서 인기 있는 해산물 식당으로 가는 길을 물어보려고 애쓰셨다.
14 운이 좋게도 그녀는 몇 마디 안 되는 엄마의 스페인어를 이해하는 듯했다.
15 그녀는 우리를 근처에 있는 작은 현지 식당으로 데려다 주었다.
16 그 해산물 볶음밥은 놀랍도록 맛있었다.
17 나는 음식 사진을 찍어 그것을 내 블로그에 올리고 싶은 마음이 정말 간절했다.
18 그러나 스마트폰이 없었기 때문에 나는 그냥 그 순간을 즐기기로 했다.
19 (여행의) 남아 있는 날들 동안, 우리는 점점 더 현지 사람들에게 의존하게 되었다.
20 우리는 거리에서, 빵집에서, 공원에서 다양한 사람들을 만나 이야기할 수 있었다.
21 그들은 항상 웃으면서 너무나 친절히도 바르셀로나의 다양한 면을 우리에게 보여 주었다.
22 또한 우리 가족은 서로 많은 대화를 나누었다.
23 우리는 스페인의 기차에서, 버스에서, 그리고 식당에서 많은 시간을 함께 보냈다.
24 우리의 '첨단 과학 기술 없는' 여행은 새롭고 색다른 경험이었다.
25 여행 전에 나는 내 스마트폰에 너무 의존해서 그것 없이는 아무것도 할 수 없었다.
26 하지만 지금은 내가 스마트폰 없이도 그 순간을 즐길 수 있음을 알고 있다.
27 그 경험을 통해, 나는 스마트폰을 균형 있게 사용하는 것이 중요함을 배우게 되었다.
28 그러면, 다음번에 나는 스마트폰 없이 여행을 하게 될까?
29 아마도 그렇지는 않을 것이다. 하지만 나는 그것을 좀 더 현명하게 사용하기 위해 노력할 것이다.

1 Last summer, my father suggested a surprising event: a family trip without smartphones!

2 He said, "I hate to see you sitting together and only looking at your smartphones."

3 My sister and I explained the need for smartphones, but he kept saying that we could not fully enjoy the trip with them.

4 So we started a technology-free trip to a new city, Barcelona, Spain.

5 Our first day was terrible.

6 On the way to our guesthouse around Plaza Reial, we got lost in downtown Barcelona.

7 Dad was busy looking at the map and asking for directions with a few Spanish words he got from a tour guidebook.

8 Even though our guesthouse was right next to the Plaza, it took us about two hours to get there.

9 We were so tired that we could not go out for dinner.

10 I went to bed but couldn't fall asleep because I was worried about what would happen the next day.

11 After looking around Gaudi's Park Guell, we decided to have seafood fried rice for lunch.

12 However, we didn't know which restaurant to go to.

13 We needed help, so Mom went up to an elderly lady and tried to ask for directions to a popular seafood restaurant.

14 Luckily, she seemed to understand Mom's few Spanish words.

15 She took us to a small local restaurant nearby.

16 The seafood fried rice was amazing.

17 I really wanted to take pictures of the food and post them on my blog.

18 But without my phone, I just decided to enjoy the moment.

19 During the remaining days, we relied more and more on the locals.

20 We were able to meet and talk with various people on the streets, in the bakeries, and in the parks.

21 They were always kind enough to show us different sides of Barcelona with a smile.

22 Also, our family talked a lot with each other.

23 We spent much of our time together on the Spanish train, on the bus, and at the restaurants.

24 Our technology-free trip was a new and different experience.

25 Before the trip, I was so dependent on my smartphone that I couldn't do anything without it.

26 But now I see that I can enjoy the moment without it.

27 From the experience, I have learned the importance of a balanced use of the smartphone.

28 So, next time, would I travel without a smartphone?

29 Probably not. But I will try to use it more wisely.

Read and Think

1. Technology-Free Trip
2. new, different experience, without
3. Troubles
4. On, on our way to
5. take pictures of, post, on
6. Joys
7. enjoyed, around
8. a lot, all the time
9. after
10. thoughts, using
11. couldn't do anything
12. importance, balanced use

Grammar in Real Life B

1. Wash, running, cut, into, pieces
2. cut, with, low, heat
3. Add, to make, mixture
4. Roll, out, put, filling
5. rolled bread, take it out, bake, minutes
6. Decorate, remaining apple filling

Read and Think

1. Technology-Free Trip to Barcelona
2. Last summer, I had a new and different experience: a family trip without smartphones.
3. Troubles
4. On the first day, we got lost on our way to the guesthouse.
5. I couldn't take pictures of the food and post them on my blog.
6. Joys

55

7. I enjoyed the places and the people around me.

8. I talked a lot with my family all the time and everywhere.

9. Changes after the Trip

10. My thoughts on using a smartphone

11. Before: I couldn't do anything without it.

12. Now: I understand the importance of a balanced use of it.

Grammar in Real Life B

1. Wash one apple under running water and cut it into small pieces.

2. Cook the cut apple pieces with brown sugar on low heat.

3. Add salt, milk, and a beaten egg to make the egg mixture.

4. Roll the bread out and put the cooked apple filling on it.

5. Put the rolled bread in the egg mixture and take it out quickly. Then bake it for 3 minutes.

6. Decorate a dish with the bread rolls and the remaining apple filling.

단어 TEST Step 1   p.78

01 수염	02 수레, 우마차	03 손주
04 아내, 부인	05 땅, 지면	06 돌
07 문제	08 파괴하다, 없애다	09 기쁜
10 건네주다	11 도착하다	12 (새끼를) 낳다
13 경고하다	14 통나무	15 마술의
16 소, 암소	17 기쁨	18 아무것도 ~아닌 것
19 보상, 보답	20 빼내다, 풀어 주다; 자유로운	
21 결심하다, 결정하다		22 계질
23 난쟁이	24 설명하다	25 들판, 밭
26 이, 치아	27 ~하지 않는 한	28 흐르다, 지나가다
29 ~을 기대하다, ~을 고대하다		30 ~을 없애다
31 ~을 버리다	32 ~을 자랑스러워하다	
33 ~으로 바꾸다	34 ~에서 멀리	35 ~하려고 노력하다
36 새끼를 낳다, 출산하다		37 떠나가다
38 ~가 …하지 못하게 하다		39 ~로 가는 길에
40 ~에 대해 걱정하다		41 계속 ~하다

단어 TEST Step 2   p.79

01 arrive	02 season	03 delight
04 free	05 ground	06 decide
07 warn	08 explain	09 unless
10 field	11 beard	12 wife
13 glad	14 hand	15 log
16 magic	17 destroy	18 tooth
19 grandchild	20 nothing	21 cart
22 stone	23 bear	24 cow
25 reward	26 dwarf	27 trouble
28 far from	29 be proud of	
30 keep ~ from -ing		31 try to
32 get rid of	33 go away	34 change into
35 keep ~ing	36 look forward to	
37 on one's way to		38 go by
39 throw away	40 worry about	41 give birth

단어 TEST Step 3   p.80

1 stone, 돌멩이   2 hand, 건네주다

3 bear, (아이나 새끼를) 낳다   4 grandchild, 손주

5 beard, 수염   6 wife, 아내, 부인   7 arrive, 도착하다

8 destroy, 파괴하나   9 log, 통나무   10 cow, 소, 암소

11 season, 계절　12 field, 들판　13 cart, 수레, 우마차
14 reward, 보상　15 warn, 경고하다
16 free, 빼내다, 풀어 주다

01 One, driving down, when
02 looked, sick, worry about
03 Later, saw, field
04 get, out, under
05 pulled, away, freed
06 have, reward, want
07 heard, that, keep, young
08 humans, wrong, keep from
09 tried, explain, with, listen
10 handed, went away
11 a few, grow, all
12 became, got upset
13 change into, slow
14 birth, got, throw, away
15 listen to, threw, out
16 found, sitting by
17 worried about, that, still
18 having trouble, tooth, seen
19 throw away, put, under
20 back, went by, grew
21 worry, look forward, nothing
22 destroy, kept, back
23 throw away, far from
24 On, way, got angry
25 didn't, warn, about
26 tried, wouldn't listen
27 explained, rid of, unless
28 more, Whatever, let, happen
29 throw, onto, back
30 as, arrived, changed, bore
31 with delight, tooth, mouth
32 their, lived for, years
33 proud of, beard

01 driving down, on his horse, when
02 looked, sick, to worry about growing old
03 Later that day, dwarf
04 trying to get, out from
05 pulled, away, freed

06 reward, do, want
07 heard, that, keep, young
08 it all wrong, young again, keep, from getting older
09 tried to explain, didn't listen　　　10 handed him
11 a few days, grow at all
12 became, got upset
13 change into chickens, slow
14 give birth, got, angry, to throw it away
15 listen to, threw, out
16 However, found, sitting by
17 worried about, glad that, still young
18 having trouble, No tooth, seen
19 to throw away, put, under the ground
20 came back, went by, nothing grew, changed
21 to worry, nothing to look forward to
22 tried to destroy, kept coming back
23 decided to throw away, far from
24 On his way to, got angry
25 didn't you warn　　　　　26 tried to, listen
27 explained, get rid of, unless, wanted to
28 no more of, Whatever, let, happen
29 to throw, onto, go back home
30 did, said, arrived, changed into, bore
31 laughed with delight, his baby's mouth
32 lived for many years　　　33 was proud of

1 어느 날, Maibon이 한 노인을 보았을 때, 그는 마차를 타고 길을 내려가고 있던 중이었다.
2 그 노인은 매우 아파 보였다. Maibon은 늙어 가는 것이 걱정되기 시작했다.
3 그날 오후, 그는 들판에서 Doli라는 난쟁이를 보았다.
4 그는 통나무 아래에 깔린 그의 다리를 빼내려고 하고 있었다.
5 Maibon은 통나무를 잡아당겨서 난쟁이를 풀어 주었다.
6 "너는 보상을 받게 될 거야. 원하는 게 뭐니?"
7 "나는 네가 사람의 젊음을 유지해 주는 마법의 돌들을 가지고 있다고 들었어. 나는 그것을 원해."
8 오, 너희 인간들은 잘못 알고 있어. 그 돌들은 너희들이 다시 젊어지게 해 주지 않아. 단지 더 늙지 않게 막아 줄 뿐이라고."
9 "그것대로 좋아!" Doli는 그 돌에 관한 문제를 설명하려고 했지만, Maibon은 듣지 않았다.
10 그래서 Doli는 그에게 마법의 돌을 건네고는 가버렸다.
11 며칠이 지나서, Maibon은 그의 수염이 전혀 자라지 않았음을 알았다.
12 그는 행복해졌지만, 그의 아내 Modrona는 화가 났다.
13 "달걀이 닭이 되지 않아요!" "아, 시기가 더딘 거예요. 그 뿐이에요."

14 하지만 그녀는 탐탁해하지 않았다. "소가 새끼를 낳지 않아요!" 그때 Maibon은 그 돌에 대해 그녀에게 이야기를 했고 그녀는 매우 화를 내며 그에게 그것을 버리라고 말했다.

15 그는 원하지 않았지만, 아내의 말을 듣고 창밖으로 돌을 던졌다.

16 그러나 다음날 아침 그는 창가에 그 돌이 있는 것을 발견했다!

17 Maibon은 동물들이 걱정되긴 했지만, 자신이 여전히 젊어서 기뻤다.

18 이제 Maibon의 아기에게 문제가 생겼다. 아기의 입에서 이가 보이지 않았다.

19 그의 아내는 그에게 그 돌을 버리라고 말했고 Maibon은 이번엔 그 돌을 땅속에 묻었다.

20 그런데 그 다음날 그 돌은 다시 돌아왔다! 시간이 흘렀고 어떤 것도 자라거나 변하지 않았다.

21 Maibon은 걱정이 되기 시작했다. "기대할 것도 내 일의 결과를 보여 줄 것도 아무것도 없어."

22 Maibon은 그 돌을 없애려고 노력했지만 돌은 계속 되돌아왔다.

23 Maibon은 그 돌을 그의 집에서 멀리 떨어진 곳에 버리기로 결심했다.

24 그는 들판으로 가는 길에 난쟁이를 보았다. Maibon은 그에게 화를 냈다.

25 "너는 왜 내게 그 돌에 대해 경고하지 않았어?"

26 "나는 하려고 했지만, 너는 들으려 하지 않았어."

27 Doli는 Maibon이 진심으로 원하지 않는 한 그 돌을 없앨 수 없다고 설명했다.

28 "나는 그것을 더 이상 원하지 않아. 무슨 일이 있어도 일어나게 해!"

29 Doli는 그에게 그 돌을 땅에 던지고 집으로 돌아가라고 말했다.

30 Maibon은 Doli가 말한 대로 했다. 그가 집에 도착했을 때, Modrona는 그에게 달걀이 닭이 되고 소가 새끼를 낳았다는 좋은 소식을 말해 주었다.

31 그리고 Maibon은 아기의 입에 첫 이가 난 것을 보고 기뻐서 웃었다.

32 Maibon과 Modrona, 그리고 그들의 자녀들과 손주들은 오랫동안 살았다.

33 Maibon은 그의 흰 머리와 긴 수염을 자랑스러워했다.

1 One day, Maibon was driving down the road on his horse and cart when he saw an old man.

2 The old man looked very sick. Maibon began to worry about growing old.

3 Later that day, he saw a dwarf, Doli, in the field.

4 He was trying to get his leg out from under a log.

5 Maibon pulled the log away and freed the dwarf.

6 "You'll have your reward. What do you want?"

7 "I've heard that you have magic stones that can keep a man young. I want one."

8 "Oh, you humans have it all wrong. Those stones don't make you young again. They only keep you from getting older."

9 "Just as good!" Doli tried to explain the problem with the stones, but Maibon didn't listen.

10 So Doli handed him a magic stone and went away.

11 After a few days, Maibon saw that his beard didn't grow at all.

12 He became happy, but his wife, Modrona, got upset.

13 "The eggs don't change into chickens!" "Oh, the season's slow, that's all."

14 But she was not happy. "The cow doesn't give birth!" Maibon, then, told her about the stone, and she got very angry and told him to throw it away.

15 He didn't want to, but he listened to his wife and threw the stone out the window.

16 However, the next morning, he found the stone sitting by the window!

17 Maibon was worried about the animals, but he was glad that he was still young.

18 Now Maibon's baby was having trouble. No tooth was seen in his mouth.

19 His wife told him to throw away the stone and this time, Maibon put the stone under the ground.

20 But, the next day, the stone came back! Time went by and nothing grew or changed.

21 Maibon began to worry. "There's nothing to look forward to, nothing to show for my work."

22 Maibon tried to destroy the stone, but it kept coming back.

23 Maibon decided to throw away the stone far from his house.

24 On his way to the field, he saw the dwarf. Maibon got angry with him.

25 "Why didn't you warn me about the stone?"

26 "I tried to, but you wouldn't listen."

27 Doli explained that Maibon couldn't get rid of the stone unless he really wanted to.

28 "I want no more of it. Whatever may happen, let it happen!"

29 Doli told him to throw the stone onto the ground and go back home.

30 Maibon did as Doli said. When he arrived home, Modrona told him the good news — the eggs

changed into chickens and the cow bore her baby.

31 And Maibon laughed with delight when he saw the first tooth in his baby's mouth.

32 Maibon, Modrona and their children and grandchildren lived for many years.

33 Maibon was proud of his white hair and long beard.

MEMO

적중 100 + 특별부록

Plan B

우리학교 최신기출

비상 · 김진완 교과서를 배우는

학교 시험문제 분석 · 모음 · 해설집

전국단위 학교 시험문제 수집 및 분석
출제 빈도가 높은 문제 위주로 선별
문제 풀이에 필요한 상세한 해설

중2-2
영어

비상 · 김진완

2학년 영어 2학기 중간고사(5과) 1회

반		점수
이름		

문항수 : 선택형(27문항) 서술형(1문항)　　　20 ． ． ．

◎ 선택형 문항의 답안은 컴퓨터용 수정 싸인펜을 사용
하여 OMR 답안지에 바르게 표기하시오.
◎ 서술형 문제는 답을 답안지에 반드시 검정 볼펜으
로 쓰시오.
◎ 총 28문항 100점 만점입니다. 문항별 배점은 각
문항에 표시되어 있습니다.

[서울 강남구 ○○중]

01 다음 영영풀이에 대한 단어가 괄호에 들어갈 수 없는 단어는?
(어형 변화 가능)　　　　　　　　　　　　(4점)

- simple or easy; basic
- to prevent something bad from happening
- to stop being angry with someone and stop blaming
- why something happens, or why someone does something
- a line of written words, for example in a play or film

① I can't memorize the (　) at all.
② I'll take an (　) Spanish course.
③ I don't like the man for that (　).
④ You can overcome your (　) of water.
⑤ There are useful tips on how to (　) catching a cold.

[서울 영등포구 ○○중]

02 다음 주어진 설명과 관련이 없는 것은?　　(4점)

- to start to be seen or to exist in a place
- to hurt a person or damage a place by mistake
- to continue to give your attention to something
- to not go to bed at the time you would normally go to bed
- to look after someone who is not able to care for themselves

① appear　　　　　② attack
③ stay up　　　　　④ concentrate
⑤ take care of

[경북 ○○중]

03 다음 대화의 빈칸에 들어갈 말로 가장 적절한 것은?　(3점)

Fear: I hope Bella doesn't have any more problems like this.
Joy: Me, too. But problems are part of growing up. Just like this time, Bella will face the problems, solve them, and become _____ in the end.

① older　　　② worse　　　③ younger
④ wiser　　　⑤ prettier

[서울 광진구 ○○중]

04 다음 어법상 옳지 않은 것은?　　　　(3점)

A: What is the thing in the box?
B: It is the doll ⓐwhich ⓑmy friend ⓒgave ⓓit ⓔto me.

① ⓐ　　② ⓑ　　③ ⓒ　　④ ⓓ　　⑤ ⓔ

[경북 ○○중]

05 다음 대화에서 여자의 심경으로 가장 적절한 것은?　(4점)

M: You don't look so happy today. What's the matter?
W: I wore my sister's favorite T-shirt. But I got grape juice on it.
M: Oh, no. Did you tell your sister?
W: No, not yet. I don't know what to do.

① joyful　　　　② upset
③ excited　　　　④ pleased
⑤ satisfied

06 다음 대화 중 A의 빈칸에 쓸 수 있는 표현이 <u>아닌</u> 것은? (4점)

> A: You look upset. _____
> B: I lost my key, so I couldn't get into my house.

① What's the matter?

② What's wrong with you?

③ Is something the matter?

④ What is the problem?

⑤ How can you solve your problem?

[7~8] 다음 대화를 읽고 물음에 답하시오.

> A: I can't forgive Jenny. She didn't say a word to Bella.
> F: Jenny didn't even look at her. Jenny (A)[never, be] this cold before.
> S: Bella ate alone during lunch today. Poor Bella!
> J: Jenny is Bella's best friend. I'm sure there is a reason ⓐ_____. (우리가 잘 알지 못하는)
> A: I can't stand this any longer. Bella should just go and tell her about her feelings.
> F: I don't want Bella (B)[hurt] again. She should let it go.
> J: They are good friends. They will (C)[it, work, out].

07 위 대화의 빈칸 ⓐ를 우리말에 맞게 채울 때 옳지 <u>않은</u> 것은? (3점)

① we don't know about

② about that we don't know

③ that we don't know about

④ about which we don't know

⑤ which we don't know about

08 위 대화의 괄호 (A)~(C) 안의 단어를 문맥상 올바르게 고친 것은? (4점)

	(A)	(B)	(C)
①	was never	hurt	it work out
②	never was	hurting	work it out
③	has never been	to hurt	work out it
④	has never been	to be hurt	work it out
⑤	have never been	to be hurt	work out it

09 다음 괄호 안에 주어진 단어를 모두 사용해서 영작할 수 있는 것을 〈보기〉에서 고르면? (단, 중복 사용 불가) (5점)

> **보기**
>
> ⓐ 나는 버스를 놓쳤다. 그래서 학교로 뛰어가야 했다.
> → I missed the bus, _____ school.
>   (to, so, I, run, had)
> ⓑ Steve는 몇 번이나 프랑스로 여행을 했니?
> → How many times _____?
>   (France, Steve, traveled, to)
> ⓒ 요즘 그녀의 감정은 좋다가 안 좋다가 한다.
> → These days _____ down.
>   (feelings, going, and, up, her)
> ⓓ 네가 내 실수를 지적했을 때 화가 났다.
> → I was _____ my mistake.
>   (out, when, upset, you, pointed)
> ⓔ 나는 내 여동생과 내 방을 공유하는 것을 싫어한다.
> → I hate _____ little sister.
>   (my, sharing, my, with, room)

① ⓐ, ⓑ   ② ⓐ, ⓔ   ③ ⓑ, ⓓ

④ ⓒ, ⓓ   ⑤ ⓓ, ⓔ

[10~12] 다음 글을 읽고 물음에 답하시오.

Bella is 15 years old this year and ㉠these days her feelings are going up and down. Today, she looks down. Let's listen to Bella's feelings and find out why.

Anger: ㉡What a day! I can't believe ⓐthat Jenny yelled at Bella after the school play.

Sadness: Well, that's because Bella forgot her lines on stage.

Anger: Jenny pointed out the mistake ⓑthat Bella made. How could she do ⓒthat in front of everyone?

Joy: But I'm sure Jenny did not ㉢mean to hurt Bella. They have been best friends since elementary school. Remember?

Anger: That's what I'm saying. A true friend would never ㉣put Bella down like ⓓthat.

Fear: I'm worried ⓔthat they are not going to be friends anymore.

Joy: Come on, Fear. Don't ㉤go too far. We'll see.

10 위 글을 읽고 대답할 수 없는 것은? (3점)

① How does Bella feel these days?
② What mistake did Bella make?
③ What does Sadness want Bella to do?
④ What did Jenny do to Bella after the school play?
⑤ Does Joy think that Jenny hurt Bella on purpose?

11 위 글의 ⓐ~ⓔ 중 〈보기〉의 밑줄 친 that과 쓰임이 같은 것은? (4점)

보기

• This is the brown cat that Mary found near the train station.

① ⓐ ② ⓑ ③ ⓒ ④ ⓓ ⑤ ⓔ

12 위 글의 흐름상 밑줄 친 ㉠~㉤의 뜻이 가장 적절한 것은?(4점)

① ㉠ 이 날들
② ㉡ 정말 신나는 날이야!
③ ㉢ 나타내다
④ ㉣ 벨라를 아래로 내려놓다
⑤ ㉤ 극단적으로 생각하다

[13~14] 다음 대화를 읽고 물음에 답하시오.

Anger: I can't forgive Jenny. She didn't say a word to Bella.

Fear: Jenny didn't even look at her. ⓐJenny has never been this cold before.

Sadness: Bella ate alone during lunch today. Poor Bella!

Joy: Jenny is Bella's best friend. ⓑI'm sure there is a reason what we don't know about.

Anger: ⓒI can't stand this no longer. Bella should just go and tell her about her feelings.

Fear: ⓓI don't want Bella be hurt again. She should let it go.

Joy: They are good friends. ⓔThey will work out it.

13 위 대화의 밑줄 친 ⓐ~ⓔ 중 어법상 옳은 것은? (3점)

① ⓐ ② ⓑ ③ ⓒ ④ ⓓ ⑤ ⓔ

14 위 대화의 내용과 일치하는 것은? (4점)

① Bella ate lunch alone, so Joy says "Poor Bella."
② Sadness is afraid that Jenny won't forgive Bella.
③ Fear believes that Jenny and Bella are still best friends.
④ Joy believes that Bella and Jenny can't solve the problem.
⑤ Anger thinks that Bella should go and tell Jenny about her feelings.

[15~20] 다음 글을 읽고 물음에 답하시오.

Bella is 15 years old this year and these days her feelings are going up and down. Today, she looks down. Let's listen to Bella's feelings and find out why.

Anger:　(A)What a day! I can't believe that Jenny yelled at Bella after the school play.

Sadness: Well, ⓐthat's because Bella forgot her (B)lines on stage.

Anger:　Jenny pointed out the mistake (C)_____. How could she do ⓑthat in front of everyone?

Joy:　　But I'm sure that Jenny did not mean to hurt Bella. They have been best friends since elementary school. Remember?

Anger:　ⓒThat's what I'm saying. A true friend would never put Bella down like ⓓthat.

Fear:　　I'm (D)_____ ⓔthat they are not going to be friends anymore.

Joy:　　Come on, Fear. Don't go too far. We'll see.

16 위 글의 밑줄 친 (B)의 의미와 가장 가까운 것은? (3점)

① Draw <u>lines</u> on your paper.

② Actors are busy learning their <u>lines</u>.

③ Sam <u>lines</u> up three numbers for the lock.

④ My grandmother's face is covered with <u>lines</u>.

⑤ The people all stood in <u>lines</u> for the concert.

17 위 글의 어법상 (C)에 알맞은 것은 모두 몇 개인가? (3점)

① Bella made
② that Bella made
③ who Bella made
④ whom Bella made
⑤ which Bella made
⑥ what Bella made
⑦ that Bella made it
⑧ Bella made it

① 2개　　　② 3개　　　③ 4개
④ 5개　　　⑤ 6개

18 위 글의 밑줄 친 ⓐ~ⓔ 중 역할이 <u>다른</u> 하나는? (3점)

① ⓐ　　② ⓑ　　③ ⓒ　　④ ⓓ　　⑤ ⓔ

15 위 글의 흐름으로 보아 (A)의 의미로 가장 알맞은 것은? (4점)

① What a good day!

② What a nice day!

③ What a terrific day!

④ What a beautiful day!

⑤ What an unbelievable day!

19 위 글의 흐름으로 보아 (D)에 가장 알맞은 것 2개는? (3점)

① happy　　　　② afraid

③ worried　　　④ careless

⑤ surprised

20 위 글을 읽고 답할 수 없는 것은? (3점)

① What mistake did Bella make?

② What does 'Fear' want Bella to do?

③ How does Bella feel these days?

④ What did Jenny do to Bella after the school play?

⑤ Since when have Jenny and Bella been best friends?

[서울 광진구 ○○중]

21 다음 대화에 이어질 내용으로 가장 적절한 것은? (4점)

> W: You look tired. What's the matter?
>
> M: I didn't have breakfast this morning. I'm so hungry.
>
> W: Oh, that's too bad. We still have two more hours until lunch break.
>
> M: Our school should have a snack bar. Then, we could have a quick breakfast or snacks.
>
> W: I think so, too. How can we make that suggestion?
>
> M: We can post it on the suggestion board.

① 학교 내의 매점을 간다.

② 보건실에 가서 휴식을 취한다.

③ 건의 게시판에 글을 작성한다.

④ 식당에 가서 점심을 먼저 먹는다.

⑤ 학생들에게 아침을 먹고 등교할 것을 제안한다.

[경기 ○○중]

[22~25] 다음 글을 읽고 물음에 답하시오.

> **Voices in Our Mind**
> Bella is 15 years old this year and these days her feelings are going up and down. Today, she looks (A)_____ . Let's listen to Bella's feelings and find (B)_____ why.

<Day 1>

> Anger: What a day! I can't believe Jenny yelled at Bella after the school play.
>
> Sadness: Well, @that's because Bella forgot her lines on stage.
>
> Anger: Jenny pointed (B)_____ the mistake ⓑthat Bella made. How could she do ⓒthat in front of everyone?
>
> Joy: But I'm sure Jenny did not mean to hurt Bella. (가)They have been best friends since elementary school. Remember?
>
> Anger: That's what I'm saying. A true friend would never put Bella (A)_____ like ⓓthat.
>
> Fear: I'm worried ⓔthat they are not going to be friends anymore.
>
> Joy: Come on, Fear. Don't go too far. We'll see.

22 위 글을 읽고 답할 수 없는 질문은? (3점)

① How does Bella feel these days?

② What did Jenny do after the school play?

③ What was Bella's mistake on stage?

④ How many times has Jenny hurt Bella?

⑤ What does Fear worry about?

23 위 글의 @~ⓔ 중에서 which로 바꿔 쓸 수 있는 것은? (3점)

① @   ② ⓑ   ③ ⓒ   ④ ⓓ   ⑤ ⓔ

24 위 글의 빈칸 (A), (B)에 들어갈 단어로 바르게 짝지어진 것은? (4점)

① up, out   ② down, out

③ down, for   ④ out, for

⑤ out, at

25 위 글의 밑줄 친 (가)와 현재완료시제의 용법이 다른 것은?

(3점)

① Joshua has never seen a UFO.

② How long have you studied French?

③ Kirk has worked with Joshua since 2016.

④ Daniel has stayed in Rome for 4 years.

⑤ Daniel and Joshua have been best friends for 10 years.

26 위 글의 ⓐ~ⓔ 중에서 올바르게 고친 것을 2개 고른 것은?

(4점)

① ⓐ look → look like

② ⓑ for → while

③ ⓒ any long → any longer

④ ⓓ work out it → work it out

⑤ ⓔ become wise → become more wise

[경기 ○○중]

[26~28] 다음 글을 읽고 물음에 답하시오.

<Day 2>

Anger: I can't forgive Jenny. She didn't say a word to Bella.

Fear: Jenny didn't even ⓐlook her. Jenny has never been this cold before.

Sadness: Bella ate alone ⓑfor lunch today. Poor Bella!

Joy: Jenny is Bella's best friend. (A)I'm sure of there are a reason whom we don't know.

Anger: I can't stand this ⓒany long. Bella should just go and tell her about her feelings.

Fear: (B)나는 Bella가 다시 상처 입는 것을 원하지 않는다. She should let it go.

Joy: They are good friends. They will ⓓwork out it.

<Day 3>

Joy: Whew! I'm so happy that they are talking again.

Anger: Yeah, Bella went to Jenny and talked to her first.

Joy: Jenny didn't avoid Bella on purpose.

Sadness: Yeah, Jenny didn't know a way to say sorry.

Fear: I hope Bella doesn't have any more problems like this.

Joy: Me, too, But problems are part of growing up. Just like this time, Bella will face the problems, solve them, and ⓔbecome wise in the end.

27 위 글의 밑줄 친 (A)를 올바르게 고친 문장은? (3점)

① I'm sure of there is a reason whom we don't know.

② I'm sure of there is a reason which we don't know.

③ I'm sure of there is a reason what we don't know about.

④ I'm sure that there is a reason whom we don't know about.

⑤ I'm sure that there is a reason which we don't know about.

28 위 글의 밑줄 친 (B)를 주어진 단어를 이용하여 영어로 옮기시오. (want, hurt) (8 words) (5점)

→ _____

2학년 영어 2학기 중간고사(5과) 2회

문항수 : 선택형(27문항) 서술형(3문항)　　　20 ．　．　．

◎ 선택형 문항의 답안은 컴퓨터용 수정 싸인펜을 사용
하여 OMR 답안지에 바르게 표기하시오.

◎ 서술형 문제는 답을 답안지에 반드시 검정 볼펜으
로 쓰시오.

◎ 총 30문항 100점 만점입니다. 문항별 배점은 각
문항에 표시되어 있습니다.

[서울 영등포구 ○○중]

01 다음 밑줄 친 부분의 의미가 가장 어색한 것은?　(3점)

① Puppies grow very quickly. (자라다)
② This story is really touching. (만지다)
③ We can work out a problem. (해결하다)
④ John pushed me hard on purpose. (고의로)
⑤ What's more, it was going to be dark soon.
　(더욱이)

[경기 ○○중]

02 어법상 다음 (A)~(C)에 들어갈 알맞은 표현으로 짝지어진 것은?　(3점)

W: Hello, Dr. Watson. Can you tell us about
　your study?
M: I study animals (A)[which / where] lived
　millions of years ago.
W: Oh, I'm curious about those animals.
　Were there any interesting (B)[one /
　ones]?
M: Yes, there were many. This is the giant
　kangaroo. It lived in Australia. It was as
　heavy as three men and it couldn't jump
　well.
W: That's (C)[amazing / amazed]!

	(A)	(B)	(C)
①	where	ones	amazed
②	where	one	amazed
③	which	ones	amazed
④	which	one	amazing
⑤	which	ones	amazing

[서울 광진구 ○○중]

03 다음 대화에 알맞은 그림은?　(3점)

W: I was late for class again. I just can't
　wake up in the morning.
M: Do you set an alarm?
W: Yeah, but I turn it off and go back to
　sleep.
M: I think you should put it far from your
　bed. That way, you'll have to get out of
　bed.

①  ②

③  ④

⑤

[서울 중랑구 ○○중]

04 빈칸에 들어갈 수 없는 것은?　(3점)

- You should _____ the problem at
  hand.

① make　　② take　　③ face
④ solve　　⑤ focus on

[5~6] 다음 대화를 읽고 물음에 답하시오.

> W: You look tired. (A)_____
> M: I didn't have breakfast this morning. I'm so hungry.
> W: Oh, that's too bad. We still have two more hours until lunch break.
> M: Our school should have a snack bar. Then, we could have a quick breakfast or snacks.
> W: I think so, too. How can we make that (B)_____?
> M: We can post it on the (B)_____ board.

05 위 대화의 흐름상 빈칸 (A)에 들어가기 적절하지 <u>않은</u> 문장은?

(3점)

① What's wrong with you?

② What's the matter?

③ Why did you make the problem?

④ What happened to you?

⑤ Is something the matter?

06 위 대화의 흐름상 빈칸 (B)에 들어가기 가장 적절한 단어는?

(3점)

① suggestion ② trouble ③ advice

④ mistake ⑤ poster

07 빈칸에 공통으로 들어갈 단어는?

(4점)

> • If you _____ someone who did something bad or wrong, you stop being angry with them and no longer want to punish them.
> • How could you do this to me? I can't _____ you.

① forgive ② stand ③ avoid

④ hurt ⑤ mean

08 Which of the following is correct?

(4점)

① They appeared TV for the first time.

② My best friend became part of our family.

③ He is one of the most famous female leaders.

④ David can speak five language with his friends.

⑤ I received the award thank to my parents.

09 빈칸에 들어갈 것으로 알맞은 것은?

(3점)

> • The Green Friends are looking for volunteers with _____ they will clean up the park.

① that ② which

③ whose ④ what

⑤ whom

10 두 문장을 한 문장으로 바꾸어 쓸 때 빈칸에 들어갈 것으로 알맞은 것은?

(3점)

> • She started to play the violin fifteen years ago.
> • She still plays the violin.
> ⇒ She _____ the violin for fifteen years.

① played ② have played

③ is playing ④ has played

⑤ started to play

[11~13] 다음 글을 읽고 물음에 답하시오.

Bella is 15 years old this year and these days her feelings are going up and down. Today, she looks ⓐ_____. Let's listen to Bella's feelings and find out why.

Anger: What a day! I can't believe Jenny yelled at Bella after the school play.

Sadness: Well, that's because Bella forgot her ⓑ lines on stage.

Anger: Jenny pointed out the mistake that Bella made. How could she do that in front of everyone?

Joy: But I'm sure Jenny did not mean to hurt Bella. They have been best friends since elementary school. Remember?

Anger: That's what I'm saying. A true friend would never put Bella ⓒ_____ like that.

Fear: I'm worried that they are not going to be friends anymore.

Joy: Come on, Fear. Don't go too far. We'll see.

11 다음 중 위 글의 내용과 일치하는 문장들을 <u>모두</u> 고르면? (3점)

① 요즘 Bella는 감정 기복이 심하다.

② Jenny와 Bella는 초등학교 때는 서로 알지 못하는 사이였다.

③ Jenny는 여러 사람들 앞에서 Bella를 깎아내리는 행동을 했다.

④ Joy는 Anger의 말에 전적으로 동의하고 있다.

⑤ Bella가 무대에서 대사를 잊어버리는 실수를 했다는 것은 사실이 아니다.

12 위 글의 내용으로 보아 빈칸 ⓐ와 ⓒ에 들어갈 표현이 순서대로 바르게 짝지어진 것은? (3점)

① down – up   ② down – out

③ up – down   ④ down – down

⑤ out – down

13 밑줄 친 ⓑ와 같은 의미로 쓰인 문장은? (3점)

① Please stand in <u>line</u> for concert tickets.

② Connect the <u>lines</u> and make a square.

③ You should memorize your <u>lines</u> before the play starts.

④ You can transfer to the orange <u>line</u> here at Dongdaemun subway station.

⑤ Don't cut in <u>line</u>! We're waiting here.

14 어법상 밑줄 친 부분이 옳은 것은? (4점)

① I can't remember the story <u>what</u> I read last night.

② I'm afraid of talking with people <u>which</u> I don't know well.

③ This is the yellow cat <u>whom</u> was found near the train station.

④ Paul lost the watch <u>which</u> was given to him on his fifteenth birthday.

⑤ The Green Friends are looking for volunteers <u>whom</u> are going to clean up the park.

15 빈칸에 들어갈 것으로 알맞은 것은? (3점)

• I have learned English _____.

① last year   ② in 1987

③ yesterday   ④ three years ago

⑤ since last winter

[16~18] 다음 글을 읽고 물음에 답하시오.

Bella is 15 years old this year and these days her feelings are going up and down. Today, she looks down. Let's listen to Bella's feelings and find out why.

Anger: What a day! I can't believe Jenny yelled at Bella after the school play.
(A)
Sadness: Well, that's because Bella forgot her lines on stage.
(B)
Anger: Jenny pointed out the mistake Bella made. How could she do that in front of everyone?
(C)
Joy: But I'm sure Jenny did not mean to hurt Bella. They ⓐ_____ since elementary school. Remember?
(D)
Anger: That's what I'm saying. A true friend would never put Bella down like that.
(E)
Joy: Come on, Fear. Don't go too far. We'll see.

16 위 글의 (A)~(E) 중 문맥상 다음 문장이 들어갈 곳은? (4점)

Fear: I'm worried that they are not going to be friends anymore.

① (A)   ② (B)   ③ (C)   ④ (D)   ⑤ (E)

17 위 글의 빈칸 ⓐ를 〈보기〉의 어구를 문맥에 맞게 적절하게 배열하여 완성하시오. 필요하면 어형 변화를 할 것. (4점)

보기
friends / have / best / be

→ _____

18 위 글의 내용과 일치하지 않는 것은? (3점)

① Bella는 15살이며 요즘 감정이 좋았다가 나빴다가 한다.
② Anger는 연극이 끝난 후 Bella가 소리친 것에 화가 나 있다.
③ Sadness는 Bella가 무대에서 대사를 잊어버렸기 때문에 Jenny가 화났다고 했다.
④ Joy는 Jenny가 일부러 Bella에게 상처를 주려고 한 건 아니라고 확신한다.
⑤ Joy는 너무 극단적으로 나가지 말라고 경계하고 있다.

19 다음 남자의 말에 이어질 대화를 순서대로 바르게 배열한 것은? (4점)

M: Ms. Morris, I just can't stop playing computer games. What should I do?

(A) Oh, that's a good idea.
(B) I think I should. Thank you for the advice, Ms. Morris.
(C) Well, why don't you use a special program? When you set a time limit, the computer shuts down at that time.
(D) And I think you should move the computer out of your room and into the living room.

① (A) - (B) - (C) - (D)
② (A) - (C) - (B) - (D)
③ (C) - (A) - (D) - (B)
④ (C) - (B) - (A) - (D)
⑤ (D) - (B) - (C) - (A)

[20~21] 다음 대화를 읽고, 물음에 답하시오.

> W: You look tired. What's the matter?
> M: I didn't have breakfast this morning. I'm so hungry. (A)
> W: Oh, that's too bad. (B) We still have two more hours until lunch break. (C)
> M: Our school should have a snack bar. (D)
> W: I think so, too. How can we make that suggestion?
> M: We can post it on the suggestion board. (E)

20 위 대화의 (A)~(E) 중 다음 문장이 들어갈 곳은? (4점)

> Then, we could have a quick breakfast or snacks.

① (A) ② (B)) ③ (C ④ (D) ⑤ (E)

21 위 대화가 끝나고 주인공들이 할 일로 적절한 것은? (3점)

① 학생회에 가입하기
② 간식 먹기
③ 매점 가기
④ 의견 제안 게시판에 게시하기
⑤ 게시판 정리하기

[22~23] 다음 대화를 읽고 물음에 답하시오.

> - Hello, you're on the air.
> (A) Hi, Solomon. I'm Amy.
> (B) ⓐI think you should tell her your feelings. And you should also make some rules with your sister.
> (C) What's the matter?
> (D) Oh, I'll try that. Thanks for the advice.
> (E) I hate sharing my room with my little sister. She uses my stuff without asking me first. What should I do?

22 위 대화를 내용에 맞게 올바르게 배열한 것은? (4점)

① (A) - (B) - (C) - (E) - (D)
② (A) - (B) - (E) - (C) - (D)
③ (A) - (C) - (E) - (B) - (D)
④ (A) - (C) - (B) - (E) - (D)
⑤ (A) - (E) - (C) - (B) - (D)

23 위 대화의 밑줄 친 ⓐ 대신 들어가기에 적절하지 않은 문장은? (3점)

① Why don't you tell her your feelings?
② How about telling her your feelings?
③ I advise you to tell her your feelings.
④ What about telling her your feelings?
⑤ I wish I could tell her my feelings.

[24~26] 다음 글을 읽고 물음에 답하시오.

> Anger: I can't forgive Jenny. She didn't say a word to Bella.
> Fear: Jenny didn't even look at her. Jenny ⓐhas never been this cold before.
> Sadness: Bella ate alone ⓑduring lunch today. Poor Bella!
> Joy: Jenny is Bella's best friend. I'm sure there is a reason (A)that we don't know about.
> Anger: (B)I can't stand this any longer. Bella should just go and tell her about her feelings.
> Fear: I don't want Bella ⓒto be hurt again. She should let it ⓓto go.
> Joy: They are good friends. They will ⓔwork it out.

24 위 글의 밑줄 친 ⓐ~ⓔ 중에서 어법상 어색한 것은? (3점)

① ⓐ ② ⓑ ③ ⓒ ④ ⓓ ⑤ ⓔ

25 위 글의 밑줄 친 (A)와 같은 용법으로 쓰인 that은? (3점)

① <u>That</u> was so expensive.

② <u>That</u>'s what I am saying.

③ I heard <u>that</u> Bella ate alone.

④ The mistake <u>that</u> Bella made was terrible.

⑤ I can't believe <u>that</u> Jenny yelled at Bella after the school play.

26 위 글의 Anger가 밑줄 친 (B)와 같이 말한 이유를 쓰시오. (4점)

→ _____

[서울 금천구 ○○중]

[27~30] 다음 글을 읽고 물음에 답하시오.

Anger: What a day! I can't believe Jenny yelled at Bella after the school play.

Sadness: Well, that's because Bella forgot her lines on stage. (A)

Anger: Jenny pointed out _____ (a) _____. How could she do that in front of everyone?

Joy: But I'm sure Jenny did not mean to hurt Bella. (B) They (b)<u>have been</u> best friends since elementary school. Remember?

Anger: (C) A true friend would never put Bella down like that.

Fear: I'm worried that they are not going to be friends anymore. (D)

Joy: (E) Come on. Fear. Don't go too far. We'll see.

27 (A)~(E) 중에서 다음 문장이 들어갈 알맞은 곳은? (3점)

That's what I'm saying.

① (A) ② (B) ③ (C) ④ (D) ⑤ (E)

28 위 글의 내용과 일치하지 <u>않는</u> 것은? (3점)

① Bella forgot her lines on stage.

② *Joy* is sure Jenny meant to hurt Bella.

③ Jenny yelled at Bella after the school play.

④ Bella and Jenny were best friends in elementary school.

⑤ *Fear* worried that Bella and Jenny aren't going to be friends anymore.

29 자연스러운 문장이 되도록 빈칸 (a)에 아래 단어를 바르게 배열하시오. (4점)

Bella / the / made / that / mistake

→ _____

30 밑줄 친 (b)와 같은 용법으로 쓰인 것은? (3점)

① I <u>have finished</u> my homework.

② He <u>has traveled</u> to America twice.

③ How long <u>have</u> you <u>learned</u> English?

④ Sally <u>has met</u> the math teacher before.

⑤ My brother <u>has had</u> two piano concerts

2학년 영어 2학기 중간고사(6과) 1회

문항수 : 선택형(23문항) 서술형(6문항)　　20　.　.　.

◎ 선택형 문항의 답안은 컴퓨터용 수정 싸인펜을 사용하여 OMR 답안지에 바르게 표기하시오.
◎ 서술형 문제는 답을 답안지에 반드시 검정 볼펜으로 쓰시오.
◎ 총 29문항 100점 만점입니다. 문항별 배점은 각 문항에 표시되어 있습니다.

[서울 강남구 ○○중]

01 다음 괄호 안에 주어진 단어들을 배열하여 대화를 완성하시오. (4점)

> Soowon: What did you learn about elephants?
> Hoon: I learned (to, that, elephants, a, thick, protect, make, baby, wall, elephants).

→ I learned _____.

[경기 ○○중]

02 다음에서 단어와 그 뜻풀이가 바르지 않게 연결된 것을 〈보기〉에서 모두 고른 것은? (4점)

> **보기**
> ⓐ care for: to take care of somebody who is sick, very old, very young, etc.
> ⓑ keep one's eyes on: to look after somebody/something and make sure that they are not injured, damaged, etc.
> ⓒ blind: not able to see
> ⓓ appear: to stop existing
> ⓔ careless: not giving enough attention to what you are doing, so that you are able to complete the work
> ⓕ feed: the things such as food, medicines, fuel, etc. that are needed by a group of people
> ⓖ restless: unable to stay calm or be satisfied with where you are because you are bored or need a change

① ⓐ, ⓒ, ⓔ　　② ⓑ, ⓒ, ⓓ　　③ ⓒ, ⓓ. ⓔ
④ ⓓ. ⓔ, ⓕ　　⑤ ⓔ, ⓕ, ⓖ

[서울 관악구 ○○중]

03 아래 〈보기〉의 문장과 뜻이 같은 것은? (3점)

> **보기**
> • A friend is not as important as a family in my country.

① A friend is more important than a family in my country.
② A friend is less important than a family in my country.
③ A friend is so important as a friend in my country.
④ A friend is the most important person in my country.
⑤ A family is not more important than a friend in my country.

[서울 관악구 ○○중]

04 밑줄 친 부분의 의미가 알맞지 <u>않은</u> 것은? (3점)

① I hope you do not <u>make a mistake</u>.
　(실수를 하다)
② Members all want to <u>fix a problem</u>.
　(문제를 확인하다)
③ In the end, he <u>admitted his mistake</u>.
　(실수를 인정했다)
④ I <u>have a problem</u> with my parents.
　(문제가 있다)
⑤ You should <u>focus on the problem</u> at hand.
　(문제에 집중하다)

05 다음 문장들 중 어법상 바르지 <u>않은</u> 것은? (3점)

① I ran as fast as I could.

② I spoke as slowly as I could.

③ Today is as hot as yesterday.

④ My sister speaks Chinese as better as you.

⑤ The bread is not so heavy as the banana.

06 괄호 안의 단어들 중 빈칸에 들어 갈 수 있는 단어의 개수는? (3점)

• Stella is as _____ as Tom.
  (smart, cheaper, colder, big, fastest, oldest, funny, lighter)

① 2개　　② 3개　　③ 4개　　④ 5개　　⑤ 6개

07 아래 그림을 보고, 질문에 대한 답을 〈조건〉에 맞게 쓰시오. (4점)

조건
• 그림과 일치하며 비교를 나타내는 문장을 써야 함. (shark와 boat는 같은 속도입니다.)
• 주어와 동사를 포함한 <u>한 문장의 영어</u>로 어법에 맞게 써야 함.
• 반드시 a shark, a boat, swim, as를 포함.

Q: How fast can a shark swim?

A: _____

08 다음 우리말과 뜻이 같도록 빈칸에 알맞은 말을 〈보기〉에서 골라 문장을 완성하시오. (6점)

보기
worry, for, tell, during, useless, mysterious, stand, regularly, while, feed, rescue, restless, suggestion, shelter

(1) My kids became _____ on long journeys. (나의 아이들은 긴 여행에 가만히 있지 못했다.)

(2) Can you _____ the difference between the two versions? (당신은 두 버전 사이의 차이를 구별할 수 있나요?)

(3) Dolphins can swim _____ they are sleeping. (돌고래는 잠자는 동안에 수영을 할 수 있다.)

09 다음 중 Toby의 발표 내용과 일치하는 것을 고르면? (3점)

Toby: Hi, I'm Toby. I'm going to give a presentation about the blue whale. It's the biggest sea animal in the world. How big is it? Well, it's about 30m long. That means it's longer than a basketball court. Another interesting thing is that its tongue is as heavy as an elephant! Surprising, isn't it?

① Toby gives a presentation about a basketball.

② The blue whale is the biggest sea animal in the world.

③ The blue whale's tongue is heavier than an elephant.

④ A blue whale is shorter than a basketball court.

⑤ A blue whale is as heavy as an elephant.

10 다음 중 밑줄 친 It의 쓰임이 나머지 넷과 <u>다른</u> 것은? (3점)

① <u>It</u> is fun to grow these plants.

② <u>It</u> is hard to become an animal doctor.

③ <u>It</u> is difficult for her to enter the company.

④ <u>It</u> is about 50 meters from here to the store.

⑤ <u>It</u> is important to obey the safety rules.

11 글의 흐름으로 보아 주어진 문장이 들어가기에 가장 적절한 곳은? (4점)

Date/Time: July 13th / 6:00 a.m.

Notes: (A) A new elephant group appeared and Stella approached them. (B) But I was wrong. (C) An elephant, probably the oldest female, allowed Stella to become part of the group. (D) The other elephants also seemed to welcome Stella. (E) Unbelievably, one of the female elephants fed Stella. She cared for Stella as warmly as Stella's mom did. This was such an amazing moment!

At first, I thought that they would not let Stella in their group.

① (A) ② (B) ③ (C) ④ (D) ⑤ (E)

12 괄호 안의 단어를 사용해서 우리말을 영작하시오. (필요시 단어 추가, 변형 가능) (6점)

(1) 시간은 돈만큼 가치 있다. (valuable / as)

→ Time is _____.

(2) 그 소파가 침대만큼 비쌌다. (bed / as)

→ The sofa was _____.

(3) 축구 경기를 시청하는 것은 신난다. (it / watch / to / exciting)

→ _____.

13 아래 그림을 묘사한 문장으로 적절한 것은? (3점)

① A feather is as light as this box.

② A feather is twice as heavy as this box.

③ This box is as lighter as a feather.

④ This box is not as heavier as a feather.

⑤ This box is not as lightest as a feather.

[14~15] 다음 글을 읽고, 물음에 답하시오.

Hi, I'm Toby. I'm going to ⓐ발표하다 about the blue whale. It's the biggest sea animal in the world. ⓑ얼마나 크니 is it? Well, it's about 30m long. ⓒ그것은 의미해 it's longer than a basketball court. Another ⓓ흥미로운 점 is that its tongue (A)an / as / is / as / heavy / elephant! ⓔ놀랍죠, isn't it?

14 위 글의 ⓐ~ⓔ 중 어법상 옳지 <u>않은</u> 것은? (3점)

① ⓐ give a presentation

② ⓑ How big

③ ⓒ That means

④ ⓓ interesting thing

⑤ ⓔ Surprised

15 위 글의 밑줄 친 (A)의 단어들을 바르게 배열하여 쓰시오. (4점)

→ Its tongue _____!

[16~17] 다음 글을 읽고, 물음에 답하시오.

Date/Time: July 8th / 2:35 p.m.
Notes: Today was my first day in Africa. I took lots of pictures of elephants. This morning, I found an elephant group by a small water hole. I saw a baby elephant ⓐdrinking water beside her mother. Her eyes were as bright as stars. I gave her a name, Stella. Around noon, I saw a group of lions approaching Stella. The elephants stood around Stella and made a thick wall. Thanks to them, Stella was safe.

16 위 글의 내용과 일치하는 것은? (3점)

① 8월 8일에 쓴 관찰 일지이다.
② 글쓴이의 이름은 Stella이다.
③ 글쓴이는 코끼리와 사자를 보았다.
④ 글쓴이는 아프리카에서 길을 잃었다.
⑤ 코끼리는 사진 찍히는 것을 좋아한다.

17 문맥상 위 글 ⓐ와 바꿔 쓸 수 있는 것은? (3점)

① drink ② drank ③ to drink
④ to be drunk ⑤ to have drunk

[18~20] 다음 글을 읽고, 물음에 답하시오.

Date/Time: July 12th / 7:20 p.m.

Notes: Around sunset, I heard a strange sound. I followed the sound and found Stella crying next to ⓐher mom. ⓑShe was lying dead and Stella was alone. It is dangerous to stay alone in such a wild area. What's more, it was going to be dark soon. Elephants can't see well at night. So ⓒStella could easily be attacked. I called the elephant shelter and asked for help. I decided to stay by her until the rescue team came.

Date/Time: July 12th / 10:40 p.m.

Notes: The night was dark and quiet. I kept my eyes on Stella with my night camera. Stella was still next to her mom. ⓓShe was touching her mom's lifeless body with ⓔher nose. It was sad to see Stella staying close to her mom. I hope Stella stays safe throughout the night.

18 위 글에서 답을 찾을 수 없는 질문은? (3점)

① Where did the writer call?
② Around sunset, what did the writer hear?
③ What did the writer find when he followed the sound?
④ Why did the writer give a baby elephant a name, Stella?
⑤ What was Stella doing next to her mother during the night?

19 위 글의 ⓐ~ⓔ 중 가리키는 대상이 다른 하나는? (2점)

① ⓐ ② ⓑ ③ ⓒ ④ ⓓ ⑤ ⓔ

20 아래의 영영풀이에 해당하는 단어를 위 글에서 찾아 영어로 쓰시오. (4점)

(1) the part of each day when the sun has set and it is dark outside, especially the time when people are sleeping

_____

(2) a small building or covered place which is made to protect people or animals from bad weather or danger

_____

(3) all your physical parts, including your head, arms, and legs

_____

[21~22] 다음 글을 읽고, 물음에 답하시오.

Today was my first day in Africa. I took lots of pictures of elephants. This morning, I found an elephant group by a small water hole. I saw a baby elephant drinking water beside her mother. Her eyes were as bright as stars. I gave her a name, Stella. Around noon, I saw a group of lions approaching Stella. The elephants stood around Stella and made a thick wall. ⒶThanks to them, Stella was safe.

21 위 글을 읽고 대답할 수 없는 질문은? (3점)

① What did a group of lions do?

② Where did the writer keep this diary?

③ Why did elephants stand around Stella?

④ What did the writer find this morning?

⑤ Why did the writer name a baby elephant Stella?

22 위 글의 밑줄 친 표현 Ⓐ를 빈칸에 넣었을 때 의미가 통하는 것은? (3점)

① _____ her injury, she continued to play.

② _____ his help, I finished my homework.

③ _____ the high price, I bought the ticket.

④ _____ the bad weather, we went on our trip.

⑤ _____ my backache, I went swimming on weekends.

[23~24] 다음 글을 읽고, 물음에 답하시오.

Around sunset, I heard a strange sound. I followed the sound and found Stella ㉠_____ next to her mom. [A] She was lying dead and Stella was alone. [B] It is dangerous to stay alone in such a wild area. [C] Elephants can't see well at night. [D] So Stella could easily be ㉡_____. [E] I called the elephant shelter and asked for help. I decided to stay by her until the rescue team came.

23 [A]~[E] 중 다음 문장이 들어갈 곳은? (3점)

What's more, it was going to be dark soon.

① [A]　② [B]　③ [C]　④ [D]　⑤ [E]

24 ㉠, ㉡에 알맞은 형태로 짝지어진 것은? (4점)

	㉠	㉡
①	cry	attack
②	cry	attacking
③	crying	attacking
④	crying	attacked
⑤	cried	attacked

[25~26] 다음 글을 읽고, 물음에 답하시오.

A new elephant group appeared and Stella approached them. At first, I thought that they would not let Stella in their group. But I was wrong. An elephant, probably the oldest female allowed Stella to become part of the group. The other elephants also seemed to welcome Stella. Unbelievably, one of the female elephants fed Stella. She cared for Stella (A)as warmly as Stella's mom did. This was such an amazing moment!

25 Which one can not be answered from the passage? (3점)

① What appeared in front of Stella?

② What did the writer think at first?

③ How did the other elephants seem?

④ Until when should the female elephant take care of Stella?

⑤ Which elephant allowed Stella to become part of the group?

26 위 글의 밑줄 친 (A)의 용법과 다르게 쓰인 것은? (3점)

① I am <u>as blind as</u> a bat.

② Her face is <u>as white as</u> a sheet.

③ This box is <u>as light as</u> a feather.

④ Dogs can't see <u>as well as</u> humans.

⑤ We'll be there <u>as soon as</u> possible.

[경기 ○○중]

[27~29] 다음 글을 읽고, 물음에 답하시오.

[A]
Notes: A new elephant group appeared and Stella approached them. At first, I thought that they would not let Stella in their group. But I was wrong. An elephant, probably the oldest female allowed Stella to become part of the group. The other elephants also seemed to welcome Stella. Unbelievably, one of the female elephants fed Stella. ⓐ<u>She cared for Stella as warm as Stella's mom did.</u> This was such an amazing moment!

[B]
Notes: Today was my first day in Africa. I took lots of pictures of elephants. This morning, I found an elephant group by a small water hole. ⓑ<u>I saw a baby elephant drink water beside her mother.</u> Her eyes were as bright as stars. I gave her a name, Stella. Around noon, I saw a group of lions approaching Stella. ⓒ<u>The elephants stood around Stella and made a thick wall.</u> Thanks to them, Stella was safe.

[C]
Notes: The night was dark and quiet. I kept my eyes on Stella with my night camera. Stella was still next to her mom. She was touching her mom's lifeless body with her nose. ⓓ<u>It was sad to see Stella staying close to her mom.</u> I hope Stella stays safe throughout the night.

[D]
Notes: Around sunset, I heard a strange sound. I followed the sound and found Stella crying next to her mom. ⓔ<u>She was lying dead and Stella was alone.</u> It is dangerous to stay alone in such a wild area. What's more, it was going to be dark soon. Elephants can't see well at night. So Stella could easily be attacked. I called the elephant shelter and asked for help. I decided to stay by her until the rescue team came.

27 위 글의 이야기의 시간적 흐름을 고려할 때 (A)~(D)의 순서로 가장 적절한 것은? (3점)

① (A) - (C) - (B) - (D)

② (B) - (C) - (D) - (A)

③ (B) - (D) - (C) - (A)

④ (C) - (A) - (D) - (B)

⑤ (D) - (A) - (C) - (B)

28 위 글의 내용과 일치하지 않는 것은? (4점)

① On the first day in Africa, the writer found a baby elephant and gave it a name.

② With the help of elephants, Stella could be safe from another group of elephants.

③ The writer heard Stella crying and found her with her dead mother.

④ After the mother elephant died, Stella was in danger of being attacked by other animals.

⑤ The writer stayed up all night paying close attention to Stella.

29 위 글의 밑줄 친 ⓐ~ⓔ 중 어법상 옳지 않은 것은? (3점)

① ⓐ   ② ⓑ   ③ ⓒ

④ ⓓ   ⑤ ⓔ

◎ 선택형 문항의 답안은 컴퓨터용 수정 싸인펜을 사용하여 OMR 답안지에 바르게 표기하시오.
◎ 서술형 문제는 답을 답안지에 반드시 검정 볼펜으로 쓰시오.
◎ 총 31문항 100점 만점입니다. 문항별 배점은 각 문항에 표시되어 있습니다.

[경기 ○○중]

01 단어의 영영풀이가 옳지 <u>않은</u> 것은?　　(3점)

① alone: being by yourself without anyone
② feed: to give food to a person or animal
③ hole: an empty space in something solid
④ forgive: to continue feeling anger toward someone
⑤ shelter: a small building to protect people from bad weather or danger

[서울 송파구 ○○중]

02 밑줄 친 단어의 쓰임이 바르지 <u>않은</u> 것은?　　(3점)

① You are in <u>danger</u>! Be careful!
② We laughed at the comedian's <u>humorous</u> stories.
③ It's <u>adventure</u> and exciting to travel all over the world.
④ Did you have a <u>restless</u> night? You seemed tired.
⑤ I'm sorry to hurt your feelings by my <u>careless</u> words.

[경기 ○○중]

03 다음 글에서 필자가 느낀 감정으로 가장 알맞은 것은?　　(3점)

The night was dark and quiet. I kept my eyes on Stella with my night camera. Stella was still next to her mom. She was touching her mom's lifeless body with her nose. It was sad to see Stella staying close to her mom. I hope Stella stays safe throughout the night.

① urgent　　② worried　　③ excited
④ hopeful　　⑤ mysterious

[경기 ○○중]

04 다음에서 유추할 수 있는 내용으로 적절하지 <u>않은</u> 것은?　(3점)

Hi, I'm Toby. I'm going to give a presentation about the blue whale. It's the biggest sea animal in the world. How big is it? Well, it's about 30m long. That means it's longer than a basketball court. Another interesting thing is that its tongue is as heavy as an elephant! Surprising, isn't it?

① blue whale의 길이는 약 30m이다.
② blue whale은 농구 코트보다 더 길다.
③ Toby는 blue whale에 대해서 발표한다.
④ blue whale은 세계에서 가장 큰 바다 동물이다.
⑤ blue whale의 혀는 코끼리의 혀와 무게가 같다.

[경기 ○○중]

05 다음 대화의 내용과 일치하지 <u>않는</u> 것은?　　(3점)

A: Hello, Dr. Watson. Can you tell us about your study?
B: I study animals that lived millions of years ago.
A: Oh, I'm curious about those animals. Were there any interesting ones?
B: Yes, there were many. This is the giant snake. It lived in South America. It was as long as a bus and it had two legs.
A: That's amazing!

① B는 고대 동물을 연구한다.
② giant snake는 남미에 살았다.
③ giant snake는 다리가 두 개였다.
④ A는 고대 동물에 대해 호기심이 많다.
⑤ giant snake는 버스만큼 무게가 나갔다.

06 다음 중 어법상 쓰임이 옳지 <u>않은</u> 것은? (3점)

Today was my first day in Africa. I ①took many pictures of elephants. This morning, I ②found an elephant group by a small water hole. I saw a baby elephant drinking water beside her mother. Her eyes were as bright as stars. I ③gave her a name, Stella. Around noon, I ④saw a group of lions approach Stella. The elephants ⑤stood around Stella and make a thick wall. Thanks to them, Stella was safe.

①　　　②　　　③　　　④　　　⑤

07 다음 표의 내용과 일치하지 <u>않는</u> 것은? (4점)

	A-phone	B-phone	C-phone
Price	$500	$400	$400
Size	6×15cm	6×15cm	5×11cm
Weight	190g	120g	190g

① A-phone is as big as B-phone.

② C-phone is not as big as B-phone.

③ A-phone is not as cheap as B-phone.

④ B-phone is not as heavy as C-phone.

⑤ C-phone is as expensive as A-phone.

08 다음 대화를 읽고 답할 수 <u>없는</u> 질문은? (3점)

Kelly: George, that red house over there is my house.

George: Wow, the tree by the house is really big.

Kelly: Actually, that tree is as old as me, thirteen years old.

George: How do you know that, Kelly?

Kelly: My father planted the tree in 2004 when I was born.

① How old is Kelly now?

② When was Kelly born?

③ What color is Kelly's house?

④ How tall is the tree by Kelly's house?

⑤ When was the tree by Kelly's house planted?

09 다음 대화의 밑줄 친 (A)~(E) 중 내용의 흐름상 <u>어색한</u> 부분은? (3점)

Clare: Do you think we can be friends with lions, Todd?

Todd: No, Clare. (A)I don't think so.

Clare: (B)Well, I watched a video clip about friendship between two men and a lion.

Todd: Really? (C)I'm not curious about the story. Can you tell me more?

Clare: (D)The two men raised a baby lion and sent her back into the wild. When the men and the lion met a year later, she remembered them.

Todd: (E)Wow, that's so touching.

① (A)　　　② (B)　　　③ (C)

④ (D)　　　⑤ (E)

10 주어진 단어를 이용하여 다음 우리말을 영어로 쓰시오. (4점)

• 자전거를 타는 것은 좋은 운동이다.
(it / exercise / ride a bike)

→ _____

[11~12] 다음을 읽고 물음에 답하시오.

Date/Time: July 8th / 2:35 p.m.

Notes: Today was my first day ⓐat Africa. I took lots of pictures of elephants. This morning, I found an elephant group ⓑby a small water hole. I saw a baby elephant ⓒdrinking water ⓓbeside her mother. Her eyes were as ⓔbright as stars. I gave her a name, Stella.

(A) The elephants stood around Stella and made a thick wall.
(B) Thanks to them, Stella was safe.
(C) Around noon, I saw a group of lions approaching Stella.

11 위 글의 ⓐ~ⓔ 중 쓰임이 옳지 <u>않은</u> 것은? (3점)

① ⓐ   ② ⓑ   ③ ⓒ   ④ ⓓ   ⑤ ⓔ

12 위 글의 흐름에 맞게 위의 (A)~(C) 문장을 배열할 때 가장 옳은 것은? (2점)

① (A) - (B) - (C)   ② (A) - (C) - (B)
③ (B) - (A) - (C)   ④ (C) - (A) - (B)
⑤ (C) - (B) - (A)

[13~16] 다음을 읽고 물음에 답하시오.

Date/Time: July 13th / 6:00 a.m.

Notes: A new elephant group appeared and Stella approached them. (A) At first, I thought ⓐ[which / that] they would not let Stella in their group. (B) An elephant, probably the oldest female allowed Stella ⓑ[become / to become] part of the group. (C) The other elephants also seemed ⓒ[welcome / to welcome] Stella. (D) Unbelievably, one of the female elephants fed Stella. <u>그 코끼리는 Stella의 엄마만큼 따뜻하게 Stella를 보살폈다.</u> (E) This was such an amazing moment!

13 위 글의 (A)~(E) 중 아래 주어진 문장이 들어가기에 가장 알맞은 곳은? (3점)

> But I was wrong.

① (A)   ② (B)   ③ (C)
④ (D)   ⑤ (E)

14 위 글의 ⓐ~ⓒ 중 문맥상 올바른 것은? (3점)

	ⓐ	ⓑ	ⓒ
①	that	become	to welcome
②	that	to become	to welcome
③	that	to become	welcome
④	which	become	welcome
⑤	which	to become	to welcome

15 위 글에 대한 내용에서 유추할 수 있는 것으로 옳은 것은? (3점)

① Stella is still alone.
② One of the female elephants acted as Stella's mom.
③ Stella will be able to meet her mom with a new group.
④ At first, the writer thought that Stella could be part of a new elephant group.
⑤ The oldest female elephant didn't seem to be happy with Stella.

16 위 글에서 주어진 우리말 뜻에 맞는 영어 문장을 쓰시오. (as ~ as 원급 비교 사용할 것. 9 단어) (4점)

→ She _____.

[17~21] 다음 글을 읽고 물음에 답하시오.

Note A: The night was dark and quiet. I kept my eyes on Stella with my night camera. Stella was still next to her mom. She was touching her mom's lifeless body with her nose. It was sad to see Stella ⓐstayed close to her mom. I hope Stella stays safe throughout the night.

Note B: A new elephant group appeared and Stella approached them. At first, I thought that they would not let Stella in their group. But I was wrong. 아마도 가장 나이가 많은 암컷인 듯한 코끼리 한 마리가 Stella가 그 무리의 일원이 되도록 허락했다. The other elephants also ⓑseemed welcome Stella. Unbelievably, one of the female elephants fed Stella. She cared for Stella as (A)_____ as Stella's mom did. This was such an amazing moment!

Note C: Around sunset, I heard a strange sound. I followed the sound and found Stella ⓒto cry next to her mom. She was lying (B)_____ and Stella was alone. It is dangerous to stay alone in ⓓsuch wild area. What's more, it was going to be dark soon. Elephants can't see well at night. So Stella could easily be attacked. I called the elephant shelter and asked for help. I decided to stay by her until the rescue team came.

Note D: Today was my first day in Africa. I took lots of pictures of elephants. This morning, I found an elephant group by a small water hole. I saw a baby elephant ⓔdrinking water beside her mother. Her eyes were as (C)_____ as stars. I gave her a name, Stella. Around noon, I saw a group of lions approaching Stella. The elephants stood around Stella and made a thick wall. Thanks to them, Stella was safe.

17 위 글의 Note A~D를 시간의 순서에 맞게 바로 배열한 것은?

(3점)

① Note A - Note D - Note C - Note B
② Note A - Note C - Note B - Note D
③ Note C - Note A - Note D - Note B
④ Note D - Note C - Note A - Note B
⑤ Note D - Note C - Note B - Note A

18 위 글을 읽고 대답할 수 없는 것은? (3점)

① Why did Stella's mom die?
② Where did the writer write this diary?
③ Why could Stella be attacked easily at night?
④ What did the writer find when he followed the sound?
⑤ What was Stella doing next to her mother during the night?

19 위 글의 빈칸 (A)~(C)에 들어갈 것으로 가장 적절한 것은?

(4점)

	(A)	(B)	(C)
①	warm	die	bright
②	warm	dead	brightly
③	warmly	dead	bright
④	warmly	dead	brightly
⑤	warmly	die	brightly

20 위 글의 밑줄 친 ⓐ~ⓔ 중 어법상 올바른 것은? (3점)

① ⓐ   ② ⓑ   ③ ⓒ   ④ ⓓ   ⑤ ⓔ

21 위 글의 밑줄 친 우리말을 영어로 바르게 옮긴 것은? (4점)

① Maybe Stella was allowed to become the oldest female in the group.

② Maybe the oldest female elephant wanted Stella to become her daughter.

③ An elephant, probably the leader of the group allowed Stella to be one of the best in the group.

④ An elephant, probably the oldest female allowed Stella to become part of the group.

⑤ Probably, an elephant, the oldest female Stella allowed to become part of the group.

[충북 ○○중]

[22~25] 다음 글을 읽고 물음에 답하시오.

Date/Time: July 12th / 7:20 p.m.

Notes: Around sunset, I heard a strange sound. I followed the sound and found Stella crying next to her mom. She was lying dead and Stella was alone. ⓐ_____ in such a wild area. What's more, it was going to be dark soon. Elephants can't see well at night. So Stella could easily be attacked. I called the elephant shelter and asked for help. I decided to stay by her (A)_____ the rescue team came.

Date/Time: July 12th / 10:40 p.m.

Notes: The night was dark and quiet. I kept my eyes (B)_____ Stella with my night camera. Stella was still next to her mom. She was touching her mom's lifeless body with her nose. It was sad to see Stella staying close to her mom. I hope Stella stays safe (C)_____ the night.

22 위 글을 읽고 답할 수 <u>없는</u> 질문은? (3점)

① Around sunset, what did the writer hear?

② Why did Stella's mother die?

③ Where did the writer call?

④ Why could Stella be attacked easily at night?

⑤ What was Stella doing next to her mother during the night?

23 위 글의 빈칸 (A)~(C)에 어법상 들어갈 말로 짝지어진 것은? (4점)

	(A)	(B)	(C)
①	to	at	during
②	by	on	for
③	by	to	throughout
④	until	at	for
⑤	until	on	throughout

24 위 글의 내용을 바탕으로 전화 대화를 했을 때, <u>어색한</u> 부분은? (3점)

W: ⓐHi. This is the elephant shelter. How can I help you?

M: Hello. I'm calling about a baby elephant. ⓑShe is alone now.

W: ⓒOh, she is not safe in the wild.

M: ⓓYes. It's going to be bright soon, so I'm very worried about her.

M: ⓔWe'll be there as soon as possible.

① ⓐ　　② ⓑ　　③ ⓒ　　④ ⓓ　　⑤ ⓔ

25 위 글의 빈칸 ⓐ를 아래 〈조건〉에 맞게 영작하여 완성하시오. (4점)

조건
1. 가주어(It)를 사용하여 문장을 시작할 것.
2. danger, alone, stay, be 등의 단어를 반드시 이용하되, 문맥에 맞게 변형하거나 단어를 추가할 수 있음.
3. 반드시 '현재 시제'로 문장을 만들 것.
4. 6 단어로 영작할 것.

ⓐ _____ in such a wild area.

[26~28] 다음을 읽고 물음에 답하시오.

(A) A new elephant group appeared and Stella approached them. (B) At first, I thought that they would not let Stella in their group. (C) An elephant, probably the oldest female allowed Stella to become part of the group. (D) The other elephants also seemed to welcome Stella. (E) Unbelievably, one of the female elephants fed Stella. She cared for Stella ⓐStella의 엄마가 했던 만큼 따뜻하게. This was such an amazing moment!

26 (A)~(E) 중 주어진 문장이 들어가기에 가장 적절한 곳은? (3점)

But I was wrong.

① (A)　　　② (B)　　　③ (C)

④ (D)　　　⑤ (E)

27 위 글을 읽고 답할 수 <u>없는</u> 질문은? (3점)

① What appeared in front of Stella?

② What did the writer think at first?

③ Where did the writer see the new elephant group?

④ How did one of the female elephants care for Stella?

⑤ Which elephant allowed Stella to become part of the group?

28 위 글의 밑줄 친 ⓐ의 우리말을 영작하시오. (필요시 단어를 추가하거나 변형할 것.) (4점)

ⓐStella의 엄마가 했던 만큼 따뜻하게
→ _____
(warm, as ~ as, Stella's mom, do)

[29~31] 다음을 읽고 물음에 답하시오.

Around sunset, I heard a strange sound. I followed the sound and found Stella ⓐto cry next to her mom, She was lying ⓑdeadly and Stella was alone. It is dangerous ⓒto stay alone in such a wild area. _____(A)_____, it was going to be dark soon. Elephants can't see well at night. So Stella could easily ⓓattack. I called the elephant shelter and asked for help. I decided ⓔstaying by her until the rescue team came.

29 위 글에서 밑줄 친 ⓐ~ⓔ 중 어법상 쓰임이 옳은 것은? (3점)

① ⓐ　　　② ⓑ　　　③ ⓒ

④ ⓓ　　　⑤ ⓔ

30 위 글의 빈칸 (A)에 들어갈 말로 가장 알맞은 것은? (3점)

① So　　　　　　② However

③ As a result　　　④ Furthermore

⑤ For example

31 위 글의 내용과 일치하지 <u>않는</u> 것은? (3점)

① 코끼리들은 밤에 잘 볼 수 없다.

② 작가는 이상한 소리를 따라갔다.

③ Stella는 엄마 옆에서 울고 있었다.

④ 작가는 도움을 요청하기 위해 코끼리 보호소에 전화를 걸었다.

⑤ Stella는 구조팀이 올 때까지 엄마 옆에서 머물기로 결정했다.

2학년 영어 2학기 기말고사(7과) 1회

문항수 : 선택형(28문항) 서술형(1문항)   20 . . .

◎ 선택형 문항의 답안은 컴퓨터용 수정 싸인펜을 사용하여 OMR 답안지에 바르게 표기하시오.

◎ 서술형 문제는 답을 답안지에 반드시 검정 볼펜으로 쓰시오.

◎ 총 29문항 100점 만점입니다. 문항별 배점은 각 문항에 표시되어 있습니다.

[서울 서초구 ○○중]

01 다음 빈칸에 들어갈 단어가 <u>아닌</u> 것은?　(4점)

- We should know the _____ of the environment.
- I try to _____ work and play.
- What kind of work _____ do you have?
- My brother works in _____ Seattle.
- My parents _____ money every year.

① important　　　② balance
③ downtown　　　④ experience
⑤ donate

[경북 ○○중]

02 다음 대화의 빈칸에 들어갈 말로 가장 적절한 것은?　(3점)

W: I saw an interesting painting in an art book. Look at this.
M: Wow, it looks like da Vinci's *Mona Lisa*.
W: Actually, it's *Mona Lisa* by Fernando Botero. Which do you prefer?
M: _____
　Da Vinci's *Mona Lisa* has an interesting smile.

① I prefer Botero's to da Vinci's.
② I prefer da Vinci's to Botero's.
③ There are various kinds of painting.
④ I'm looking forward to watching the painting.
⑤ Da Vinci's *Mona Lisa* is as interesting as Botero's *Mona Lisa*.

[서울 노원구 ○○중]

03 주어진 문장 다음에 이어질 대화가 자연스럽도록 (a)~(e)를 바르게 배열한 것은?　(4점)

Anna: (*ringing*) Hello, Steve.
Steve: Hi, Anna. We're meeting at the arts festival tomorrow at 1:30, right?

(a) I want to watch the hip-hop dance performance first.
(b) Oh, the one at the Main Hall near the gym? Sure!
(c) Right. What kind of performance do you want to watch first?
(d) Sounds good. It's at 2 p.m. at the gym, right?
(e) Yeah, and how about watching the play, *Romeo and Juliet*, at 4 p.m.?

① (a)-(b)-(c)-(d)-(e)　　② (b)-(a)-(c)-(e)-(d)
③ (c)-(a)-(d)-(e)-(b)　　④ (d)-(b)-(c)-(a)-(e)
⑤ (e)-(b)-(a)-(c)-(d)

[부산 ○○중]

04 다음 대화의 빈칸 (A)에 가장 알맞은 말은?　(3점)

W: Brian, is your band going to play at the Teen Music Festival?
M: Yes, we're practicing almost every day.
W: What kind of music are you going to play this year?
M: (A)_____ We'll play songs from the nineties.

① The piano.　　　② The guitar.
③ Every year.　　　④ Rock music.
⑤ In the festival.

05 다음 대화의 내용과 일치하지 않는 것은? (4점)

> W: (ringing) Hello, Steve.
> M: Hi, Anna. We're meeting at the arts festival tomorrow at 1:30, right?
> W: Right. What kind of performance do you want to watch first?
> M: I want to watch the hip-hop dance performance first.
> W: Sounds good. It's at 2 p.m. at the gym, right?
> M: Yeah, and how about watching the play *Romeo and Juliet*, at 4 p.m.?
> W: Oh, the one at the Main Hall near the gym? Sure!

① 내일 남자와 여자는 예술 축제에서 만나기로 했다.
② 여자와 남자는 어떤 공연을 먼저 볼지 정하고 있다.
③ 남자는 힙합 댄스 공연을 마지막 순서로 보고 싶어 한다.
④ 힙합 댄스 공연은 2시에 체육관에서 있을 예정이다.
⑤ 4시에는 로미오와 줄리엣 공연을 보려고 한다.

[6~8] 다음 글을 읽고 물음에 답하시오.

Welcome to the World Art Museum tour. When you go to an art museum, how much time do you ⓐspend to look at each painting? Many visitors ⓑglance to one painting for only ⓒa few second before they move on. But you might miss the important details of paintings (A)since it is hard ⓓto notice them right away. Today, we'll look at two paintings closely and I'll ⓔhelp you to see interesting details.

06 위 글 다음에 올 내용으로 가장 적절한 것은? (3점)

① 미술 박물관 여행기
② 두 가지 미술 작품 설명
③ 훌륭한 미술 작품의 특징
④ 미술 박물관에서의 주의 사항
⑤ 한 미술 작품 당 할애해야 할 시간

07 위 글의 밑줄 친 ⓐ~ⓔ 중 글의 내용이나 어법상 옳은 것을 두 개 고른 것은? (4점)

① ⓐ ② ⓑ ③ ⓒ
④ ⓓ ⑤ ⓔ

08 위 글의 밑줄 친 (A)since의 의미로 사용되지 않은 것은? (3점)

① I'll buy you lunch <u>since</u> it's your birthday.
② <u>Since</u> it was getting darker, I decided to go home.
③ I can't hang out with you <u>since</u> my mother asked me to come home early.
④ I have a good friend and I have known her <u>since</u> I was seven years old.
⑤ Emma has seen this movie many times <u>since</u> there are lots of great special effects.

[9~12] 다음 글을 읽고 물음에 답하시오.

Look at this painting first. The seaside landscape is so peaceful and beautiful, ⓐisn't it? (ⓐ) The title of this painting is (A)_____. So, can you see where Icarus is? (ⓑ) Do you see two legs ⓑthat is sticking ⓒout of the water near the ship? This is Icarus in the famous myth in Greece. (ⓒ) However, Icarus didn't listen. He flew too close to the sun. So, the wax melted and he ⓓfell into the water. (ⓓ) Now, look at the entire painting again. ⓔDespite the tragedy of Icarus, people are going on with their everyday activities. (ⓔ) Does the painting still look peaceful? (B)화가가 우리에게 무엇을 말하고자 노력하고 있다고 생각하나요?

09 위 글의 (A)에 들어갈 작품의 제목으로 가장 적절한 것은? (4점)

① Landscape with the Fall of Icarus
② Landscape with the Rise of Icarus
③ Landscape with the Tragedy of Greece
④ The Story of Icarus' Peaceful Life
⑤ The Rise of Icarus' Tragedy

10 위 글의 ⓐ~ⓔ 중에서 보기의 문장이 들어가기에 문맥상 가장 어울리는 곳은? (3점)

> 보기
> In the myth, Icarus' father made wings for him with feathers and wax and told him to stay away from the sun.

① ⓐ　　② ⓑ　　③ ⓒ　　④ ⓓ　　⑤ ⓔ

11 위 글을 읽고 밑줄 친 ⓐ~ⓔ 중 어법상 어색한 것은? (3점)

① ⓐ　　② ⓑ　　③ ⓒ　　④ ⓓ　　⑤ ⓔ

12 우리말 (B)를 영작한 것으로 적절한 것은? (4점)

① Do you think what is the artist trying to tell us?
② Do you think what the artist is trying to tell us?
③ Do you think what the artist is trying telling us?
④ What do you think the artist is trying to tell us?
⑤ What do you think the artist is trying telling us?

[13~14] 다음 글을 읽고 물음에 답하시오.

Welcome to the World Art Museum tour. When you go to an art museum, how many time do you spend looking at each painting? Many visitors glance at one painting during only a few seconds before they move on. But you might miss the important details of paintings as it is hard ⓐto notice them right away. Today, we'll look at two paintings close and I'll help you see interesting details.

13 위 글에서 어법상 바르지 못한 단어 표현은 모두 몇 개인가? (3점)

① 2개　　② 3개　　③ 4개　　④ 5개　　⑤ 6개

14 위 글의 ⓐto notice와 쓰임이 같은 것은? (3점)

① It is better for you to leave early.
② To get a good job, you should try hard.
③ I've prepared it to satisfy your curiosity.
④ She needs someone to fix her computer.
⑤ They must be foolish to believe her again.

[15~18] 다음 글을 읽고 물음에 답하시오.

Now, ⓐlet's move on to the next painting. Do you see the artist behind the large canvas? He is Diego Velázquez, and he actually painted this picture. Who is he painting? Take a (a)_____ look. The young princess ⓑseems that be the main person because she is ⓒin the center of the painting. But the title of the painting is *The Maids of Honour*. Then, is the artist drawing the ⓓtwo women beside the princess? Take a (b)_____ look. It will ⓔmake you wonder about the painting more. Try to see (A)(which, the artist, direction, is, at, looking). Can you see the king and the queen in the mirror in the background of the painting? Who is he painting now?

15 위 글의 밑줄 친 ⓐ~ⓔ 중 어법상 어색한 것은?　(4점)

① ⓐ　② ⓑ　③ ⓒ　④ ⓓ　⑤ ⓔ

16 위 글의 빈칸 (a), (b)에 각각 들어갈 말로 가장 적절하게 짝지은 것은?　(4점)

	(a)	(b)
①	quick	close
②	quick	open
③	close	open
④	close	short
⑤	long	short

17 위 글의 밑줄 친 (A)에 제시된 단어들을 배열하여 완성한 문장으로 가장 적절한 것은?　(3점)

① which is the artist looking at direction
② which the artist is looking at direction
③ which at direction the artist is looking
④ which direction the artist is looking at
⑤ is the artist looking at which direction

18 위 글을 읽고 대답할 수 없는 것은?　(3점)

① Who drew the painting, *The Maids of Honour*?
② What is the job of the man behind the large canvas?
③ Who is the girl in the middle of the painting?
④ What are the people beside the princess doing?
⑤ How many people can we see in the mirror in the painting?

[19~20] 다음 글을 읽고 물음에 답하시오.

Look at this painting first. (A) The seaside landscape is so peaceful and beautiful, ⓐis it? (B) So, can you see ⓑwhere Icarus is? Do you see ⓒtwo legs who are sticking out of the water near the ship? (C) This is Icarus in the famous myth in Greece. In the myth, Icarus' father ⓓmade wings to him with feathers and wax and ⓔtold him stay away from the sun. However, Icarus didn't listen. (D) He flew too close to the sun. So, the wax melted and he fell into the water. (E) Now, look at the entire painting again. Despite the tragedy of Icarus, people are going on with their everyday activities. Does the painting still look peaceful?

19 위 글의 (A)~(E)에서 다음 문장이 들어가기에 가장 알맞은 곳은?　(4점)

> The title of this painting is *Landscape with the Fall of Icarus*.

① (A)　② (B)　③ (C)　④ (D)　⑤ (E)

20 위 글의 ⓐ~ⓔ 중 내용과 어법 둘 다 올바른 것은?　(3점)

① ⓐ　② ⓑ　③ ⓒ　④ ⓓ　⑤ ⓔ

[21~24] Read and answer the questions.

Welcome to the World Art Museum tour. When you go to an art museum, [A]how much time do you spend look at each painting? Many visitors look at one painting for only a few seconds before they move on. But you might miss the important details of paintings since it is hard to notice them right away. Today, we'll look at two paintings closely and [B]I'll help you see interesting details. Look at this painting first. The seaside landscape is so peaceful and beautiful, isn't it? The title of this painting is *Landscape with the Fall of Icarus*. So, where is Icarus in the painting? Do you see [C]two legs that are sticking the water near the ship? This is Icarus in the famous myth in Greece. In the myth, Icarus' father made wings for him with feathers and wax and [D]told him stay away from the sun. However, Icarus didn't listen. He flew too close to the sun. So, the wax melted and he fell into the water. Now, look at the entire painting again. People don't care about him and are going on with their everyday activities. Do you still think that the painting is peaceful? Ⓐ_____?

Now, let's move on to the next painting. Do you see the artist behind the large canvas? He is ⓐDiego Velázquez, and he actually painted this picture. Who is he painting? Take a quick look. [E]The young princess seems the main person because she is in the center of the painting. But the title of the painting is *The Maids of Honour*. Then, is ⓑthe artist drawing the two women beside the princess? Take a close look. You will wonder about ⓒhis painting more. Try to see the direction he is looking at. Can you see ⓓthe king and the queen in the mirror in the background of the painting? Who is ⓔhe painting now?

21 Which of the following is correct? (3점)

① [A] ② [B] ③ [C] ④ [D] ⑤ [E]

22 Which of the following is correct according to the text? (4점)

① Icarus flew too close to the water and fell down.
② Icarus made wings with feathers and wax himself.
③ Two women are behind the princess in the painting, *The Maids of Honour*.
④ The artist, Diego Veláquez, is behind the canvas.
⑤ The king and the queen are in the center of the painting.

23 Which of the following is different in the text? (3점)

① ⓐ   ② ⓑ   ③ ⓒ
④ ⓓ   ⑤ ⓔ

24 다음 우리말 뜻과 동일한 문장이 되도록 반드시 간접의문문과 제시 단어를 활용하여 빈칸 Ⓐ에 들어갈 문장을 단어 수에 맞게 영작하시오. (11단어) (5점)

Ⓐ: 당신은 그 화가가 우리에게 무엇을 말하려 한다고 생각하나요?
*제시 단어: tell, think, try

→ _____

[25~27] 다음 글을 읽고 물음에 답하시오.

Look at this painting first. The seaside landscape is so peaceful and beautiful, isn't it? The title of this painting is *Landscape with the Fall of Icarus*. (A) Do you see two legs that are sticking out of the water near the ship? (B) This is Icarus in the famous myth in Greece. (C) In the myth, Icarus' father made wings for him with feathers and wax and told him to stay away from the sun. (D) However, Icarus didn't listen. (E) He flew too close to the sun. So, the wax melted and he fell into the water. Now, look at the entire painting again. Despite the tragedy of Icarus, people are going on with their everyday activities. Does the painting still look peaceful? What do you think the artist is trying to tell us?

25 위 글의 (A)~(E) 중 주어진 문장이 들어가기에 가장 적절한 곳은? (3점)

So, can you see where Icarus is?

① (A)　② (B)　③ (C)　④ (D)　⑤ (E)

26 위 글의 내용으로 답할 수 <u>없는</u> 질문은? (3점)

① What is the title of the painting?

② Where is Icarus in the painting?

③ What did Icarus' father make for Icarus?

④ What mistake did Icarus' father make?

⑤ What were the other people in the painting doing when Icarus fell into the water?

27 위 글을 요약한 대화를 만들 때 빈칸에 들어갈 말로 가장 적절한 것은? (4점)

Q: Where is Icarus?

A: He's _____ the ship. You can see his legs sticking out of the water.

Q: What happened to Icarus?

A: He flew too _____ to the sun and the wax of his wings _____.

① in – close – melt　② in – low – turn

③ near – close – melted　④ near – low – turned

⑤ below – high – fell

[28~29] 다음 글을 읽고 물음에 답하시오.

Welcome to the World Art Museum tour. ⓐWhen you go to an art museum, how much time do you spend ⓑlooking at each painting? Many visitors glance at one painting for only a few seconds before they ⓒmove on. But you might miss the important details of paintings (A)<u>since</u> it is hard ⓓ<u>to notice</u> them right away. Today, we'll look at two paintings closely. It will make you ⓔ<u>seeing</u> interesting details.

28 위 글의 밑줄 친 ⓐ~ⓔ 중 어법상 <u>어색한</u> 것은? (3점)

① ⓐ　② ⓑ　③ ⓒ　④ ⓓ　⑤ ⓔ

29 위 글의 밑줄 친 (A)와 쓰임이 같은 것은? (3점)

① You don't need to go to school <u>since</u> it's Sunday.

② It has been 9 years <u>since</u> I started playing the guitar.

③ Ryan has grown these plants <u>since</u> last year.

④ Jill has been interested in space <u>since</u> 2013.

⑤ You have changed a lot <u>since</u> I saw you last year.

2학년 영어 2학기 기말고사(7과) 2회

문항수 : 선택형(26문항) 서술형(2문항) 20 . . .

◎ 선택형 문항의 답안은 컴퓨터용 수정 싸인펜을 사용하여 OMR 답안지에 바르게 표기하시오.
◎ 서술형 문제는 답을 답안지에 반드시 검정 볼펜으로 쓰시오.
◎ 총 28문항 100점 만점입니다. 문항별 배점은 각 문항에 표시되어 있습니다.

[경북 ○○중]

01 다음 빈칸에 들어가기에 가장 적당한 말은? (3점)

> A: Brian, is your band going to play at the Teen Music Festival?
> B: Yes, we're practicing almost every day.
> A: _____ are you going to play this year?
> B: Rock music. We'll play songs from the nineties.

① Where　　　　② How often
③ Who　　　　④ How many musics
⑤ What kind of music

[경기 ○○중]

02 다음 Arts Festival의 일정을 정리한 표에서, 대화의 내용과 일치하지 <u>않는</u> 것은? (4점)

> John: Hello, Anna.
> Anna: Hi, John. We're meeting at the arts festival tomorrow at 1:30, right?
> John: Right. What kind of performance do you want to watch first?
> Anna: I want to watch the hip-hop dance performance first.
> John: Sounds good. It's at 2 p.m. at the gym, right?
> Anna: Yeah, and how about watching the play, *Romeo and Juliet*, at 4 p.m.?
> John: Oh, the one at the Main Hall? Sure!

Arts Festival Schedule		
Performance	Time	Place
① Dance: Hip-Hop	② 2:00 p.m.	③ Gym
④ Movie: Romeo & Juliet	⑤ 4:00 p.m.	Main Hall

[서울 노원구 ○○중]

[3~4] 다음 대화를 읽고 질문에 답하시오.

> Jack: Hi, we are planning a school festival, so we want to find out students' favorite types of performances. May I ask you a few questions?
> Serin: Sure.
> Jack: What kind of performance do you like best?
> Serin: I like music performances best.
> Jack: Okay. Then, (A)_____
> Serin: I prefer rock to hip-hop.
> Jack: Who's your favorite musician?
> Serin: My favorite musician is TJ.
> Jack: Great. Thank you for your answers.

03 빈칸 (A)에 가장 알맞은 표현은? (3점)

① which festival do you want to go to?
② which do you prefer, rock or hip-hop?
③ what type of movie do you want to watch?
④ what do you like to do in a music festival?
⑤ what are you going to do in a school festival?

04 Which is the true statement? (4점)

① Jack's favorite musician is TJ.
② Serin is not interested in the school festival.
③ The performance that Jack likes most is music.
④ Serin doesn't have time to answer the questions.
⑤ Jack wants to know what types of performances students like.

[5~7] 다음 글을 읽고 물음에 답하시오.

Now, let's move on to the next painting. Do you see the artist behind the large canvas? He is Diego Velázquez, and he actually painted this picture. Who do you think he is painting? Take a quick look. The young princess seems to be the main person because she is in the center of the painting. But the title of the painting is *The Maids of Honour*. Then, is the artist drawing the two women beside the princess? Take a close look. It will make you (A)_____ about the painting more. Try (B)_____ which direction the artist is looking at. Can you see the king and the queen in the mirror in the background of the painting? Who do you think he is painting now?

05 위 글의 내용과 일치하는 것은? (3점)

① 그림 속 화가와 그림을 그린 화가는 다른 사람이다.
② 재빨리 그림을 보면 화가가 왕과 왕비를 그리고 있다.
③ 공주는 그림의 왼쪽에 위치하고 있다.
④ 두 명의 시녀의 시선은 화가를 향해 있다.
⑤ 그림의 배경에 있는 거울 속에 왕과 왕비가 있다.

06 위 글에 쓰인 문장을 참고로 하여, 다음 중 어법상 어색한 문장을 고르면? (3점)

① The woman lets the cat go out of the house.
② The man wants her to buy the exhibition tickets.
③ The woman hears the bell ring.
④ The man helps him to do his best.
⑤ The woman has people to make the food.

07 위 글의 빈칸 (A), (B)에 가장 알맞은 것은? (3점)

	(A)	(B)
①	wonder	to see
②	wonder	see
③	to wonder	to see
④	to wonder	seeing
⑤	wondering	seeing

[8~10] 다음 글을 읽고 물음에 답하시오.

Look at this painting first. The seaside landscape is so peaceful and beautiful, ⓐis it? The title of this painting is *Landscape with the Fall of Icarus*. So, can you see ⓑwhere is Icarus? Do you see ⓒ two legs that are sticking out of the water near the ship? This is Icarus in the famous myth in Greece. In the myth, Icarus' father ⓓmade wings to him with feathers and wax and ⓔtold him to stay away from the sun. However, Icarus didn't listen. He flew ⓕtoo close to the sun. So, the wax melted and he fell into the water. Now, look at the entire painting again. ⓖDespite the tragedy of Icarus, people are going on with their everyday activities. Does the painting ⓗstill look peace? ⓘWhat do you think the artist is trying to tell us?

08 위 글의 ⓐ~ⓘ 중, 어법상 올바른 것은? (4점)

① ⓐ, ⓒ, ⓓ, ⓕ, ⓖ   ② ⓑ, ⓔ, ⓕ, ⓗ, ⓘ
③ ⓒ, ⓓ, ⓔ, ⓕ, ⓖ   ④ ⓑ, ⓓ, ⓗ, ⓖ, ⓘ
⑤ ⓒ, ⓔ, ⓕ, ⓖ, ⓘ

09 위 글에서 다음 영영풀이에 해당하는 단어를 찾아 쓰시오. (4점)

It is a well-known story which was made up in the past to explain natural events or to justify religious belief or social customs.

→ _____

10 위 글의 내용을 한 문장으로 요약하고자 한다. (A), (B)에 들어갈 말로 가장 적절한 것은? (4점)

> The text explains how we can find out more in painting by looking at the details carefully. In *Landscape with the Fall of Icarus*, the figure of Icarus in the water adds a (A)_____ to a painting that seems (B)_____.

	(A)	(B)
①	twist	peaceful
②	result	dark
③	parody	scary
④	change	lonely
⑤	romance	joyful

[대구 ○○중]

[11~13] 다음 글을 읽고 물음에 답하시오.

Now, let's move on to the next painting. (A) Do you see the artist behind the large canvas? He is Diego Velázquez, and he actually painted this picture. ⓐ_____? Take a quick look. (B) The young princess seems to be the main person because she is in the center of the painting. But the title of the painting is *The Maids of Honour*. (C) Take a close look. It will make you wonder about the painting more. Try to see which direction the artist is looking at. (D) Can you see the king and the queen in the mirror in the background of the painting? (E) ⓑ_____?

11 위 글에서 다음 문장이 들어갈 위치로 가장 적절한 곳은? (4점)

> Then, is the artist drawing the two women beside the princess?

① (A)　② (B)　③ (C)　④ (D)　⑤ (E)

12 위 글의 ⓐ, ⓑ에 공통으로 들어갈 문장을, 〈보기〉의 단어들을 배열하여 영작하시오. (4점)

> **보기**
>
> do / think / who / he / you / is / painting

→ _____

13 위 글을 읽고 답할 수 <u>없는</u> 질문은? (3점)

① What is the title of the painting?
② When did the artist paint the painting?
③ Where is the princess in the painting?
④ How many people are there in the picture?
⑤ Who is the person behind the large canvas?

[경기 ○○중]

14 다음 대화의 ⓐ~ⓔ 중 어법상 옳은 것의 개수로 알맞은 것은? (3점)

> Harry: Hey, Ron. Why are you so late? You ⓐ<u>made me wait</u> for a long time.
> Ron: I'm sorry. My mother ⓑ<u>made me did</u> my homework before going out. After finishing my homework, she ⓒ<u>let me go</u> out.
> Harry: Oh, I see. Let's go in. I can't wait to see the paintings.
> Ron: OK. Wow! Take a look at this painting. The farmer ⓓ<u>makes two cows to work</u> for him. It is so realistic.
> Harry: I like this one, too. The green color ⓔ<u>makes me feel</u> peaceful.

① 1개　　② 2개　　③ 3개
④ 4개　　⑤ 5개

[15~17] 다음 글을 읽고 물음에 답하시오.

Look at this painting first. ⓐThe seaside landscape is so peaceful and beautiful, is it? The title of this painting is *Landscape with the Fall of Icarus*. ⓑSo, can you see where is Icarus? ⓒDo you see two legs sticking out of the water near the ship? This is Icarus in the famous myth in Greece. In the myth, Icarus' father made wings for him with feathers and wax and told him not to fly too close to the sun. However, Icarus didn't listen. He flew too close to the sun. So, the wax melted and he fell into the water. Now look at the entire painting again. ⓓIn spite the tragedy of Icarus, people are going on with their everyday activities. No one notices as Icarus falls into the sea. A farmer is working in the field. A man is fishing by the sea. And the *shepherd is looking after his sheep. ⓔDoes the painting look peacefully?

*shepherd: 양치기

15 위 글의 내용과 일치하면 T, 일치하지 않으면 F로 표시할 때, 알맞게 표시된 것은? (3점)

① Icarus in the painting is related to Greek myth. - F

② Icarus' father used feathers and wax to create wings for Icarus. - T

③ The Icarus' body part we can see in the painting is his legs. - F

④ Icarus chose to follow his father's advice. - T

⑤ The people in the painting are interested in Icarus' tragedy. - T

16 위 글의 밑줄 친 ⓐ~ⓔ 중 어법상 옳은 것은? (4점)

① ⓐ   ② ⓑ   ③ ⓒ   ④ ⓓ   ⑤ ⓔ

17 위 글 속의 단어에 대한 설명이 <u>아닌</u> 것은? (4점)

① to see or become conscious of something or someone

② an area of countryside, especially in relation to its appearance

③ one of the parts of a bird's or insect's body that it uses for flying

④ an ancient story, especially one invented in order to explain natural or historical events

⑤ to tell someone that something bad or dangerous may happen

18 다음 Jen이 기록한 목록을 보고 쓴 문장 중 어법상 옳은 것은? (4점)

What do I want to know?	• How much is the picture? • What does the picture mean? • Why did the painter use the color?
What did I learn?	• When was the picture painted? • What material did the artist use? • What is the name of the painter?

① Jen wants to know how much the picture is.

② Jen learned when was the picture painted.

③ Jen learned what material the artist did used.

④ Jen wants to know what meant the picture.

⑤ Jen wants to know why did the painter use the color.

[19~21] 다음 글을 읽고 물음에 답하시오.

Welcome to the World Art Museum tour. When you go to an art museum, how much time do you spend (A)_____ at each painting? Many visitors glance (B)_____ one painting for only a few seconds before they move on. But you might miss the important details of paintings (C)_____ it is hard to notice @them right away. Today, we'll look at two paintings closely and I'll help you see interesting details.

19 위 글의 빈칸 (A)~(C)에 들어갈 단어로 알맞은 것은? (4점)

	(A)	(B)	(C)
①	looking	at	since
②	looking	on	because of
③	looking	on	despite
④	look	with	since
⑤	look	at	because

20 위 글에 이어질 내용으로 알맞은 것은? (3점)

① 두 명의 화가에 대해 알아본다.
② 그림 두 개의 세부 사항을 살펴본다.
③ 그리스 신화에 대해 알아본다.
④ 그림의 제목을 맞춘다.
⑤ 그림을 빠르게 감상하는 법을 알아본다.

21 위 글의 밑줄 친 @가 가리키는 것은? (3점)

① the World Art Museums
② paintings
③ many visitors
④ the important details of paintings
⑤ a few seconds

[22~24] 다음 글을 읽고 물음에 답하시오.

Look at this painting first. The seaside landscape is so peaceful and beautiful, isn't it? The title of this painting is *Landscape with the Fall of Icarus*. (A) So, can you see where Icarus is? Do you see two legs that are @sticking out of the water near the ship? This is Icarus in the famous myth in Greece. (B) In the myth, Icarus' father made wings for him with feathers and wax and told him to stay away from the sun. (C) He flew too close to the sun. So, the wax melted and he fell into the water. Now, look at the entire painting again. (D) Despite the tragedy of Icarus, people are going on with their everyday activities. (E) Does the painting still look peaceful?

22 위 글을 읽고 답할 수 없는 질문은? (3점)

① What is the title of the painting?
② What did Icarus' father make for Icarus?
③ What did Icarus' father tell Icarus?
④ Why did Icarus's wing melt?
⑤ How many people are in the painting?

23 위 글의 (A)~(E) 중 다음 문장이 들어갈 곳은? (4점)

> However, Icarus didn't listen.

① (A)   ② (B)   ③ (C)   ④ (D)   ⑤ (E)

24 위 글의 밑줄 친 @와 같은 뜻으로 쓰인 것은? (4점)

① Her arms and legs were like <u>sticks</u>.
② The boys were throwing <u>sticks</u>.
③ Don't <u>stick</u> your arm out of the car window.
④ The <u>stick</u> is out of the bag.
⑤ He feels the ground with a <u>stick</u>.

Look at this painting first. It is painted by a painter named Pieter Bruegel. The seaside landscape is so peaceful and beautiful, isn't it? (A)The title of this painting is *Landscape with the Fall of Icarus*. So, can you find Icarus in this picture? (B)Do you see two legs that ⓐare sticking out of the water near the ship? (C)This is Icarus in the famous myth in Greece. In the myth, Icarus' father made wings ⓑfor him with feathers and wax and ⓒtold him to stay away from the sun. However, Icarus didn't listen. (D)He flew too close to the sun. So, the wax melted and he fell into the water. Now, look at the entire painting again. (E)Despite the tragedy of Icarus, people ⓓare going on with their everyday activities. Does the painting still look ⓔpeacefully? What does the artist want to tell us?

(가)

25 Icarus에 대한 설명으로 옳지 <u>않은</u> 것은? (4점)

① Pieter Bruegel painted the scene of his death.

② In the picture, he is in the water near the ship.

③ He is the one of the Greek gods who never died.

④ He didn't follow his father's advice and fell into the water.

⑤ His father made him wings with feathers to help him to fly.

26 ⓐ~ⓔ 중 어법상 옳지 <u>않은</u> 것은? (3점)

① ⓐ ② ⓑ ③ ⓒ ④ ⓓ ⑤ ⓔ

27 (A)~(E) 문장 중, 그림의 (가)에 대한 설명으로 적절한 것은? (4점)

① (A) ② (B) ③ (C) ④ (D) ⑤ (E)

28 다음 대화의 내용과 일치하는 것은? (4점)

W: (ringing) Hello, Steve.
M: Hi, Anna. We're meeting at the arts festival tomorrow at 1:30, right?
W: Right. What kind of performance do you want to watch first?
M: What about the teen orchestra performance?
W: Umm, I think the orchestra performance begins at 12:00 in the Concert Hall. It's quite earlier than our appointment time.
M: Then, I want to watch the hip-hop dance performance first.
W: Sounds good. It's at 2 p.m. at the gym, right?
M: Yeah, and how about watching the play, *Romeo and Juliet*, at 3 p.m.?
W: Oh, the one at the Main Hall near the gym? Sure!
M: Before we go back home, let's go to the art gallery to see Gogh's work. The Van Gogh exhibition starts at 4:00 p.m.

Performance	Time	Exhibition Place
① Hip-Hop	3:00 p.m.	gym
② Romeo & Juliet	1:30 p.m.	Main Hall
③ Arts festival	12:00	Concert Hall
④ Teen Orchestra	2:00 p.m.	Main Hall
⑤ The Van Gogh	4:00 p.m.	art gallery

2학년 영어 2학기 기말고사(8과) 1회

문항수 : 선택형(27문항) 서술형(1문항)   20 . . .

◎ 선택형 문항의 답안은 컴퓨터용 수정 싸인펜을 사용하여 OMR 답안지에 바르게 표기하시오.
◎ 서술형 문제는 답을 답안지에 반드시 검정 볼펜으로 쓰시오.
◎ 총 28문항 100점 만점입니다. 문항별 배점은 각 문항에 표시되어 있습니다.

[서울 관악구 ㅇㅇ중]

01 밑줄 친 부분의 쓰임이 <u>다른</u> 하나는?   (3점)

① His job is <u>playing</u> the guitar in a band.
② This is a <u>sleeping</u> bag.
③ I love <u>listening</u> to classical music.
④ The girl <u>dancing</u> on the street is my sister.
⑤ Tom has his own <u>swimming</u> pool.

[서울 관악구 ㅇㅇ중]

02 밑줄 친 부분의 영어 표현이 우리말의 의미와 맞지 <u>않는</u> 것은?   (4점)

① Wash one apple under <u>running water</u> and cut it into small pieces. (흐르는 물)
② Cook the <u>cut apple pieces</u> with brown sugar on low heat. (잘라진 사과 조각)
③ Add salt, milk, and <u>a beating egg</u> to make the egg mixture. (휘저은 계란)
④ Roll the bread out and put the <u>cooked apple filling</u> on it. (요리된 사과 소)
⑤ Decorate a dish with the bread rolls and the <u>remaining apple filling</u>. (남아 있는 사과 소)

[서울 관악구 ㅇㅇ중]

03 〈보기〉 중 밑줄 친 부분이 바르게 쓰인 문장의 개수는?   (4점)

보기
• I heard <u>disappointed</u> news.
• The <u>broken</u> window looked dangerous.
• The movie had a <u>shocked</u> ending.
• Look at the <u>smiling</u> face in the picture.
• Wouldn't it be exciting to ride a <u>flying</u> car?

① 1개 ② 2개 ③ 3개 ④ 4개 ⑤ 5개

[서울 송파구 ㅇㅇ중]

[4~5] 다음 대화를 읽고 물음에 답하시오.

(1) M: Jenny, I really enjoyed watching the new online comic *Scary Night*. What about you?
W: Ⓐ_____ I thought it had too many sound effects.
M: Really? I thought they made the story more interesting.
W: Not me. I couldn't focus because I was too scared.

(2) M: Hey, Lisa. I've got over a hundred comments on my SNS posts.
W: Oh, I wouldn't feel comfortable to share my posts with so many people.
M: Really? I think it's great that a lot of people see my posts.
W: Ⓐ_____ I only want to share my posts with my close friends.

04 빈칸 Ⓐ에 공통으로 들어갈 표현은?   (3점)

① I didn't agree.
② That's a great idea.
③ I'm with you on that.
④ What do you think about it?
⑤ I don't agree with you.

05 위 대화문 (2)에 대한 내용이다. 틀린 것은?   (4점)

ⓐ They are talking about sharing their SNS posts with other people.
ⓑ The man likes sharing his SNS posts with many other people.
ⓒ The man has already gotten many comments on his SNS posts.
ⓓ The woman only wants to share her posts with her close friends.
ⓔ Getting a comment from an unknown person would probably make the woman comfortable.

① ⓐ ② ⓑ ③ ⓒ ④ ⓓ ⑤ ⓔ

After ⓐ<u>looking</u> around Gaudi's Park Guell, we decided to have seafood fried rice for lunch. However, we didn't know which restaurant ⓑ<u>to go</u> to. We needed help, so Mom went up to an elderly lady and tried to (A)＿＿＿＿＿＿＿ to a popular seafood restaurant. Luckily, she seemed ⓒ<u>to understand</u> Mom's few Spanish words. She took us to a small local restaurant nearby. The seafood fried rice was amazing. I really wanted ⓓ<u>to take</u> pictures of the food and ⓔ <u>posted</u> them on my blog. But without my phone, I just decided to enjoy the moment.

06 위 글의 빈칸 (A)에 알맞은 것은?　(4점)

① let her go

② ask for directions

③ ask her the way

④ communicate with

⑤ keep her eyes on it

07 위 글의 내용과 일치하는 것은?　(3점)

① Mom didn't speak Spanish.

② I was not satisfied with the food.

③ I couldn't eat the seafood fried rice.

④ Mom and I finally got to the restaurant with a lady's help.

⑤ They had to take a local bus to get to the restaurant.

08 위 글의 밑줄 친 ⓐ~ⓔ 중 옳지 않은 것을 고르고, 바르게 고쳐 쓰시오.　(3점)

→ ＿＿＿＿＿＿＿＿＿＿＿＿＿

Last summer, my father suggested a surprising event: a family trip without smartphones! He said, "I hate to see you sitting together and only looking at your smartphones." My sister and I explained the need for smartphones, but he kept saying that we could not fully enjoy the trip with them. So we started a technology-free trip to a new city, Barcelona, Spain. Our first day was terrible. On the way to our guesthouse around Plaza Reial, we got lost in downtown Barcelona. Dad was busy looking at the map and asking for directions with a few Spanish words he got from a tour guidebook. Even though our guesthouse was right next to the Plaza, it took us about two hours to get there. <u>우리는 너무 피곤해서 저녁을 먹으러 나갈 수 없었다</u>. I went to bed but couldn't fall asleep because I was worried about what would happen the next day.

09 위 글의 우리말을 영어로 바르게 옮긴 것은?　(3점)

① We were so tired that we cannot go out for dinner.

② We were too tired that we can go out for dinner.

③ We were very tired and we could go out for dinner.

④ We were too tired not to go out for dinner.

⑤ We were so tired that we couldn't go out for dinner.

10 위 글을 읽고 대답할 수 <u>없는</u> 것은?　(4점)

① What is a technology-free trip?

② How long did Dad learn Spanish?

③ Where was the family's guesthouse located?

④ What surprising event did Dad suggest last summer?

⑤ Why did Dad suggest a family trip without smartphones?

[11~13] 다음 글을 읽고 물음에 답하시오.

After looking around Gaudi's Park Guell, we decided to have seafood fried rice for lunch. (A)_____, we didn't know which restaurant to go to. We needed ⓐhelp, so Mom went up to an elderly lady and tried to ask for ⓑdirections to a popular seafood restaurant. (B)_____, she seemed to understand Mom's few Spanish words. She took us to a small ⓒlocal restaurant nearby. The seafood fried rice was amazing. I really wanted to take pictures of the food and post them on my blog. But without my phone, I just decided to enjoy the moment.

During the remaining days, we relied more and more on the ⓓforeigners. We were able to meet and talk with various people on the streets, in the bakeries, and in the parks. They were always kind enough to show us ⓔdifferent sides of Barcelona with a smile. (C)_____, our family talked a lot with each other. We spent much of our time together on the Spanish train, on the bus, and at the restaurants.

11 위 글의 밑줄 친 ⓐ~ⓔ 중 문맥상 어색한 것은? (4점)

① ⓐ   ② ⓑ   ③ ⓒ   ④ ⓓ   ⑤ ⓔ

12 위 글의 내용으로 보아 답할 수 없는 질문은? (4점)

① How did the family find a popular seafood restaurant?

② What did the writer want to do with a smartphone at the restaurant?

③ Where did the family meet and talk with the locals?

④ How were the locals to the family?

⑤ How often did the family get on the Spanish train?

13 위 글의 빈칸 (A)~(C)에 들어갈 말로 알맞게 짝지어진 것은? (4점)

	(A)	(B)	(C)
①	However	Luckily	Also
②	However	Yet	Also
③	However	Luckily	Still
④	So	Yet	Still
⑤	So	Luckily	Finally

[14~15] 다음 글을 읽고 물음에 답하시오.

Last summer, my father suggested a ⓐsurprising event: a family trip without smartphones! He said, "I hate to see you ⓑsitting together and only ⓒlooked at your smartphones." My sister and I explained the need for smartphones, but he kept ⓓsaying that we could not fully ⓔenjoy the trip with (A)them. So we started a technology-free trip to a new city, Barcelona, Spain.

14 위 글의 ⓐ~ⓔ 중 어법상 어색한 것은? (4점)

① ⓐ   ② ⓑ   ③ ⓒ   ④ ⓓ   ⑤ ⓔ

15 위 글의 (A)them이 가리키는 것은? (3점)

① events   ② my family

③ smartphones   ④ technologies

⑤ my sister and I

[16~17] 다음 글을 읽고 물음에 답하시오.

ⓐLast summer, my father suggested a surprised event: a family trip without smartphones! He said, ⓑ"I hate to see you to sit together and only to look at your smartphones." My sister and I explained the need for smartphones, but he kept saying that we could not fully enjoy the trip with them. So we started a technology-free trip to a new city, Barcelona, Spain.

Our first day was terrible. On the way to our guesthouse around Plaza Reial, we got lost in downtown Barcelona. ⓒDad was busy looking at the map and asking for directions with a few Spanish words he got from a tour guidebook. Even though our guesthouse was right next to the Plaza, it took us about two hours to get there. We are too tired to go out for dinner. I went to bed but couldn't fall asleep because I was worried about what would happen the next day.

ⓓAfter looking around Gaudi's Park Guell, we decided to have seafood frying rice for lunch. However, we didn't know which restaurant to go to. We needed help, so Mom went up to an elderly lady and tried to ask for directions to a popular seafood restaurant. ⓔLuckily, she seemed understanding Mom's few Spanish words. She took us to a small local restaurant nearby. The food was amazing. I really wanted to take pictures of the food and post them on my blog. But without my phone, I just decided to enjoy the moment.

16 위 글의 밑줄 친 ⓐ~ⓔ 중 어법상 옳은 것은? (3점)

① ⓐ   ② ⓑ   ③ ⓒ   ④ ⓓ   ⑤ ⓔ

17 위 내용을 옳게 이해한 이를 <u>모두</u> 고르면? (5점)

Amy: I want to try technology-free trip to a new city like the writer did. Even though I can't use my smartphone, I can find a popular restaurant by asking people.

Bella: I think it is amazing that the writer suggested a trip without smartphones first. It could cause so many difficulties on his family's trip.

Cindy: The writer's mom asked an elderly lady about a popular seafood restaurant, and it was very nice of her to take the family to a small local restaurant.

Jenny: I am planning to go to Barcelona, Spain next month. I should search for the writer's blog to see the pictures of the food he or she took.

Will: I can't believe it took the family about two hours to get to their guesthouse around Plaza Reial even though the writer's dad knew many Spanish words and the direction of the place.

① Amy, Bella   ② Amy, Cindy

③ Bella, Jenny   ④ Cindy, Will

⑤ Jenny, Will

18 다음 중 스마트폰 사용의 심각성을 나타내는 내용과 관련이 가장 적은 것은? (4점)

① I use my phone when I walk and when I eat.

② I can't focus on my work because of my phone.

③ I feel nervous when I don't have my phone with me.

④ I check my phone first when I wake up in the morning.

⑤ I like meeting my friends better than playing with my phone.

[19~21] 다음 글을 읽고 물음에 답하시오.

After looking around Gaudi's Park Guell, we decided to have seafood fried rice for lunch. However, we didn't know which restaurant to (a)go. We needed help, so Mom went up to ⓐan elderly lady and (b)tried to ask for directions to a popular seafood restaurant. Luckily, she seemed to understand Mom's (c)few Spanish words. ⓑShe took us to a small local restaurant nearby. The seafood fried rice was amazing. I really wanted to take pictures of the food and post ⓒthem on my blog. But without my phone, I just decided to enjoy the moment.

During the (d)remaining days, we relied more and more on Ⓐthe locals. We were able to meet and talk with ⓓvarious people on the streets, in the bakeries, and in the parks. ⓔThey were always kind enough to show us different sides of Barcelona with a smile. Also, our family talked a lot with each other. We spent much of our time together on the Spanish train, on the bus, and at the restaurants.

Our technology-free trip was a new and different experience. Before the trip, I was so dependent on my smartphone that I couldn't do anything without it. But now I see that I can enjoy the moment without it. From the experience, I have learned the importance of a (e)balanced using of the smartphone. So, next time, would I travel without a smartphone? Probably not. But I will try to use it more wisely.

19 위 글의 (a)~(e) 중 어법상 옳은 것을 <u>모두</u> 고르면? (4점)

① (a), (b), (d) ② (a), (b), (e)
③ (a), (c), (d) ④ (b), (c), (e)
⑤ (b), (c), (d)

20 위 글의 밑줄 친 ⓐ~ⓔ 중 Ⓐthe locals에 해당되지 <u>않는</u> 것은? (3점)

① ⓐ ② ⓑ ③ ⓒ ④ ⓓ ⑤ ⓔ

21 위 글을 읽고 알 수 있는 사실은? (3점)

① The writer's family went to Gaudi's Park Guell.
② The writer has a sister.
③ The locals didn't help the writer's family often.
④ The writer's mom can speak Spanish very well.
⑤ The writer couldn't learn anything from the technology-free trip.

[22~23] 다음 글을 읽고 물음에 답하시오.

Our technology-free trip was a new and different experience. (A) Before the trip, ⓐI was so dependent on my smartphone that I couldn't do anything without it. (B) From the experience, I have learned the importance of a balanced use of the smartphone. (C) So, next time, would I travel without a smartphone? (D) Probably not. But I will try to use it more wisely. (E)

22 위 글의 (A)~(E) 중 다음 문장이 들어갈 곳은? (4점)

But now I see that I can enjoy the moment without it.

① (A) ② (B) ③ (C) ④ (D) ⑤ (E)

23 위 글의 밑줄 친 ⓐ를 바르게 바꾼 문장은? (3점)

① I was so dependent on my smartphone to do anything with it.
② I was too independent on my smartphone to do anything without it.
③ I was so dependent on my smartphone not to do anything without it.
④ I was too independent on smartphone that I couldn't do anything with it.
⑤ I was too dependent on my smartphone to do anything without it.

[24~25] 다음 글을 읽고 물음에 답하시오.

Our technology-free trip was a new and different experience. Before the trip, I was so (A)[independent / dependent] on my smartphone that I couldn't do anything without it. But now I see that I can enjoy the moment (B)[with / without] it. From the experience, I have learned the importance of a (C)[balanced / unbalanced] use of the smartphone. So, next time, would I travel without a smartphone? Probably not. But I will try to use it more wisely.

24 위 글의 각각의 괄호 안에서 문맥에 맞는 낱말로 가장 적절한 것은? (4점)

	(A)	(B)	(C)
①	independent	with	unbalanced
②	independent	with	balanced
③	dependent	without	balanced
④	dependent	without	unbalanced
⑤	dependent	with	unbalanced

25 위 글의 내용을 한 문장으로 요약하고자 할 때, 빈칸 ⓐ와 ⓑ에 들어갈 말로 가장 적절한 것은? (3점)

> My thoughts on using a phone have ⓐ_____ into a ⓑ_____ way.

	ⓐ	ⓑ
①	moved	balanced
②	not changed	strange
③	remained unchanged	predictable
④	not decided	strict
⑤	shifted	negative

[26~28] 다음 글을 읽고 물음에 답하시오.

Last summer, my father suggested a ⓐsurprising / surprised event: a family trip without smartphones! He said, "I hate to see you sitting together and only looking at your smartphones." My sister and I explained the need for smartphones, but he kept ⓑto say / saying that we could not ⓒfull / fully enjoy the trip with (가)them. So we started a technology-free trip to a new city, Barcelona, Spain.

26 위 글의 ⓐ~ⓒ에 들어갈 가장 알맞은 것은? (4점)

	ⓐ	ⓑ	ⓒ
①	surprising	to say	full
②	surprising	saying	full
③	surprising	saying	fully
④	surprised	saying	fully
⑤	surprised	to say	fully

27 위 글을 읽고 답할 수 <u>없는</u> 질문은? (3점)

① What is the technology-free trip?

② Why did Dad suggest a family trip without smartphones?

③ What did the writer and the writer's sister try to explain to Dad?

④ How long have the writer and the writer's sister used their smartphones?

⑤ Where did the family go for a technology-free trip?

28 다음 중 밑줄 친 (가)them이 의미하는 것은? (3점)

① family ② my sister and I

③ smartphones ④ events

⑤ trip to a new city

◎ 선택형 문항의 답안은 컴퓨터용 수정 싸인펜을 사용하여 OMR 답안지에 바르게 표기하시오.

◎ 서술형 문제는 답을 답안지에 반드시 검정 볼펜으로 쓰시오.

◎ 총 28문항 100점 만점입니다. 문항별 배점은 각 문항에 표시되어 있습니다.

[서울 양천구 ○○중]

01 다음 게시물의 내용과 일치하지 <u>않는</u> 것은? (4점)

Age: 5 months old / Lost Date: Yesterday
Owner: James

① James lost his five-month-old cat, Leon.

② This poster was made to find James' cat, Leon.

③ The cat owner left his phone number on the poster.

④ It is easy to see the title "LOST CAT" in big letter at the top on the poster.

⑤ Even though there is Leon's picture on the poster, it doesn't show Leon's face well.

[서울 송파구 ○○중]

[2~3] 다음 글을 읽고 물음에 답하시오.

Last month, my family spent a week in a resort with no digital devices at all. These are messages I left on my SNS after I returned to my digital life.
Oct. 9th / Here we are. There are no TVs, no computers, no cellphones and worst of all no refrigerators! I realized that I cannot eat ice cream this week! Last week, my mom shouted, "I want to reset my life!" Ⓐ_____ we are here, in the digital detox camp. I miss my smartphone so much.
Oct. 10th / We went hiking early in the morning. My father took pictures of me and my younger sister. I wanted to send pictures to my friends and show off what I was doing here. Ⓑ_____ the film is still inside the camera. At night, we went stargazing. We were lucky since we saw the Milky Way in the sky. I really wished I could take a picture of it.
Oct. 11th / We went to a nearby farm and picked lettuce and tomatoes. My father cooked dishes with the vegetables. My mom said, "Everything is so fresh." She looked happier than ever. After lunch, I was just lying down with my sister on the grass. She talked about her best friend whom she met at the animal shelter. I didn't know that my sister is such an animal lover.
Oct. 15th / I don't know how I spent a week here. A week has already gone by. I feel closer to my family.

*detox: 해독 *stargaze: 별을 관찰하다

02 위 글의 Ⓐ, Ⓑ에 알맞은 말로 짝지어진 것은? (4점)

	Ⓐ	Ⓑ
①	That's why	But
②	Because	Also
③	Even though	Because
④	That's because	However
⑤	So	Then

03 위 글의 내용과 일치하는 것은? (4점)

① 글쓴이가 SNS에 올린 글을 리조트 내 디지털 수업 때 올린 글들이다.

② 리조트 내엔 일체의 디지털 기기가 없었다.

③ 글쓴이가 본인의 삶을 재시작하고 싶은 마음에 여행을 떠나게 되었다.

④ 여행 중간에 친구들에게 근황을 알릴 수 있는 사진이나 글들을 올릴 수 있었다.

⑤ 이번 한 달간의 여행으로 가족 간의 대화도 늘고 자연과 함께 할 수 있었다.

04 내용상 빈칸에 차례대로 알맞은 표현은? (3점)

During the remaining days, we relied more and more on the _____. We were able to meet and talk with various people on the streets, in the bakeries, and in the parks. They were always _____ enough to show us different sides of Barcelona with a smile. Also, our family talked a lot with each other. We spent much of our time together on the Spanish train, on the bus, and at the restaurants.

① locals – kind

② strangers – kind

③ guidebooks – talkative

④ locals – talkative

⑤ smartphones – unkind

05 다음 주어진 글에 이어질 알맞은 내용은? (3점)

Last summer, my father suggested a surprising event: a family trip without smartphones! He said, "I hate to see you sitting together and only looking at your smartphones." My sister and I explained the need for smartphones, but he kept saying that we could not fully enjoy the trip with them. So we started a technology-free trip to a new city, Barcelona, Spain.

① City tour with my friends

② Surprising presents for my mom

③ Living for a week without smartphones

④ The trip to Barcelona without smartphones

⑤ How to use apps with smartphones

06 다음 글이 들어가기에 가장 알맞은 곳은? (4점)

Before the trip. I was so dependent on my smartphone that I couldn't do anything without it.

ⓐ Our technology-free trip was a new and different experience. ⓑ But now I see that I can enjoy the moment without it. ⓒ From the experience, I have learned the importance of a balanced use of the smartphone. ⓓ So, next time, would I travel without a smartphone? ⓔ Probably not. But I will try to use it more wisely.

① ⓐ   ② ⓑ   ③ ⓒ   ④ ⓓ   ⑤ ⓔ

07 주어진 문장 뒤에 이어질 대화의 순서로 바른 것은? (4점)

Excuse me. Can you help me order with this machine?

ⓐ Wow, it's so simple. This machine is much faster than ordering at the counter.

ⓑ Touch the Done button at the bottom and pay for them.

ⓒ I'm with you on that. It really saves a lot of time when there's a long line.

ⓓ Sure. First, press the Hot Dog button and choose your hot dog and drink.

ⓔ Okay. How do I pay for my order?

① ⓑ-ⓔ-ⓓ-ⓐ-ⓒ   ② ⓓ-ⓔ-ⓑ-ⓐ-ⓒ

③ ⓓ-ⓐ-ⓑ-ⓔ-ⓒ   ④ ⓔ-ⓓ-ⓑ-ⓒ-ⓐ

⑤ ⓔ-ⓐ-ⓓ-ⓑ-ⓒ

08 두 문장이 같은 뜻이 되도록 〈보기〉와 같이 문장을 바꿔 쓸 때 빈칸을 채우시오. (4점)

보기

• My brother is too young to stay home alone.

⇒ My brother is so young that he can't stay

I was too sick to go on a field trip.

⇒ I was _____.

[9~10] 다음 글을 읽고 물음에 답하시오.

Our first day was (A)[terrible / easy]. On the way to our guesthouse around Plaza Reial, we got lost in downtown Barcelona. Dad was busy looking at the map and asking for directions with a few Spanish words he got from a tour guidebook. Though our guesthouse was (B)[quite far from / right next to] the Plaza, it took us about two hours to get there. We were so tired that we could not go out for dinner. So I went to bed but couldn't (C)[fall asleep / wake up] because I was worried about what would happen the next day.

09 위 글의 괄호 (A)~(C) 안에서 문맥에 맞는 낱말로 가장 적절한 것은? (4점)

	(A)	(B)	(C)
①	terrible	quite far from	fall asleep
②	easy	quite far from	fall asleep
③	terrible	right next to	fall asleep
④	easy	right next to	wake up
⑤	terrible	right next to	wake up

10 위 글에서 그 내용을 미루어 짐작할 수 있는 것은? (4점)

① The first day went on well as we planned.

② We failed to arrive at the guesthouse since it wasn't on the map.

③ It took less time to go to the guesthouse than we expected.

④ Dad looked like a native Spanish speaker.

⑤ Because we arrived at the guest house late, we decided not to go out for dinner.

[11~12] 다음 글을 읽고 물음에 답하시오.

After looking around Gaudi's Park Guell, we decided to have seafood fried rice for lunch. However, we didn't know which restaurant to go to. We needed help, so Mom went up to an elderly lady and tried to ask for directions to a popular seafood restaurant. ⓐLuckily, she seemed to understand Mom's few Spanish words. ⓑSpanish is the second most popular language after English in the world. ⓒShe took us to a small local restaurant nearby. ⓓThe seafood fried rice was amazing. ⓔI really wanted to take pictures of the food and post them on my blog. But without my phone, I just decided to enjoy the moment.

11 위 글의 ⓐ~ⓔ 중, 글의 흐름과 관계 없는 문장은? (3점)

① ⓐ   ② ⓑ   ③ ⓒ

④ ⓓ   ⑤ ⓔ

12 위 글에서 다음 중 그 답을 찾을 수 없는 질문은? (4점)

① What did the writer want to do with a smartphone at the restaurant?

② What kind of food did the family decide to have for lunch?

③ What did Mom do when the family needed help finding a restaurant?

④ How many hours have passed since the family had lunch?

⑤ How was the seafood fried rice at the small local restaurant?

[13~17] 다음 글을 읽고 물음에 답하시오.

(A)

Last summer, my father suggested a ①surprised event: a family trip without smartphones! He said, "I hate to see you ②sitting together and only looking at your smartphones." My sister and I explained the need for smartphones, but he kept saying that we could not fully enjoy the trip with them. So we started (가)_____ to a new city, Barcelona, Spain.

(B)

After looking around Gaudi's Park Guell, we decided to have seafood ③fried rice for lunch. However, we didn't know which restaurant to go to. We needed help, so Mom went up to an elderly lady and tried to ask for directions to a popular seafood restaurant. The seafood fried rice was ④amazing. I really wanted to take pictures of the food and post them on my blog. But without my phone, I just decided to enjoy the moment.

(C)

Our first day was terrible. On the way to our guesthouse around Plaza Reial, we got lost in downtown Barcelona. Dad was busy looking at the map and asking for directions with a few Spanish words he got from a tour guidebook. (나)_____ our guesthouse was right next to the Plaza, it took us about two hours ⑤to get there.

(D)

(다)_____ the remaining days, we relied more and more on the locals. We were able to meet and talk with various people on the streets, in the bakeries, and in the parks. They were always kind enough to show us different sides of Barcelona with a smile. Also, our family talked a lot with each other. We spent much of our time together on the Spanish train, on the bus, and at the restaurants.

13 위 글의 (A)에 이어질 가장 알맞은 순서는? (4점)

① (B) - (C) - (D)   ② (B) - (D) - (C)
③ (C) - (D) - (B)   ④ (C) - (B) - (D)
⑤ (D) - (B) - (C)

14 위 글 (A)의 빈칸 (가)에 들어갈 어휘로 가장 적절한 것은? (3점)

① a backpacking trip   ② a volunteer trip
③ a honeymoon trip   ④ a smartphone trip
⑤ a technology-free trip

15 ①~⑤ 중 단어의 쓰임이 잘못된 것은? (3점)

① surprised   ② sitting   ③ fried
④ amazing   ⑤ to get

16 위 글 빈칸 (나), (다)에 들어갈 말이 바르게 짝지어진 것은? (4점)

	(나)	(다)
①	Even though	During
②	Besides	Since
③	Despite	For
④	Moreover	Therefore
⑤	In spite of	As

17 다음 중 위 글에서 알 수 있는 내용으로 가장 거리가 먼 것은? (4점)

① 숙소를 찾는 데 어려움을 겪었다.
② 가족들과 많은 시간을 보낼 수 있었다.
③ 맛집의 음식을 블로그에 올릴 수 있었다.
④ 다양한 사람들과 만나 이야기할 수 있었다.
⑤ 현지인들은 매우 친절했다.

[18~25] 다음 글을 읽고 물음에 답하시오.

Last summer, my father suggested a surprising event: a family trip without smartphones! He said, "I hate to see you sitting together and only looking at your smartphones." My sister and I explained the need for smartphones, ⓐ_____ he kept saying that we could not fully enjoy the trip with them. So we started a technology-free trip to a new city, Barcelona, Spain.

Our first day was ⓑ_____. On the way to our guesthouse around Plaza Reial, we got lost in downtown Barcelona. Dad was busy looking at the map and asking for directions with a few Spanish words he got from a tour guidebook. Even though our guesthouse was right next to the Plaza, it took us about two hours to get there. ⓒWe were so tired that we could not go out for dinner. I went to bed but couldn't fall asleep because I was worried about what would happen the next day.

After looking around Gaudi's Park Guell, we decided to have seafood fried rice for lunch. However, we didn't know which restaurant to go to. We needed help, so Mom went up to an elderly lady and tried to ask for directions to a popular seafood restaurant. Luckily, ⓓshe seemed to understand Mom's few Spanish words. She took us to a small local restaurant nearby. The seafood fried rice was amazing. I really wanted to take pictures of the food and post them on my blog. But without my phone, I just decided to enjoy the moment.

During the remaining days, we relied more and more ⓔ_____ the locals. We were able to meet and talk with various people on the streets, in the bakeries, and in the parks. They were always kind enough to show us different sides of Barcelona with a smile. Also, our family talked a lot with each other. We spent much of our time together on the Spanish train, on the bus, and at the restaurants.

Our technology-free trip was a new and different experience. Before the trip, I was so dependent ⓕ_____ my smartphone that I couldn't do anything without it. But now I see that I can enjoy the moment without it. From the experience, I have learned the importance of a balanced use of the smartphone. So, next time, would I travel without a smartphone? Probably not. But I will try to use it more wisely.

18 위 글의 여행에 대해 알 수 없는 것은? (3점)

① 여행지   ② 동행자
③ 숙소 위치   ④ 여행 비용
⑤ 여행 조건

19 위 글의 빈칸 ⓐ에 들어갈 접속사로 가장 적절한 것은? (3점)

① so   ② or
③ and   ④ but
⑤ because

20 위 글의 빈칸 ⓑ에 가장 적절한 표현은? (3점)

① great   ② good
③ fearful   ④ terrible
⑤ perfect

21 위 글의 ⓒ와 같은 의미로 빈칸에 들어갈 단어를 괄호에서 골라 바르게 연결한 것은? (4점)

> We were _____ _____ _____ _____ out for dinner. (㉠ to ㉡ too ㉢ go ㉣ tired)

① ㉠-㉡-㉢-㉣   ② ㉡-㉢-㉣-㉠
③ ㉢-㉠-㉡-㉣   ④ ㉠-㉢-㉣-㉡
⑤ ㉡-㉣-㉠-㉢

22 위 글의 밑줄 친 ⓓshe는 누구인가? (3점)

① 엄마   ② 여동생
③ 글쓴이   ④ 현지인
⑤ 여행 가이드

23 위 글의 빈칸 ⓔ, ⓕ에 공통으로 들어갈 전치사는? (4점)

① in   ② at
③ on   ④ for
⑤ with

24 다음 중 위 글에 드러난 현지인들에 대한 느낌으로 가장 적절한 것은? (3점)

① noisy   ② friendly
③ nervous   ④ calm
⑤ unpleasant

25 위 글의 여행의 장단점(Joy/Trouble)을 요약할 때, 내용을 잘못 이해한 학생은? (4점)

만월: Trouble - They got lost on their way to the guesthouse.

진구: Joy - They could learn the importance of smartphones.

봉림: Joy - They talked a lot with their family all the time and everywhere.

보검: Trouble - They couldn't take pictures of the food and post them on their blog.

혜리: Joy - They enjoyed the places and the people around them.

---

① 만월   ② 진구   ③ 봉림   ④ 보검   ⑤ 혜리

[전남 ○○중]

[26~27] 다음 글을 읽고 물음에 답하시오.

After ⓐlooking around Gaudi's Park Guell, we decided ⓑto have seafood fried rice for lunch. However, we didn't know which restaurant to go to. We needed help, so Mom went up to an elderly lady and tried ⓒto ask for directions to a popular seafood restaurant. Luckily, she seemed to understand Mom's few Spanish words. She took us to a small local restaurant nearby. The seafood fried rice was ⓓamazing. I really wanted to take pictures of the food and ⓔposted them on my blog. But without my phone, I just decided to enjoy the moment.

26 위 글의 ⓐ~ⓔ 중 어법상 어색한 것은? (3점)

① ⓐ   ② ⓑ   ③ ⓒ   ④ ⓓ   ⑤ ⓔ

27 위 글의 내용과 일치하지 않는 것은? (4점)

① 현지 식당 해산물 볶음밥은 아주 맛있었다.
② 엄마가 해산물 식당 가는 길을 물어보았다.
③ 점심으로 해산물 볶음밥을 먹기로 했다.
④ 한 노부인이 식당에 가는 방법을 말해 줬다.
⑤ 가족은 Gaudi의 Guell 공원을 둘러보았다.

[전남 ○○중]

28 다음 우리말을 영어로 바르게 옮긴 것은? (3점)

• 나는 너무 약해서 그 상자를 들 수 없었다.
---

① I was too weak to lift the box.
② I was weak enough to lift the box.
③ I was so weak to lift the box.
④ I was so weak that I could lift the box.
⑤ I was so weak that I can't lift the box.

정답 및 해설

Lesson 5 (중간)

1회

01 ④	02 ②	03 ④	04 ④	05 ②	06 ⑤	07 ②	08 ④
09 ⑤	10 ③	11 ②	12 ⑤	13 ①	14 ④	15 ⑤	16 ②
17 ②	18 ⑤	19 ②, ③		20 ②	21 ③	22 ④	23 ②
24 ②	25 ①	26 ③, ④		27 ⑤			

28 I don't want Bella to be hurt again.

01 영영풀이에 해당하는 말을 순서대로 써 보면, • elementary, • avoid, • forgive, • reason, • script이고, 각 괄호에는 ① script, ② elementary, ③ reason, ⑤ avoid, ④에는 fear가 들어가야 한다.

02 영영풀이에 해당하는 말을 순서대로 써 보면, • appear, • injure, • concentrate, • stay up, • take care of이므로, ②attack에 대한 설명은 찾아볼 수 없다.

03 문제들을 통한 성장통을 겪고 나면, ④ '더 지혜로워지고', 성숙하게 된다.

04 두 문장을 관계대명사를 이용해서 하나로 연결하면, 관계대명사 뒤에 있던 본래의 대명사는 사라지게 된다. ④it을 삭제하는 것이 적절하다.

05 언니의 셔츠를 입었다가, 포도 주스를 쏟았으니, 긍정적인 심경은 아닐 것이다. ②번 '속상한'이 정답이다.

06 상대방이 난처해 보이는데, 그 이유나 원인을 묻는 표현이 들어가야 한다. ⑤번, '어떻게 너의 문제를 해결할 수 있니?'라는 질문은, 문제의 원인에 대해서 알기도 전에 해결 방법을 묻게 되는 상황이 되는 것이므로 적절하지 않다.

07 관계대명사 that은 앞에 전치사를 쓸 수 없다.

08 (A) 현재완료 부정으로 has never been (B) want+목적어+to be p.p.(다치는 것으로 수동이므로 be p.p.) (C) work it out ('타동사+부사'의 대명사 목적어는 그 사이에 나온다.)

09 알맞게 영작하면 빈칸에 ⓐ so I had to run <to> ⓑ <has> Steve traveled to France ⓒ her feelings <are> going up and down ⓓ upset when you pointed out ⓔ sharing my room with my가 들어간다. ⓐ, ⓑ, ⓒ의 경우, < >로 표시한 단어들이 부족하다.

10 위 글로는 ③ 'Sadness가 Bella가 어떻게 하기를 원하는지' 대답할 수 없다.

11 <보기>와 ⓑ의 that은 관계대명사, 나머지 ⓐ, ⓔ는 접속사, ⓒ, ⓓ는 지시대명사이다.

12 ① 요즘 ② 속상한 날이야! ③ 의도하다 ④ 깔보다

13 ⓑ what → that[which] ⓒ no → any ⓓ be → to be ⓔ work out it → work it out

14 ① Joy → Sadness ② 그런 내용이 없다. ③ Fear → Joy ④ 두 사람이 문제를 해결할 수 없을 거라고 여기는 화자는 없다. ⑤가 글의 내용과 일치한다.

15 ①~④는 모두 긍정적이다. ⑤는 '긍정·부정' 모두 가능하고, 글의 내용상 '믿을 수 없을 만큼 속상한 날'로 해석 가능하다.

16 (B)의 lines는 연극의 대사를 가리킨다. ②가 정답이다.

17 관계대명사 that 또는 which를 쓸 수 있고, 생략해도 되기 때문에, 어법상 가능한 것은 ①, ②, ⑤ 세 개다.

18 ⓐ, ⓑ, ⓒ, ⓓ에 쓰인 that은 모두 지시대명사인데, ⓔ의 that만 접속사이다.

19 글의 흐름상 '걱정된다'는 단어가 들어가는 것이 적절하다. 'be worried', 'be afraid' 모두 '염려한다'라는 뜻이다.

20 위 글을 읽고, ② 'Fear가 Bella에게 어떻게 하기를 원하는지'를 묻는 질문에는 대답할 수 없다.

21 대화를 통해 학교에 '어떤 요청'을 해야 하며, 그 '방법'이 무엇인지도 알았으므로, '건의 게시판에 글을 작성하는 것'이 가장 자연스러운 흐름이다.

22 위 글을 읽고, ④ 'Jenny가 몇 차례나 Bella에게 상처를 줬는가?'라는 질문에는 대답할 수 없다.

23 that을 which로 바꿔 쓸 수 있는 것을 묻는 경우, 보통 관계대명사 that을 찾는 문제이다. 관계대명사는 ⓑ이며, 나머지 ⓐ, ⓒ, ⓓ는 지시대명사, ⓔ는 접속사이다.

24 (A) look down 우울해 보이다, put somebody down 깔보다 (B) find out 찾아내다, point out 지적하다, 가리키다

25 (가) '계속' ① '경험', 나머지는 모두 '계속'적 용법

26 ① look like → look at ② while → during ⑤ more wise → wiser

27 우선 '~를 확신하다'는 표현은 be sure를 쓴다. be sure 뒤에 '명사'만 올 때는 '전치사 of', '절'이 올 때는 '접속사 that'을 써야 한다. 그리고 a reason 뒤에 관계대명사는 that 또는 which가 가능하고, 이 경우 '관계부사 why'를 쓰지 않도록 유의한다.

28 5형식 문장 구조에서 want의 목적보어로 to부정사를 쓰는 것에 유의한다.

Lesson 5 (중간)

01 ② 02 ⑤ 03 ④ 04 ① 05 ③ 06 ① 07 ① 08 ②
09 ⑤ 10 ④ 11 ①, ③   12 ④ 13 ③ 14 ④ 15 ⑤
16 ⑤ 17 have been best friends   18 ② 19 ③ 20 ④
21 ④ 22 ④ 23 ⑤ 24 ④ 25 ④
26 Jenny와 Bella가 예전에는 가장 친한 친구였기 때문이다.
27 ③ 28 ② 29 the mistake that Bella made   30 ③

01 touching은 '만지다'의 현재분사형도 있지만, '감동적인'이라는 뜻으로도 쓰는데, ②번 문장에서는 '감동적인'으로 쓰였다.

02 각각 (A) 관계대명사 주격 which (B) Were there로 물었으므로, 복수대명사인 ones (C) '놀랍다'라는 뜻으로, '놀라움'을 느끼는 객체가 아니라 '놀라움'을 주는 주체이므로 현재분사형 amazing이 적절하다.

03 대화의 내용은 알람시계를 맞춰 놓지만, 듣고서 다시 끄기 때문에 아침에 지각을 하는 학생의 고민이다. 이 대화에 관련된 적절한 그림은 ④번이다.

04 각각 '현재의 문제에[를] ① 만들라 ② 받아들여라 ③ 직면해라 ④ 해결하라 ⑤ 집중하라'가 되므로, ①이 어색하다.

05 '피곤해 보이는 원인'을 묻는 표현이 적절하다. ③은 '왜 그 문제를 일으켰는지?'를 묻기 때문에 적절하지 않다.

06 대화를 하는 두 사람의 학교에 간단한 식사를 할 매점이 없어서 '건의'(suggestion) 게시판에 글을 올리려고 한다.

07 두 글에 공통적으로 '용서하다'라는 단어가 들어가야 한다.

08 ① appeared TV → appeared on TV
③ He → She ④ language → languages
⑤ thank → thanks

09 선행사는 volunteers이고, 뒤의 문장에서 앞으로 나온 전치사 with의 목적어 자리이므로, whom이 적절하다. 관계대명사 that은 전치사의 목적어 자리에 쓸 수 없다는 것에 유의한다.

10 15년 전에 바이올린 연주를 시작했고, 현재도 하는 것이므로 현재완료시제를 사용한다. 3인칭 단수 주어이므로 has를 쓰는 것에 유의한다.

11 ①, ③은 위 글의 내용과 일치한다. ② 두 사람은 초등학교 이후로 가장 친한 친구였다. ④ Anger의 말에 Joy가 동의한 것이 아니라 그 반대이다. "That's what I'm saying"은 Anger가 한 말이다. ⑤ Bella는 실수를 했고, Jenny가 그것에 대해 지적했다.

12 ⓐ look down: 침울해 보이다 ⓒ put A down: A를 깎아내리다

13 ⓑ lines는 연극의 '대사'를 뜻한다. ③ '연극이 시작되기 전에 너의 대사를 모두 암기해야 한다'가 같은 뜻으로 쓰였다. ① 줄(서기) ② 선(도형) ④ 노선(지하철) ⑤ 줄(새치기)

14 ① what → which[that]

② which → who[whom/that]
③ whom → which[that]
⑤ whom → who[that]

15 현재완료시제 문장이므로, 명백한 과거 표현이 있으면 정답이 될 수 없다. 그러므로 ⑤ '작년 겨울 이후로'가 적절하다.

16 '두 사람이 더 이상 친구로 지낼 것 같지 않다'고 걱정하는 것은 약간 극단적이다. 따라서, Fear를 달래며 '너무 극단적으로 생각하지 말라'고 하는, 마지막 Joy의 말 바로 앞인 (E)가, 주어진 문장이 들어갈 적절한 위치이다.

17 'since+과거시제'로 보아, '현재완료' 시제로 영작하는 것이 적절하다.

18 위 글에 따르면, ② Bella가 소리친 것이 아니라, Bella에게 Jenny가 소리쳤다. 그러므로 ②가 일치하지 않는다.

19 Ms. Morris, 컴퓨터 게임을 멈출 수가 없어요. 어떻게 하죠? [(C) 특별한 프로그램을 써 보는 게 어때? 시간 제한을 설정하면, 그 시간에 컴퓨터가 꺼진단다. (A) 오, 좋은 아이디어네요. (D) 그리고, 방에서 거실로 컴퓨터를 옮기는 것도 좋겠어. (B) 그래야겠네요. 조언 감사드려요.]의 순이다.

20 '그러면 우리가 아침이나 간식을 사 먹을 수 있을 텐데.'라는 문장이므로, '학교에 매점이 있어야 돼.'의 다음인 (D)가 적절하다.

21 필요성을 느끼고, 방법을 알았으니, ④ '글을 올릴 것이다.'

22 [(A) 안녕? Amy예요. (C) 문제가 뭔가요? (E) 동생과 방을 같이 쓰기 싫어요. 묻지도 않고 내걸 갖다 써요. 어쩌죠? (B) 우선 솔직히 얘기하시고, 규칙을 만드세요. (D) 오, 해볼게요. 조언 감사드려요.]의 순이다.

23 다른 문장들은 모두 '제안'하는 표현인데, ⑤는 ⓐ 대신 들어가기에 적절하지 않다.

24 let은 목적어 뒤에 원형을 쓴다. to부정사는 쓸 수 없다.

25 (A)와 ④의 that은 관계대명사(목적격)이다. ①, ②는 지시대명사, ③, ⑤는 접속사로 사용되었다.

26 친구들 간의 문제를 해결하는 데는 솔직함이 가장 중요하다.

27 주어진 문장은 앞의 내용을 강하게 긍정하고 동의하는 표현이다. Joy가 Jenny와 Bella가 초등학교 이후로 친한 친구였음을 상기시키자, Anger가 긍정하면서 '진정한 친구라면 Bella를 깎아내리면 안 된다.'는 말을 하는 사이인 (C)가 적절하다.

28 Joy는 'Jenny가 Bella에게 의도적으로 상처를 주려고 했다고 확신하고 있다.'는 말은 정반대이다. 도리어, Joy는 그 반대의 경우를 확신하고 있다. 그러므로 ②번이 내용과 일치하지 않는다.

29 관계대명사 that을 이용하여, 어법에 맞게 적절히 배열한다.

30 (b)는 '계속'적 용법이다. 예문들은 각각 ① '완료' ② '경험' ③ '계속' ④ '경험' ⑤ '경험'으로, ③이 적절하다.

Lesson 6 (중간) 1회

01 that elephants make a thick wall to protect baby elephants
02 ④ 03 ② 04 ② 05 ④ 06 ②
07 A shark can swim as fast as a boat.
08 (1) restless (2) tell (3) while   09 ② 10 ④ 11 ②
12 (1) as valuable as money
   (2) as expensive as the bed
   (3) It is exciting to watch a soccer game.
13 ① 14 ⑤ 15 is as heavy as an elephant 16 ③ 17 ①
18 ④ 19 ② 20 (1) night (2) shelter (3) body   21 ⑤
22 ② 23 ③ 24 ④ 25 ④ 26 ⑤ 27 ③ 28 ② 29 ①

01 '코끼리들이 새끼 코끼리들을 보호하기 위해 두꺼운 벽을 만든다'
는 것을 알게 되었다.
02 ⓓ appear → disappear ⓔ able → unable
   ⓕ feed → supplies
03 'not as ~ as'는 'less 원급 than'으로 바꿔 쓸 수 있다. '우리나라
에서 친구는 가족만큼 중요하지 않다.' = '친구가 가족보다 덜 중
요하다.'
04 ② 'fix a problem'은 '문제를 해결하다'라는 뜻이다.
05 'as 원급 as' 구문이므로 비교급은 쓸 수 없다.
06 'as 원급 as'구문에 비교급, 최상급은 쓸 수 없다.
07 질문의 주어가 'a shark'임에 유의하여, 적절히 영작한다.
08 (1) restless: 가만히 있지 못하는 (2) tell: 구분하다 (3) while:
   ~ 동안
09 the blue whale은 세계 최대의 바다 동물이다.
10 ④ '거리'를 뜻하는 비인칭 주어, 나머지는 모두 가주어이다.
11 처음엔 Stella가 배척당할 것이라고 생각했으나, 내가 틀렸다.
12 동등 비교와 가주어를 적절히 사용하여, 영작한다.
13 비교하는 두 사물의 무게가 같으므로 동등 비교를 이용한다.
14 That's surprising의 줄임말이다.
15 혀의 무게가 코끼리만큼 된다는 내용에 맞게 배열한다.
16 글쓴이의 Africa 동물 관찰 일지이다.
17 지각동사의 능동 목적보어 자리에 원형 또는 현재분사를 쓴다.
18 '글쓴이가 Stella라고 이름 붙인 이유'는 알 수 없다.
19 ⓑ는 Stella의 엄마를 가리키며, 나머지는 모두 Stella이다.
20 (1) 태양이 지고 캄캄한 하루의 일부
   (2) 사람이나 동물을 보호하려고 만들어진 건물 또는 장소
   (3) 머리와 손발을 포함한 모든 신체
21 Stella라고 이름 붙인 이유는 위의 글로 알 수 없다.
22 ② Thanks to: ~ 덕분에, 나머지는 'Despite(~에도 불구하고)'
   가 맞다.
23 Stella가 공격받기 쉬운 다른 이유이므로, (C)가 적절하다.

24 ⊙ found는 목적격보어로 '현재분사', ⓛ 공격받는 것이므로 '수
동태' 표현이 적절하다.
25 다른 무리의 암컷이 언제까지 Stella를 돌봐야 하는지는 알 수 없
다.
26 나머지는 모두 원급 비교 형태로서 'as+형용사/부사+as' 형태로
쓰인데 반해, ⑤의 'as soon as'는 관용적 표현으로 possible과
함께 써서 '가능한 빨리'를 나타내는 데 쓰인다.
27 (B) 첫날 (D) 엄마의 죽음 (C) 밤의 위기
   (A) 새 무리 합류
28 Stella가 다른 무리들로부터 안전한 것이 아니라, 다른 무리들 덕
분에 사자나 여러 위협들로부터 안전하게 된 것이다.
29 ① warm → warmly로 고치는 것이 적절하다.

Lesson 6 (중간) 2회

01 ④ 02 ③ 03 ② 04 ⑤ 05 ⑤ 06 ⑤ 07 ⑤ 08 ④
09 ③ 10 It is a good exercise to ride a bike. 11 ① 12 ④
13 ② 14 ② 15 ②
16 cared for Stella as warmly as Stella's mom did   17 ④
18 ① 19 ③ 20 ⑤ 21 ④ 22 ② 23 ⑤ 24 ④
25 It is dangerous to stay alone   26 ③ 27 ③
28 as warmly as Stella's mom did   29 ③ 30 ④ 31 ⑤

01 ④ to continue → not to continue로 해야 옳다.
02 ③ adventure → adventurous가 적절하다.
03 홀로 남겨진 아기 코끼리의 안위를 걱정하고 있다.
04 blue whale 혀는 코끼리 혀가 아니라, 코끼리 무게와 같다.
05 giant snake와 버스의 비교는 '무게'가 아니라 '길이'이다.
06 병렬 구조로 쓰이는 동사는 같은 시제로 표현해야 한다. ⑤ make
   → made가 적절하다.
07 C-phone 가격과 같은 것은 B-phone이다.
08 위 글을 읽고, 'Kelly네 나무가 얼마나 큰지'를 알 수 없다.
09 자세히 질문하면서 '궁금하지 않다'고 하는 것은 어색하다.
10 '자전거를 타는 것'이 주어이므로 이를 진주어로 하여 문장을 쓰
며, to부정사를 진주어로 쓴다.
11 ① Africa는 전치사 in을 앞에 쓴다.
12 (C) 정오 무렵, 사자들이 접근했다. (A) 코끼리들이 Stella를 둘
   러쌌다. (B) 그들 덕에 Stella는 안전했다.
13 처음엔 Stella가 배척당할 것이라고 생각했으나, 내가 틀렸다.
14 ⓐ 목적어를 이끄는 접속사 that ⓑ allow의 목적격보어로 to부
   정사 ⓒ 'seem+to부정사'가 적절하다.
15 위 글을 통해, 암컷들 중 한 마리가 Stella의 어미 노릇을 해주는
   것으로 유추할 수 있다.

16 warmly의 형태에 유의하여, 적절히 영작한다.

17 D(첫날) - C(어미 코끼리의 죽음) - A(밤의 위기) - B(다른 무리에 합류)

18 위 글로는 'Stella의 엄마가 왜 죽었는지' 답할 수 없다.

19 (A) 동사를 수식하는 부사 자리 warmly (B) lie+형용사: ~한 채로 누워 있다 (C) be동사의 주격보어로 형용사 bright가 적절하다.

20 ⓐ stayed → stay(ing)

ⓑ seemed welcome → seemed to welcome

ⓒ to cry → crying

ⓓ such wild → such a wild

21 'allow+목적어+to부정사' 형태에 유의하여, 적절하게 영작한 것을 찾는다.

22 위 글로는 'Stella의 엄마가 왜 죽었는지' 답할 수 없다.

23 (A) '~할 때까지'(계속) (B) keep one's eyes on (C) '~ 내내'

24 ⓓ bright → dark로 고치는 것이 적절하다.

25 가주어 It과 to stay alone을 활용하여, 적절히 영작한다.

26 처음엔 Stella가 다른 무리로부터 따돌림을 당할 것이라고 생각했지만, 내가 틀렸다.

27 위 글로는 '필자가 어디에서 새 코끼리 무리를 봤는지'는 알 수 없다.

28 대동사 did와 부사 warmly에 유의하여 적절히 영작한다.

29 ⓐ to cry → crying ⓑ deadly → dead

ⓓ attack → be attacked ⓔ staying → to stay

30 야생에 홀로 남겨진 코끼리에게 닥칠 어려움을 나열하고 있다. 교과서 원래 지문은 'What's more'(게다가)인데, 같은 의미인 Furthermore, Moreover 등이 가능하다.

31 Stella가 결정한 것이 아니라, 필자가 구조팀이 Stella를 구하러 올 때까지 그 곁에서 머물기로 결정했다는 내용이다.

Lesson 7 (기말) 1회

```
01 ①  02 ②  03 ③  04 ④  05 ③  06 ②  07 ④, ⑤
08 ④  09 ①  10 ③  11 ②  12 ④  13 ②  14 ①  15 ②
16 ①  17 ④  18 ④  19 ②  20 ②  21 ②  22 ④  23 ④
24 What do you think the artist is trying to tell us?  25 ①
26 ④  27 ③  28 ⑤  29 ①
```

01 빈칸 순서대로 importance, balance, experience, downtown, donate가 들어가야 한다. ① important → importance

02 흐름상 앞뒤의 문맥과 호응하려면, Botero가 그린 모나리자보다, da Vinci의 모나리자가 더 좋다는 내용이 나와야 한다.

03 내일 1시 반, 예술제에서 볼 거지? (c) 응, 먼저 뭐 보고 싶어? (a) 힙합 먼저. (d) 좋아, 체육관에서 2시? (e) 응. 4시엔 연극? (b) 응, 좋아.

04 음악의 종류를 물었으므로, ④가 적절하다.

05 남자가 가장 먼저 보고 싶은 것이 힙합 댄스 공연이다.

06 위 글의 마지막 부분을 보면, '오늘 두 점을 자세히 보고, 세부 사항을 이해할 수 있도록 도와주겠다'는 말이 있다.

07 ⓐ to look → looking ⓑ glance to → glance at ⓒ a few second → a few seconds

08 ④의 since는 '~ 이후로'라는 의미의 접속사로 사용되었다. (A)와 나머지 선택지에 쓰인 since는 '~이기 때문에'라는 의미의 접속사이다.

09 '그리스 비극과 함께 보여지는 (일상) 풍경' 이야기이다.

10 아버지의 당부를 기억하는 ⓒ가 가장 적절하다.

11 선행사가 복수이므로, ⓑ that is → that[which] are

12 주절에 동사 think가 있으므로 의문사를 문두에 쓰고 간접의문문 어순(의문사+주어+동사)에 유의한다.

13 how many time → how much time, during → for, close → closely 이렇게 총 3개이다.

14 ① to부정사의 명사적 용법으로 '진주어' 역할을 찾는다. ②, ③, ⑤는 부사적 용법 ④는 형용사적 용법이다.

15 ② seems that → seems to

16 take a [quick/close] look: [빨리/자세히] 보다

17 which direction에 유의한다.

18 위 글로는 공주의 옆에 있는 사람들이 무엇을 하는지 알 수 없다.

19 Icarus가 들어가는 제목임을 알아야 (B) 뒤의 질문이 가능하다.

20 ⓐ → isn't it? ⓒ who → which ⓓ to → for

ⓔ stay → to stay

21 ① look → looking

③ sticking → sticking out of

④ stay → to stay

⑤ seems → seems to be

22 캔버스 뒤에 있는 사람은 화가인 Diego Velázquez이다. 그러므로 ④가 본문 내용과 일치한다.

23 ⓐ, ⓑ, ⓒ, ⓔ는 모두 화가를 가리키는데, ⓓ는 글자 그대로 왕을 가리킨다. 그러므로 ④가 다르다.

24 주절의 동사에 think가 있는 것에 유의하여, 적절히 영작한다.

25 '그림 속 Icarus의 위치'를 물어야 (A) 뒤의 내용이 나올 수 있다.

26 이 글로는 Icarus의 아버지가 무슨 실수를 했는지 알 수 없다.

27 Icarus는 배 부근(near)에 있고, 태양에 너무 가까이(close) 날았으며, 날개의 밀랍이 녹았다(melted).

28 사역동사 make의 목적보어 자리이므로, ⑤ seeing → see로 고치는 것이 적절하다.

29 since는 접속사, 전치사로 모두 쓰일 수 있고, 의미도 다르다. (A)는 접속사 '~이기 때문에'로 쓰였으며, 같은 쓰임으로 사용된 것은 ①이다. 나머지는 모두 '~ 이후로'의 의미이다.

Lesson 7 (기말)

> **01** ⑤ **02** ④ **03** ② **04** ⑤ **05** ⑤ **06** ⑤ **07** ① **08** ⑤
> **09** myth **10** ① **11** ③
> **12** Who do you think he is painting? **13** ② **14** ③ **15** ②
> **16** ③ **17** ⑤ **18** ① **19** ① **20** ② **21** ④ **22** ⑤ **23** ③
> **24** ③ **25** ③ **26** ⑤ **27** ⑤ **28** ⑤

01 빈칸이 포함된 질문에 대한 답변으로 보아, 빈칸에는 어떤 종류의 음악을 연주할 것인지 묻는 것이 적절하다.

02 ④ Romeo and Juliet은 영화가 아니라 연극(play)이다.

03 (A) 뒤의 답변으로 보아, 선호를 묻는 질문이 가장 적절하다.

04 학교 축제를 기획하며, 학생들이 어떤 공연을 좋아하는지 알아보고자 하는 것이므로 ⑤가 일치한다.

05 'the king and the queen in the mirror in the background of the painting'으로 보아 그림 뒤의 배경에 있는 거울 속에 왕과 왕비가 있다.

06 사역동사 have[has] 뒤의 목적보어 자리에 to V는 안 된다.

07 (A) make 뒤 목적보어 (B) try to V: ~하려고 노력하다

08 ⓐ→ isn't it? ⓑ→ Icarus is ⓓ→ for him
ⓗ→ peaceful

09 자연 현상을 설명, 종교/관습을 정당화하려고 과거에 만든 이야기

10 Icarus의 모습은 (B) 평화로워(peaceful) 보이는 그림에 (A) 반전(twist)을 일으킨다.

11 제목 '시녀들'을 소개하며, 자연스럽게 공주에게서 두 여성들로 초점을 옮기는 (C)가 적절하다.

12 의문사를 문두로 보내는 것에 유의하여, 적절히 배열한다.

13 위 글을 통해서는 화가가 언제 그 작품을 그렸는지에 대한 질문에 답할 수 없다.

14 ⓑ did → do ⓓ to work → work 옳은 것은 총 3개이다.

15 Icarus에게 아버지가 밀랍과 깃털을 사용해서 날개를 만들어 주었다는 사실은 '참'이다. 그러므로 ②가 정답이다.

16 ⓐ is it? → isn't it? ⓑ where is Icarus → where Icarus is ⓓ In spite → In spite of 또는 Despite ⓔ peacefully → peaceful로 고치는 것이 적절하다.

17 각 단어는 ① notice, ② landscape, ③ wing, ④ myth, ⑤ warn이다. warn은 위 글에 나와 있지 않다.

18 간접의문문의 '의문사+주어+동사' 어순이 바르게 된 것을 찾는다.

19 (A) '~하느라 시간을 쓰다': spend+시간+V-ing (B) '힐끗 보다': glance at (C) '~이기 때문에'(접속사): since, as, because

20 'we'll look at two paintings closely'로 보아, ②가 적절하다.

21 them은 ④'중요한 세부 사항들'을 가리킨다.

22 그림 속에 모두 몇 명이 있는지는 확실하게 대답할 수 없다.

23 '아버지의 경고'와, '날개가 녹아 추락'하는 사이인 (C)가 적절하다.

24 문맥상 '밖에 빠져나온, 튀어나온'이라는 뜻이다.

25 'Icarus가 불멸하는 그리스 신들 중의 하나이다.'라는 문장은 옳지 않다.

26 ⓔ peacefully → peaceful로 고치는 것이 적절하다.

27 Icarus의 비극에도 불구하고, 다른 사람들은 평온한 일상을 지속하고 있다는 내용이므로, (E)가 가장 적절하다.

28 미술관에서 오후 네 시에 Van Gogh 전시를 시작한다.

Lesson 8 (기말)

> **01** ④ **02** ③ **03** ③ **04** ⑤ **05** ⑤ **06** ② **07** ④
> **08** ⓔ, post **09** ⑤ **10** ② **11** ④ **12** ⑤ **13** ① **14** ③
> **15** ③ **16** ③ **17** ② **18** ⑤ **19** ⑤ **20** ③ **21** ① **22** ②
> **23** ⑤ **24** ③ **25** ① **26** ③ **27** ④ **28** ③

01 ①, ②, ③, ⑤는 동명사 ④만 현재분사로 쓰였다.

02 ③ beating → beaten

03 첫 번째 문장(→ disappointing), 세 번째 문장(→ shocking)에 어법상 틀린 부분이 있으므로, 바르게 쓰인 문장은 총 3개이다.

04 '동의하지 않음'이 들어가야 한다. ①은 '시제'가 틀렸다.

05 ⓔ comfortable → uncomfortable

06 흐름상 '길 또는 방향'을 묻는 내용이어야 한다.

07 어느 할머니 덕에 우리 가족은 식당에 도착할 수 있었다.

08 ⓔ posted → post (wanted 뒤의 to부정사, and로 연결되는 병렬 구조)

09 were, couldn't 등의 시제에 유의하여, so ~ that을 활용한다.

10 아빠가 스페인어를 얼마나 오래 배웠는지 답할 수 없다.

11 '현지인들'에게 더 의지하게 되었다. ⓓ foreigners → locals

12 위 글로는 얼마나 자주 스페인 기차를 탔는지 답할 수 없다.

13 (A) 점심을 먹기로 했지만, 어느 식당으로 가야 할지 몰랐다. (B) 다행히, 현지 할머님이 알아들으셨다. Luckily = Fortunately (C) 이번 여행의 장점이 계속 나열되고 있다. Also = Moreover

14 sitting과 병렬구조이다. ⓒ looked → looking

15 나와 여동생은 스마트폰을 가져갈 필요성을 계속 설명했지만, 아빠는 그것들(스마트폰)이 있으면, 여행을 온전히 즐길 수 없다고

16 ⓐ surprised → surprising

ⓑ to sit, to look → sitting, looking

ⓓ frying → fried

ⓔ understanding → to understand

17 Bella, Jenny, Will 등은 내용을 잘못 이해하고 있다.

18 스마트폰 사용의 심각성을 나타내는 내용은 ① '걸을 때와 먹을 때도 폰을 쓴다.' ② '일에 집중 못한다.' ③ '폰이 없으면 불안하다.' ④ '아침에 일어나면 폰부터 확인한다.' 등과 같은 부정적인 내용이다. ⑤ '폰으로 게임하는 것보다 친구들을 만나는 것을 좋아한다.'는 것은 오히려 반대의 내용이다.

19 (a) → go to, (e) → balanced use

20 ⓒ them은 '사진들'을 가리킨다.

21 글쓴이 가족이 Guell 공원에 간 사실이 첫 문장에 나와 있다.

22 '여행 전 지나친 의존'과 '여행의 교훈' 사이인 B가 적절하다.

23 'so 형용사 that 주어 can't'는 'too 형용사 to V'로 전환한다.

24 문맥상 (A) 의존적인 (B) ~ 없이 (C) 균형 잡힌 등이 적절하다.

25 '스마트폰 사용에 대한 생각이 균형 잡힌 방식으로 이동/변화했다'는 것이므로 ⓐ moved, changed, shifted 등이, ⓑ balanced, healthy, sound 등이 들어가는 것이 적절하다.

26 ⓐ 놀라운 이벤트(surprising event) ⓑ 계속 얘기했다(kept saying) ⓒ 온전히 즐기다(fully enjoy)

27 그들이 얼마나 오래 스마트폰을 썼는지 위 글로는 알 수 없다.

28 '스마트폰을 가져가면 여행을 온전히 즐길 수 없다'는 내용.

Lesson 8 (기말)   2회

> **01** ⑤ **02** ① **03** ② **04** ① **05** ④ **06** ② **07** ②
> **08** so sick that I couldn't go on a field trip   **09** ③ **10** ⑤
> **11** ② **12** ④ **13** ④ **14** ⑤ **15** ① **16** ① **17** ③ **18** ④
> **19** ④ **20** ④ **21** ⑤ **22** ④ **23** ③ **24** ④ **25** ② **26** ⑤
> **27** ④ **28** ①

01 '사진이 있어도 얼굴이 잘 안 보인다'는 일치하지 않는다.

02 Ⓐ 여행 시작의 계기가 앞에 나왔으므로 'That's why'가, Ⓑ 사진을 자랑하고 싶지만, 필름이었으므로 'But'이 적절하다.

03 ②는 'a resort with no digital devices at all'과 일치한다.

04 '친절한' '현지인들'에게 점점 더욱 더 의존하게 되었다.

05 아버지의 제안에 따라 스마트폰 없이 하는 여행을 하게 됐다.

06 '여행 전의 스마트폰에 대한 지나친 의존'은 '현재의 깨달음' 앞인 ⓑ가 적절하다.

07 자동 주문기계 사용법이다. ⓓ-ⓔ-ⓑ-ⓐ-ⓒ의 순서이다.

08 시제(couldn't)에 유의하여, 'so ~ that'으로 적절히 영작한다.

09 (A) 첫날은 힘들었으므로 terrible (B) '양보 의미의 접속사' Though와 글의 문맥으로 보아, 꽤 가까웠으므로 right next to (C) 다음 날 걱정에 잠들 수 없었으므로 fall asleep

10 ①~④는 틀린 내용이다. ⑤에서 '늦게 도착해서'라는 표현이 본문에 있지는 않지만 '너무 피곤해서' 저녁을 먹으러 나갈 수 없었다는 것으로 짐작컨대 '늦게 도착한 것'이 저녁 식사를 못한 이유라고 볼 수 있다.

11 '스페인어가 영어 다음으로 세계에서 두 번째로 많이 사용되는 언어'라는 ⓑ 문장은 글의 전체 흐름과 무관하다.

12 위 글로는 '가족이 점심 식사를 하고 몇 시간이 흘렀는가'라는 질문에 대한 답을 찾을 수 없다.

13 글의 흐름상 (C) 첫날 (B) 다음날 점심 (D) 나머지 날들 순이다.

14 전자기기 없는 여행, 'a technology-free trip'을 말한다.

15 '놀라운(놀랍게 하는) 이벤트'이므로, '현재분사'를 써야 한다.

16 (나) '양보' 의미의 '접속사' (다) 특정한 '기간'을 뜻하는 '전치사'

17 스마트폰을 가져가지 않았으므로, 맛집의 음식 사진을 찍어서 블로그에 올리고 싶었지만, 그럴 수 없었다.

18 위 글을 통해서 여행 비용에 대해서는 알 수 없다.

19 나와 여동생이 설명했지만 아빠가 고집부리셨다.

20 '부정적'인 의미가 들어가야 한다. ④만 부정적이다.

21 전체는 We were too tired to go out for dinner.이다.

22 ⓓ she는 현지의 an elderly lady를 가리킨다.

23 rely on, be dependent on은 모두 '의존하다'라는 뜻이다.

24 '친절하고 좋은' 인상을 받았으므로 'friendly'가 적절하다.

25 '스마트폰의 중요성'이 아니라 '균형 있는 사용'의 중요성이다.

26 ⓔ → post, wanted to take pictures의 to take와 병렬구조

27 '식당에 가는 방법'을 말해 준 것이 아니라, 노부인이 '필자의 가족들을 직접 식당으로' 데려갔다.

28 'too ~ to V'가 적절히 활용된 것은 ①이다. 같은 의미를 다르게 표현하면, I was so weak that I couldn't lift the box.가 된다.